BOTANY

AN INTRODUCTION TO PLANT SCIENCE

BOTANY

SECOND EDITION

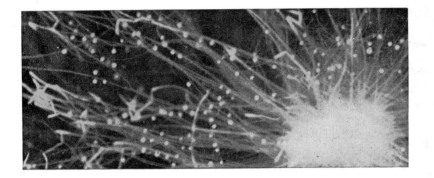

AN INTRODUCTION
TO PLANT SCIENCE

WILFRED W. ROBBINS

T. ELLIOT WEIER

C. RALPH STOCKING

John Wiley & Sons, Inc., New York

London

SECOND EDITION

Sixth Printing, July, 1961

To Wilfred W. Robbins

For him botany was alive, human, to be used and enjoyed by himself and his students, in classroom and out; in agricultural specialists' offices and on their experimental plots, and by commercial growers and home gardeners.

Preface

The philosophy of the second edition of *Botany*, despite the absence of Dr. W. W. Robbins' guiding hand, varies little, if any, from that of the first edition. We have missed him in the many decisions concerning revision, but we have endeavored to keep all changes in line with his concepts of teaching.

We must emphasize that the second edition, like the first, has been written with the student in mind. New concepts are developed from known reference points and new scientific terms are presented after, or in intimate relation with, the explanation of the concepts the new terms convey. It is our belief that all concepts can be initially explained in simple language and that the student's understanding of scientific concepts is a prerequisite to his accurate use of scientific terms. A balance must be struck between the beginning student's interest, training, and ability and the professional's desire for erudition. It is upon success in attaining this balance, probably more than any other single factor, that the production of a successful elementary text ultimately depends. We have written with this problem constantly before us. We are sure that students new to botany have a surprisingly small knowledge of plants, and we are careful, in the use of examples, not to assume a knowledge on the part of the student that does not exist.

The instructor is the most important element of any course; the text can only complement him and all courses must mirror his personality regardless of the text. *Botany* complements the instructor in a variety of ways: in presenting botanical concepts in an orderly and logical fashion; in its illustrations, closely integrated with the text material; in its well-placed and numerous summaries; and in its review diagrams and charts.

Both student and instructor demand a significant reason for any course. The authors believe strongly that the significance of botany lies in its being that area of plant science which integrates and adds to the store of basic knowledge about plants, and from which must be drawn by amateurs and professionals alike, all of the details which make gardening a pleasure and agriculture the single most important industry in the country. Any text book can only indicate this significance; the instructor must make it live for the student. It is sometimes more important to interest the beginning student than to have him memorize scientific minutiae.

It is sometimes held that the biological sciences, particularly the introductory courses, being largely descriptive, may not accurately present a full picture of the scientific method. We have tried to present botany in a fashion that will give all students some feeling for both descriptive and experimental phases of science. The discussion of physiology in *Botany* makes it possible to emphasize the experimental nature of this field and to give it a much more satisfactory treatment. We feel that the text will give, in an entirely suitable manner, both a thorough grounding in botany for the science major and a terminal course in science for the nonscience major.

Two major changes have been made in the second edition, both designed to emphasize the fact that the plant as a whole is a living, functioning organism. Function and structure comprise a unit, understandable only in terms of each other. To this end, as in the first edition, the general functions of structures are discussed as the structures are first described.

However, a detailed discussion of physiology is not undertaken in the second edition until the structure of the plant as a whole is understood. To accomplish this, the piecemeal discussion of absorption, conduction, transpiration, and photosynthesis have been deleted from the first edition's chapters on the stem, root, and leaf, combined with some material from the chapter called "The Plant as a Living Mechanism," and accompanied by a new discussion of respiration, united into three new chapters called "Soil and Mineral Nutrition," "Transpiration, Conduction, and Absorption," and "Photosynthesis and Respiration." This arrangement, well tested in our own classes, makes possible a more logical, understandable discussion of the whole plant as a living mechanism. Should others, however, disagree, it will still be possible to follow the discussion of stem structure with the section on conduction, the discussion of root structure with the section on absorption, and the discussion of leaf structure with transpiration and photosynthesis, as was done in the first edition.

Second, the angiosperm portion of Chapter 21 has been entirely rewritten to emphasize the life cycle story in angiosperms and to compare it with the life cycle of primitive forms. This new material, combined with a description of selected families of angiosperms, comprises a new chapter dealing only with angiosperms.

No chapter has escaped some rewriting. Revisions worthy of note include a rearrangement of the stem chapter with some addition to the discussion on the external morphology of the stem and an expansion of the section on wood anatomy. A discussion of monocotyledonous leaves has been added to the leaf chapter and the section on leaf fall rewritten. Descriptions of grass and composite flowers are included in the flower chapter. Photosynthesis has been brought up to date and a discussion of respiration has been added. The chapter called "The Plant as a Living Mechanism" has been rewritten to include recent information. A discussion of *Chlamydomonas* has been added to the Algae and *Vaucheria* moved from the Chlorophycophyta to the Chrysophycophyta. The sections dealing with nuclear details in the Ascomycetes and Basidiomycetes have been rewritten and *Penicillium* transferred from the Fungi Imperfecti to the Ascomycetes. Summaries and review charts have been added at many significant points. There are many new illustrations.

To the long list of colleagues mentioned as helping with the first edition, we must add Dr. Vernon Cheadle, and we again thank those whom we consulted for information and advice. We wish particularly to thank Dr. Ernest Gifford for his constant help and advice, and Drs. John Torrey, George Pappenfuss, and Johannas Proskauer for their many helpful suggestions, criticisms, and reading of the manuscript. We are indebted to Mr. James Dunning for a critical reading of the manuscript and to Dr. Robert Parke for many helpful suggestions. We are indebted to Ansel Adams for suggestions regarding illustrations and to Miss Jeanette Klute for Plate IV. Mr. Paul of the University Press has been most cooperative, and Miss June McCaskill has aided materially in the preparation of the many new line drawings. We are particularly indebted to Mr. Walter Russell, Collector to the Botany Department, for his untiring efforts in supplying us with fresh material for many of the new illustrations. And last, but not least, we must thank Mrs. Betty Pearson and Mrs. Mary Brinton for their patience and strong intuitive sense in the seemingly hopeless, yet successful, task of typing.

T. Elliot Weier
C. Ralph Stocking

Davis, California
December, 1956

Contents

1   *Introduction*   **1**

2   *The Plant World*   **13**

3   *Classification and Naming of Plants*   **33**

4   *The Plant Body of Seed Plants*   **45**

5   *The Plant Cell*   **50**

6   *The Stem*   **81**

7   *The Root*   **136**

8   *The Leaf*   **154**

9   *Soil and Mineral Nutrition*   **172**

10   *Transpiration, Conduction, and Absorption*   **184**

11   *Photosynthesis and Respiration*   **202**

12   *The Flower*   **219**

13   *The Fruit, Seed, and Seedling*   **257**

14   *Inheritance*   **285**

15   *The Plant as a Living Mechanism*   **303**

16   *The Groups of Plants*   **324**

17   *The Fission Plants*   **331**

18   *The Algae*   **351**

19   *The Fungi*   **378**

20   *The Fungi (Continued)*   **397**

21   *The Viruses*   **431**

22   *The Bryophytes*   **441**

23   *The Vascular Plants*   **461**

24   *The Vascular Plants (Continued)*   **478**

25   *Angiospermae*   **503**

26   *Evolution*   **531**

Glossary   **543**

Index   **563**

1

Introduction

An educated person is one who has a fair knowledge and an appreciative understanding of the environment in which he lives, and who is able to adjust himself to it. Our environment is most complex. It embraces everything that surrounds us, both living and nonliving. It includes the air we breathe, the food we eat, the water we drink; it includes temperature, rainfall, light, humidity of the atmosphere, wind, soil, and atmospheric pressure; it involves the varied plant and animal life, both wild and domesticated; and it includes the human beings with whom we are associated, their racial characteristics, and their social and economic systems. All elements of the environment affect our lives, our health, our well-being, our happiness, our freedom, and our philosophic and religious views.

In the long struggle upward, man has sought knowledge of his environment, the better to know how to adjust himself to it, modify it, and control it. He has been successful in a large measure. Life of the average educated individual in normal times can be, and usually is, more complete, satisfying, and productive, happier, and freer from fear than that of his aboriginal ancestor or of the backward peoples now living.

The Importance of Plants to Man. In all parts of the world where races of men developed, the kinds of plants about them influenced and largely determined their whole mode of existence: the kind of food they ate, the material from which their clothing was made, and the type of shelter over their heads. *Food, clothing, and shelter have always been the primary needs of man.* Moreover, from the earliest times, plants have influenced man's religious expressions, his architecture, and his use of ornaments and in a large measure have determined the degree of civilization which he has attained.

Although man's early interest and concern with plants were mainly as sources of food, clothing, and shelter, the earliest written records of the Chinese, the Hindus, and the Egyptians reveal that all sorts of plants were used also for their actual or supposed medicinal properties. Primitive peoples the world over, including the Indian tribes of this country, have always utilized many different kinds of plants as cures for various human ailments. Although it is known today that the great majority have no medicinal properties, still the list of those that are used advantageously in the treatment of sickness is very sizable; and still there are

1

Fig. 1.1. Inca jug showing corn motif. (Courtesy of C. Rick.)

1947 quinine was synthesized, although not in commercial quantities.

Not all drugs are thus derived from the practical experience of primitive peoples or even from the trial-and-error methods of modern peoples. Modern research laboratories have been the sources of many new and dramatic drugs. The *antibiotics* (see page 427) are complex substances which, having relatively minor effects on the tissues of man or animals, are able to prevent the growth, within tissues, of harmful microorganisms. The antibiotics are produced by common molds or mold-like organisms. Penicillin, the first truly effective antibiotic substance, is produced by a very common green mold, *Penicillium notatum,* and was discovered in 1929 by Dr. A. Fleming in an English laboratory. Since then an energetic search has been carried out for other molds or microorganisms which produce other antibiotics. This search has been rewarded by the discovery of about 10 additional such compounds.

no wholly satisfactory synthetic substitutes for such important drugs as opium, quinine, penicillin, and streptomycin.

Opium is the dried juice that exudes from the injured fruit of the opium poppy, a plant grown extensively in China and India. From opium are derived a number of refined drugs, morphine being one of the more widely used, which serve the medical profession in relieving pain. Morphine is now made synthetically and in learning how to do this a compound similar to morphine was discovered which relieves pain but which is much less habit forming than morphine. Quinine, the specific cure and preventive of malaria, comes from the bark of *Cinchona,* a small tree native to the high mountains of South America and now grown on large plantations in India and Java. During World War II the shortage of quinine became acute. As a substitute a synthetic organic compound, atabrine, became familiar to nearly every member of the fighting forces in the South Pacific. In

We are dependent upon plants for other things than drugs. We are dependent upon them for food, clothing, shelter, and a host of modern gadgets, from tires to the plastic of your fountain pen and the paper in the book you are reading. Use of plant materials is as old as man, but because of *research,* plant materials serve man in many hundreds of ways that were undreamed of a century ago. New uses for plants and new methods of cultivation may bring about vast changes in our economy. For instance, the substitution of rayon for natural fibers such as cotton, combined with the mechanical harvesting of cotton and the resulting growing of cotton in California has had a considerable impact upon the economy of the southern states which must eventually influence their culture. A glance at a road map will reveal the great influence vegetation has upon population density. Neither the Everglades of Florida nor the pine barrens of New Jersey have the network of roads or concentration of towns that occur in central Ohio. Roads are scarce in mountain and desert states of the west; few people make their homes amid sagebrush, but when irrigation makes it possible to grow cotton or apples or wheat, what was a desert becomes a populous countryside.

The growing of plants and animals is a basic industry. We consider this activity as *Agriculture*. In its broadest sense it may be defined as the growing of plants and animals for human needs. Considering only the plant half of agriculture we may subdivide this half into a number of categories; the growing of field crops (Agronomy), of fruit and vegetable crops (Horticulture), of flowers (Floriculture). The collection of information concerning all phases of the growing and processing of plants may be termed *Plant Science*. This information comprises data concerning, among other things, the structure, reproduction, chemistry, breeding, disease, physiology, processing, and distribution of plants or plant parts. *Botany* is the science which deals with the basic information concerning plants. It considers plants for their own sake without an immediate consideration of their usefulness. But it is to this basic information that the agriculturist must turn for the details which make possible an increase in yield or the introduction of new varieties of crops or flowers to assure us of food and clothing and to beautify our homes and parks. It is the function of the Plant Scientist, and in particular of the Botanist, to insure for future generations, which will be much greater numerically than our own, an adequate supply of plant materials for food, shelter, medicine, and pleasure.

It will be profitable to consider further the role of plant life in the world. Our first evidence of man on the earth dates back to approximately 1,500,000 years ago. This was in the late Cenozoic epoch (see page 532). In that early period the plant life of the earth was much as it is today. It is rather significant that the intensive development on the earth of annual herbs, that is, of small, nonwoody plants that flower and produce seed in one season, had its beginnings in this early period and that during this same epoch man was emerging from the primitive stage. In fact, this epoch has been called the age of man and herbs. Herbaceous annual plants were an important factor in human development, not only in the early period but also throughout man's entire history.

Primitive man was not an agriculturist. He was a hunter and gatherer of food; plants, as well as animals, were an all-important source of his food. About 6000 B.C., in the New Stone Age, there is the first evidence of plant cultivation, as well as animal domestication. Man had become a food producer; he had discovered that certain plants, chiefly herbaceous annuals like wheat, rice, barley, rye, and peas, possess seeds with food stored in them; he had found out that these plants could be grown in plots about his hut or cave and that he need not wander far and wide as a hunter of food. This was the birth of agriculture. Thus, when man began the stirring of the soil with sticks and the growing, harvesting, and storing of seeds, it was possible for him to give up his hunting life and to lead a more settled existence. In this way did villages and small settlements arise—a primitive urban existence. In fact, agriculture, involving both the cultivation of plants and the domestication of animals, made urban life possible. Peoples lived together; social and economic problems arose; it was now possible to begin the development of what we are pleased to call a civilization. With the supply of food, shelter, and clothing not only assured but also rather easily obtained, man had the leisure to develop the arts and industries identified with civilization.

Ancient Centers of Agriculture. Ancient centers of agriculture and ancient civilizations developed in three distinct areas or centers on the earth (Fig. 1.2). These were the **Mediterranean**, the **Oriental**, and the **American** centers. (1) The **Mediterranean center** embraced all shores of the Mediterranean Sea and was the meeting ground of three continents. Any plants cultivated in one part were sure to be carried to other parts. The peoples of this great Mediterranean area were provided with a wide selection of grains, chief of which were wheat, rye, and barley, and of vegetables and fruits. (2) The **Oriental center** included China, Indo-China, the Malay Peninsula, Japan, Korea, and Manchuria. The most important food plant was rice; other cultivated plants were cotton, soybean, and certain fruits. The Orientals had relatively few species of food plants; their diet lacked variety in ancient times, as it does even today. (3) The **American center** included central and southern Mexico, Central America, and northern South America. The important food plants were corn (maize), potato, kidney bean, and lima bean.

Thus, the three great centers of civilization developed in association with, and were largely dependent upon, three important herbaceous cereals, namely: wheat, rice, corn. Probably 60 per cent of the total diet of the world's population today

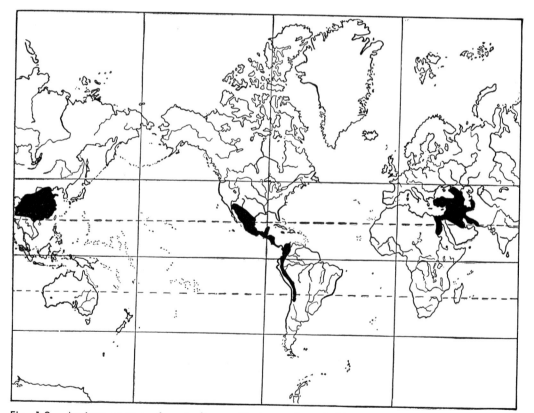

Fig. 1.2. Ancient centers of agriculture. (Redrawn from Robbins and Ramaley, *Plants Useful to Man,* The Blakiston Co.)

comes from the grass family, including wheat, corn, barley, oats, rye, and rice; next in importance are the legumes, such as peas, beans, and soybeans. (In 1952, there were produced in the world 7150 million bushels of wheat, 1565 million bushels of rye, 7823 million bushels of rice, and 5600 million bushels of corn.)

Agriculture—a Basic Industry. Agriculture is the industry that furnishes our food and many raw materials, such as fibers, wood, cork, rubber, gums, resins, essential oils, many kinds of fatty oils and waxes, and animal products. In the United States approximately 40 per cent of the population depends directly upon agriculture. We hear it stated time and again that agriculture is our basic industry. Human beings derive their very sustenance from plants and animals. Obviously, in the world today, with approximately 2400 million mouths to feed, these human beings cannot survive on the berries, roots, and seeds of wild plants and on animals they shoot or run down in forests. They must grow plants and animals under *controlled conditions,* striving for high yields and rapid multiplication. Agriculture is essentially concerned with growing plants and animals. But, of these two food sources, plants have a peculiar importance, because animals must derive their food from plants. Only green plants, that is plants that contain a green pigment, called **chlorophyll,** are able to make foods. These foods are chiefly carbohydrates (sugars and starches), fats, and proteins. Cattle, sheep, and hogs eat plants, derive foods from them, and we human beings, in turn, may obtain foods from both plants and animals.

Animals, including man, derive from plants other essential substances besides carbohydrates, fats, and proteins. It is now known that *plants constitute the major source of vitamins.* We are constantly told, from every source, including the radio, that man may suffer from certain vitamin deficiencies. Ailments due to vitamin deficiency are an established fact. Man's diet may contain water, mineral salts, carbohydrates, fats, and proteins in sufficient quantities to supply his energy requirements, but still something may be lacking in the diet which results in abnormal development or poor health. If this "something," this substance we call a **vitamin,** is added, even in very minute quantities, the individual recovers from the deficiency symptoms. Some animals, among them poultry, pigs, and cattle, manufacture their own vitamin C, while others, including man and guinea pigs, must get it from their food. Although vitamin A is not found in higher plants, the yellow carotene pigments that they contain can be converted into the nearly colorless vitamin A in the bodies of animals. Animal cells are of primary importance in the synthesis of vitamin D_2 and microbial action is the chief source of vitamin B_{12}. In the ultimate analysis, human beings and all other animals are dependent upon plants (chiefly green plants) for nourishment and for vitamins. In another chapter (Chapter 15) dealing with growth, we shall have more to say about plant and animal foods, various vitamins, and the close relationship between plants and animals.

Productive Capacity of the World. There is evidence, accumulated by experienced agriculturists and economists, that the productive capacity of the earth is sufficient to supply the required food and other materials derived from plants for a world population much greater than now exists. The total land area of the earth is estimated to be approximately 57 million to 58 million square miles. Of this, 6 million square miles are in the polar zones. Of the remaining 52 million square miles, about 13 million are grassland, about 17 million desert, and the remainder forests. Approximately 48 per cent of the world land areas are snow and ice, tundras, mountains, and deserts. Of the land outside the polar regions, about 40 per cent or 21 million square miles may be regarded as arable. However, there are physical limitations to the production of any essential crop plant. Let us consider wheat, one of the staple foods of the world. Wheat, like every other plant, grows successfully only under certain environmental conditions. It is a plant of temperate climates; it is not productive in the tropics or in polar regions. It must have a moderate amount of water; it will not grow in the desert, nor will it grow in water, as does rice. It thrives in a soil that is neither too alkaline nor too acid and that has the proper supply of mineral salts. The total area of the earth available for wheat constitutes but a small fraction of the total land area. There are, however, ways of increasing the acreage devoted to wheat. For example, breeding methods have developed quick-maturing wheat varieties that can be grown profitably in Canada and other northern regions. Also, drought-resistant varieties have been developed which have made possible a greatly increased acreage of wheat in semiarid regions, such as the western Great Plains of the United States. A knowledge of fertilizers, of methods by which excess acidity or alkalinity of the soil can be corrected, and of other agronomic practices has enabled man to overcome some of the limitations imposed by the soil. It has been estimated that the area of the world physically available for wheat production is 10 to 11 times the area at present used for wheat growing.

The Bureau of Plant Industry, Soils, and Agricultural Engineering, U. S. Department of Agriculture, has estimated the "attainable increase in yield due to improved practices" in the United States as tabulated below.

| | Average Yield per Acre | |
Crop	1935–1939	1960
Corn (bushels)	28.1	36.7
Oats (bushels)	31.7	38.5
Hay (tons)	1.4	1.8
Potatoes (bushels)	124.0	152.0
Soybeans (bushels)	18.5	21.9
Peanuts (pounds)	765.0	916.0
Wheat (bushels)	12.4	14.6
Rice (bushels)	47.5	53.6

We are under obligation to the thousands of research workers in many fields of science for the knowledge that makes possible increased production of plants and animals. It may seem at times that we produce too much, and in terms of one community that may be so. If, however, the world situation is considered as a whole it will be found that plant products are unequally distributed, some peoples have too much, others too little. In short, we know better how to produce plants, animals and gadgets, than we know how to distribute these things, or how they will affect peoples when distributed. But scientific research will and must go forward. Man's natural inquisitiveness will continue to result in new discoveries. New kinds of plants, new products, greater yields, greater utilization of all sorts of plant and animal waste products, new building materials, better nutrition, all will be realized. The plant scientist will play an important role in this advance.

BOTANY

One may rightly ask: What does the preceding discussion have to do with botany? We shall attempt an answer. The student should keep in mind that the gradual acquirement of knowledge and understanding of the vast assemblage of plants in the world—their distribution, habits, adaptation to climates and soils, chemical composition, culture, breeding, propagation, and utilization—has made possible the production of useful plants to meet the needs of a rapidly increasing world population.

In the United States, as well as in several other countries, the yield per acre of our most important crop plants has been increased. New varieties have been developed by plant breeders—varieties resistant to certain diseases, better adapted to certain climatic and soil conditions, more satisfactory from the standpoint of chemical composition, food value, etc. In addition new uses have been found for old crops and new industrial techniques have brought about the introduction of new crops for both new and old products.

Could such changes have taken place without research, without the gaining of new knowledge of plants and how to grow them? Can the efficient use of our land, production of plants, and their distribution as food, clothing or industrial products be continued and improved upon, without research? Research, the acquisition of new knowledge, gives us an understanding of how plants absorb substances from the soil, how they make food, how they breathe, how they reproduce, what nourishment they need, how they may be processed into food, clothing, or plastics, and scores of other facts. Research gives us an understanding of how the environment and heredity of plants may be modified so that they may be better suited to our needs. Continued research will supply additional information resulting in new varieties of plants, new uses for both old and new plants, new and better methods of processing, and ways and means of equalizing production and consumption for the benefit of both farm and urban communities. Research in plant science is not dramatic in terms of the life and health of individuals as is medical research, but it is dramatic in terms of whole communities.

Not all research involves plants associated with farm, factory, and consumer. Plants make all of our food, whether we eat it directly as corn on the cob, or corn in corn-fed pork. How plants make this food is not yet fully known and we should very much like to know the secret. The search involves meticulous work on plant cell structure, on plant pigments, enzymes, and other compounds. Knowledge of this work still spreads but a short distance from the laboratories where botanists, chemists, physicists, radiation experts, and others work together.

It is the function of the research worker in plant science to discover the basic facts concerning plants, *all plants*, not just those that are of immediate economic importance. Occasionally one fact or a set of observations will lead to improvement in the production or processing of a certain crop; more frequently an immediate application of the observation is neither likely nor expected. But it is only upon a broad base of botanical knowledge that the agriculturist, whether farmer, agronomist, agricultural economist, or agricultural engineer, can bring to every-day use new and better plant products.

Interrelationship of the Sciences. Man has always had a natural curiosity about all aspects of the universe. From small beginnings, among all the principal races of the earth, the sciences developed. In the early centuries, scientists were amateurs; they were not professional men gaining a livelihood from their work. Rather they were driven on by an urge or curiosity to inquire into the ways of the universe. Often they were held in ill repute, scoffed and laughed at, and sometimes they were persecuted. Today, as then, thousands of workers in all parts of the world are spurred on by this same urge to discover, know, and understand; but today they are regarded with respect and appreciation.

From the late sixteenth to the eighteenth century, academies of science and universities were established. During this period lived many of the great men associated with early advancement of knowledge, such men as Francis Bacon, Harvey, Boyle, Newton, Linnaeus, Priestley, Lamarck, Volta, Cuvier, and Humboldt. It must be remembered that the biological sciences—botany and zoology—have been greatly furthered by discoveries of chemists and physicists. We realize today that it is impossible to study plants understandingly and comprehensively without some knowledge of physical and chemical facts and principles. Many of the processes in plant life, such as food manufacture and respiration, are essentially chemical processes; and such processes as absorption of materials from the soil, their movement through the plant, and the loss of water from the plant are largely physical phenomena. The student will soon discover that the various branches of science—chemistry, physics, geology, zoology, and botany, including all their various applications, such as engineering, agriculture, pharmacy, forestry, and plant breeding—are strictly interdependent.

In time, the pursuit of science became an honorable profession instead of a mere avocation. Scientists have become numerous, as teachers and research workers in universities and colleges, as investigators in industrial scientific laboratories, of which there are more than 2000 in the United States, in scientific bureaus of state and federal governments, and in museums, zoologic gardens, and botanic gardens. In 1955, the American Association for the Advancement of Science had a membership of 48,660. This great organization of scientific workers has stated, in part, in a resolution:

The implications of the scientific spirit for the advantage of all peoples are becoming increasingly evident. Even the moral consequences of scientific understanding are being recognized and appreciated. Objectively demonstrable knowledge about ourselves and our environment is the solid foundation for faith in a brighter future. Fully justified now is the confidence that science can contribute mightily to the satisfaction of common human desire—freedom from want, freedom from fear, freedom from toilsome drudgery, and freedom from oppression. In such freedom science thrives and thus can continue its benefactions.

What Is a Botanist, and What Does He Do? The popular conception of a botanist is "an individual who can name plants." One is likely to visualize a more or less eccentric person, with plant press in hand, tramping through woods, meadows, swamps, and fields, collecting plants, neatly pressing them, giving them long, "meaningless" Latin names, and then filing the mounted specimens away in a herbarium that smells of naphthalene. The individual who knows the names of plants is indeed a botanist but in only one special subdivision of the field of plant science. In the broad field of plant science as it is developed today, there are many subdivisions and there are many workers who properly may be called **botanists,** or, if we prefer, **plant scientists.** They are working in many specialized fields of plant science. All are endeavoring to advance our knowledge of the plant world.

Let us inquire as to the number of botanists or plant scientists in the world and in this country. In accordance with a resolution passed at the Fifth International Botanical Congress, at Cambridge, England, in 1930, the *International Address Book of Botanists* was prepared. It is a directory of individuals and scientific institutions, universities, societies, etc., in all parts of the world, interested in the study of botany. This address book listed at that date 11,422 botanists and 2324 institutions and societies furthering botanical knowledge.

In 1939, the American Society of Plant Physiologists published the *International Address List of Plant Physiologists.* This list, by countries, totals 2701.

In 1947, Dr. Robert F. Griggs, formerly chairman of the Division of Biology and Agriculture, National Research Council, Washington, D. C., listed the main societies in the United States, together with the number of members in each, which have to do with plant science or with both plant and animal science. His findings are presented herewith.

PLANT SCIENCE

Society	Number of Members
Phytopathological Society	1130
Society of Agronomy	1200
Horticultural Science	740
Plant Physiologists	640
Botanical Society	1380
Mycological Society	380
Society of American Foresters	4550
Soil Science Society	500

SOCIETIES, BOTH PLANT AND ANIMAL

American Genetic Association	3530
Society of Biological Chemistry	600
Ecological Society	740
Genetics Society	560
Society of Bacteriologists	1500
Development and Growth	250

Each botanist, regardless of his specialized interest, is a plant scientist. It would be out of place here to relate what each of the above special fields of botanical science includes. We may suggest, however, that the interested student may consult his instructor or a library.

Subdivisions of Botany

The broad subdivisions of botany are: (1) **systematic botany** or **taxonomy,** (2) **morphology,** and (3) **physiology.**

Systematic Botany or Taxonomy. This phase of botany concerns the names of plants and their relationships. The number of different kinds (species) of plants recognized in the world today is well in excess of 300,000. A great many kinds that flourished in the geologic past are now extinct.

Many living plants are useful to man. Consider the economic importance of wheat, oats, barley, rice, corn, sugar cane, sorghum, date palm, coconut, rubber tree, banana, manioc, sugar beet, hop, fig, hemp, jute, cotton, flax, potato, tobacco, apple, melons, beans, alfalfa, soybean, the spices, the citrus fruits, olive, tea, coffee, and the great number of medicinal plants, and ornamental plants. And we should not fail to mention the many different kinds of fungi and bacteria, which have such an important bearing upon the health of man and other animals, the health of other plants, the fertility of the soil, and the preservation and decay of foods. Also of inestimable value are many species of trees, and of grasses and other forage plants of pastures, meadows, and ranges.

New species of plants are being discovered every year. It is estimated that the yearly average for the higher groups of plants alone is approximately 4700 proposed new species. It is obvious that, from the practical as well as from a scientific standpoint, it is necessary that attention be given to the naming and proper classification of the vast assemblage of plants, both native and cultivated. The botanists who do these things are systematic botanists or taxonomists. Most certainly it is essential for those working in the various fields of plant science, whether they are agriculturists, florists, foresters, physiologists, or morphologists, to know with what plants they are dealing; they must know their proper scientific names and their relationships. There must be those who are qualified to make accurate identifications of plants. There are so many kinds of plants, in so many different groups, that no one taxonomist can be expected to know them all. So it is that taxonomists usually give special attention to one or a few groups or to the plants of a limited area. For example, we may cite a noted taxonomist who is regarded as an authority on grasses; another, on orchids; another, on willows; another, on legumes; another, on various molds and mildews; another, on algae; another, on the floras of Indo-Malaya, Polynesia, China, and the Philippines; another, on the flora of peat bogs; etc.

Taxonomists are concerned with more than the identification and classification of plants, however. Their specialty also embraces problems of evolution and plant geography.

Plant Morphology. In a broad sense, plant morphology is concerned with the structure of plants. It involves external morphology, i.e., the external form, arrangement, and relationships of the various organs (such as roots, stems, leaves, and flowers); **anatomy,** the internal structure, including the finer details of tissues, **histology,** and of cells, **cytology. Cells** are the small chambers or compartments with their living substance, **protoplasm,** which make up the plant body. Let us cite specific examples that illustrate, in part, the scope of plant morphology. The plant breeder may be making crosses of wheat varieties in order to combine in the hybrids and their offspring certain desired qualities, such as resistance to disease, or high protein content of flour, or adaptation to soil and climatic conditions. In the first place, the plant breeder must know the structure of the wheat flower in order to be successful in the technique of cross pollination. He would call upon the morphologist not only for information about the external form of the flower and its various organs but also for the details of cellular structure.

If he is breeding for resistance to some disease that affects the leaves, it is essential to know the structure of the leaves. In fact, the wheat breeder should have a fairly clear picture of the form and structure, that is the morphology, of the entire wheat plant. In all higher plants there are reproductive structures, such as flowers and fruits, and vegetative structures, such as roots, stems, and leaves. There may be little resemblance between the vegetative portions of two species, although their reproductive structures may be very similar. For example, cabbage and watercress have quite different form and appearance and thrive in very different habitats. Their vegetative structures are quite different. The flowers of the two, however, are constructed on the same general plan. On the basis of similarity in flower structure, cabbage and watercress are placed in the same plant family. Reproductive structures are less influenced by environmental conditions than are vegetative organs. On account of this greater stability, the reproductive structures are of greater value than the vegetative structures in showing actual relationships and are of prime importance in classification. Thus, through his study of the form and structure, particularly of reproductive organs, the morphologist has assisted the taxonomist in establishing a natural system of classification of the plants of the world.

Certain chemical herbicides used to kill weeds profoundly alter the morphology of organs (such as leaves) formed by the treated plants (Fig. 1.3). A study of these morphological changes and a comparison with the development of normally produced organs may lead not only to a better understanding of the action and more effective use of the herbicides but may also help in the understanding of problems concerned with the normal development of plant organs.

The wood technologist can identify different kinds of wood by microscopic examination of sections that show its structure. The food microscopist can detect adulterations in food products, such as spices, breakfast foods, and canned products, because of his knowledge of the characteristic anatomy of the fragments of plant tissues which he observes under the microscope. Industrial fibers, such as cotton, flax, hemp, and jute, have individual structural characters that enable the expert to identify them in any manufactured article. A detailed knowledge of the structure of the wheat kernel is a guide to the milling processes that involve the separation of various tissues and the contents of the cells. Numerous other examples could be given indicating the value of a knowledge of plant structure and the work of a plant morphologist.

Plant Physiology. Plants absorb water and mineral salts from the soil; they take in oxygen and carbon dioxide from the atmosphere; they give off water to the atmosphere; they manufacture sugars, starch, fats, proteins, and scores of other substances; they conduct materials from one part of the plant to another; they respire; they grow; they react to the environment in which they live; they reproduce. In short, plants carry on a number of activities; they do work; they have functions. Plant physiology is the area of botany concerned with a study of these activities and functions. It is an experimental science. The plant physiologist observes the effects of variations in

Fig. 1.3. Grape leaves (*Vitis vinifora*), A, normal leaf; B, abnormal development of leaves after application of 2,4-D. ×½. (Photo courtesy of Gifford.)

environment and in heredity upon life processes and uses this information to explain and to control plant behavior. This branch of botany is an exceedingly important one, because it has contributed much knowledge that has found practical application in the growing of plants.

Let us cite a few examples that show the scope of plant physiology and the work of the plant physiologist. Fruits, such as apples, plums, and grapes, and vegetables, such as potatoes, peas, carrots, beets, and asparagus, are composed primarily of living cells, all of which are respiring. In this process, chemical reactions take place in the living cells, and the fruit or vegetable may change in quality. As a matter of fact, most fruits and vegetables lose in quality between the time of harvesting and the time of eating. The plant physiologist has studied these changes and the influence of such factors as temperature and humidity of the atmosphere upon the rate and nature of the changes. As a result of his studies we know now how best to store and refrigerate fruits and vegetables and how to ship them long distances across country or even to distant lands, so that they will reach the consumer in first-class condition.

Many kinds of commercial seeds do not germinate well, even though freshly harvested and kept under the most suitable conditions. The plant physiologist speaks of such seeds as exhibiting **dormancy.** For example, in a lot of alfalfa seed a consider-able percentage may not germinate but lie dormant in the soil. These seeds may germinate after a period of months or even years. The cause of this dormancy has been determined by the plant physiologist. In alfalfa, dormancy is caused by a hard seed coat impervious to water. The dormancy can be overcome and the seed made to germinate promptly by scratching the seed coat and thus rendering it permeable to water. Scratching or "scarifying" the seeds of alfalfa, sweet clover, and other legumes is now commercial practice.

Many other specific examples of physiological investigations could be cited.

Why Study Botany? From the discussion in this chapter, it is quite evident that the plant sciences are not detached from the world in which we live. Plants are a part of our environment. We depend upon them. We must study them. We must learn how to grow them and encourage them to produce more. We must learn new uses for the varied plants that grow in the far corners of the earth.

In the next chapter a brief picture will be given of the varied plant life of the world, and, in the chapters that follow, more details of the structure and functions of plants. Certain fundamentals of plant structure and function must be understood by the student if he is to have an intelligent comprehension of any phase of growing plants, whether for pleasure or for profit.

2

The Plant World

Plants clothe the earth. It is difficult to find any part of the earth entirely devoid of plant life. The bleak Aleutians have no tree growth, but there is a variety of herbs, including grasses, sedges, and rushes, and there are low shrubs, such as willows, birches, and alders, and also simpler forms of plants, such as lichens, mosses, and algae. In arctic and antarctic regions, and on high mountains well above timberline, there is plant life. Alpine meadows in midsummer may be luxuriant in the foliage and blossoms of a great variety of herbs. Even in the thin film of water on the surface of melting snow fields a one-celled plant (*Chlamydomonas*), containing a red pigment, sometimes occurs in such countless millions that it imparts to the surface a red color. "Red snow," as it is called, is not infrequently observed on polar and high-mountain snow fields.

Not only in very cold parts of the world do we find plants, but also where it is very hot. For example, certain microscopic blue-green plants form the principal vegetation of hot springs, where they have been found living in water at a temperature as high as 87° C (179° F). The beautiful coloration of the hot springs in Yellowstone National Park is partly due to such blue-green plants.

The hottest deserts of the world support various forms of plants. Deserts may be quite barren most of the year, but following periods of even moderate showers there may be a sudden burst of activity and the landscape becomes a profusion of flower colors. The face of a rock cliff exposed to the direct rays of the sun is an extremely hot and dry site. Yet on such cliffs one may find specialized plants that are able to withstand great extremes of both temperature and moisture (Fig. 2.1). Waters of the earth, both fresh and salt, support extensive plant growth. Fresh waters contain many kinds of algae, some fungi, and even certain flowering plants. Algae make up the greater part of the vegetation of marine waters. The free-floating marine plants are generally one-celled forms. In addition, large seaweeds, including the kelps, and the rockweeds (Figs. 18.20, 18.23) grow attached to the ocean floor. Seaweeds are used as food by some peoples; they also are a source of agar and of fertilizers.

There are no ferns or mosses in the sea, and the few flowering plants that occur are in shallow water close to shore. Marine algae (seaweeds) are sometimes found at considerable depths. As an example, in the Bay of Naples near the Isle of Capri,

Fig. 2.1. Mountain phlox (*Phlox douglasii*) growing on an exposed rock in the Sierra Nevada. (Photo courtesy of Ansel Adams.)

algal vegetation occurs at a depth of 390 to 425 feet.

The soil teems with bacteria and various fungi and algae. Here they play an indispensable role in soil fertility. Bacteria and fungi thrive in and on the bodies of plants and animals. In fact, plants of some kind are everywhere: in the air, the soil, the water; in the coldest and hottest, the wettest and driest parts of the world.

Different Kinds of Plants

Let us briefly survey the world of plants, and observe how they differ in size, form, color, life history, geographical distribution, manner of adjustment to environmental conditions, and usefulness. We have said that the number of distinct kinds (species) of plants in the world is well in excess of 300,000. Of course, the best-known plants are the trees, shrubs, and herbs, which include all sorts of plants used for food, clothing, shelter, ornament, medicine, and a great variety of industrial purposes. Less conspicuous and less well known are the mosses, liverworts, pond scums, and seaweeds; and still less well known, at least in their general appearance, are the thousands of different kinds of microscopic plants, such as bacteria, and certain fungi.

Plants Vary Greatly in Size. The largest plants in the world are the giant sequoias of California. For example, the General Sherman Tree in Sequoia National Park, California, is 272 feet in height. It has a base circumference of 94.8 feet and a volume of 450,000 board feet. The lumber from this giant tree could supply that required for thirty-five five-room houses covering three square city blocks. There is as much lumber in this one tree as could be obtained from 20 acres of average California pine forest. It is estimated that the General Sherman Tree has the largest amount of woody material of any living tree.

The smallest plants in the world are the bacteria (Fig. 17.1). Among the smallest known bacteria is a rod-shaped form that is $\frac{1}{2}$ micron long and $\frac{1}{5}$ micron wide. (A micron, the unit of microscopic measurement, is $\frac{1}{1000}$ of a millimeter or about $\frac{1}{25,000}$ of an inch.)

Plants Differ in Form. Plants have a body, just as animals do. A plant body has a form; the body of a common tree, shrub, or herb has organs, such as roots, stems, and leaves, serving its individual needs, as well as reproductive organs that make possible the formation of new individuals. Also we must recognize that even very simple plants, those *without* roots, stems, leaves, flowers, and fruit, have a distinct body form, with various structures for maintaining life and for reproducing. We readily recognize tall, erect trees, herbs, bushes, spreading shrubs, vines that trail over the branches of trees or other support—like hops, grapes, and pole beans—and plants that grow prostrate on the ground—such as cucumber, squash, watermelon, strawberry, and wild morning-glory. We are familiar with the so-called **succulent plants** (Fig. 6.58) with very fleshy stems or leaves, such as the cacti. Then there are plants with stems underground as well as aboveground, like the Irish potato (Fig. 6.52), onion (Fig. 6.54), iris, and gladiolus (Fig. 6.55). There are plants with roots in the air as well as underground, for example, *Symphonia* (Fig. 2.2), certain orchids, corn, and ivy. There are plants that shed their leaves with the approach of unfavorable growing conditions, such as cold weather or dry weather; we call such plants **deciduous.** Other plants, the so-called **evergreens,** bear foliage the year round; these include the pines, spruces, firs, cedars, sequoias, and many broadleaf evergreen shrubs of mild winter climates.

Fig. 2.2. *Symphonia globulifera,* a tree with aerial roots. (Photo by Beard, used in *Journal of the New York Botanical Garden.*)

Thus far we have mentioned the varied forms of trees, shrubs, and herbs, that is, of seed-bearing plants. Quite different in habits of growth and general character of the plant body are the many different kinds of non-seed-bearing plants; among these are pond scums, seaweeds, mushrooms, molds, mildews, rusts, smuts, liverworts, and the numerous species of microscopic plants.

Green and Nongreen Plants. Plants may be divided into two large groups distinguished by the manner in which they secure their food. (1) Green plants, that is, those which possess a green pigment (chlorophyll), are able to make their own food, and therefore are independent of any other organism. (2) Nongreen plants, that is, those devoid of chlorophyll, are unable to make food, and therefore are dependent upon a source of food supply outside their

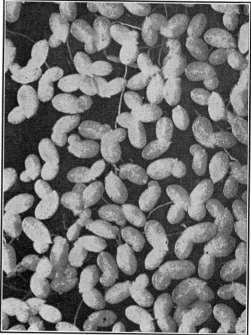

Fig. 2.3. Duckweed (*Lemna*), a free-floating flowering plant. ×1½.

Plants of cold or dry, exposed situations, as may be found on high mountain peaks or in polar regions, may take the form of cushions or mats or rosettes. In addition, some plants live in water. Some of these are free-floating, like duckweed (*Lemna*) (Fig. 2.3); others are attached to the bottom of the stream or pond and bring their leaves, flowers, and fruits above the water surface (waterlilies, *Elodea, Myriophyllum*); others are anchored to the bottom but are completely submerged, even the flowers and fruits developing underwater.

own bodies. In this second group of plants, which, like animals, must secure their food ready-made, are the fungi, most bacteria, a few algae, and a relatively few flowering plants, such as dodder, which is parasitic on stems and leaves of alfalfa and other flowering plants, Indian pipe (*Monotropa*) (Fig. 2.4), and the Sierran snow plant (*Sarcodes*). From the standpoint of man's food supply and of other uses man makes of

Fig. 2.5. Sword-fern (*Nephrolepsis*); a non-seed bearing plant. A, the fern plant, ×⅟₁₅; B, underside of a spore-bearing leaf, ×1.

Fig. 2.4. Indian pipe (*Monotropa*), a saprophytic flowering plant. ×½. (Courtesy of F. Herman.)

plants, green plants are the more important of the two groups. However, as we shall learn later, bacteria and fungi play an indispensable role in nature, particularly in relation to chemical changes that take place in the soil, and to the decomposition of organic substances.

Seed-bearing and Non-seed-bearing Plants. Another broad grouping of the plants of the world is as follows: (1) seed-bearing plants and (2) non-seed-bearing plants. Essentially, this grouping is based upon the method of reproduction. It may be somewhat surprising to learn that there are plants which reproduce by means other than seeds. As a matter of fact, all algae and fungi, all mosses and liverworts, all ferns (Fig. 2.5) and their relatives, a total of approximately 140,000 species, reproduce by other means than seeds. Recall that the total number of species of plants in the world is well over 300,000.

Although seed plants dominate the surface of the earth today, there was a time in the geologic history of the earth when there were no seed plants. Plants without seeds, that is, those reproducing by small bodies called **spores,** were then the only kinds of plants. Gradually in the development of plant life on the earth seed plants appeared. We recognize in the seed an extremely efficient structure for reproduction and multiplication, a structure able to retain its vitality for many years and very resistant to desiccation and to great extremes of temperature. Seeds are well adapted to wide dissemination. However, on account of the well-advanced state of development of the young plant (embryo) within the seed and the supply of stored food available to it, the new plant after germination is able to become well established before it must become self-supporting. Thus, plants with seeds are evidently successful in the struggle for existence, and they, like man in the animal kingdom, now dominate the surface of the earth.

It is very largely from seed plants that we derive foods and materials for shelter, clothing, and other industrial products.

Useful and Nonuseful Plants. We are inclined to evaluate different plants, to distinguish between those that are useful and those that appear to be useless. Such distinctions, however, are difficult to make. It has been emphasized that green plants are the food makers of the world, that all animals and all plants that are not green are dependent, directly or indirectly, on green plants. The very small animals (protozoans, crustaceans, and insect larvae) of both fresh and salt water, which are an important food supply of fish, are dependent mainly upon microscopic green aquatic plants for their food. Therefore, inasmuch as fish constitute an important food of man, we must conclude that these microscopic green aquatic plants are highly useful. Many inconspicuous herbs, other than grasses, which are fully recognized for their

forage value, and a considerable number of native shrubs are often browsed by animals on the western ranges and may constitute an important source of their food. Such plants cannot be classed as useless. Some plants that are useless or even harmful in certain places may be useful in others. For example, wild oats in many parts of the world is a weed in cultivated fields, but on western range lands of the United States it may supply a fairly good early feed for grazing animals. Tansy, a weed in certain parts of the United States, is cultivated as a medicinal plant in other parts. Such examples might be multiplied.

It is known with certainty that, although many bacteria and fungi cause diseases of plants and animals, a great many of these organisms are indispensable in nature in that they bring about the decomposition of plant and animal products and thus play a role in maintaining soil fertility. The relation of bacteria to soil fertility will be discussed in Chapter 17.

Man is continuously discovering new uses for plants. Most striking are his discoveries involving the utilization of wood as a basis for various plastics and also the utilization of the waste products of the agricultural industry, such as straw, corn cobs, fruit pits, and cull fruits and vegetables. As an example, the corn plant is put to a variety of uses: it provides food for human beings and livestock; it is a source of oil, starch, glucose (grape sugar), and artificial gums; pith from the stalks is made into explosives; pipes and charcoal are made from the cob; paper and building boards are produced from the stalks.

So intensive has been man's search for ways to utilize plants of the world and so productive have been his findings that one scarcely dares to label a given plant as wholly worthless. Someone has defined a weed as "a plant whose virtues have not been found out." This definition implies that all plants are of some benefit to man, that we simply have not discovered the benefits of weeds. This extreme view is probably unjustifiable.

Not all plants valuable to man are domesticated. Many native or "wild" plants are highly useful, although man thus far has not brought them under cultivation and improved them by selection and breeding. The student will find interest in a book entitled *Edible Wild Plants of Eastern North America*, by M. L. Fernald and A. C. Kinsey.*

Forest trees for the most part are not domesticated, although in many parts of the world trees are grown as a crop, planted in rows, and cared for until ready to be cut for lumber. Also, the improvement of forest species by breeding is under way in a limited fashion.

It will be of interest to classify the useful plants of the world, although it will not be possible to give here a list of plants in each group. This classification follows closely that given in A. F. Hill's *Economic Botany*,† a book replete with valuable information about useful plants and plant products.

1. Food plants.
   (*a*) Cereals.
   (*b*) Legumes and nuts.
   (*c*) Vegetables.
   (*d*) Fruit vegetables.
   (*e*) Fruits of temperate regions.
   (*f*) Tropical fruits.
2. Industrial plants and plant products.
   (*a*) Fiber plants.
   (*b*) Forest products.
   (*c*) Tanning and dye materials.
   (*d*) Rubber and other latex products.
   (*e*) Gums and resins.
   (*f*) Essential oils.
   (*g*) Fatty oils and waxes.
   (*h*) Sugars, starches, and cellulose products.

* Idlewild Press, 1943.
† McGraw-Hill Book Co., 1937.

3. Medicinal plants.
4. Spices and other flavoring materials.
5. Beverage plants and beverages.

Our classification does not include ornamental plants. Thousands of different kinds of plants are used to adorn public parks and streets, home gardens and lawns; the cut-flower industry in this country amounts to millions of dollars annually; large sums are represented in nurseries, seed farms, and greenhouses; in fact, we must regard ornamentals as among our indispensable useful plants.

The harmful plants include: (1) those that cause disease, (2) weeds, and (3) poisonous plants. All are of economic importance because of their harmful nature. They must be studied and understood; we must know how to control and eradicate them. It has been estimated that the annual losses in the United States from plant diseases (affecting ten leading crops plus forest trees) amount to $1190 million, and from weeds approximately $3000 million. The annual losses among cattle from eating poisonous plants amount to several million dollars.

The Distribution of Plants

Rarely in nature do individual plants grow isolated from all others. Plants, like human beings and other animals, generally live in associations, groups, or communities, such as forest and meadow. **Climate,** in the broad sense, and **soil** determine what kinds of plants dominate a given situation. This means that plants respond to a given set of environmental conditions. Environment is a complex set of factors; it includes light, heat, atmospheric humidity, precipitation, air movements, nature of the soil (including its structure, texture, temperature, and chemical composition), plants, and animals.

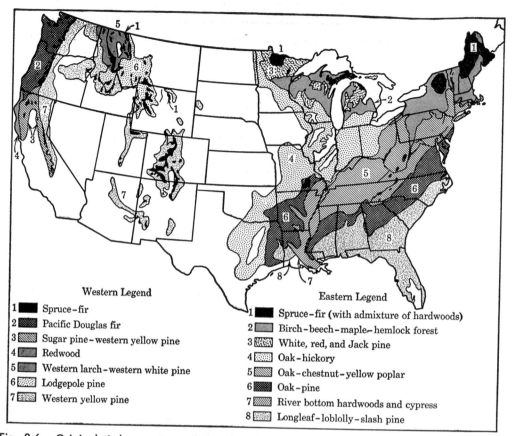

Western Legend

1 Spruce–fir
2 Pacific Douglas fir
3 Sugar pine–western yellow pine
4 Redwood
5 Western larch–western white pine
6 Lodgepole pine
7 Western yellow pine

Eastern Legend

1 Spruce–fir (with admixture of hardwoods)
2 Birch–beech–maple–hemlock forest
3 White, red, and Jack pine
4 Oak–hickory
5 Oak–chestnut–yellow poplar
6 Oak–pine
7 River bottom hardwoods and cypress
8 Longleaf–loblolly–slash pine

Fig. 2.6. Original timber regions of the United States. (From Jones, *Economic Geography,* The Macmillan Co.)

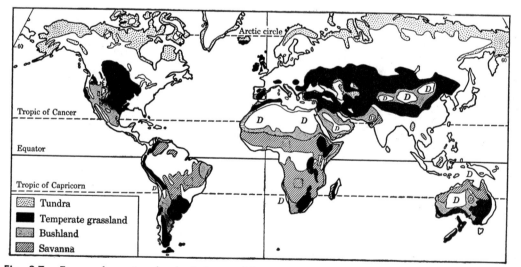

Tundra
Temperate grassland
Bushland
Savanna

Fig. 2.7. Types of grazing land of the world. *D* indicates deserts. (From Jones, *Economic Geography,* The Macmillan Co.)

The effect of the various combinations of environmental factors is seen in the characteristic plant communities in different parts of the world. If we travel from the Atlantic to the Pacific Coast, we see great changes in the plant life (Fig. 2.6). Although much of the original vegetation has been disturbed by cultivation, we can see enough of it to know what the original vegetation was like. From the East Coast to a point a hundred miles or more west of Chicago, we pass through mixed deciduous forests of oak, hickory, elm, ash, maple, linden, poplar, and other broadleaf trees. Across the Appalachians is a narrow belt of forest, composed principally of hemlock, eastern white pine, red pine, red spruce, sugar maple, red maple, yellow birch, American beech, and black cherry. From the mixed deciduous forests west to the foot of the Rocky Mountains is the great central grassland belt of our country—one of the richest agricultural regions in the world (Fig. 2.7). The eastern half of this grassland belt is the **prairie**, where the characteristic vegetation consists of tall grasses. Here the average annual precipitation is from 35 to 40 inches. The western half is drier, the average annual precipitation being 10 to 18 inches. This half is called the **Great Plains**, and its characteristic vegetation is short grasses, such as grama grass and buffalo grass. Then we come to the Rocky Mountains and see forests of western yellow pine, Douglas fir, lodgepole pine, Engelmann spruce, fir, and other conifers. Westward over the Continental Divide is the Great Basin, a well-named area between the Rocky Mountains and the Sierra Nevada. This is a desert **shrubland** with sagebrush (Fig. 2.8) predominating in the north and creosote bush in the south. In

Fig. 2.8. Sagebrush in western United States. (Photo by R. C. Wilson, courtesy California Forest and Range Station, U. S. Forest Service.)

the Sierra are evergreen forests, and on the western slope **chaparral** on the lower stretches, grassland in the great valley of the Sacramento and San Joaquin rivers, and then coastal forests.

A transcontinental trip such as briefly described illustrates the influence of climatic factors upon the character of the plant life. In any locality, however, a walking trip will show various kinds of plant communities resulting from differences in the local environment. For example, around almost every lake or pond is a striking arrangement of the vegetation in more or less concentric zones (Fig. 2.9). A well-chosen radius from free water to shore line and up a gradually sloping bank will show these zones best. In the water may be some plants that are completely submerged. Then there are marsh plants in shallow water, with their roots and rootstocks and possibly some of their leaves underwater but with much of the plant above the surface, thus exposed to the evaporating action of the air. Along the shore line, where the water table is high, may be willows and alders and many other plants that thrive only if soil moisture is ample. Higher on the slopes are plants of a different character which have roots penetrating the soil to considerable depths and have habits of growth and structures which enable them to withstand periodic dry spells.

Fig. 2.9. Zones of vegetation around a lake in the Rocky Mountains. (Courtesy of Ansel Adams.)

A Vegetation Map of the World

The principal types of vegetation which cover large expanses of the earth's land surface are forest, shrub, grassland, desert, and tundra (Figs. 2.6 and 2.7). There are, of course, other kinds of plant associations less extensive, such as those of fresh water, salt water, marsh and swamp, and saline and alkaline soils. But the five associations above include the principal ones that cover vast areas and give character to the landscape.

Water and **temperature** are the two principal factors that determine the general distribution and character of the vegetation that clothes the earth's surface. For example, in the tropics where temperatures are high and rainfall abundant throughout the year, an evergreen hardwood forest flourishes and the vegetation is luxuriant. But, in the tropics where the temperatures are high and the rainfall meager, a desert type of vegetation occurs.

Plants absorb water from the soil. Most of this water moves through the plant and is lost to the atmosphere as water vapor escaping from the leaves. If the plant is to survive it must take in as much water from the soil as it loses to the atmosphere, in addition to that utilized in its vital processes. If the air temperature is high, the wind movement great, and the atmosphere dry, that is, the relative humidity low, the leaves of plants lose water rapidly. When this happens and the amount of soil water available is inadequate, the plant is likely to succumb. Evergreen trees with broad leaves, exposing a large evaporating leaf surface to the air throughout the year, could not long survive under such conditions. Rather would we expect to find in such an environment plants with a reduced leaf surface, with water-storage tissue, and with other structural features that tend to maintain a balance between water intake and water outgo. Plants with these characters are better able to survive under conditions of high temperature, low relative humidity, and low rainfall. Plants of the deserts have these features, which are so well seen in various cacti. In another chapter the water relations of plants will be discussed more fully. As regards the principal vegetation types of the world, indicated above, the student should keep in mind the combined influence of temperature and available water in the soil, the two chief factors determining the geographical distribution of vegetation types.

Forests of the World

The forests of the world are broadly classified as follows: (1) **conifers** or **softwoods**, (2) **temperate hardwoods**, (3) **tropical hardwoods**, and (4) **mixed conifers and hardwoods** (Fig. 2.10). Conifers or softwoods are such trees as pine, spruce, fir, larch, cypress, juniper, and redwood. Hardwoods are, for the most part, broadleaf trees that in temperate climates are represented by such common plants as oak, maple, walnut, and ash, and in tropical climates by a very large number of different kinds of trees, many of which are not well known. The forest resources of the tropics are enormous and as yet scarcely touched.

It is estimated that approximately 22.5 per cent of the earth's land surface is forest. This is about 7500 million acres, but not more than 5500 million acres is productive.

In many countries the present forested area is only a small percentage of that which originally covered the land. This is particularly true of China, where large forests are now rare. In Great Britain only 5 per cent of the original forest remains; in France, Spain, Belgium, Italy, and Greece but 10 to 20 per cent; in Sweden and Finland about 50 per cent; and in the United States about 60 per cent. Today, the largest forested areas are in South America and Asia, including the East Indies.

	Percentage of Land Area in Forests	Percentage of Conifers	Percentage of Temperate Hardwoods	Percentage of Tropical Hardwoods
North America	26.8	72.4	20.1	7.5
South America	44.0	5.2	5.5	89.3
Europe	31.3	74.0	24.0	1.6
Asia	21.6	42.4	27.3	30.3
Africa	10.7	0.9	2.2	96.9
Australia	5.8	4.0	11.0	85.0
New Zealand	25.7	68.0	32.0	0.0
Oceania	71.0	0.0	0.0	100.0

Tropical Rain Forests. One of the most striking types of vegetation in the world is the tropical rain forest (Fig. 2.11). Many Americans who were in the armed forces during World War II became very familiar with it. It has almost daily rain, the air is constantly humid, and the temperatures are high. There is no definite dry season. The annual rainfall is over 75 inches and, in some regions, more than twice that much.*

* Average annual precipitation in inches in regions with tropical rain forests: Suva, Fiji, 113; Jaluit, Marshall Islands, 159; Kusaie,

The tropical rain forest is evergreen and consists almost entirely of broadleaf species. Characteristic is the very large number of species. It is reported that on 3 square miles of rain forest around Lagoa Santa in Brazil a total of over 400 species of trees was recorded. Over 2500 different tree species are said to occur in the Amazon forest. Some tropical rain forests have such a dense mass of foliage from the ground up to the tops of the trees that they are nearly impassable; others are "like immense dark-columned halls which afford a free passage and a clear outlook in all directions" (Schimper). In those of the "jungle" type, the ground may be covered with ferns, mosses, and low herbs; low palms, tree ferns, and various shrubs may form another vegetative story; above these are trees of moderate height; and the highest story or

Caroline Islands, 255; Kau Kau, Guadalcanal, 180; Annaville, New Caledonia, 109; Pago Pago, Samoa, 196; Kieta, Bougainville, 120; Rendova, Solomon Islands, 175; Finschhafen, New Guinea, 115; Colón, Panama, 116; Kamerun, Africa, 99.

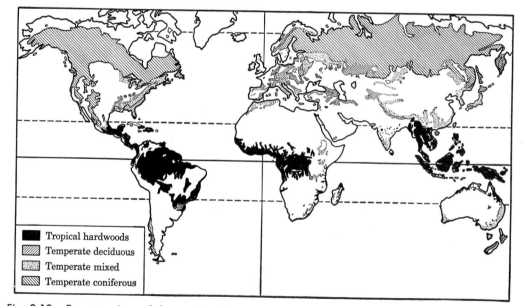

Tropical hardwoods
Temperate deciduous
Temperate mixed
Temperate coniferous

Fig. 2.10. Forest regions of the world. (From Jones, *Economic Geography*, The Macmillan Co.)

Fig. 2.11. Humid tropical forest in Hawaii National Park. (Photo courtesy of Ansel Adams.)

tier is composed of trees with tall, thick trunks unbranched up to 100 to 150 feet.

Fig. 2.12. The staghorn fern (*Platycerium andinum*) and a tropical fern (*Polypodum Ulei*) living side by side as epiphytes on a Brazilian jungle tree. (Photo by E. Ule, used in the *Journal of the New York Botanical Garden.*)

In some cases the shade may be so dense that the forest floor is almost bare. In tropical rain forests woody climbing plants, **lianas,** abound. Also, there are many species of **epiphytes** (Fig. 2.12)—plants that grow attached to the trunks and branches of trees and have no contact with the soil.

The most extensive continuous rain forest in the world is in the Amazon drainage basin.

Tropical Deciduous Forests and Woodlands. In contrast to the evergreen rain forests of the tropics are those forests in tropical regions which experience a periodic dry season. The leaves of many species are shed with the approach of the dry season. Schimper recognizes three types of such tropical forests: (1) **monsoon forest,** (2) **savannah forest,** (3) **thorn forest.**

The deciduous forests of tropical Burma are the best example of the **monsoon type.** These Burmese forests are described by Schimper as folows: "Here the trees average in height 70–80 feet, but in many parts of the country are even 120 feet high. They grow straight and are often accompanied by lianas; these epiphytes are practically confined to the tops of the trees. The intervals between the trees are frequently filled with a tall bamboo thicket; but shrubby and herbaceous vegetation, particularly grass, is very scanty." The teak tree (dati tree) is a characteristic plant of monsoon forests not only in Burma and British India but also in East Java.

The **savannah forest** is parklike in appearance. The trees, which shed their leaves during the dry season, are usually less than 60 feet tall; there are relatively few woody shrubs, lianas, and epiphytes but an abundance of herbs, especially grasses. Savannah forests are found in East Africa, tropical America, Burma, and other tropical areas, often merging into the monsoon type of forest. The bush forests of

Africa and the "campos serrados" of Brazil also belong here.

The thorn forests of the tropics occur where the climate is somewhat drier than that of the savannah forest. The trees are less than 60 feet tall; there is a considerable amount of woody undershrubs and slender lianas, but herbs, including grasses, are sparse. Thorny plants are characteristic. Typical thorn forests and woodlands occur in the interior of Brazil, where they are known as "caatinga," in parts of central India, and along the coast of East Africa.

From the standpoint of forest resources, those of the tropics are unexcelled but as yet scarcely touched. When we realize that the present forest area of the United States is but slightly more than half that of the primeval forests that existed when the country was settled, that but 5 per cent of the original forest of Great Britain remains, that in the thickly settled parts of Europe and China very little of the original forested area remains, it seems evident that we will look more and more to the tropics for the products of the forest, especially lumber. One might pause to consider the possibility of a considerable unbalance in natural conditions should these great tropical forests be depleted as have been those of Great Britain, Europe, China, and the United States. Some of the important tropical woods, among the several thousand, are balsa, boxwood, ebony, cocuswood, lignum vitae, mahogany, rosewood, satinwood, and teak.

Coniferous Forests. Examples of coniferous or cone-bearing trees are pines, spruces, firs, cedars, junipers, redwoods, hemlocks, larch, and arborvitae. Their seeds are borne in cones (Fig. 24.18), and they have no flowers in the ordinary sense. The leaves are small and needlelike (Fig. 24.19) and with few exceptions (larch) remain attached to the tree for several years; that is, coniferous forests are ever-green. These small, needlelike leaves are characteristics that enable conifers to withstand dry conditions.

Coniferous forests occupy approximately 35 per cent of the total forested area of the world, an area estimated at about 7500 million acres. Coniferous forests are most extensive in the cold temperate zone of the Northern Hemisphere; in warmer climates they are restricted to the higher altitudes. Coniferous forests include one of the greatest sources of lumber and turpentine and also of pulpwood for paper.

The coniferous forests of the United States are shown in Fig. 2.6. The **great northern** or **subpolar coniferous forest** stretches across the northern part of the continent from Labrador and Newfoundland to Alaska, the principal species being balsam fir, larch, white spruce, and black spruce, interspersed with aspen, paper birch, and balsam poplar. The **southeastern coniferous forest** occurs along the Atlantic coastal plain from Virginia to Texas, where the principal coniferous species are longleaf pine, shortleaf pine, loblolly pine, southern white cedar, and cypress, with a mixture of such broadleaf species as live oak, magnolia, red gum, and tupelo. The **Rocky Mountain coniferous forest** stretches from Central America to Northern British Columbia, the principal coniferous species being lodgepole pine, western yellow pine, Douglas fir, white fir, Engelmann spruce, and alpine fir. The **Pacific Coast forests** include such commercially important species as the Sitka spruce, Douglas fir, the redwoods, western yellow pine, lodgepole pine, Engelmann spruce, sugar pine, and red fir.

Coniferous forests, chiefly of Scotch pine and Norway spruce, extend across northern Europe including Scandinavia. In the central and southern mountainous districts of Europe are forests of silver fir. In the Pyrenees and Alps the Swiss mountain pine forms impressive forests. A primeval forest of pines, larches, and spruces covers great stretches of Siberia. Extensions of the Siberian forests occupy the northern Chinese plateau from the Altai Mountains to Lake Baikal, the southeastern corner of Siberia, northeastern China, Kamchatka, and the island of Saghalin southward towards Japan. There are extensive forests of Aleppo pine in southern Europe and, along the Mediterranean, forests of Italian stone pine.

Deciduous Forests of Temperate Zones. The tree species of deciduous forests are commonly spoken of as hardwoods, as contrasted with the so-called softwoods of coniferous forests. Deciduous forests occur in those regions that have marked seasonal temperature changes, that is, in the Temperate Zones. As we have seen, however, there are deciduous forests also in tropical and subtropical regions that experience a dry season. In North America, temperate-climate hardwoods constitute approximately 20 per cent of the forests. Figure 2.6 shows the extent of the great eastern deciduous forest of the United States. This is a mixed forest of elm, ash, walnut, tulip-tree, chestnut, hickory, oak, beech, maple, and other species. In South America temperate hardwoods constitute only about 5 per cent of the forests; in Europe, about 24 per cent; in Asia, about 27 per cent; in Africa, slightly over 2 per cent; in Australia, 11 per cent; and in New Zealand, 32 per cent.

Shrub Vegetation

A shrub or bushland type of vegetation occupies those regions with a rainfall intermediate between that which supports forests and that which makes for true desert. In the United States, typical shrub or bushland is represented by the sagebrush of the northern part of the Great Basin (Fig. 2.8) and by the creosote bush of the southern part of this same area. There are portions of western Colorado, Utah, Idaho, Nevada, and eastern Oregon and Washington that are dominated by sagebrush, an almost pure stand as far as the eye can see. Sagebrush lands that can be irrigated are among our most productive agriculturally. There are boundless areas of shrub or brush in southern Russia, in central, western, and southwestern Australia, and in other scattered parts of the world. On the foothills of the Rocky Mountains and the Sierra Nevada, extensive areas are covered with drought-resistant, often thorny shrubs or bushes; such vegetation is known as **chaparral.** The chaparral of western United States is utilized chiefly for grazing.

Grasslands of the World

There are many types of grasslands in the world (Fig. 2.7). In all of them perennial grasses dominate, but these may be intermixed with many different kinds of other herbs and a few shrubs or trees. Two general types of grasslands are recognized: (1) **steppe** and (2) **savannah.** The grasslands of the central United States are examples of **steppes.** The meadow type of steppe, represented by the **prairies** of the so-called Corn Belt, is composed of relatively tall grasses growing in a region where the annual precipitation is from 35 to 40 inches. West of the prairies are the **Great Plains.** The dominant vegetative covering is short grasses (buffalo grass and grama grass). Here the average annual precipitation is from 10 to 18 inches. The steppes of southern Russia, bounded on the east by the Caspian desert and on the south by the Black Sea, and including the famed Ukraine, are among the most extensive grasslands of the world. Here the rainfall averages approximately 16 inches a year.

The **pusztas** of Hungary are similar to the steppes of Russia. The **pampas** of South America represent another extensive grassland area.

The **savannah** type of grassland (Fig. 2.13) occurs in dry tropical and subtropical climates and contains isolated trees. Brazilian savannahs are known as "campos," those of Venezuela as "llanos," those of Ceylon as "patanas," and those of the Congo as "campine."

The grasslands of the world have become the richest of the agricultural lands, as witness the Ukraine of Russia and the prairies and plains of the United States. Many million acres of these grasslands are now in cultivated crops, orchards, and pastures. The native grasslands of western United States, unsuitable for cultivation, are usually designated as "range lands." The "range" area of the United States is estimated to be about 728 million acres.

These range lands in western Kansas, the panhandle of Oklahoma, northern Texas and eastern Colorado and New Mexico have been plowed and planted to wheat. The rainfall in this region is between 14 and 18 inches a year and the soil and winds are such that under proper conditions the soil under cultivation "blows." In 1954 this "Dust Bowl" area involved some 12 million acres and presented a problem of considerable magnitude to the agricultural policy makers of the country. From a strictly botanical viewpoint there is no problem; native grasses will hold the land. However, under wartime conditions wheat gives a much greater financial return, so the land is cultivated and money and men invested in its development. This development can

Fig. 2.13. Savannah type dry grasslands of California. (Courtesy of P. Jones.)

only end in the destruction of the land. The problem concerns not only plants and what the botanist knows of their requirements but also important human relationships.

Deserts of the World

Extensive areas of the world have a very low annual rainfall (usually less than 5 inches *), frequently high air and soil temperatures, and very dry air (Fig. 2.14). Consequently, their vegetation is sparse. Because of these conditions the soil in these areas is almost devoid of humans. How-

* The average annual rainfall (in inches) of certain desert localities is as follows: Copcapo, Chile, 0.4; Aden, Arabia, 2; Suez, Egypt, 2.4; Fort Mohave, Ariz., 2.4; Walvis Bay, South Africa, 0.24.

ever, many desert and semidesert soils respond to irrigation, and great areas of desert land have become valuable agriculturally.

The most extensive deserts of the world are as follows:

1. Across North Africa (between 20° and 30°N.) including much of Algeria, Libya, Egypt, north Anglo-Egyptian Sudan, eastward into Arabia, Iraq, southern Iran, Afghanistan, Baluchistan, and northern India. This large area includes such deserts as the Sahara, Libyan and Nubian, and Thar.

2. Central Asia, from the Caspian Sea to the mountains that stand between Mongolia and Manchuria. The Gobi Desert is included in this area.

3. Western America, including parts of the states of Utah, Nevada, Arizona, and Southern California, and south to the Mexican plateau. This area includes the Colorado, the Mohave, Sonora, and Chihuahua deserts.

Fig. 2.14. Desert of Southwestern United States. (Photo courtesy of Ansel Adams.)

4. Central Australia.

5. South Africa, including the Kalahari and Namib deserts.

6. Western strip of the South American coast, and western Argentina.

The characteristic plants of the deserts of North America are the cacti, of which there are many species. Other conspicuous plants are mesquites, acacias, and yuccas, of which the Joshua tree (Fig. 2.15) is an example. Generally, plants able to exist in the desert have various structural devices for storing water or for preventing the loss of water from the plant surface. Cacti are characteristic only of American deserts. The typical native plants of the Sahara Desert, although succulent and spiny, thus resembling cacti, are members of entirely different plant families (chiefly spurge family and milkweed family). American cacti, however, have been introduced into deserts of other parts of the world. Contrary to the general impression, deserts are not always bare stretches of burning sands almost totally devoid of plant life. As a matter of fact, the deserts of southwestern United States, for example, blossom with a profusion of flowering plants, after the short rainy period. Most of these plants are annuals.

Fig. 2.15. Joshua tree (*Yucca brevifolia*) in the Mohave Desert of California.

Tundra

The treeless wastes on arctic islands and mainlands not covered by ice support a vegetation composed mostly of various mosses and lichens (see page 427). Low herbs and some dwarf shrubs may occur. The tundra soil is wet and cold, the air moist. Typical tundras are found in northern Russia and Siberia, Greenland, Iceland, northern Canada, and on such islands as the Aleutians. The sparse vegetation of the tundra is not uniform; mosses predominate in moister soil, and lichens in drier soil.

Native and Alien Plants

A distinction may be made between those plants *native* to a region and those which have been *introduced* from some other part of the world. Most of the plants we grow in orchard, garden, and field are introduced; they are desirable aliens. It is apparent that man has greatly changed the vegetative aspect of many parts of the world. He has plowed up the native grasses of plains and prairies and has planted cereals, legumes, and other introduced species. He has cleared the forests and developed farms, using as crops mostly those native to some other part of the world. There are many regions where cultivation of the land is so extensive that it is difficult to find even small vestiges of the original plant covering. In Central Europe much of the original forest land is replaced by forest trees that have been planted.

In addition to the useful alien crop plants, there are many **weeds.** These are species that, in some instances, are harmless in their native home but behave as weeds under other conditions of soil and climate. For example, in one state, California, 360 species or 72 per cent of the total number of weeds are from Europe and Western Asia, and fully 15 per cent of these are from the Mediterranean region. Eastern Asia, South Africa, and Australia have contributed about 10 per cent; South America, approximately 10 per cent; and the United States, east of California, about 8 per cent. Relatively few native plants of California have become pernicious weeds in that state.

In the United States, the movement of populations westward, the reclamation and settlement of new lands, the planting of agricultural crop plants and the development of the livestock industry have all been factors in the introduction and establishment of alien plants, many of which are undesirable. For example, in western states many of the range lands have been invaded by European and North African annual grasses that have replaced the original native grasslands, consisting largely of perennial species. This invasion by alien species has been brought about chiefly by overgrazing or by plowing and subsequent abandonment of the land. Burned-over forest areas are sometimes invaded by species that are not native to the region. The building of roads, levees, ditches, etc., disturbs the natural plant covering, and on the disturbed areas one may usually find a great variety of weeds, most of which are from a foreign land.

It will be of interest to the student to learn the native home of the various field, orchard, and garden crops and of the orna-

mental trees, shrubs, and herbs, and the weeds in the garden or home plantings. Many of these alien plants have been introduced purposively; others, the weeds, have arrived in our midst from faraway lands, against our wishes and desires. In what ways did these weeds get here? How did they escape the vigilant eye of the border guard? We can deport an undesirable alien human being but not an alien plant. What means are available to rid our lands of these undesirable alien plants?

Indicator Plants

Native plants have served to indicate the agricultural possibilities of a region. Any native plant community, which obviously is one that has become established and survived successfully in a region for many thousands of years, is a response to and an index of both soil and climate. As a matter of fact, farmers have long been in the habit of judging the value of land for crops largely by the natural plant covering. In the Great Basin between the Rocky Mountains and the Sierra Nevada, sagebrush (*Artemisia tridentata*) (Fig. 2.8) usually indicates land free from alkali, whereas greasewood (*Sarcobatus vermiculatus*) is an indicator of alkali soil. Sagebrush land is capable of crop production but greasewood land is not, unless the alkali in the soil is removed by drainage. In the Great Plains of eastern Colorado, wire-grass land or bunch-grass land is freer from crop failure than is land dominated by short grass of the grama-buffalo grass type, although short-grass land is darker in color and looks like better soil. Wire-grass and bunch-grass associations indicate soil that is moist to a considerable depth, whereas short grass indicates land from which there is considerable water runoff and consequently less water in the deeper layers of soil.

3

Classification and
Naming of Plants

Chapter 1, page 9, contains a brief discussion of systematic botany or taxonomy, one of the main subdivisions of the plant sciences. The systematic botanist or taxonomist is concerned with (1) the grouping or classification of plants, together with the principles involved, and also with (2) a phase known as nomenclature or naming of plants. For example, there are many kinds of clovers (Fig. 3.1): there is a small, trailing white clover common in lawns, pastures, and meadows; there is red clover, a forage and hay crop. In fact, about 300 kinds of clover are recognized in the world today. Some are cultivated; many are known only in the wild state. These clovers may differ not in just one character, like flower color or leaf shape, but in several characters: size, habit of growth, shape, color, and structural details of the flower, fruit, seed, etc.

Categories of Classification

The Species. It is customary to speak of each recognizable **kind** of plant as a **species** (plural, also **species**). Although the spe-

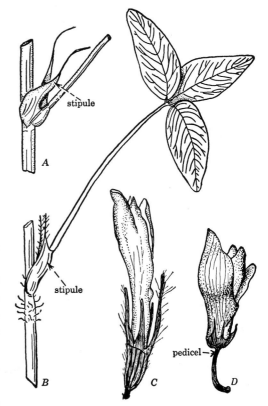

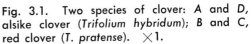

Fig. 3.1. Two species of clover: A and D, alsike clover (*Trifolium hybridum*); B and C, red clover (*T. pratense*). ×1.

33

cies is the basic unit in plant classification, it is very difficult to give a concise definition of the term. Provisionally, we may say that a *species is a group of similar plants that normally breed freely among themselves*. Under natural conditions they do not usually cross with dissimilar groups of plants. Many exceptions to this definition can be found. In spite of the difficulty of defining a species, this unit forms the "building stone" of classification.

Most species, such as white clover, **are** represented by millions of individual plants. These individuals are alike in all their *essential* characters, but they are *not exactly alike;* in fact, no two plants are identical in all their characteristics. All members of a species show individual variations of a minor or nonspecific nature. Whereas most species of plants are represented by millions of individuals, a few species are represented in the world today by only a relatively small number of individual plants. Notable examples are the Monterey cypress (*Cupressus macrocarpa*) (Fig. 3.2), found naturally only on the headlands at the mouth of the Carmel River in Monterey County, California, and the Big Tree (*Sequoiadendron giganteum*), occurring over a limited area on the western slope of the Sierra Nevada at elevations between 5000 and 8000 feet.

Fig. 3.2. Monterey cypress (*Cupressus macrocarpa*) along Del Monte's Seventeen-mile Drive, California. (Photo courtesy of Julian P. Graham.)

There is an obvious relationship among plants. For example, it is evident that the various species of clover and peas are more closely related than the species of clover and melons, and that the species of wheat and barley have a closer relationship than species of wheat and tobacco. We judge clover and peas as close relatives because of the striking similarity in flower structure, character of fruit, and type of foliage; and we are equally certain of the distant relationship of clover and melons because of the great dissimilarity in flower structure, nature of fruit, type of foliage, and whole manner of growth.

The Genus. If plants are to be grouped or classified intelligently, it would seem desirable to arrange them so as to bring together those *most closely related.* For example, there are many distinct species of clover; they are similar in many respects and more closely related to each other than to other kinds of plants; accordingly, species of clover are grouped and constitute a **genus** (plural, **genera**). The name of the genus to which all clover species belong is *Trifolium.* From the noun genus there is the adjective **generic.** Therefore, we would say that *Trifolium* is the **generic name** of clovers. When we use the name *Trifolium,* we refer to all kinds or species of clovers.

The question naturally is asked: How do we designate a certain species of clover, such as white clover or red clover? This is done by using a **binomial,** that is **two names.** For example, white clover is *Trifolium repens,* and red clover is *Trifolium pratense. Trifolium* alone refers to all clovers; *repens* alone refers to no kind of plant; but the binomial *Trifolium repens* refers to a distinct species, and the binomial *Trifolium pratense* to another distinct species. As stated, there are close to 300 species of *Trifolium* in the world. It is apparent that a genus is a more inclusive and larger group than a species.

The Family. Let us continue with the explanation of the method of classifying plants. Because of the similarity in flower, fruit, and other characters, it is believed that such plants as clovers, garden peas, beans, vetches, alfalfas, peanuts, and many similar plants are closely related. But the foregoing common plants are sufficiently unlike, according to the judgment of competent systematic botanists, to place them in different genera. Species of clovers belong to the genus *Trifolium,* garden peas to the genus *Pisum,* beans to the genus *Phaseolus,* vetches to the genus *Vicia,* alfalfas to the genus *Medicago,* and peanuts to the genus *Arachis.* But these different genera have so many characters in common that they are brought together in a single group called a **family.** The family that includes the above genera and many others closely related to them is the Leguminosae, or legume family. A family is more inclusive than a genus, and a genus, in turn, more inclusive than a species. To state it differently, species are collections of closely related individual plants, genera are collections of closely related species, and families are collections of genera.

Other Categories. Families of plants are grouped into **orders,** orders into **classes,** classes into **phyla,** each, in the order given, being more inclusive than the foregoing. This system is followed by taxonomists in the naming and classification of animals, also. In both plant and animal kingdoms the largest groupings are the **phyla.**

THE PLANT PHYLA

The method of classifying or grouping the many species of plants now recognized may be clarified by beginning with the largest group and following with the smaller and smaller subgroups. All plants in the world, constituting the **plant kingdom,** may be placed into a number of fairly distinct groups that we will designate as **phyla** (singular, **phylum**). Certain phyla are divided up into smaller groups called classes. These groups are as follows:

1. Phylum Schizophyta (fission plants).
   Class Schizomycetes (bacteria).
   Class Schizophyceae (blue-green algae).
2. Phylum Euglenophycophyta (euglenoids).
3. Phylum Chlorophycophyta (green algae).
4. Phylum Charophycophyta (stoneworts).
5. Phylum Chrysophycophyta (diatoms and related forms).
6. Phylum Pyrrophycophyta (golden-brown algae).
7. Phylum Phaeophycophyta (brown algae).
8. Phylum Rhodophycophyta (red algae).
9. Phylum Myxomycophyta (slime molds).
10. Phylum Eumycophyta (true fungi).
    Class Phycomycetes.
    Class Ascomycetes.
    Class Basidiomycetes.
    Class Imperfecti,
11. Phylum Bryophyta.
    Class Hepaticae (liverworts).
    Class Anthocerotae (anthoceros).
    Class Musci (mosses).
12. Phylum Psilophyta—represented chiefly by fossil forms.
13. Phylum Lycophyta (clubmosses and quillworts).
14. Phylum Sphenophyta (horsetails).
15. Phylum Pterophyta.
    Class Filicinae (ferns).
    Class Gymnospermae (cone-bearing seed plants).
    Class Angiospermae (flower-bearing seed plants).

Note that all phyla have the termination *phyta*, which is derived from the Greek word *phyton* meaning plant. The ending *ae* is used generally to designate classes and it will be seen that most family names end in *aceae*. In the algae the class ending is *phyceae* and in the fungi it is *mycetes*. Some of the common families of flowering plants end in *eae*, or even *ae* rather than the normal *aceae*, i.e., the grass family, Gramineae; the pea family, Leguminosae; and the usual, the rose family, Rosaceae.

Characteristics of Plant Phyla

The first ten phyla are often referred to as the **thallophytes** or the "thallus plants," a **thallus** being a very simple plant body lacking true roots, stems, and leaves. Moreover, the majority of thallophytes have *unicellular reproductive structures.* The **bryophytes** (phylum 11) or "moss plants" are primitive land plants, like thallophytes in that they have no true roots, stems, and leaves and no specialized system for the conduction of food and water from one part of the plant to another, but unlike thallophytes in that they possess *multicellular reproductive structures.* The last four phyla are often referred to as the **vascular plants** because they possess a vascular or specialized conducting system. Three of these four phyla, 12, 13, and 14, are of interest because the living plants belonging to them are the remnants of ancient vegetation. The Psilophyta are represented by only two genera and four species of living plants, and one of these is so primitive that it lacks roots and has only much-reduced leaves. The other two phyla are represented by the clubmosses and horsetails. These plants are small and form a rather inconspicuous part of the present-day flora. Once the earth's vegetation was comprised of extensive forests of these plants. Indeed, much of the coal burned today is the carbonized trunks of representatives of these two phyla. To the last phylum, the Pterophyta, belong the ferns and the seed plants. This phylum is divided into three large classes: one class (Filicinae) comprises the ferns; another class (Gymnospermae) contains the cone-bearing trees (conifers); and the third class

(Angiospermae), the largest, includes all the flowering plants.

Clover has a vascular system, flowers, and seeds. It belongs to the class Angiospermae in the phylum Pterophyta. When the clover seed germinates, *two* cotyledons or seed leaves are evident; therefore, clover is in the subclass Dicotyledoneae. This subclass is a very large assemblage of plants. It is divided into many **orders**, that to which clover belongs being the order Rosales. This order of flowering plants includes around 15,000 species, all of which have certain characters in common. It is subdivided into **families**, including such well-known ones as the rose family (Rosaceae), the mimosa family (Mimosaceae), the legume family (Leguminosae), and the gooseberry family (Grossulariaceae). Clover is a member of the legume family. This family of plants, a very large, cosmopolitan one, has about 400 genera and more than 5000 species. Clovers belong to the genus *Trifolium*. This genus in turn has many species (about 300). White clover is *Trifolium repens*.

Summarizing, the complete classification of white clover (*Trifolium repens*) is as follows:

Phylum—Pterophyta
Class—Angiospermae
Subclass—Dicotyledoneae
Order—Rosales
Family—Leguminosae
Genus—*Trifolium*
Species—*repens*
Scientific name—*Trifolium repens*

Thus one species (*Trifolium repens*) is seen in its relationship to all other groups of plants. To the student, the above may mean no more than a list of names difficult to pronounce. But it must be admitted that it is necessary and convenient to have the plants of the world classified, to have order and system. Various attempts have been made in the past to classify plants,

and various systems have been proposed. Usually each has represented a distinct advance over the preceding one. The reason for this is that research in the plant sciences has revealed new facts; in short, we know more about the plant kingdom today than we did last year, or in the last century.

Plant Characters Used as a Basis of Classification. The efforts to classify or group the 300,000 or more kinds of plants in the world have been in the direction of arriving at a **natural system of classification.**

Plants have ancestors, just as people do. Some of these are now extinct and known only in the fossil form. In any natural system of classifying plants, an attempt is made to express their ancestry. A classification of the races of mankind has the same objective; and, when the origin and relationships of the different races are being studied, evidence is derived from various sources: fossils, methods of securing food, comparative body form and anatomy, geographical distribution, migration paths, etc. The same sort of evidence is sought in arriving at the natural relationships of plants. In other words, this system is based on the actual relationships among different kinds of plants and not upon superficial characters (flower color, for example) which vary with each slight change in environmental conditions.

The reproductive organs of a plant, flowers, are less influenced by environmental conditions than are vegetative organs (roots, stems, leaves). Suppose that you plant two bean seeds of the same species, one in poor soil, the other in rich soil; the first is placed in the shade, the second in the sun; the first is caused to suffer from lack of water, the second has ample water. The two bean plants may look quite different as to size, vigor, extent of root system, size and thickness of leaves, and other vegetative characters; but, when they develop flowers, those of both plants are typical of the species, even in the details of structure. Because of the greater stability of reproductive structures, as compared with vegetative structures, we can place more reliance in them as a basis for showing actual relationships. Why are strawberries and raspberries placed in the same plant family (Rosaceae, rose family)? Their habits of growth are quite dissimilar: strawberries are herbs with a trailing habit, whereas raspberries are shrubs with more or less erect woody stems. The flowers of the two, however, have the same essential structure and indicate a close relationship between the two plants.

Nomenclature or Naming of Plants. The necessity of naming objects and the practical advantage of doing so are self-evident. This applies not only to plants and animals, but also to the parts of an automobile, the types of airplanes, the goods on the druggist's shelf, the kinds of soil, etc. There is a special set of terms and names associated with every trade, business, and profession. The terms and names used in the sciences are usually regarded as "technical" and therefore "difficult." But they seem technical and difficult only because of unfamiliarity with them and lack of opportunity or a disinclination to use them.

Every species of plant has a name—a **scientific name.** Many kinds of plants also have a common name, such as wheat, carrot, oak, daisy, poison ivy, white pine. But many species of plants are so small and inconspicuous or so little known that no common names are attached to them. Of course, cultivated plants, weeds, and most other conspicuous plants that occur in many different countries have common names in the language of each country. For example, the widespread weed usually called *black mustard* in the United States is *Khardal aswad* in Arabia, *moutarde noire* in France, *Senfkohl* in Germany, *mostarda*

in Italy, and *kara hardal* in Turkey. Even in English-speaking countries it has several common names: cadlock, warlock, scurvy, senvil, brown mustard, kerlock, and scurvy-senvil. If, in the scientific literature, this plant is referred to solely by its common name, the reader might be hard-pressed to know exactly to which species reference is made. This problem is further complicated by the fact that the same common name may be applied to totally different species. Accordingly, it is readily apparent that for the benefit of plant scientists throughout the world every distinct species should have *one name,* understood by all. This is its scientific name. Black mustard is *Brassica nigra.* When this binomial appears in the literature, every plant scientist, no matter what language he speaks, knows that reference is made to a specific mustard with certain characteristics.[*]

As stated, a binomial, such as *Brassica nigra,* is a combination of the name of the genus (*Brassica*) and the name of the species (*nigra*). The method of binomial nomenclature has been in use by zoologists and botanists the world over since the middle of the eighteenth century. The great

[*] Realizing that many species of plants have several common names, thus giving rise to confusion, the American Joint Committee on Horticultural Nomenclature has prepared a book entitled *Standardized Plant Names,* which in the second edition is described as "a revised and enlarged listing of approved scientific and common names of plants and plant products in American commerce or use." In the preface to the second edition the statement is made that "the purpose of *Standardized Plant Names* is to bring intelligent order out of the chaos in names of plants and plant products existing the world over. Such standardization, supported by adequate authority, will not only promote satisfactory understanding between those who sell and those who buy, but will also improve the multifarious relations, scientific, educational and social, into which the advancing plant consciousness of America has grown."

Swedish naturalist, Linnaeus (Fig. 3.3), published his monumental work the *Species Plantarum* in 1753, and in it the binomial system of nomenclature was well established.

Several thousand new species of plants are discovered every year. The plant specimens may have been collected in parts of the world previously unexplored by botanists, although new species are being discovered every year in areas many times traversed by botanists. These specimens ultimately fall into the hands of a systematic botanist who is interested in and has given special attention to the group (family or genus) to which the plant in question belongs. This botanist sets out to identify the species. In so doing, he compares it with allied forms, of which he has herbarium specimens or published descriptions. He may find that the plant has characters similar to those of a species heretofore described; or he may find that the plant has characters so different from those of any known species that he concludes it is a new species (**species novum, sp. nov.**). In other words, it is a species that has never been described. Accordingly, he describes this new species and gives it a name. The description is published in one of the many recognized botanical journals, and the specimen or specimens he used in making the description are properly labeled and placed in one or more of the herbaria of the world. This specimen is known as the **type specimen** (Fig. 3.4).

The one who described it places the initial letter or abbreviation of his name after the scientific name. For example, Linnaeus named a great number of our common plants, and accordingly we find the letter *L.* after these so-called Linnaean species, such as *Beta vulgaris* L. (common beet), *Brassica rapa* L. (turnip), and *Medicago sativa* L. (alfalfa).

Fig. 3.3. Linnaeus (Carl von Linné) (1707–1778), the founder of modern systematic botany. (Photo courtesy of Brooklyn Botanic Garden.)

The botanist who describes a new species is confronted with the problem of giving it an appropriate specific name. Many specific names are descriptive of some characteristic feature of the plant. For example, black mustard is *Brassica nigra;* *nigra* refers to the black seed. White mustard is *Brassica alba; alba* describes the color of the seed. Sometimes a specific name is formed from the name of the person who first collected the plant in question or of some person whom the botanist naming the plant wished to honor. An example is *Lupinus grayi* (Gray's lupine).

It is the general opinion among botanists that specific names that are descriptive of some outstanding character of the plant are preferable to those that describe habitat or geographical distribution or honor some individual. Specific names descriptive of a plant character have more meaning than others; also, they are of more interest and are an aid to the student in his memorization of plant names. The fact that they are Latinized, for the most part, does not make it difficult to find their meanings, even though the student has had no Latin. The definition of most specific names may usually be found readily in an unabridged

Fig. 3.4. Herbarium sheet showing "type specimen," and label. (Photo courtesy of Herbarium of the Univ. of Calif., Berkeley.)

dictionary by reference to the Latin or Greek roots of allied words. For example, consider *Populus angustifolia,* narrowleaf poplar or cottonwood (Fig. 8.1). Look up "*angusti*" in the dictionary, and note the Latin meaning. Or, consider *Pinus ponderosa* (yellow pine); the dictionary gives the meaning and derivation of *ponderosa* under the word "ponderous."

Generic names are often merely the words by which the plants in question were known to those who spoke Latin. Examples of such names are *Avena* (oat), *Pinus* (pine), *Quercus* (oak), *Phaseolus* (certain kinds of beans), *Pisum* (pea), *Ficus* (fig), and *Rosa* (rose).

Botanical Manuals or Floras. The plants of an area, in the aggregate, are spoken of as the **flora.** Thus we may refer to the flora of western United States, or the flora of Sumatra, or the flora of eastern Massachusetts. The term may also be used as a synonym of botanical manual; thus, a flora or manual of Texas is a description of all the plant species known to occur in that state. The species in a flora or manual are arranged systematically by genera, families, classes, and phyla. In addition, brief data on the geographic distribution and habitat of each species are generally given, and sometimes accompanying illustrations. Also, **keys** are usually a part of the manuals. Keys are simple devices for identifying species or larger groups. By means of a key a plant that one may wish to identify can be "run down" and its name determined with the minimum of effort.

A key to several important species of *Trifolium* (clovers) is given herewith.

KEY TO PRINCIPAL SPECIES OF *Trifolium*

Flowers in spikelike heads, much longer than
    thick: *T. incarnatum* (crimson or scarlet
    clover).
Flowers in globular or ovoid heads.
    Corolla white or yellowish white, sometimes

touched with pink; stems creeping: *T.*
    repens (white clover).
Corolla red, red-purple, or rose-colored;
    stems erect or nearly so.
    Flowers pediceled (Fig. 3.1); stipules
      acuminate (Fig. 3.1): *T. hybridum*
      (Alsike or Swedish clover).
    Flowers sessile (Fig. 3.1); stipules
      abruptly acute (Fig. 3.1): *T. pratense*
      (red clover).

Herbaria. An herbarium is a systematic collection of appropriately preserved plants. The plant, properly pressed and dried, is mounted on a sheet of heavy paper and labeled (Fig. 3.5). The label gives the scientific name of the species, place, and date of collection, name of collector, and sometimes notes on habitat. Photographs showing the plant's habit of growth and habitat may be attached to the herbarium sheet. The folders in which the mounted specimens are contained are filed in appropriate herbarium cases, the arrangement of which is systematic. By this we mean that a certain section of the herbarium would contain representatives of one plant family. The herbaria of the world are repositories of its plant life. Some of them have several million specimens from all parts of the world. Herbaria are associated with botanic gardens, universities, and colleges, and there are also many very valuable private herbaria. Facilities are provided in herbaria for research work: reference books, monographs, manuals, floras, and also the equipment required for pressing plants and identifying them, such as dissecting microscopes.

Botanic Gardens. The small booklet *Botanic Gardens of the World,* by C. Stuart Gager, published in 1937 in the Brooklyn Botanic Garden Record, contains data concerning the history, organization, and work of over 400 botanic gardens. They are found in nearly every country of the world. Many of them are very old, and a considerable proportion of them were organized primarily for botanical research or instruction or both. Among the oldest and best-known botanic gardens of the world (with date of establishment in parentheses) are the following:

Royal Botanic Garden of Padua, Padua, Italy (1545).
Botanic Garden of Heidelberg, University of Heidelberg, Germany (1593).
National Museum of Natural History, Paris, France (1635).
Botanical Garden and Museum, Berlin, Germany (1646).

Royal Botanic Garden, Edinburgh, Scotland (1670).
Botanic Garden of the Academy of Sciences, Leningrad, Russia (1712).
University Botanic Gardens, Cambridge, England (1762).
Botanic Garden and Botanical Institute of the University of Vienna, Vienna, Austria (1754).
Royal Botanic Garden, Calcutta, India (1787).
Botanic Garden of University of Innsbruck, Innsbruck, Germany (1793).
Botanic Garden of Harvard University, Cambridge, Mass. (1807).
Botanical Garden of Rio de Janeiro (1808).

Fig. 3.5. View in the Herbarium of the University of California, Berkeley. (Photo courtesy of Herbarium of the Univ. of Calif., Berkeley.)

Botanic Garden, Munich, Germany (1809).

Royal Botanic Gardens, Peradeniya, Ceylon (1810).

Botanic Gardens of New South Wales, Sydney, Australia (1816).

Government Botanic Gardens, Buitenzorg, Java (1817) (Fig. 3.6).

U. S. Botanic Garden, Washington, D. C. (1820).

Botanic Garden, Hamburg, Germany (1821).

Royal Botanic Garden, Kew, England (1841).

Missouri Botanical Garden, St. Louis, Mo. (1859).

Arnold Arboretum of Harvard University, Jamaica Plain, Mass. (1872).

The New York Botanical Garden, New York City (1895).

Brooklyn Botanic Garden, Brooklyn, N. Y. (1910).

Montreal Botanical Garden, Montreal, Canada (1936).

These gardens have plantings of species from all parts of the world, arranged by plant families or according to habitats. They contain outdoor plantings and often greenhouses controlled to grow tropical plants. Their reference libraries may contain thousands of volumes of books, pamphlets, and photographs, and the herbaria may be extensive. For example, the New York Botanical Garden, of 40 acres, has a reference library of 43,500 volumes and many thousands of pamphlets; an herbarium of approximately 1,706,000 specimens; and a systematic plantation, arboretum, fruticetum, rose gardens, and rock gardens. The Missouri Botanical Garden, at St. Louis, with 75 acres, has a library of 50,000 volumes,

Fig. 3.6. View in the Government Botanic Gardens, Buitenzorg, Java. (Photo courtesy of Douglas Campbell, *Outline of Plant Geography*, The Macmillan Co.)

an herbarium of 1,050,000 specimens, 6500 species growing under glass, and 7500 species growing out-of-doors. The Botanic Garden in Leningrad has an herbarium of approximately 3 million specimens. The Botanic Garden and Museum in Berlin had before World War II an herbarium of 4 million specimens and an arboretum and fruticetum that together contained about 15,000 labeled plants. The famed Royal Botanic Garden at Kew, England, with 288 acres, has a reference library of 44,000 volumes, an herbarium of 4 million specimens, an arboretum and fruticetum together of 7000 species and varieties, 13,000 species growing under glass, and 8000 herbaceous species growing out-of-doors.

Botanic gardens are of value not only to botanists, horticulturists, nurserymen, seedsmen, landscape gardeners, home gardeners, and foresters but also to thousands of tourists. Most of them are open to the public, and many offer instruction with special lectures and demonstrations to meet the needs and interests of individuals in all walks of life.

4

The Plant Body of Seed Plants

In this chapter we will give attention to the general structure and functions of a familiar seed plant, the common garden bean. Any one of many thousands of seed plants would serve our purposes as well. It is recognized that seed plants are very complex organisms, as compared with unicellular, filamentous, and platelike plant bodies or even multicellular plants like the mushrooms. Other types of plants have different types of plant bodies. They will be discussed in some detail after the structure and function of the plant body of seed plants is understood. See Figs. 18.22, 19.3, and 22.11 for other plant body types.

The bean seed is borne in a pod on a "mother plant." Under suitable growing conditions the bean seed germinates and a young plant (seedling) emerges (Fig. 4.1D) having roots, stems, and leaves. The plant *grows*, extends its roots into the soil and its stems with their leaves into the atmosphere, and after a number of weeks attains adult size. Flowers are formed, then pods "set," and in the pods are seeds ("beans"). The bean plant has then completed a **life cycle.** The series of structural changes and physiological processes through which a plant passes in the course of its development are complicated. Many of the physiological processes involved are complex and require a knowledge of chemistry and physics in order to be understood. A bean plant is an individual—it has a birth, a young life, an adult life, a period of reproduction, then death. It has **organs,** just as does the human being, which perform various functions necessary to maintain its life. These organs—**roots, stems, leaves, flower parts**—are composed of **tissues,** groups of cells that carry on different activities (Figs. 4.1E and F and 4.2). The cells are the small compartments that make up tissues; they possess living material (**protoplasm**) and hence are the *living units of plant structure and function* (Fig. 5.2). The plant body is composed of cells and the products of cells. All the different kinds of work the plant does are really the work of its cells.

A plant body like that of the bean (Fig. 4.1D) possesses all the organs and tissues necessary to maintain life. The stem (1) supports the foliage leaves and flowers, (2) conducts water and mineral salts from the soil, (3) conducts plant foods from tissues where they are manufactured to tissues where they are needed in growth or where they are stored for future use, and (4) may store foods. The roots (1) anchor the plant

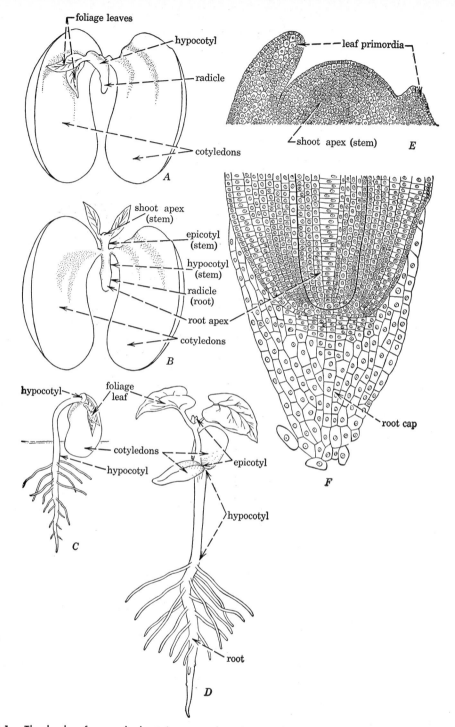

Fig. 4.1. The body of a seed plant (common bean). A, dormant embryo showing natural position of the organs; B, embryo straightened to show the axis of the plant body and the relative position of the organs; C and D, stages in the development of the plant body; E, shoot apex; F, root apex. (A, C, D redrawn from Holman and Robbins, A Textbook of General Botany, John Wiley & Sons, Inc.)

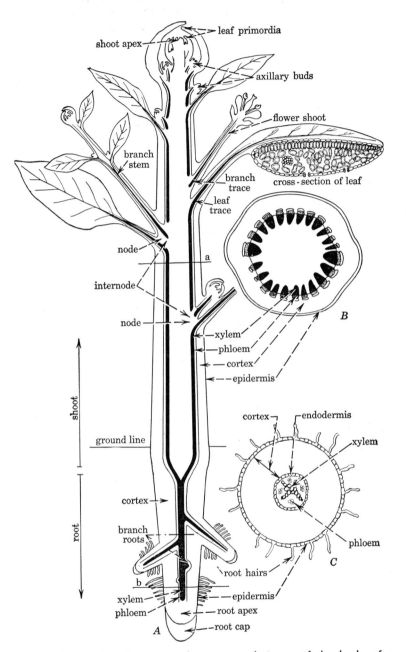

Fig. 4.2. Diagram A, showing the principal organs and tissues of the body of a seed plant; B, cross section of stem; C, cross section of root. (A redrawn from Holman and Robbins in A *Textbook of General Botany*, John Wiley & Sons, Inc.)

in the soil, (2) absorb water and mineral salts from the soil, and (3) may store food. The leaves (1) manufacture foods and (2) give off water in the form of water vapor. These activities involve both chemical and physical processes, which will be discussed in later chapters.

One cannot have a clear understanding of the structures and functions of a plant without a knowledge of its anatomy, such as is revealed by the use of a compound microscope. All-important at the very beginning is an understanding of cells—the units of plant structure and function. The following chapter deals with the cell.

The gross development of the seed plant body is shown in Fig. 4.1A to D. After soaking a bean seed in water for several hours, the outer skin or seed coat is easily removed. The body exposed is the **embryo** (Fig. 4.1A, B). The term embryo as used in biology refers to a living organism in the early stages of development, and, in most plants and the higher animals, at least, it is more or less dependent upon the maternal parent for its food. The embryo is a well-advanced young bean plant. There are two large **cotyledons** or seed leaves, several young **foliage leaves,** a **stem** (composed of epicotyl and hypocotyl), and a **rudimentary root (radicle).** The two cotyledons contain stored food, chiefly starch. Although the young foliage leaves are small, their veins can be easily seen with a lens.

Figure 4.1A, B shows the bean embryo spread open so that the relationship of the different parts is more easily observed. The embryo of the mature seed is an organism which already possesses many thousands of cells distributed in essential organs (root, stem, leaves) so well advanced that they can be recognized as such. Already established are those organs that will grow upward and those that will grow downward.

The embryo plant body has two regions of importance to future growth—the **shoot tip** and the **root tip** (Fig. 4.1E, F). The shoot tip includes (1) the dome-shaped mass of meristematic cells, known either as the **shoot apex** or **apical meristem,** at the very end of the young plant between rudimentary leaves, and (2) the cells below the meristem that are enlarging and in early stages of differentiation. The root tip, at the lower end of the young plant, is composed of similar tissues, (1) the **root apex** or **apical meristem,** and (2) the elongating and differentiating cells above the meristem plus (3) a **root cap** protecting the apical meristem. The cells that make up these two tips are capable of division, differentiation, and growth. Meristematic cells are cells capable of active cell division with a resulting increase in the number of cells. Until the death of the plant, there are always meristematic tissues at the tips of stems and roots. After differentiation certain types of cells may lose their power of division. In the bean embryo most cells are meristematic, but those of the apical meristems are of peculiar interest because as a result of their multiplication, enlargement, and eventual differentiation both the shoot and root increase in length and become roots and shoots.

During the early stages in the development of the seedling bean plant, the cells are nourished by food (chiefly starch) stored in the cotyledons. Before this food moves from the cotyledons to other parts of the plant, it is changed to sugar. Sugar, unlike starch, is soluble in the water of cells, and in solution it moves from the cotyledons to all other cells of the embryo, especially to those actively growing cells of the shoot tip and root tip. As soon as the cotyledons are raised into the light by the lengthening of the shoot, they become green, and then they begin the manufacture of food. By this time the roots are well established in the soil and are absorbing water and mineral salts. The foliage leaves that were present in the seed expand; they, too, engage in the process of food making. As food moves from the cotyledons, they shrivel and after a time disappear altogether. The seedling, with its roots absorbing water and mineral salts from the soil, and with its green leaves manufacturing food, is now an *independent plant*. The plant, as shown in Fig. 4.1D, is equipped with all the organs and tissues necessary to carry on the processes that are required to keep it alive and growing. At this stage the structural framework of the adult plant is established.

Branch roots arise from certain meristematic cells inside the main root (Fig. 4.2A). Branch shoots originate from meristematic cells in the leaf axils of the main stem (Fig. 4.2A). New leaves, the primordia of which are shown in Fig. 4.1E and Fig. 4.2 arise from the meristematic cells of every shoot tip.

A diagram of a seed plant (Fig. 4.2) will serve to summarize the foregoing discussion and illustrate the structural organization of a seed plant. The plant body is made up of two parts: the **shoot** and the **root**. The shoot is composed of two kinds of organs—stem and **leaves**. In the seedling there are two kinds of leaves, the cotyledons or seed leaves, which are temporary in most species, and the foliage leaves, which are relatively longer-lasting. The stem, in contrast to the root, is divided into **nodes** and **internodes,** regions that alternate throughout the length of the stem. **Nodes** are the slightly enlarged portions where leaves and buds arise and where branches originate from the buds. An **internode** is the region between two successive nodes. As we shall see later, the anatomy of nodes and internodes differs. All shoots terminate in a mass of meristematic cells, the shoot apex. The shoot apex is the region where leaves, buds, and the various tissues that make up the stem are initiated. The main root and all branch roots also terminate in a mass of meristematic cells, the root apex. Protecting this is a cap of cells, called the root cap. Below the apical meristems the cells are elongating and differentiating. *This region of meristematic and differentiating cells is referred to as the shoot or root tip.*

In Fig. 4.2 structures and tissues are shown which will be discussed in later chapters.

5

The Plant Cell

In 1590, Zacharias Jansen, a spectacle maker of Middleburg, Holland, invented the compound microscope. This instrument was later improved by Robert Hooke, an Englishman, who not only was interested in optics but also was an architect and an experimenter with flying machines. Hooke, who lived from 1636 to 1703, examined all sorts of natural objects with his improved microscope. Among these were thin slices of cork (the dead outer bark of an oak). Figure 5.1 is an illustration of the cork tissue as Hooke saw it under his microscope. This figure was published in 1665 in an article entitled "*Micrographia, or Some Physiological Descriptions of Minute Bodies Made by Magnifying Glasses.*" Hooke observed that the cork was composed of empty chambers, or minute hollow compartments, which he described as "little boxes or cells distinct from one another." He estimated that a cubic inch of cork would contain about 1259 million cells.

The term **cell**, first applied by Hooke, has come into general use for the structural unit of both plants and animals.

It is highly instructive to examine the tissue of a potato tuber, or leaf, or any other living plant structure with a binocular microscope (magnifying 30 or more times). With this instrument we get a three-dimensional view of the cells, which appear as many small chambers separated from one another by walls that are usually thin and transparent. If we cut very thin slices (sections) of living plant tissue and

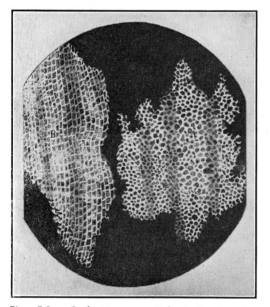

Fig. 5.1. Cork tissue as Robert Hooke observed it under his microscope. (From Hooke, *Micrographia*, 1664, The Council of the Royal Society of London for Improving Natural Knowledge.)

examine them with the compound microscope at high magnifications (150 to 500
times), the cell contents are revealed.

As early as 1835, the French zoologist
Dujardin observed in the cells of certain
simple animals a jellylike or slimy substance. He recognized this substance as
the living material of the animals. Later,
a similar substance was found in the living
cells of plants. And it was not long before
it was recognized that the properties that
we associate with life of both animal and
plant cells were the properties of the jellylike or slimy material. The term **protoplasm** was applied to this living substance.
Today it is commonly understood that the
protoplasm of plants and that of animals
are not essentially different. This is a very
significant fact; it points to unity of life
whether expressed in a lowly plant or in
a complex animal like man.

We now know that all living things, both
plants and animals, are composed of cells.
Moreover, the cell, although extremely
small, is composed of still smaller parts,
each of which has its own particular structure and function. Within each cell chemical reactions of great complexity are taking
place; most reactions associated with life
are carried out in cells.

THE PARTS OF THE CELL

The plant cell has two distinct parts:
(1) the **protoplast,** which is enclosed by
(2) the **cell wall.**

The protoplasm of the individual cell is
organized; by this we mean it has organs
or different parts (Fig. 5.2), each with functions. This organized, more or less independent, living unit of each cell is called a
protoplast. Thus the protoplast is a structural and functional unit.

The protoplast may be divided into **protoplasm** and **ergastic substances.** The proto-

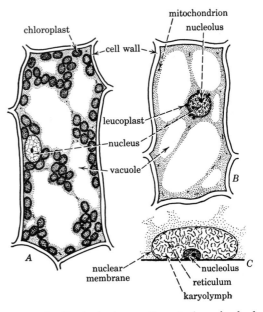

Fig. 5.2. Typical plant cells. A, from leaf of
a water plant, *Elodea,* ×1000; B, from epidermis of scale of onion bulb, ×1000; C, vegetative nucleus, ×3000.

plasm is composed of the **nucleus** and
cytoplasm. The nucleus is a spherical or
ovoid mass of protoplasm, somewhat darker
in color and denser than the protoplasm
within which it is embedded. All the protoplasm surrounding the nucleus is called
cytoplasm. The nucleus is surrounded by
a membrane (not a wall), the **nuclear membrane.** Within the nucleus are one or more
denser masses, the **nucleoli** (singular, nucleolus), and the **reticulum,** which is composed of several to many small nets. The
nuclear nets, or the reticulum, are composed
of a substance called **chromatin.** The
reticulum is embedded in a colorless nuclear material known as the **karyolymph.**
The karyolymph is sometimes called the
nuclear sap, but it must be remembered
that it is not an inert water sap similar to
the cell sap. The cytoplasm is composed
of a clear background fluid called the **hyaloplasm,** in which are embedded at least two

types of distinct denser cytoplasmic bodies, the **plastids** and the **mitochondria**. The cytoplasm is bounded both externally and internally by cytoplasmic membranes. The separate parts of the protoplast will be discussed later.

Within the protoplast may be found various substances known as **ergastic substances**. These may be (1) **vacuoles,** or (2) **crystals,** or (3) **solid bodies** of various noncrystalline forms, chiefly starch grains and protein bodies.

The different parts of a plant cell and their relations to one another are shown in the accompanying outline.

1. The protoplast

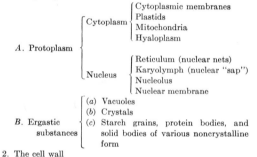

A. Protoplasm
- Cytoplasm
  - Cytoplasmic membranes
  - Plastids
  - Mitochondria
  - Hyaloplasm
- Nucleus
  - Reticulum (nuclear nets)
  - Karyolymph (nuclear "sap")
  - Nucleolus
  - Nuclear membrane

B. Ergastic substances
- (a) Vacuoles
- (b) Crystals
- (c) Starch grains, protein bodies, and solid bodies of various noncrystalline form

2. The cell wall

Thus we see that the individual plant cell is a complex unit. It has structures that bear a definite relation to one another, and these play a role in its life. An ordinary plant, such as wheat or an oak tree, is composed of many millions of these units, joined in a very definite manner to give form and structure to roots, stems, leaves, flowers, fruit, and seeds and to give form and character to the whole wheat or oak individual. Cells differ in form, in size, in thickness of walls, in chemical composition, and in the work they perform. Cells in one part of the plant influence those in another, and they are so coordinated in their activities that the multicellular individual behaves as a whole; it is a living individual composed

of units (cells), all of which, in a healthy plant, are working together harmoniously.

How do new cells arise? How do they grow? How do root cells influence the behavior of leaf cells, and vice versa? Why do certain cells begin to form flower structures and why do others not? Why does removal of the cells composing the terminal bud of a stem cause other cells some distance away to begin division? These questions will be discussed in subsequent chapters.

Obviously, if we are to understand the living plant as a whole, it is first necessary that we have knowledge of the cells of which it is made.

THE PROTOPLAST

The active living unit of the cell is the **protoplast,** which may be divided into **protoplasm** and the **ergastic substances.** We will consider first the structure and some of the properties of protoplasm.

PROTOPLASM

Protoplasm is the basic material of life. It has certain fundamental properties that are the same in all plants and animals. Yet, there are no two species of plants or animals, and probably no two individual plants or animals, in which the protoplasm is the same in all particulars.

Under the compound microscope, protoplasm appears as a translucent liquid. Tiny granules and globules are dispersed throughout. Protoplasm usually seems to have the consistency of a viscous liquid, though in some cells and under certain conditions it is more like a stiff jelly and under other conditions it may be very fluid. In active cells the viscosity of protoplasm has been likened to that of light machine oil

When a cell dies, the protoplasm loses its liquid or viscous consistency and coagulates or sets into a firm mass.

Protoplasm is a complex **colloidal system.** A colloidal system consists of an association of two or more substances in which one of them is in a finely divided state but not in complete solution. The mixture of vinegar and oil in mayonnaise is an example, although the particles formed here are generally larger than those of a true colloidal system. In the preparation of mayonnaise the oil is literally whipped into the vinegar. That is, the oil is *dispersed* in droplets in the vinegar. This arrangement results in large surfaces between the particles of oil and vinegar (Fig. 5.3). Protoplasm is such a colloidal system. In it are particles that vary in size from those easily seen with the microscope to particles which are so small that they cannot be seen. Protein molecules, which are long chains of atoms folded in various ways, may form either a disperse or a continuous phase.

Protoplasm is a very *complex mixture* of many different compounds. Approximately 75 per cent of protoplasm is water and 25 per cent is solid matter. Of the solid matter, the greater part is proteins; the lesser part is carbohydrates (chiefly sugars), fats, organic acids, and other organic compounds and also various inorganic compounds (simple compounds of the mineral elements calcium, potassium, magnesium, phosphorus, sulfur, and iron). Proteins are very complex chemical compounds. Familiar examples are gelatine and egg white, the proteins of which are dispersed in water. In addition to carbon, oxygen, and hydrogen, the proteins contain nitrogen and sulfur and sometimes phosphorus. There is ample evidence that proteins, probably the most characteristic components of protoplasm, differ in the various species of plants and animals. It is quite likely that the immunity of certain varieties of crops to specific diseases is related to their characteristic proteins.

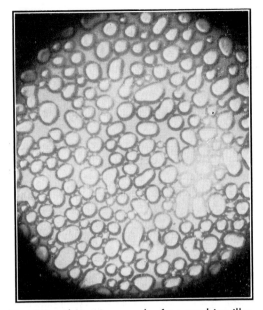

Fig. 5.3. Photomicrograph of an emulsion illustrating the colloidal state. (Photo courtesy of Seifriz.)

The Nucleus

The nucleus is a very important protoplastic body, influencing greatly the growth and metabolism of the plant. It may be spherical or ovoid, or it may be flattened against the cell wall or irregular in shape (Fig. 5.2C). It is present in all living cells except the mature food-conducting cells (sieve-tube members) of higher plants and the red blood cells of many animals. In living cells the nucleus is usually difficult to see because it is but slightly less translucent than the cytoplasm in which it is embedded. The living nucleus frequently appears to be a perfectly homogeneous globule of protoplasm. In tissues that have been killed and stained, a very definite structure becomes evident within the nucleus. We refer here to cells that are not dividing. The nuclei of such cells will be called **vegetative nuclei.** In order to explain the function of the nucleus in cell division, it is necessary to assume that the living nucleus has a very definite structure. For these reasons it is generally believed that the following description of the structures present in a fixed and stained nucleus are also present, but invisible, in the living healthy nucleus.

The nucleus is bounded by a **nuclear membrane.** This membrane is very delicate and is not to be thought of as a rigid structure like the cell wall. Within the nucleus two types of materials, differentiated by the stains applied, may be observed. One of these forms a spherical body, the **nucleolus** (singular). Generally each nucleus has either one or two **nucleoli** (plural), infrequently several.

The other nuclear material is likely to be quite indistinct because of its diffuse nature. In the best microscopic preparations this material appears in the form of fine threads with somewhat irregular diameters. These threads constitute the **reticulum.** It is believed that the reticulum is composed of units or separate threads that are constant in number for *each species* of plant. These units of threadlike reticulum are called **chromosomes.** Each chromosome has an orderly linear organization consisting of minute localized regions called **genes,** somehow associated with the threadlike structure of the chromosome. The genes control the growth and chemical processes of the living organism. In some nuclei, such as those found in the salivary glands of certain flies, this orderly linear organization may be observed under the microscope as a series of bands (Fig. 26.5). In fruit flies, corn, and many other animals and plants the exact location on the thread or chromosome of certain genes may be accurately determined. Although individual

genes have never been seen, a great deal is known about their activity. They appear either to be nucleoproteins, or at least to be associated with nucleoproteins, complex substances composed of a protein and a nucleic acid.

We have said that genes control the form and activities of the cells and of the plant as a whole. We cite two examples, one concerned with structure, the other with chemical activity: (1) Squash fruits are variously shaped and colored; they may be elongated and green, or flat and white, or round and yellow. Experiments have shown that the color and shape of these fruits are directly related to the types of genes present in the nucleus. (2) The formation of chlorophyll, the green pigment of plants, generally is under the control of the nucleus. In atom bomb tests at Bikini radiation from the explosion changed a gene in the nucleus of a corn embryo in such a manner that chlorophyll formation was retarded in developing corn seedlings (Plate III, Chapter 15).

Cytoplasm

One of the remarkable aspects of cytoplasm is its astonishing chemical activity combined with an extremely simple visible structure. We have described cytoplasm as consisting simply of a hyaline fluid, hyaloplasm, in which plastids and mitochondria and perhaps other granules may be embedded. Membranes occur at all surfaces. A very great number of the chemical conversions, characteristic of living matter take place in this medium. Obviously it must have a more complex structure than is revealed by our microscopes.

At the boundary of the cytoplasm where it comes in contact with the cell wall, and also where it is in contact with the vacuoles, membranes known as **cytoplasmic membranes** are formed. Such membranes are too thin to be seen even with the aid of the microscope, but, as will be shown later, experimental techniques have led to the conclusion that they exist. Moreover, these cytoplasmic membranes are somewhat different in physical and chemical properties from the rest of the cytoplasm, and they have long been considered of great importance because there is evidence that they control the movement of substances into and out of the cell or the vacuole. It must not be thought, however, that cytoplasmic membranes are of such structure that it is possible to peel them away from the cytoplasm of which they are a part.

Plastids. Plastids are specialized cytoplasmic bodies (Figs. 5.4, 5.5). They are portions of the cytoplasm that are specially differentiated and perform particular functions in the cell. They vary considerably in size and form but are generally rather small and spherical or ellipsoidal. In some foliage leaves, a single cell may contain 100 plastids. Cells of other leaves may have fewer. Plastids multiply by division and are present in the nongreen meristematic cells of some plants as small colorless bodies. In primitive plant forms they are present in meristematic and reproductive cells as recognizable green plastids. They are therefore considered as having a genetic

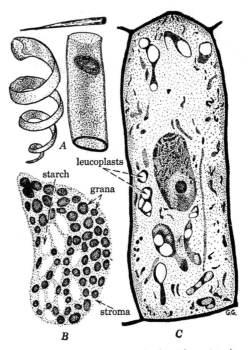

Fig. 5.5. Various types of plastids. A, chromoplasts from cells of carrot root; B, chloroplasts from leaf of *Pellonia*, ×10,000; C, cell from root tip of rye showing leucoplasts and mitochondria, ×1300. (C, redrawn from O'Brien.)

continuity from one generation to another as has the nucleus.

Three kinds of plastids, distinguished on the basis of color and the nature of the work they perform, occur in plants. They are: **chloroplasts** (green), **leucoplasts** (colorless), and **chromoplasts** (yellow, brown, or red).

Chloroplasts. The dominant color in the world about us is green. Green forests, green meadows, green lawns, green shrubbery, in fact, the great majority of green plants owe their color to pigments (colored compounds) known as **chlorophylls**. These pigments (except in the blue-green algae, and certain bacteria, page 332) occur *only in plastids*. Plastids that possess chlorophyll are called **chloroplasts** (Fig. 5.5B).

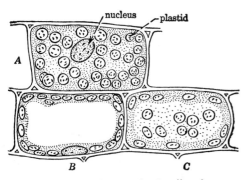

Fig. 5.4. Chloroplasts in leaf cells of a moss. A, C, plastids as seen in optical planes at upper and lower surfaces of cell; B, optical plane through middle of cell. ×700.

In the living world the chloroplasts play an indispensable role in the energy cycle. The chloroplast is the primary food laboratory of the world. Within it carbon dioxide and water undergo chemical change and sugar is formed. In this process the radiant energy of light is transformed into the potential energy of the sugar molecule. Chlorophylls absorb the light energy. The sugar is the foundation material with which the plant builds all other compounds that make up its body. Human beings and all other animals, in the final analysis, obtain their foods (energy) from green plants. They are strictly dependent upon chloroplasts.

Several kinds of pigments occur in chloroplasts, the principal ones being the green **chlorophylls** and the yellow to red **carotenoids.** There are a number of chlorophylls (about ten), differing in their chemical composition. The principal ones are as follows: *chlorophyll a* and *chlorophyll b*, which are found in the Chlorophycophyta, Bryophyta, Lycophyta, Sphenophyta and Pterophyta; and *chlorophyll c* or *chlorophyll d* that are associated with *a* in some of the algal phyla. The other chlorophylls are relatively rare. The chlorophyll pigments may be dissolved out of the plastids by means of alcohol, acetone, or other organic solvents and then may be separated by further appropriate chemical means. Associated with the chlorophylls in chloroplasts are the carotenoid pigments, **carotenes** and **xanthophylls.** Generally, chlorophylls comprise about 65 per cent, carotenes 6 per cent, and xanthophylls about 29 per cent of the total pigments in chloroplasts.

It has been known for a long time that the element iron is essential to the formation of chlorophylls. Plants deprived of iron, and of other metallic elements such as potassium, phosphorus, and zinc fail to form chlorophyll, the leaves appearing yellow or yellow green (Plate III, Chapter 15). Though these elements are essential in chlorophyll formation, magnesium is the only metallic element in the chlorophyll molecule.

Leucoplasts. Leucoplasts are colorless plastids (Fig. 5.5C). They occur in plant cells not exposed to light (roots) or in cells exposed to intense light. They are found in tubers (potato, for example), roots, seeds, and other starch-storing organs, in young dividing cells in various parts of the plant, and in the cells forming the outer cellular layers of leaves. It is well known that potatoes may become green when exposed to light. In such cases leucoplasts that were present in the cells before exposure to light are stimulated to produce chlorophyll and are thus transformed into chloroplasts.

Leucoplasts are cell organs that are concerned with food storage. For example, starch grains appear in storage tissues in leucoplasts. As these grains enlarge, the leucoplasts stretch to many times their normal size.

Chromoplasts. Chromoplasts (Fig. 5.5A) are responsible for the red, yellow, or orange color of many fruits and vegetables and of the petals of many flowers. These colors are due to the carotenoids present within the chromoplasts. The carrot root is a striking example of a plant organ that has carotene.

Plastids and Vitamins. Several carotenoids, found in both chromoplasts and chloroplasts, are known to be related to the fat-soluble vitamin A. Animals can make vitamin A from carotenoids. When eaten by animals the carotenoids may reappear in the animal and be observed as the yellow color of egg yolks, cream, yellow body fat, and butter. Plants apparently are unable to synthesize vitamin A directly. The function of carotenoids in the plant is not definitely known.

Mitochondria. These structures are small bodies, present in the great majority of cell

types as small spheres or rods (Fig. 5.2).
They have been found to occur in all animal
cells and in plants they are present in the
cells of meristematic tissue, in the epidermis, and in other nongreen tissues. It
has been clearly shown that the mitochondria in animal cells serve as focal points for
intracellular respiration (see page 214) and
available evidence indicates that they have
a similar function in plant tissue, at least
when choloroplasts are absent or inactive.
In many instances the mitochondria in the
cells of meristematic tissue cannot be distinguished morphologically from young
developing chloroplasts, **proplastids.** The
relationship between chloroplasts and mitochondria is one of great interest as it involves the two important energy changes
occurring in living organisms, respiration
and photosynthesis.

ERGASTIC SUBSTANCES

Vacuoles

In many young cells the cytoplasm occupies much of the space in the cell. Small
vacuoles are, however, present (Fig. 5.6A).
As the cell grows larger, the small vacuoles
that occur within the cytoplasm increase in
size, coalesce, and become fewer in number (Fig. 5.6B, C). Finally, when the cell
has attained its mature size, only a few
large vacuoles, or even one, may remain,
and the protoplasmic contents (nucleus and
cytoplasm) of the cell lie compressed
against the cell wall (Fig. 5.6D). The nucleus may occupy a position near the center
of the cell, in which event it is connected
with the cytoplasm around the cell wall by
strands of cytoplasm.

The similarity of the term *vacuole* to the
word *vacuum* may have led to the conclusion that vacuoles of the plant cell are cavities with absolutely nothing in them. Quite
the contrary is true. Vacuoles contain not

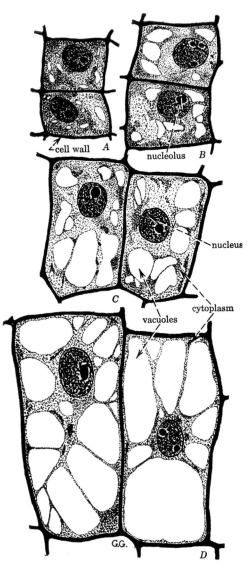

Fig. 5.6. Stages in the growth of a cell. Progressively older cells from A–D. ×2000.

pure water, but a highly dilute solution of
many substances. This aqueous solution in
the cell is termed **cell sap.** Among the substances dissolved in the water, and thus
constituents of cell sap, are the following:
(1) gases of the atmosphere, including
nitrogen, oxygen, and carbon dioxide; (2)
inorganic salts, such as nitrates, sulfates,

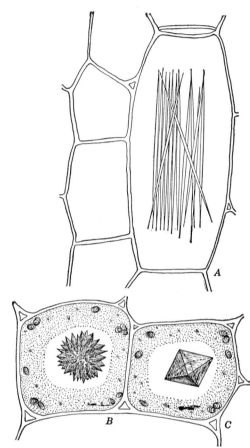

Fig. 5.7. Crystals. *A,* needlelike crystals (raphides); *B,* cluster of crystals; *C,* single crystal. ×2000.

Generally the cell sap is slightly acid. The concentration of cell sap varies from cell to cell, and it may vary in the same cell during the course of the cell's life.

Crystals

Cells with crystals can be found in almost all plants and in many different plant tissues. Crystals vary in chemical composition and in form (Fig. 5.7). The most common crystals are of calcium oxalate; it is generally held that they are an excretory product of the protoplast formed by the union of calcium and oxalic acid. This acid, a by-product of certain activities of the protoplast, is soluble in cell sap and is toxic to the protoplasm if it attains a high concentration in the cell. By its union with calcium, the soluble oxalic acid is converted into the highly insoluble calcium oxalate, which will not injure the protoplasm. In

phosphates, and chlorides of potassium, sodium, calcium, iron, and magnesium; (3) organic acids, such as oxalic, citric, malic, tartaric; (4) salts of organic acids; (5) sugars, such as grape sugar (glucose) and cane sugar (sucrose); (6) water-soluble proteins, alkaloids, and certain pigments, such as anthocyanin.

The most prevalent pigments of the vacuolar sap are the **anthocyanins**. These pigments are responsible for the red color of the roots and leaves of garden beet and the red, purple, or blue of the petals of many flowers or of other parts of plants.

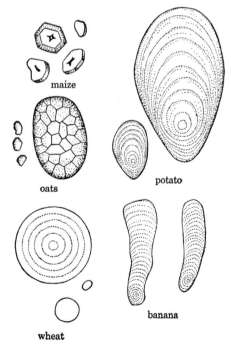

maize

oats

potato

wheat

banana

Fig. 5.8. Starch grains of different plants.

addition to calcium oxalate, crystals of calcium sulfate or of protein sometimes occur.

Starch Grains

The stored starch of plants is perhaps the single most important compound used as food by the animal kingdom (Fig. 5.8). Moreover, it is the principal type of reserve food of most plants. Starch is a complex carbohydrate. It occurs in plant cells in the form of grains or granules.

THE CELL WALL

The protoplast is surrounded by a plasma or cytoplasmic membrane. Outside this membrane, and surrounding the entire protoplast, is a relatively rigid wall. The wall is secreted by the protoplast that it encloses. When, as is usual, protoplasts are separated from each other by walls, the walls are cemented together by an intercellular substance, the **middle lamella** (Fig. 5.9) which is characterized by pectates and certain other substances. The first wall formed by the protoplast is the **primary wall** (Fig. 5.9) and is composed mainly of **cellulose**. Further aging of the cell may bring about the deposition by the protoplast of more wall material, which is laid down on the primary wall. Thus a **secondary wall**

(Fig. 5.9) is formed, and the complete mature cell wall may finally come to have a thickness many times as great as the primary wall. In some tissues the secondary wall is stratified and composed of several layers. In others the cells do not lay down secondary wall material, in which event the common wall between two adjacent protoplasts is composed of the middle lamella with primary wall material on each side. The secondary wall may be of cellulose or of cellulose impregnated with other substances. Some of these substances, notably **lignin**, lend hardness to wood; others, like **suberin** and **cutin**, are waxy and protect leaves and stems against water loss. In addition, certain other materials may enter into the composition of the cell wall—gums, tannins, minerals, pigments, proteins, fats, and oils. It should be emphasized that in mature hard tissues, such as wood, lignin may be deposited not only in the secondary wall but also in the primary wall and middle lamella.

Although the walls of cells vary considerably in composition in different species, and from one part to another in the same individual plant, **cellulose** constitutes the greatest percentage of the material of which cell walls are made. It is elaborated by the protoplast. Chemically it is a carbohydrate. Other familiar examples of carbohydrates

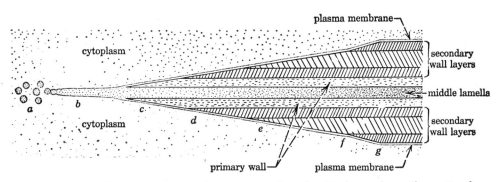

Fig. 5.9. Diagram showing structure of a mature cell wall. (Redrawn from Sharp, *Fundamentals of Cytology*, McGraw-Hill Book Co.)

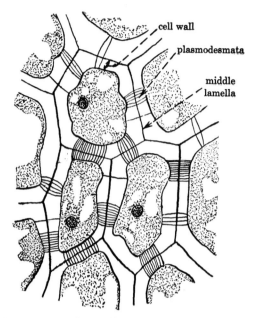

cell wall

plasmodesmata

middle
lamella

Fig. 5.10. Plasmodesmata in endosperm of persimmon, ×1500. (Redrawn from Eames and MacDaniels, *Introduction to Plant Anatomy*, McGraw-Hill Book Co.)

are sucrose (cane sugar), glucose (grape sugar), and starch. Cellulose, as well as other carbohydrates, is composed of only three elements—carbon, hydrogen, and oxygen. As will be explained later, these elements are derived from water in the soil and from carbon dioxide in the atmosphere. Cellulose contains no nitrogen, phosphorus, potassium, or other elements that are absorbed by the plant from the soil and are in part responsible for the soil's fertility. Cellulose is formed through the linkage of many molecules of glucose in a characteristic way.

Other than cellulose, the commonest and most widely found substance in the walls of plant cells is **lignin**, a material that adds to their hardness. By appropriate chemical treatments, cellulose and lignin can be separated. For example, when wood is treated with 72 per cent sulfuric acid, cellu-

lose is changed and becomes water-soluble, whereas lignin remains as an insoluble precipitate. Or, when wood is treated with aqueous or alcoholic sodium hydroxide, lignin is dissolved, and cellulose is left as an insoluble residue. For industrial uses it is desirable to have cellulose in as pure a form as possible, that is, free from lignin and other substances. For example, in pulping wood, lignin is brought into a soluble form and cellulose is recovered as nearly lignin-free as possible. Most paper pulp is from 1 to 5 per cent lignin. The walls of cotton fibers (cells) are almost pure cellulose. Cotton linters (the short fibers that cling to cotton seed and are too short to be spun into yarn) are the principal source of cellulose when a pure form of this substance is required.

Cellulose, like coal, limestone, sulfur, and petroleum, is a fundamental material upon which the chemist depends to make many hundreds of products. For example, (1) cellulose treated with sodium hydroxide and carbon disulfide gives viscose rayon and Cellophane; (2) cellulose treated with acetic anhydride and acetic acid gives cellulose acetate (pyroxylin), acetate rayon, safety film, plastics, Cel-o-glass; (3) cellulose treated with etherifying agents gives cellulose ethers and textile finishes; (4) cellulose treated with sulfuric acid and nitric acid gives nitrocellulose, celluloid, lacquers, plastics, explosives; and (5) cellulose treated with cuprammonium and a caustic gives cuprammonium cellulose and cuprammonium rayon.

Suberin is a waxy substance associated with cellulose in the walls, particularly of cork cells. Since neither water nor gases can pass through suberin, cork tissue is an excellent protection against excessive loss of water.

Cutin is a fatty substance usually found as an external coating on the outer cellulose wall of the epidermal cells of leaves and stems.

Other substances, besides lignin, suberin, and cutin, that may be associated with cellulose in the walls of cells will be discussed at other points in the text.

Plasmodesmata (singular, **plasmodesma**). As we have seen, the plant cell as a structural unit has a somewhat rigid wall enclosing an organized structure, the protoplast. Although in a multicellular plant, each protoplast is a more or less independent unit, it has been demonstrated that very fine channels in the walls connect adjacent protoplasts and that through these channels extend fine threads of protoplasm, each thread being called a **plasmodesma** (Fig. 5.10). These threads are so delicate that they are not seen unless stained by a special technique. The function of plasmodesmata is not entirely clear. There is some evidence that certain materials may be transferred through them from protoplast to protoplast and, also, that they may transmit stimuli from one cell to another.

SUMMARY OF CELL STRUCTURE

1. All animals and plants are composed of microscopic units called cells.

2. Each cell is composed of a protoplast, generally, in the case of plants, surrounded by a cell wall.

3. The protoplast may be divided into the protoplasm and ergastic substances.

4. Protoplasm consists of cytoplasm and the nucleus.

5. Embedded in the hyaloplasm, the clear background fluid of the cytoplasm, may occur various types of plastids, bodies whose concern is food manufacture, and mitochondria, whose function involves respiration.

6. The nucleus, whose function involves inheritance, has a membrane bounding the karyolymph in which are embedded one or more nucleoli and the reticulum (chromosomes).

7. Within most plant cells there are one or more aqueous vacuoles. Together with the cytoplasm the vacuoles function in water and solute absorption and movement throughout the plant.

8. The cell wall is secreted by the protoplast and may be composed of a cellulosic primary wall and a secondary wall also of cellulose. This cellulose wall may be impregnated with a hardening material, lignin, or with waxy substances, cutin or suberin. A middle lamella formed of pectates cements cells together.

THE PHYSIOLOGY OF THE CELL

We have studied the structure of the individual plant cell and seen that most plants are composed of countless numbers of these units. A knowledge of structure, be it of a cell, a tissue or an organ, is essential to an understanding of the activities or functions of the cell, tissue, or organ. An automobile is composed of several thousand parts, each of which has a particular composition, shape, and location upon which depends its special role in the proper operation of the machine. The human eye is a complex organ in which the many individual parts are "put together" in such a way that the function of sight is possible. Likewise, the cell is a most complex structure— a *living structure*. It is the structural and functional unit of the plant. It has work to do; that is, it has functions or activities. **Physiology** is the study of the functions or activities of organisms.

Our study of the physiology of cells will be simplified if we consider a chlorophyll-containing plant such as a unicellular alga (Fig. 18.4) floating freely in water. This cell carries on all the functions that are necessary to maintain its life. Within this microscopic bit of living substance a number of physical and chemical processes are occurring simultaneously. Each cell is (1) absorbing materials such as water, mineral salts, and gases from outside its own body, and simultaneously losing materials to the external environment; (2) building foods from the materials and light energy that it absorbs; (3) digesting foods (changing complex foods to a simple form); (4) respiring, thus releasing energy for various activities; (5) building protoplasm from the foods; (6) growing; and (7) it may also be producing new cells.

We shall briefly discuss each of these physiological processes. However, it is not possible to elaborate on several of them without a knowledge of the structure of the plant as a whole. Therefore, the following discussion merely defines some of these processes, reserving a more complete discussion for later chapters.

ABSORPTION

Water and the different substances dissolved in the water of the river, pond, or lake in which a plant is floating are absorbed by the plant. These substances pass through the cell wall and through the membrane surrounding the cytoplasm immediately inside the wall. They may then pass through the cytoplasm itself, and finally through the membrane between the cytoplasm and the vacuole. The substances are then within the vacuole (Fig. 5.2). Some, however, may remain in the protoplasm.

In order to understand the nature of substances entering a freely floating plant from the surrounding medium in which it is living and the processes involved in the transfer, it will be necessary for us to discuss the following topics: **solution, diffusion, permeability of membranes, osmosis, absorption of solutes.**

Solution

All substances that enter the plant cell are in solution in water. This statement applies to gases as well as to various crystalline substances. There may be solutions of a gas in a liquid, or a liquid in a liquid, or a solid in a liquid. A familiar example of a solution is sugar in water. When sugar is added to water, the sugar molecules become separated from one another and uniformly distributed throughout the resulting solution. It is a solution containing no particles larger than **molecules,** which are the smallest particles in which an element or a substance can exist and still retain the properties of the element or substance in mass. The components of this particular solution are water molecules and sugar molecules. Water is spoken of as the **solvent,** sugar as the **solute.** It is possible, of course, to have a solution with several components. For example, a quantity of sugar, ordinary table salt (sodium chloride), and sodium nitrate could be added to water. The resulting solution would be composed of the solvent—water, and the solutes—sugar, sodium chloride, and sodium nitrate. Soil water, sea water, and the waters of rivers, ponds, and lakes are solutions containing small amounts of many different solutes.

Ions and Molecules. The dissolved particles in a solution may be molecules, ions, or a mixture of molecules and ions. When molecules of materials, such as salt ($NaCl$), that will conduct an electric current are present in water some of them dissociate into their component parts, Na^+ and Cl^-, called **ions.** Notice that the Na^+ ion carries a positive charge and the Cl^- ion carries a negative charge. Thus when crystals of common table salt, sodium chloride ($NaCl$), are dissolved in water, there will be some NaCl molecules, some Na^+ ions, and some Cl^- ions. Most of the substances that green plants absorb from the soil water, or from the water in which they are floating, are more or less ionized when in solution in water. However, plant cells contain many substances, such as glucose and sucrose, that do not ionize at all. The point in mentioning ions is that ions, rather than whole molecules, are often the particles that are absorbed by cells. Thus it usually happens that a cell in a dilute sodium nitrate ($NaNO_3$) solution absorbs Na^+ ions and NO_3^- ions *independently and in different proportions*. Note that the molecules are composed of several **elements**. Sugar is composed of the elements carbon, hydrogen, and oxygen (Fig. 11.1). Elements are forms of matter that cannot be further decomposed by chemical means. Gold, iron, iodine, carbon, oxygen are examples of elements.

Frequent reference will be made to the *concentration of a solution*. A solution made by adding 1 gram of sodium chloride to 99 grams of water is a 1 per cent solution; one made by adding 2 grams to 98 grams of water is a 2 per cent solution. Ordinarily, it would be said that the latter solution has double the concentration of the former. In diffusion phenomena the expression of concentration on the percentage basis as above is not satisfactory, for it is important to know the relative numbers of dissolved particles (molecules and ions) of solute dispersed in a given volume of solvent. Grape sugar ($C_6H_{12}O_6$) has a molecular weight of 180; cane sugar ($C_{12}H_{22}O_{11}$), a molecular weight of 342. To make two solutions, one of grape sugar and another of cane sugar, *equal in concentration*, that is, with the same number of dissolved particles, volume molar solutions are used. A volume molar solution of grape sugar is made by dissolving 180 grams (the molecular weight) of the substance in enough water to make 1000 milliliters of solution; a molar solution of cane sugar is made by dissolving 342 grams (the molecular weight) of this sugar in enough water to make one liter (1000 ml) of solution. If the molecular weight in grams of any soluble substance is dissolved in 1000 grams of water, the solution is said to be a molal solution.

Diffusion

When a cube of sugar is placed in a cup of water the sugar dissolves, and, after a time, even without stirring, the molecules of sugar become uniformly distributed among the water molecules. Sugar molecules have moved from the bottom of the cup toward the top, and water molecules have moved in among the sugar molecules. In all solutions, the molecules or ions of the solute and of the solvent are in constant motion. A visual demonstration of this motion can be made by placing a large crystal of copper sulfate in the bottom of a glass container filled with water. The color of the solution is seen to be most intense near the crystal and to become less and less intense as the distance from it increases. Obviously, dissolved particles of copper sulfate are moving into the water. In time (many days) the whole solution becomes uniform in color, indicating that the dissolved particles of the solute have become uniformly distributed among the water molecules. The experiment shows that the rate of diffusion of the substance through water is slow. This conclusion assumes, of course, that the container holding the water and copper sulfate is not shaken. Ordinarily in making a solution we do not wait for diffusion to become complete under its own force but hasten the process by shaking or stirring the mixture. When diffusion is complete, any unit volume (a cubic centimeter or cubic inch, for example) of the solution has the same concentration as any other unit volume. This means that the number of dissolved particles relative to water molecules in any unit volume of the solution is the same as that in any other unit of equal volume.

In the experiment just cited it is apparent that particles of copper sulfate (molecules and ions) move from a place where there are many such particles to places where there are fewer or none. Water molecules are likewise moving from regions of their higher concentration to regions of their lower concentration. This dispersion of substances by the movement of their ions or molecules is **diffusion.**

Diffusion may also be demonstrated with gases. The air itself is a solution of oxygen, nitrogen, carbon dioxide, and other gases. If, in one corner of a room in which air currents are reduced to a minimum, a bottle is opened containing some volatile substance with a strong and characteristic odor, it is detectable throughout the room in a very short time. As a result of their random kinetic activity, molecules of the volatile substance have moved between the molecules of the other components of the atmosphere; and they have moved from a region where there are many of them per unit volume of atmosphere to a region where there are fewer or none in the same unit volume. Or, we can say that the direction of the diffusion of the gas has been from a region of its *greater partial pressure* to regions of its *lesser partial pressure.*

Diffusion Pressure. To illustrate **diffusion pressure,** let us consider a toy rubber balloon expanded with an odoriferous gas, hydrogen sulfide for instance. The gas molecules are confined in a small space. Their activity results in a pressure on the rubber walls of the balloon. Suppose that we now prick the balloon; it releases the gas molecules that have been exerting a pressure, and it collapses. Freed from the confines of the rubber balloon these molecules now move rapidly across the room. The concentration of the molecules in a small space brings about the development of a pressure by these molecules. Since this pressure results in the diffusion of the molecules we may speak of it as **diffusion pressure.**

In the experiments described above in which sugar or copper sulfate is dissolved in water, we may refer to the diffusion pressure of water and also to the diffusion pressure of the solute sugar or of the solute copper sulfate. The presence of sugar molecules or copper sulfate molecules among the water molecules reduces the diffusion pressure of the water. We may define *diffusion pressure as a tendency of different particles* (ions or molecules) *to diffuse;* it is the *cause* of diffusion rather than the result. As will be shown later, it is possible to measure the pressures developed by diffusing particles.

Permeability of Plant Membranes

The Permeable Membrane. Let us again consider the green plant floating in water. Bathing the cell on all sides is a dilute but exceedingly complex solution of molecules and ions that are constantly bombarding the outer surface of the cell, the cell wall. This membrane, though apparently continuous when viewed through a microscope, is in reality quite porous with **microcapillary spaces** existing between the interwoven cellulose **microfibrils** (Fig. 5.11). Many of these spaces may be filled with other wall substances such as pectates or lignin, but many also are filled with liquid. There is a strong attraction between the insoluble cell wall materials and water. Consequently water is found throughout the wall, thus forming a continuous pathway through which solute particles can freely diffuse. The process in which water is attracted to (**adsorbed on**) the surfaces of the cellulose microfibrils, causing them to move apart and the wall to swell, is called **imbibition.** Cellulose imbibes water and the cell wall thus allows the relative free passage of water and dissolved materials. The cell wall is a **permeable membrane.** Cell walls found in the outer surface of higher plants may be impregnated with fatty materials such as cutin and suberin. These walls do not imbibe water and are impermeable to water and dissolved substances though they may be permeable to substances soluble in fat.

Differentially Permeable Membrane. Lying in intimate contact with the wall of a living cell is the outer cytoplasmic or plasma membrane, the **plasmolemma,** the first important barrier to the free passage of the molecules and ions that bombard the cell from the outside. This limiting surface of the protoplast is characterized by a different physical and chemical composition than the rest of the protoplasm. It is not a rigid, unchanging surface but an ever changing dynamic "guardian of life," for if it is destroyed the cell dies. Although the exact nature of this membrane is not definitely established, it is thought to be a mosaic of fatty and protein material through which water can readily pass but which restricts or prevents the passage of many dissolved materials. It is a **differentially permeable membrane,** allowing some substances to pass freely, others to pass slowly, and others to pass hardly at all. Although the cell cannot select those substances which are beneficial to it and prevent from entering those which are harmful or toxic, the presence of the cytoplasmic membranes does prevent the free diffusion of materials into and out of the cell.

The inner cytoplasmic membrane, the **tonoplast,** surrounding the vacuole, is also differentially permeable. It is more fatty in nature than the plasmolemma and consequently certain substances diffuse through the cell wall and the plasmolemma into the cytoplasm but do not readily find their way into the vacuole. As we have already seen, the vacuolar sap frequently contains high concentrations of plant products such as anthocyanins that are not found in the cytoplasm. Destruction of the cytoplasmic membranes, by immersing the cell in alcohol, for instance, renders the membranes

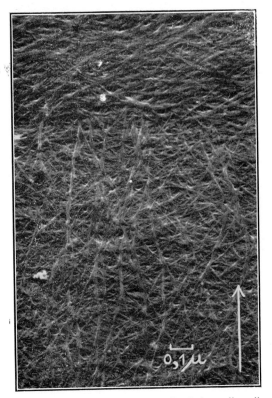

Fig. 5.11. Electron micrograph of the cell wall of a cotton fiber. ×60,000. (Courtesy of Roelofsen.)

permeable, allows the outward diffusion of vacuolar materials, and results in the death of the cell.

Within the cell itself solutes are not free to diffuse at random throughout the protoplast. In addition to the tonoplast that restricts the movement of materials between the cytoplasm and the vacuole, there are the nuclear and plastid membranes that restrict the free diffusion of materials into and out of these bodies. Moreover the colloidal nature of the hyaloplasm itself presents a delicate but ever changing architecture within which the foods, vitamins, hormones, enzymes, and inorganic ions are so distributed that the intricate yet precise processes of life proceed.

Diffusion through Differentially Permeable Membranes

Nonliving Membranes. The differentially permeable membranes of the cell play their role in the maintenance of life activities. Certain features of their behavior can best be explained by reference to the simple apparatus called an **osmometer** (Fig. 5.12). The cylindrical sac of an osmometer is made of parchment paper, collodion, or other material that is differentially permeable. This sac is filled with a concentrated sugar solution, stoppered with a tight-fitting rubber stopper through which a glass tube is fitted, and the sac immersed in distilled water (pure solvent). In fol-lowing this discussion one should keep in mind that the cell sap of a living algal cell is usually more concentrated in total solutes (salts, sugars, etc.) than is the pond water in which it may be floating. The movement of water into the plant cell obeys the same laws as those that govern the movement of water into an osmometer.

Turgor Pressure. On the outside of the osmometer are water molecules, and on the inside are water molecules and sugar molecules. The membrane, being differentially permeable, permits the free movement of water molecules inward or outward and retards or prevents the free movement of sugar molecules outward. After a short time the liquid rises in the tube, and the

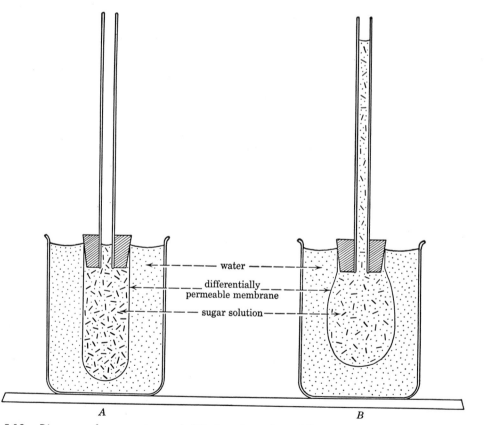

water

differentially permeable membrane

sugar solution

A   *B*

Fig. 5.12. Diagram of osmometer and diffusion through a differentially permeable membrane. A, before osmosis has occurred; B, after osmosis.

sac becomes distended, **turgid.** The pressure of the solution against the sac, the **turgor pressure,** is a measurable pressure opposed by an equal and opposite pressure of the wall of the sac against its contents, the wall pressure. Evidently water molecules are moving inward more rapidly than outward. The diffusion pressure of pure water outside the sac exceeds the diffusion pressure of water in the solution inside the sac. Thus water molecules tend to diffuse into the sac.

In other words the concentration of water molecules per unit volume outside of the sac is greater than the concentration of water molecules per unit volume within the sac. As water continues to move in, turgor pressure is built up in the sac and the tendency for water to diffuse back out of the sac gradually increases. Finally this outward diffusion of water equals the inward diffusion. At this point there is no further net movement of water into the sac and the system is at equilibrium. Water molecules are passing through the membrane in both directions at the same rate. The diffusion pressures of water on both sides of the sac are now equal. An important conclusion to be drawn from this demonstration is that (1) the diffusion pressure of water (in this case water within the sac) is reduced by the presence of solute particles that reduce the concentration of the water, and (2) the diffusion pressure of water (in this case water within the sac) is increased by the development of a physical turgor pressure in the solution. These two factors, solutes and turgor pressure, then have opposite effects on the diffusion pressure of water. In our example, equilibrium was attained when these two factors balanced each other and water within the sac had the same diffusion pressure as the pure water outside.

Osmosis. The diffusion of water (a solvent) through a differentially permeable membrane is called **osmosis.** Osmosis is not mysterious but is simply a special example of diffusion in which a differentially permeable membrane of a sac, or of a cell, separates the internal water having a given diffusion pressure from the water of the surrounding environment which has a different given diffusion pressure. Osmosis occurs, i.e., water diffuses across the membrane, along the diffusion gradient from a region of higher to a region of lower diffusion pressure of water. The cell gains or loses water until the diffusion pressures of water on both sides of the membrane are equal.

Water movement into living cells is usually controlled by two major factors that affect the diffusion pressure and hence the direction of diffusion of water. These are (1) the presence of solute particles in the water and (2) the existence of a turgor pressure. Other factors, for example, a change in temperature, or the presence of water attracting materials such as some colloids also affect the diffusion pressure of water in a cell. As we have seen, the presence of solute particles, i.e., molecules or ions, lowers the diffusion pressure of the water in which they are dissolved. This effect on the diffusion pressure of water is proportional to the total number of dissolved particles (molecules and ions) in a given volume of water. Ten grams of sugar dissolved in 50 ml of water will lower the diffusion pressure of water approximately twice as much as will 5 grams of sugar dissolved in 50 ml of water.

This reduction of the diffusion pressure of water caused by the presence of dissolved particles in it can be measured and is a characteristic of the concentration of the solution. If this solution is placed in an osmometer with pure water outside, osmosis will occur and turgor pressure will develop as long as there is any difference in the diffusion pressure of water across the

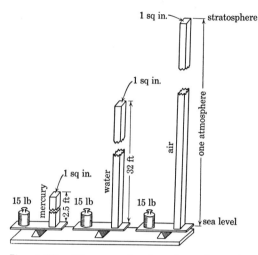

Fig. 5.13. Diagram showing the relationship of one atmosphere pressure to the height of mercury and water columns that it will balance.

membrane. The theoretical maximum turgor pressure that could develop in this system just equals the amount that the diffusion pressure of water in the solution is reduced because of the solute particles in it.

Osmotic Pressure. The term **osmotic pressure,** sometimes called osmotic concentration, or osmotic potential, is used to express these two properties of solutions, namely, (1) the amount of reduction of diffusion pressure of water in the solution caused by the presence of dissolved particles, and (2) the potential maximum turgor pressure that could develop as a result of osmosis. The osmotic pressure of a solution is usually expressed in units of atmospheric pressure. One atmosphere pressure is approximately 15 pounds per square inch (Fig. 5.13). The osmotic pressure of a solution is not an actual physical pressure that exists in the solution. We might say that it is a power rating of the solution just as an automobile engine has a rating of 150 horsepower. We do not mean that when the motor is idle it is doing the work of 150 horses. It is only when the proper con-

ditions exist, i.e., when the motor is operating, that the ability to do work, the power, actually results in the work being done. Thus a solution having an osmotic pressure of five atmospheres and standing in a beaker has the capacity to develop a turgor pressure of five atmospheres under the proper conditions, i.e., when placed in an ideal osmometer with pure water outside. This turgor pressure will develop because the diffusion pressure of pure water is five atmospheres higher than the diffusion pressure of water in the solution. If the solution were placed in an osmometer and immersed in another solution having an osmotic pressure of three atmospheres, osmosis would occur only until a turgor pressure of two atmospheres had developed in the osmometer because in this case the diffusion pressure of water in the solution outside the sac is only two atmospheres higher than the diffusion pressure of water inside the sac.

Living Membranes. Water moves from the external environment into the plant cell, whether it is a single-celled alga, a root cell of a flowering plant, or a seed, along a gradient of diffusion pressure of water. Usually the concentration of the osmotically active solutes (the osmotic pressure of the cell sap) and the turgor pressure in the cell largely determine the diffusion pressure of water in the cell. In certain instances, air-dried seeds for example, there is present a high percentage of colloidal material such as starch, protein, and cellulose, all of which have a great affinity for water and hence a large capacity for imbibing water. When these seeds are planted in moist soil, the water in the seeds has a very low diffusion pressure compared with the water in the soil. Consequently water diffuses into these seeds causing them to swell. In this case the colloidal materials are contributing largely to the low diffusion pressure of water in the seed. Although the diffusion pressure of water outside a cell floating in a pond is primarily determined by the concentration of dissolved material, in the case of water in the soil a further factor is involved, namely, the presence of colloidal soil particles that imbibe water and thus lower its diffusion pressure. Nevertheless the direction of water movement will be along a diffusion pressure gradient of water toward the region of lower diffusion pressure.

It is evident that, if particles of the different solutes in the vacuole were not restricted in their movement outward by the cytoplasmic membrane, a turgor pressure would not develop in the cell. Although the pressure outward is often very considerable, the protoplast is prevented from bursting by the elastic cell wall, which resists stretching and exerts a pressure inward. The cell wall serves the same purpose that the casing of an automobile tire does in preventing the bursting of the inner tube.

It is obvious that in a cell the *turgor pressure outward* against the wall is equal to the *wall pressure inward* against the cell contents. A cell may have varying degrees of turgidity. The maximum turgor pressure that can be developed in a cell is equal to the osmotic pressure of the cell contents. That is, when a cell has absorbed all the water it can, osmotic pressure, turgor pressure, and wall pressure are equal. Normally, most living cells are in a condition in which turgor pressure is somewhat less than the maximum pressure possible. This means they are capable of taking in more water by osmosis. However, cells may become *flaccid,* that is, lose water and have a very low turgor pressure.

The crispness of the leaves and the rigidity of the young parts of plants are due to the turgid condition of the individual cells. A young bean seedling stands erect chiefly because of the turgor pressure in all the cells of the stem. In such a young plant, strengthening tissue is not plentiful. If the cells of the seedling lose water rapidly, the whole plant becomes flaccid and droops, but it may recover if water is supplied.

Plasmolysis. If a cell or group of cells is immersed in a solution that has a higher solute concentration than that of the cell sap, water diffuses outward, and the turgor pressure in the cell is reduced. The volume of the cell decreases somewhat, but more striking is the withdrawal of the protoplast from the cell wall and the decrease in the size of the vacuole. This phenomenon is called **plasmolysis.** As shown in Fig. 5.14, the space between the cytoplasm and the cell wall in a plasmolyzed cell is filled with the solution (plasmolyzing solution) in which the cells are immersed. It is evident that there has been no movement, or very little movement, of solute particles either inward or outward through the cytoplasmic membrane. Solute particles outside the cell, however, were able to pass readily inward through the cell wall just as did water molecules. If plasmolyzed cells are immersed in water or in a solution whose concentration is less than that of the cell sap, the cells regain their turgor; water molecules diffuse inward. If cells remain long in a state of pronounced plasmolysis, death ensues. A normal, healthy, and functioning cell is one in a turgid condition.

It is instructive to plasmolyze living cells that contain a pigment dissolved in the vacuolar sap. For this purpose, cells from the root of a red garden beet may be used. When they are immersed in a strong solution, of table salt for example, plasmolysis soon follows. It will be seen, however, that the red pigment is retained in the vacuole (Fig. 5.14A). Obviously, the tonoplast is impermeable to this pigment. If the cells are heated or are treated with various chemicals, such as chloroform, alcohol, or ether, the red pigment readily dif-

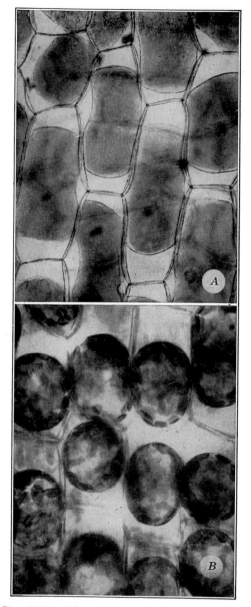

Fig. 5.14. Plasmolysis. A, photomicrograph of cells of garden beet in which a red pigment (anthocyanin) is dissolved in the cell sap; B, photomicrograph of leaf cells containing chloroplasts. Space between protoplast and wall occupied by plasmolyzing solution.   ×640. (Photo courtesy of Currier.)

fuses from the protoplast. This fact indicates that the cytoplasmic membranes manifest differential permeability *only when the cell is alive;* when the cell is killed, the cytoplasmic membranes lose their differential permeability. As we shall see later on, however, many nonliving, as well as living, membranes have differentially permeable properties.

A cell may die if plasmolysis is pronounced and prolonged. For example, if heavy applications of ordinary salt are placed on the soil where weeds are growing, so that the root cells are surrounded by a solution of high concentration, water diffuses from the cells, and they become severely plasmolyzed. If this state is prolonged, the roots die. The salt killed, not because it was toxic to root cells, but rather because severe plasmolysis was brought about by the high concentration of the soil solution. In parts of the western United States where rainfall is low and the evaporation rate high, salts of the soil may accumulate on the surface and form what are known as "alkali flats." In such soils, the concentration of the soil solution may be so high that ordinary crop plants cannot grow; only those species that are especially adapted to high salt concentration are able to survive. Plants of this type are known as **halophytes.**

Absorption of Dissolved Substances by Living Cells

In our discussion of absorption thus far we have explained how water enters the living cell. In addition to water, the cell absorbs various inorganic ions, such as nitrates, phosphates, and sulfates, and the gases, oxygen and carbon dioxide. Both oxygen and carbon dioxide are soluble in water. Apparently they enter and leave the cell by simple diffusion.

Water and the different solute particles

move into the cell *independently.* That is, if water molecules are diffusing through the cell wall and the cytoplasmic membranes and are entering the vacuole at a certain rate, it does not follow that any particular solute particle is entering the vacuole at the same rate. Moreover, in the event that the solution surrounding the cell contains $NaNO_3$, if NO_3^- ions are entering the cell, it does not follow that Na^+ ions are moving in at the same rate. Although loss of water in vapor form from a plant does affect the proportions of water and solutes absorbed, it appears that the kind and quantity of ions absorbed are chiefly determined not by the volume of water absorbed but by certain chemical and physical properties of root cells. Different solute particles diffuse independently of each other and the direction of diffusion of any solute is independent of the direction of the diffusion of any other solute that may be a part of the same solution.

It has been found experimentally that the concentration of a solute particle (ion or molecule) may be greater in the vacuole than in the solution outside the cell. For example, root cells may accumulate ions. Ions are apparently "pumped" into the vacuole of the cell from the soil solution. Referring back to diffusion of copper sulfate crystals in water, we have seen that copper sulfate molecules diffused from a point where there were many of them per unit volume to a point where there were fewer. How, then, do we harmonize this behavior (*simple diffusion*) with that in which solute particles move from a place where they are in low concentration to a place where they are in high concentration? It has been demonstrated that the **accumulation** of solute particles by plant cells is usually attended by high respiration rates. It may be assumed that the energy released by respiration is utilized by the cell to per-

form the labor of *forcing* the solute particles to move *against a concentration gradient;* and this same energy maintains the concentration difference. Thus the living cell performs work, the energy for which is derived from respiration.

SUMMARY OF ABSORPTION

1. All substances that enter the cell, gases as well as other solutes, are in solution in water.

2. The cell wall is normally permeable to all substances in true solution.

3. The cytoplasmic membranes are differentially permeable.

4. Cell colloids imbibe water and swell.

5. Osmosis is the diffusion of water through a differentially permeable membrane. Water diffuses along a gradient of diffusion pressure of water.

6. Any particular solute may accumulate in the cell and thus maintain in the vacuole a higher concentration of that substance than exists outside of the cell. To accomplish and maintain this higher concentration the cell must perform work. The energy for this work is furnished by respiration.

7. The diffusion of water and different solutes is independent.

8. Solute particles decrease the diffusion pressure of water.

9. When water diffuses into a cell the internal turgor pressure increases.

10. Turgor pressure increases the diffusion pressure of water.

11. Water enters the cell when the diffusion pressure of the water in the cell sap is less than that of the water in the solution outside the cell. Water leaves the cell if the diffusion pressure of the water in the cell exceeds that in the solution outside the cell.

12. Cells immersed in a solution of high concentration become plasmolyzed. Water diffuses out of the protoplast and the protoplast withdraws from the wall.

ENZYMES

Molecules of carbon dioxide, water, glucose, proteins, fats, and all other substances possess definite shapes. Protoplasm, a colloidal system, may be pictured as a very complex mixture of many molecules, each of which has a definite and characteristic shape. These molecular shapes, however, are not static, like the crystals in a sugar bowl. The molecules in a chemically active system, such as protoplasm, are more like the ten men on a basketball court. Each player has a definite shape; his movements are limited by his shape, structure, and the rules of the game. Likewise, a chemical reaction, because of the shape and activities of the molecules involved, proceeds from a beginning to an end point, all steps being governed by a rigid set of rules. The game may be modified; if the players put on skates and transfer to ice, the speed of the game increases. Chemical actions, too, may be modified. For instance, sugar oxidizes very slowly, if at all, at room temperature; yet in plant cells oxidation of sugar may be fairly rapid at temperatures as low as 40° F. Starch changes slowly to sugar if kept at room temperature in sterile water. It changes very rapidly when a little saliva is added. Substances that increase the rate of chemical change without appearing to enter into the reaction are known as **catalysts.** There are both *inorganic catalysts* and *organic catalysts*. Organic catalysts produced by living organisms are called **enzymes.**

Enzymes are proteins of a complex nature. They are frequently very *specific* in their activity; that is, one enzyme activates only one or two chemical changes. The specificity of enzymes and their ability to speed the rate of reaction are in many instances due to their shape, just as the shape of ice skates limits the player to ice and speeds up the game. Because of their shape and activity, enzyme molecules are able to combine with only one or two specific substances. As a result of this combination, the original compound or compounds react with each other or with surrounding substances. The resulting compounds are released from the enzyme molecule, which is now in its original form ready for further activity. Thus, an enzyme greatly speeds the rate of a reaction without being much changed itself by the reaction.

Enzymes have certain optimum conditions for their greatest activity. They may be destroyed by heat and by some metals and certain other substances.

Many of the numerous steps involved in photosynthesis, respiration, and digestion are catalyzed by enzymes. Enzymes are active in practically all cellular processes.

Protoplasm may be thought of as a very complex colloidal system in which molecules of one sort are being constantly changed into molecules of another sort. Green plant cells store energy in one process and release it in another; both processes may go on within any green cell at the same time. Enzymes help to control the precision and the rate of the changes taking place in the protoplasm.

PHOTOSYNTHESIS

Every day the combined oil wells of the world deliver some 2 billion barrels of oil for running the cars, boats, trains, and factories of our highly industrialized civilization. The energy this oil so conveniently stores came originally from the sun. It was "captured" by plants, and because of certain geological conditions was trapped and stored in the earth's crust for many millions of years. The process by which plants in the past captured, and today continue to capture, the radiant energy of the sun is known as **photosynthesis,** a term that literally means putting together (*synthesis*) by means of light (*photo*).

The principal features of this physiological process will be mentioned here, but a more complete discussion will be given in Chapter 11. Photosynthesis is a process that goes on only in cells that have *chloroplasts* and only when these cells are *illuminated.* Certain blue-green algae and purple bacteria are exceptional in carrying on photosynthesis in the absence of chloroplasts, but chlorophyll is present.

In photosynthesis, the simple compounds *water* and *carbon dioxide* are united to form *sugars* and *oxygen.* Glucose is one of the principal sugars produced during photosynthesis.

The oxygen may go into solution in the cell sap, or diffuse out of the cell, or be used in another cellular process, respiration. Carbon dioxide is dissolved in the water in which the plant is floating. As carbon dioxide is taken out of solution and used in photosynthesis, its concentration in the cell sap becomes less than that in the water outside the cell. As a result, diffusion of that gas into the cell goes on as long as active photosynthesis continues. In land plants green cells obtain carbon dioxide from the atmosphere, but this gas must go into solution in the imbibed water of the cell wall and cytoplasm before it can diffuse to the chloroplasts.

Photosynthesis is an energy-storing process. Energy is required to bring about the synthesis of glucose from carbon dioxide and water. Light is the source of energy for photosynthesis and the glucose molecule contains transformed light energy holding the atoms together. If the glucose molecule is burned, oxygen is consumed

and carbon dioxide and water are formed. The heat energy evolved in burning represents the release of chemical potential energy of the glucose molecule, which is equal to the light energy transformed and stored as chemical energy in the photosynthetic process.

Photosynthesis may be simply represented as follows:

$$6CO_2 + 6H_2O + 673 \rightarrow C_6H_{12}O_6 + 6O_2$$

carbon + water + kcal $\rightarrow$ sugar + oxygen
dioxide

Glucose may be utilized in a number of different ways: (1) broken down in the process of respiration, yielding energy; (2) converted into some closely related carbohydrate, such as sucrose (cane sugar, $C_{12}H_{22}O_{11}$), or cellulose (cell-wall building material), or starch (a reserve food supply); (3) converted into fatty substances; (4) united with the nitrogen, sulfur, and phosphorus derived from various inorganic salts absorbed from the water of the soil or the lake or stream in which the plant lives, thus forming proteins; and (5) employed as the chemical basis for a number of other substances that may be found in the cell, such as chlorophyll, or alkaloids, such as nicotine.

The conversion of glucose into other carbohydrates may be simply represented as follows:

$$nC_6H_{12}O_6 \rightarrow n(C_6H_{10}O_5) + nH_2O$$

glucose $\rightarrow$ carbohydrate + water

DIGESTION

Plants, as well as animals, **digest** *foods,* that is, they break down complex foods into simple compounds. Plants have no special organs for digestion, it is carried on *in any cell that may store food,* even temporarily. In most green cells, photosynthetic activity may proceed at such a rate during the day that the food (glucose) accumulates faster than it is used in those cells. When this occurs, the glucose may be changed temporarily to starch, which appears as granules in the chloroplasts. Glucose is soluble in the water of cell sap; starch is insoluble. When the time comes for this temporary starch reserve to be used by the cell, or transported out of the cell, it must be changed back into sugar. This chemical transformation of the insoluble starch into soluble glucose is one example of digestion. The equation for starch digestion is as follows:

$$(C_6H_{10}O_5)_n + nH_2O \rightarrow nC_6H_{12}O_6$$
$$\text{starch} \quad + \quad \text{water} \quad \rightarrow \quad \text{glucose}$$

Any other foods that are insoluble in the cell sap, such as proteins and fats, must be digested (rendered soluble) before they can diffuse and nourish the cell. Enzymes *facilitate digestion.*

Digestion may occur not only in organs that store large quantities of foods but also in any living cell where food is stored, even in small quantities and temporarily.

RESPIRATION

Many processes taking place in plants require energy. These include: the absorption of mineral salts against an osmotic gradient, the synthesis of complex compounds such as proteins, maintenance of the protoplasm in a living state, cell division and cell growth, movement, photosynthesis, and translocation. Energy for photosynthesis is supplied by sunlight; energy for translocation of water comes mainly from the evaporation of water from leaf surfaces. All other processes obtain energy from respiration.

Respiration may be defined as the **oxidation** *of organic substances, with the release of energy, within cells.* In its simplest form, oxidation involves chemical union of some substance with oxygen. However, in its broadest sense, oxidation covers the energy-releasing reactions, in which molecular oxygen itself may not be involved. In the burning of a match oxygen of the air unites with wood, heat energy is released, and the wood is broken down into carbon dioxide and water. We have seen that photosynthesis is the reverse: carbon dioxide and water united, oxygen was released, and energy was stored. This general type of reaction is termed **reduction.** Actually the details of the two reaction types are much more complicated than expressed here and will be considered in more detail in later chapters, but an understanding of the concepts given above is sufficient for elementary botany.

Sugar is the usual organic substance oxidized in all plant cells. The energy stored in the sugar is, as we have learned, derived from sunlight. Sugar is a **food,** and all foods are energy-rich compounds whose molecules are so constructed that the energy they store may be released with comparative ease.

Thus, respiration is a cellular process. All living cells respire. Although respiration is a complicated chemical process, the overall reaction occurring in cells may be described as follows: 1 gram-molecule of glucose sugar (180 grams) combines with 6 gram-molecules of oxygen (192 grams) to form 6 gram-molecules of water (108 grams) and 6 gram-molecules of carbon dioxide (264 grams) and releases 673 kilocalories of heat. A kilocalorie is the amount of heat required to raise the temperature of 1 liter of water (slightly more than a quart) $1°$ C.

This statement may be simplified as follows:

$$C_6H_{12}O_6 + 6O_2 \rightarrow 6CO_2 + 6H_2O + 673$$
$$\text{sugar} \quad + \quad \text{oxy-} \quad \rightarrow \quad \text{carbon} \quad + \quad \text{water} \quad + \quad \text{kcal}$$
$$\text{gen} \qquad \text{dioxide}$$

ASSIMILATION

We have seen how the green plant manufactures glucose from carbon dioxide and water. This sugar may be transformed into related carbohydrates, such as sucrose or starch; or it may be changed to fats; or, with the addition of chemical elements (particularly nitrogen, sulfur, and phosphorus) from the soil, proteins may be formed. Carbohydrates, fats, and proteins and simpler nitrogenous substances are the **foods** of plants, as they are of animals. They are *organic compounds*. The foods are manufactured from *raw materials*, such as water, carbon dioxide, nitrates, phosphates, and sulfates. The raw materials are *inorganic compounds*. The cell takes the foods (nonliving substances) and from them builds protoplasm (living substance). *The conversion of foods into the living material (protoplasm) of the cell is called* **assimilation.** The chemical changes involved in this conversion are not understood, but energy is probably used in the process. Except in a very general way, the chemical nature of protoplasm itself is unknown.

Animal cells also convert foods into protoplasm. Any cell of a plant, whether it possesses chlorophyll or not, can do the same. Also, any plant cell, with or without chlorophyll, can synthesize fats and proteins and can change glucose into starch and other carbohydrates. But only chlorophyll-bearing cells can manufacture glucose from carbon dioxide and water.

The steps leading up to the building of protoplasm in the free-floating water plant, or in any green cell, may be summarized as shown in the accompanying diagram.

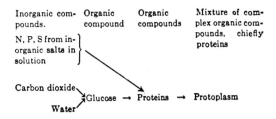

REPRODUCTION

Reproduction of Single Cells. Many plants are single-celled (unicellular). Since plants of this type have existed for ages, the single cell must either be immortal or give rise to new cells. Seeds composed of relatively few cells may develop into enormous trees composed of millions of cells. Obviously, cells divide, and the nucleus of each cell must also divide. We have stated that the genes, arranged like a string of microscopic beads on the chromosomes, are responsible for the activities of each cell and for the plant as a whole. If the nucleus divides and the daughter nuclei are identical with each other and with the original nucleus, some mechanism must exist that will supply each daughter nucleus with a complete set of similar genes. If the nucleus were simply pinched in two by chance, no two cells could be alike. That this is not what happens is apparent in that the roots of elm trees and the shoots from elm trees will reproduce elm trees. This reproduction would not be possible if the nuclei were all different.

The division of the cell involves two phases: that which parcels out the *nuclear material* so that each daughter nucleus receives its full allotment of genes is called **mitosis;** and that which involves the remainder of the cell, including wall formation, is called **cytokinesis.** These two processes normally proceed in unison.

The vegetative or resting nucleus has already been discussed. It consists of a nuclear membrane, one or more nucleoli, a reticulum, and the karyolymph. The reticulum may be composed of from six to well over a hundred individual threads, each individual thread being a **chromosome.**

Although the process of nuclear division is a continuous one, it is convenient to describe it in stages, or "phases," which are

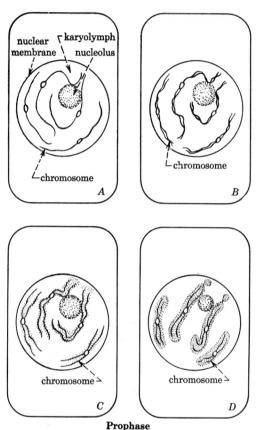

Fig. 5.15. Diagram showing prophase of mitosis.

as being elastic, stretched long and thin, and very much twisted. The first stage of cell division involves a shortening and thickening of these threads. Visualize the change that will take place in the elastic threads as the tension on them is slowly released. As they shorten and thicken they become easier to see; furthermore, they stain more heavily with certain dyes. For this reason they are called "colored (*chromo*) bodies (*soma*)" or **chromosomes.** Each chromosome is derived from an individual thread. The nucleolus slowly decreases in size and finally disappears during this stage (Figs. 5.15, 5.16, 5.17).

It becomes apparent that at late prophase each chromosome is composed not of one but of two threads coiled about each other (Fig. 5.15*B*). The nuclear membrane disappears toward the end of the prophase, but there is reason to believe that the

called the (1) **prophase,** (2) **metaphase,** (3) **anaphase,** and (4) **telophase.**

Special techniques have been devised for studies of cells. The plant tissue is first killed quickly in a chemical that coagulates the protoplasm. It is then embedded in paraffin and sectioned on a precision machine (microtome) resembling a meat slicer. The sections, about $\frac{1}{2000}$ of an inch thick, are fastened to a glass slide and stained in special dyes. These dyes stain the various cellular structures different colors, so that it is possible to distinguish them more easily.

Prophase. Let us think of the threads of the reticulum in the vegetative nucleus

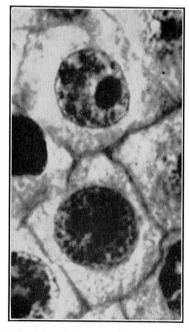

Fig. 5.16. Vegetative nucleus. *Podophyllum peltatum,* root tip. ×2000. (Photomicrograph courtesy of Brown.)

karyolymph may not mix with the general cytoplasm of the cell and that the chromosomes may remain embedded within it.

Metaphase. Forces active within the cell now arrange the chromosomes, or at least a specialized portion of each chromosome (the **kinetochore**), in the equatorial plane of the cell (Figs. 5.18, 5.20). The karyolymph appears to elongate slightly, and **tractile fibers** appear attached to the kinetochores. This structure, composed of chromosomes, fibers, and karyolymph (and possibly some cytoplasm), is the **spindle** (Figs. 5.18, 5.19). It should be mentioned that the fibers are not really strands but probably indicate an orientation of molecules within the spindle substance.

The chromosomes are now distinct bodies of two closely associated halves, each half being known as a **chromatid** (Figs. 5.18, 5.20). In those plants, such as corn, which have been intensively studied, each chro-

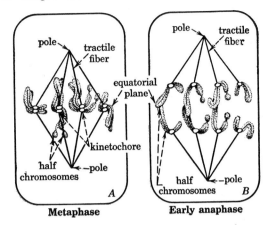

Metaphase   **Early anaphase**

Fig. 5.18. Diagram showing A, metaphase; B, early anaphase.

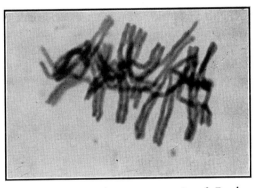

Fig. 5.19. Metaphase in root tip of *Tradescantia*. ×2000.

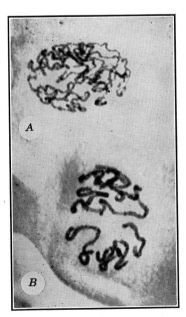

Fig. 5.17. Prophase in cells of anther wall of *Paeonia Californica.* A, early prophase; B, late prophase. ×1000. (Photomicrograph courtesy of Brown.)

Fig. 5.20. Beginning of anaphase movement in chromosomes in dividing cells of anther wall of *Paeonia Californica.* ×1000. (Photomicrograph courtesy of Brown.)

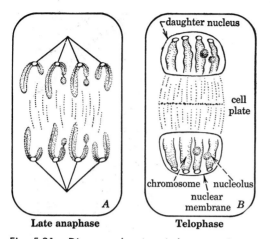

Late anaphase   **Telophase**

Fig. 5.21. Diagram showing A, late anaphase; B, telophase.

forming full-sized chromosomes once again (Figs. 5.21, 5.23).

The important characteristics of mitosis are as follows: (1) It leads to an increase in the number of cells. (2) Through the formation of chromosomes and their longitudinal division, each daughter nucleus receives a full complement of genes. (3) There is no change in the number of chromosomes; if the original nucleus had ten chromosomes, each daughter nucleus will have ten chromosomes. (4) The chromosomes maintain their individuality in the vegetative nucleus, where they are represented by the individual threads of the reticulum. Thus the chromosome is a permanent cellular body that maintains its individuality during both nuclear division and the vegetative stage of nuclear activity. (5) It should further be pointed out that, although mitosis is thought of as nuclear division, it is in reality nuclear multiplication, for during this process the nucleus, including all its parts—genes, chromosomes

mosome can be recognized and numbered. There are twenty chromosomes in corn, but only ten different types that can be distinguished by their size and form. There are thus two chromosomes of each type. The twenty chromosomes of corn may be arranged in ten pairs. Maps have been prepared of corn chromosomes showing the relative positions of the genes along them. Since the chromosomes split longitudinally, each gene is divided and each half chromosome contains a full set of genes.

Anaphase. The chromosomes do not remain long in the equatorial plane. The chromatids soon separate from each other and move to opposite poles of the cell. This period of separation of half chromosomes is called the **anaphase** (Figs. 5.18, 5.21, 5.22).

Telophase. When the divided chromosomes have reached the opposite poles of the cell, they group together and spin out into long, thin threads of the reticulum. The nuclear membrane and the nucleolus again become apparent. This period of transition from chromosomes to vegetative nucleus is known as the **telophase**. The half chromosomes that went into the constitution of the new daughter nuclei grow,

Fig. 5.22. Anaphase in root tip cell of *Podophyllum peltatum.* Note spindle fibers. ×2000. (Photomicrograph courtesy of Brown.)

and nucleoli—becomes duplicated. Where one nuclear structure existed, two now appear.

Cytokinésis. In the great majority of instances the division of the nucleus is followed immediately by the development of a cell wall near the equator of the original cell. The first material or **cell plate** (Figs. 5.21, 5.23) separating the two telophase nuclei is fluid, apparently forming from the union of droplets that develop across the spindle near the equator of the original cell. This fluid material soon undergoes physical and chemical changes so that two distinct daughter protoplasts are evident within the confines of the old cell wall. The next step is the formation of new cellulose walls adjacent to the cell plate by each daughter protoplast. The original cell plate remains as an intercellular cementing substance or **middle lamella.**

Sometimes, cytokinesis is not regularly correlated with mitosis, and cells develop with more than one nucleus or more than two sets of chromosomes. This occurs normally in portions of many plants. The beneficial nitrogen-fixing bacteria that are associated with the roots of plants belonging to the pea family invade only root cells that have more than the normal complement of chromosomes.

Reproduction of Individuals. Since most individual plants are composed of many cells, it is to be expected that special cells will be associated with their reproduction. Indeed, the sexual reproductive stages of the great majority of plants are characterized by two cellular phenomena: (1) the union of two cells (fertilization or conjugation), which *doubles the number of chromosomes,* and (2) a special reduction division by which *chromosome numbers are again halved.* In this reduction of chromosome numbers, two divisions overlap in point of time and involve an intimate association of chromosome pairs (page 286). This phenomenon involving reduction in

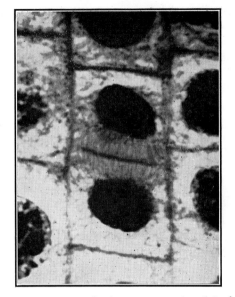

Fig. 5.23. Late telophase in root tip of *Podophyllum peltatum*. Note reconstitution of daughter nuclei and formation of cell plate. ×2000. (Photomicrograph courtesy of Brown.)

the number of chromosomes is called **meiosis,** and the divisions are called **meiotic divisions.**

Meiosis occurs in plants in the production of special reproductive cells, such as pollen grains, or spores of mosses and ferns, all of which may be called **meiospores.** We shall learn that it is a very important process, being the basis for much practical work in plant breeding.

Mitosis and meiosis differ in one very important respect: *There is no change of chromosome number in mitosis; the number of chromosomes is reduced by half during meiosis.*

GROWTH

Growth is a physiological activity of every cell. We have seen how a cell may divide to form two daughter cells. Each daughter cell "grows" to its mature size and form. The cell enlarges; the quantity of protoplasm increases; the walls may become thicker. Enlargement of the cell results in part from an increase in the quantity of protoplasm and in part from the absorption of water into the vacuole or vacuoles. As we have learned, absorption of water by the vacuole or vacuoles intensifies the turgor pressure on the cell wall, which is thereby stretched. The thickening of the wall is an activity of the protoplasm. The thickening material is usually cellulose, which is formed by the linkage of molecules of glucose.

As concerns organs and the plant as a whole, growth is much more than simple enlargement. It involves a series of physical and chemical changes. Of much interest is the role of growth-regulating substances in the growth processes. Growth will be discussed more fully in Chapter 15.

SUMMARY OF CELLULAR PHYSIOLOGY

1. Cells absorb water and mineral salts from the external environment.

2. The numerous chemical reactions that go on in the cell are controlled by organic catalysts, enzymes.

3. Green plant cells are able to synthesize carbohydrates from water, carbon dioxide, and light energy, through the process of photosynthesis.

4. Carbohydrate foods can be transformed into fats and, with the addition of certain chemicals, into proteins.

5. Complex foods are rendered simple through the process of digestion.

6. Respiration is the oxidation of organic substances within living plant cells.

7. Protoplasm is built up through the process of assimilation of foods.

8. The production of new cells is accomplished by the division of one cell into two daughter cells. This involves nuclear division or mitosis and division of the cytoplasm or cytokinesis.

9. The two daughter nuclei formed as a result of mitosis have the same number of chromosomes bearing identical genes.

6

The Stem

In our everyday observation of the common plants of garden, orchard, field, and forest, attention is attracted to the great variation in the size and form of plants. There are tall, stately trees, some with a single main trunk (stem), like the pines and spruces. There are others with many branch stems of equal size that give to the tree a spreading habit, as oaks and elms. There are woody shrubs and vines. There is an endless variety of tender nonwoody plants we call herbs. While it is convenient to divide all plants into 15 large divisions or phyla, those plants we see growing about us are quite generally limited to two subdivisions, or classes of one of these phyla known as the Pterophyta. If time is taken to observe the commonly cultivated plants, even superficially, they can easily be divided in two large classes. One class bears cones similar to the cones of pine trees. The members of this class are generally trees with needle or scale leaves, and with few exceptions are evergreen. To this class belong the firs, pines, spruces, hemlocks, etc. These are the cone-bearing Gymnospermae, the conifers (Figs. 24.2, 24.18), and they constitute the principal forest timber trees of the United States. There are other types of Gymnospermae, but we shall be concerned in the following pages only with the cone-bearing woody forms, the conifers or Coniferales.

The second large class is the Angiospermae; members of this class bear flowers, generally very different in appearance from the cones of the pines and firs (Fig. 24.3). They are of very diverse appearance, having almost any shape of leaf (Fig. 8.2); they may be evergreen or shed their leaves; they may be trees, shrubs or herbs. Grasses and oaks belong to this class. Even a cursory examination will show how grasses and oaks differ. It turns out that all Angiospermae can be divided into two subclasses depending upon whether or not they have key characteristics common to either the grasses or the oaks. These two groups of Angiospermae are called, respectively, Monocotyledoneae (Fig. 12.25) and Dicotyledoneae (Fig. 12.26). At this point these four scientific names will be little more than long words but much of the discussion on the subsequent pages is concerned with the detailed description of the structure, function, and uses of members of these three plant groups. Their relationship to each other is shown on page 330. It should be learned.

All these common plants bear leaves and seeds, either flowers and fruit, or cones. These structures are borne on stems. Obviously, a function of stems is the **support** of leaves, flowers, fruit, and seed. The flowers are raised into a position that will facilitate their pollination and the subsequent dispersal of seeds. Leaves are the principal food-making organs of the plant and are brought into a favorable position to receive air and light. Carbon dioxide of the air, and light, are essential factors in the food-making process. The food-manufacturing organs (leaves) and the reproductive organs (flowers) are not in immediate contact with water and mineral salts of the soil, as they are in plants that grow in the water. Accordingly, land plants have structures that provide for a fairly rapid conduction of water and mineral salts to organs removed from the source of these materials. Thus, another function of stems is conduction, not only of water and mineral salts from the roots to structures above the soil but also of foods, made in the leaves, to all other parts of the plant. Hence, the two principal functions of stems are **support** and **conduction**. In addition, some stems **store** food and water, and others act as **vegetative reproductive** structures.

Each individual seed plant is composed of two systems: the **root system** and the **shoot system.** The root system anchors the plant in the soil and absorbs water and mineral salts from the soil. The shoot system, either simple or branched, is composed of two kinds of organs, **stems** and **leaves.** The ordinary green **foliage leaves** are best known. In addition to these, there are modified leaves (Fig. 8.13), such as the special leaves forming the parts of the flowers. These and other kinds of modified leaves do not resemble foliage leaves in form, but they have leaf structure and a similar origin and position on the stem axis.

We see, then, that the shoot system as a whole, with its various kinds of stems and leaves, has several important functions: support, conduction, food manufacture, reproduction, and sometimes storage.

TYPES OF STEMS

There are many types of stems as regards external characters and internal structure, and they may be arbitrarily, though conveniently, classified in the following manner:

1. Stems of woody plants, including those of trees, shrubs, and woody vines. In this group we find representatives from the Gymnospermae and Angiospermae, such as oaks, maple, apple, pines and spruces.

2. Stems of the Monocotyledoneae which may be represented by wheat, oats, rice, corn and other grasses, onion, lily, asparagus and palm.

3. Stems of herbaceous plants belonging to the Dicotyledoneae, peas, beans, geranium, sunflower, etc.

4. Modified stems. They are unusual types of stems as to forms and functions, which may be found in all classes of seed plants. Examples are bulbs (onions) that store food; stems of the cacti, which store water and carry on photosynthesis; slender horizontal stems, either trailing on the surface of the ground, as in the strawberry, or creeping under the ground surface, as in many perennial weeds.

EXTERNAL CHARACTERISTICS OF YOUNG WOODY STEMS

General Appearance

The twigs of woody plants in their winter condition are particularly favorable for a study of the external characters of stems. They show methods of bud and leaf arɪangement, various kinds of buds, bark characters, and other features. A 3-year-old twig of walnut is illustrated in Fig. 6.1. Do any of the cellular details concerned with the principal functions of stems manifest themselves in the external appearance of the stem? How are the leaves and flowers arranged on a stem? And, finally, how do stems and their attached leaves and buds originate?

Buds are conspicuous structures of stems in the winter condition. From buds new stems will grow: a bud is a miniature stem. These stems may produce foliage leaves, or flowers, or both. The tip of the twig generally bears a large **terminal leaf bud** (Fig. 6.1). At regular intervals along the stem other buds may be seen; they are called **lateral buds.** Note that below the base of each lateral bud there is a scar that was made when a leaf fell from the twig; this is a **leaf scar. Vascular bundle scars** (Fig. 6.4) may be seen within each leaf scar; strands of food- and water-conducting tissues passing from the stem into the leaf stalk were broken when the leaf fell, leaving these scars. Buds and leaves are usually borne in this relationship to each other; the buds form in the angle made by the stem and the leaf stalk. This angle is termed the **leaf axil,** and consequently these buds may also be called **axillary buds.**

The passage of strands of conducting tissue into the leaves and buds must mean that the internal structure of the stem is so arranged as to make possible a continuous connection of leaves and buds with all other parts of the stem. We have thus a specialized stem region—a region to which are attached buds and leaves and within which conducting strands unite with other conducting strands of the stem. This region is known as a **node** (Fig. 6.1). The region between any two adjacent nodes is an **internode.**

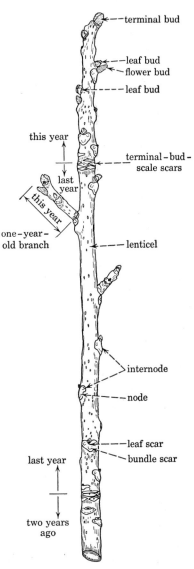

Fig. 6.1. Three-year-old twig of walnut (*Juglans regia*). $\times \frac{1}{2}$.

Protecting the young immature cells within the bud is a series of overlapping scales, the **bud scales.** They are usually shed when the bud develops into a new shoot and also leave scars, **bud-scale scars.** The part of a stem or twig between sets of terminal-bud-scale scars generally is formed during one growing season. For instance,

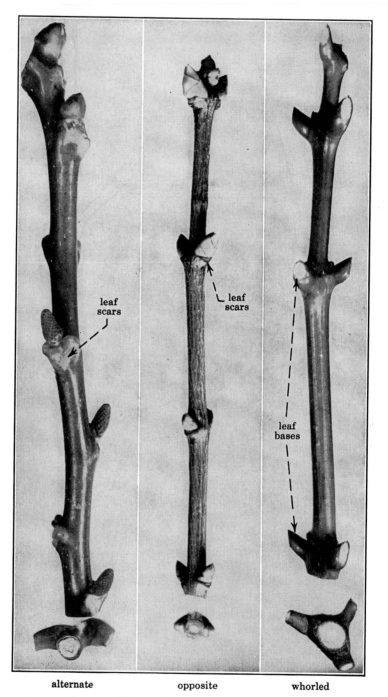

leaf
scars

leaf
scars

leaf
bases

alternate   opposite   whorled

Fig. 6.2. Twigs showing three methods of bud and leaf arrangement. The position of leaves is shown by the leaf bases and scars. Alternate, walnut (*Juglans regia*); opposite, lilac (*Syringa vulgaris*); whorled, *Catalpa*.   ×1.

growth made by the twig this year is set off from the growth made last year by means of a ring or girdle of terminal-bud-scale scars (Fig. 6.1). When the scales of a terminal bud fall off in the spring, they leave a number of closely crowded scars that form a distinct ring. Examination of several-year-old twigs shows that growth in length may vary from year to year. This fact is shown by the spacing of the terminal-bud-scale scars. It is significant that *there is no increase or decrease in the length of any portion of a stem after that portion is a year old.*

The slightly raised areas on the bark are **lenticels.** They are composed of cells that fit loosely together, with air spaces between, which permit the passage of gases inward and outward.

Fig. 6.3. Apricot (*Prunus armeniaca*) stem showing three buds in a leaf axil. Central bud becomes a side branch; the two lateral buds develop into flowers. ×5.

Arrangement and Kinds of Buds

In the walnut twig there are just *one leaf bud* and *one leaf at each node.* This arrangement of buds and leaves on the stem is spoken of as **alternate** (Fig. 6.2). It is the most common type of bud and leaf arrangement. Ash, maple, lilac and many other plants have *two leaves opposite each other at each node,* and a bud in the axil of each leaf (Fig. 6.2). This arrangement of leaves and buds is spoken of as **opposite.** *When three or more leaves and buds occur at each node,* as in catalpa, the leaf arrangement and the bud arrangement are said to be **whorled** (Fig. 6.2).

Some plants have several buds in or near the leaf axil. For example, the apricot often has a group of three buds in the leaf axil: a central bud, which develops into a side branch, and two lateral ones, which are flower buds (Fig. 6.3). All but the central one are called **accessory buds.** The walnut also may have more than one bud in the leaf axil (Fig. 6.1).

Not infrequently buds may arise on the plant at places other than leaf axils. They may appear on stems, roots, or even leaves and give rise to new shoots. Such buds are called **adventitious buds.** Their formation may be stimulated by injury, such as occurs in pruning.

Dormant or **latent buds** are ones that arose in a regular fashion in the leaf axil but for some reason did not develop at the usual time.

The walnut twig shown in Fig. 6.1 has two kinds of buds, distinguished by the structures they contain: **leaf buds** and **flower buds.** Leaf buds possess a miniature leafy branch; flower buds, one or more flowers. In some plants there are **mixed buds,** which contain both leaves and flowers. Buds are discussed in more detail on page 91.

In the identification of deciduous woody plants, it is usually considered desirable to have leaves, flowers, and even fruits. But,

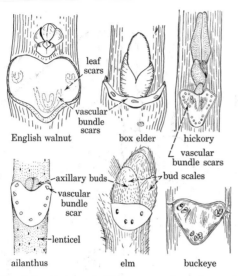

Fig. 6.4. Twigs of different species of woody plants in the winter condition, showing buds and leaf scars and distinguishing characteristics. (Redrawn from Trelease, *Winter Botany*, published by the author.)

by careful study of the twigs of such plants in their winter condition, it is possible in most instances to determine the species (Fig. 6.4).

From the above discussion it is seen that buds may be classified as to their **arrangement on the stem,** which may be (1) **alternate,** (2) **opposite,** or (3) **whorled;** as to their **position on the stem,** which may be (1) **terminal,** (2) **lateral (axillary),** (3) **accessory,** or (4) **adventitious;** and as to the **nature of the organs into which they develop,** which may be (1) **leaf,** (2) **flower,** or (3) **mixed.**

As a rule, the terminal bud of a stem is the most active and grows more vigorously than any of the axillary buds. Usually the lowest lateral buds on a year's growth of the shoot remain dormant and do not develop into branches. If the terminal bud is removed, however, as may be done in pruning, lateral buds, otherwise dormant, may become active.

Cone-bearing trees, such as pines, spruces, and firs, and also such broadleaf trees as the Carolina poplar have a single main stem with many lateral branches. In these trees the terminal bud of the main stem remains strong and dominant throughout the life of the tree, and the result is an elongated or cone-shaped shoot system. In such trees as the oak, apple, cottonwood, and elm, the terminal bud of the main stem may lose its dominance, with the result that upper lateral branches develop and a number of branches may be equal in size. In trees of this sort it is impossible to pick out any one main stem; they have a broad, spreading habit of growth.

In view of the fact that *a bud is a potential shoot,* it is possible to control or modify the form and habit of a woody plant by the removal of leaf buds or twigs. For example, flat-topped trees may be secured by the removal annually of terminal buds. And it is possible to train pear and other trees so that they grow flat against a wall, or on a trellis, to form a type of ornamental growth known as espalier (Fig. 6.5). This formation can be secured only by frequently pinching off those leaf buds that will develop into shoots which are directed outward from the wall or trellis. When one fully realizes that a leaf bud possesses the primordia that are capable of developing into a leafy shoot, one has at hand the knowledge which will enable him to train a plant to any form he may desire.

There is further evidence that leaf buds are partially developed and more or less independent shoots. In many species of plants, leaf buds may be removed from the stems on which they originated and grafted on to the stems of other plants where they will later develop into branches of the first species.

The buds of most woody plants, except those of the moist tropics, usually bear overlapping, leaflike bud scales. But herba-

Fig. 6.5. Espalier fruit tree. (Photo courtesy of U. S. Espalier Nursery Co., Portland, Ore.)

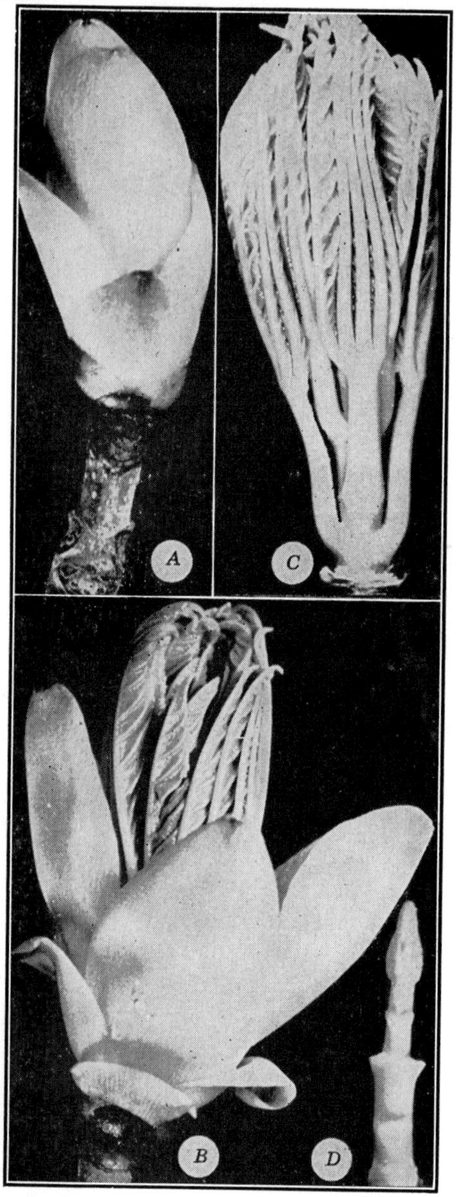

ceous plants and some woody plants (grape) possess **naked buds,** that is, buds with no special protective structures. The outermost organs of naked buds are foliage leaves, not bud scales. The bud scales differ markedly in different species of plants. They may be covered with hairs, as in willow, or with a waxy secretion, as in cottonwood.

Leaf Buds. A terminal bud of buckeye in external view and with parts of the bud removed is shown in Fig. 6.6. When the bud scales are carefully removed, several small rudimentary foliage leaves are found within (Fig. 6.6C). These leaves are much like fully expanded leaves in shape and venation. When scales and the largest leaves are removed rudimentary leaves still protect the shoot tip (Fig. 6.6D). In Fig. 6.7 we observe that the leaf bud is in reality a **miniature branch (shoot)** with nodes, each bearing a small rudimentary leaf and bud primordium, and separated by very short internodes.

Flower Buds. We have seen that a leaf bud is one that develops or "grows out" into a leafy stem. The terminal bud is usually a leaf bud, and many lateral buds are also leaf buds; that is, they form leafy branches of the main stem. Although most of the buds on a plant are leaf buds, some contain partially developed floral leaves (sepals, petals, stamens, and carpels).

In many plants the external appearance of leaf buds and flower buds is quite similar. It is often possible, however, to distinguish a leaf bud from a flower bud by its external characters or its position on the stem. For example, in magnolia, flower buds are much plumper than leaf buds (Fig. 6.8). In almond, flower buds are longer, narrower, and more pointed than leaf buds. In apple, flower buds are rather thick and rounded, whereas leaf buds are more pointed and smaller. Often, in apricots, three buds occur at a node, the middle

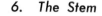

Fig. 6.6. Leaf bud of buckeye (*Aesculus californica*), dissected. A, leaf bud ready to open; B, expanding leaf bud showing young leaves protruding through bud scale covering; C, bud scales removed; D, bud scales and young leaves removed to show shoot tip still protected by rudimentary foliage leaves. ×1.

one being a leaf bud, and the two laterals flower buds (Fig. 6.3). Suffice it to say that experienced orchardists soon learn to distinguish between leaf buds and flower buds and to estimate well in advance the prob-

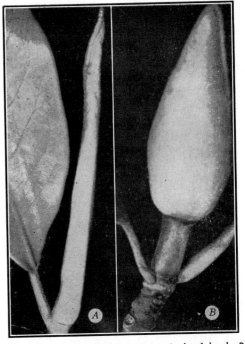

Fig. 6 8. Buds of *Magnolia*. A, leaf bud; B, flower bud. ×½.

able amount of bloom during the coming season.

The flower bud, like the leaf bud, is a miniature shoot; that is, it has an axis (stem) and foliar (leaflike) appendages. If a flower bud contains several flowers, each flower is regarded as a branch shoot.

Mixed Buds. A bud that has both rudimentary leaves and flowers is called a **mixed bud.** For example, in apple, blackberry, and grape, when a bud of this type unfolds, it produces a leafy shoot that terminates in a flower cluster; and, in mulberry, fig, oak, and a number of other trees, the leafy shoot bears flowers or flower clusters in the leaf axils.

EXTERNAL CHARACTERISTICS OF MONOCOTYLEDONOUS STEMS

Since all of the common monocotyledons of the temperate regions are herbaceous

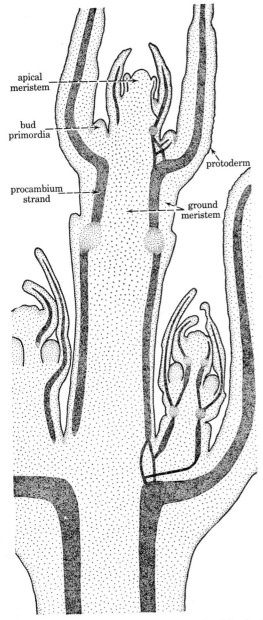

Fig. 6.7. Median lengthwise of a leaf bud of lilac (*Syringa*) showing the shoot tip. ×25.

Fig. 6.9. Palm (*Washingtonia robusta*). A, tree; B, external characteristics of trunk.

forms, the external features of their stems vary to a considerable degree from those of the woody stems just described. The woody monocotyledons, such as the palms (Fig. 6.9) and Joshua trees, are limited to warmer regions and because of their characteristic type of growth, their stems also present quite different external features. The stem of corn is an example of one of the more familiar types of herbaceous monocotyledonous stems. If a corn plant be examined (Fig. 8.4B) it will be noted that the stem is completely sheathed by the base of the leaves. When these are removed it is seen that the stem is smooth and green and is divided into prominent nodes and internodes. In the internodal region the stem is almost circular in cross section, but at the nodes it is somewhat more oval and, at one point, concave (Fig. 8.4B). Buds, which will produce the familiar ear and occasional branches or suckers arise very early in the development of the stem in these concavities.

Palms do not branch; their increase in height, the production of leaves and flowers occur as the result of the cells formed only at the single apical meristem and if this is destroyed the tree usually dies. The single apex of the palm is very broad, the leaves originate here, very close together, and the internodes are consequently very short. The palms thus do not have the distinct buds, nodes, or internodes so characteristic of woody dicotyledons. Their external appearance depends upon the age of the tree.

At the top, the trunk is completely covered by the leaves. When the leaves fall the trunk is marked by leaf bases which are gradually weathered away, a process which at first exposes a mass of vascular bundles. While this weathering process is going on a periderm or cork is being formed from a cork cambium (page 118) which develops just beneath the leaf bases. The trunk of older palms is thus completely covered by a ridged periderm. The external stages of this development are shown in Fig. 6.9.

EXTERNAL CHARACTERISTICS OF HERBACEOUS DICOTYLEDONOUS STEMS

In general, herbaceous plants have naked buds which are normally active throughout the life of the plant, even though the terminal bud may, in many forms, grow more actively than many of the lateral buds. The stems of herbaceous plants are divided characteristically into nodes and internodes with leaves occurring quite generally at the nodes. Buds, in many instances, may develop and grow in the axils of these leaves. Since these buds, even in such perennial herbs as alfalfa, are not protected by bud scales when not actively growing, girdles of bud-scale scars do not occur. Nor do the leaves fall away to produce leaf scars.

Modified stem types will be discussed in a later section.

SUMMARY OF EXTERNAL CHARACTERISTICS OF STEMS

1. There are, in general, four stem types: (1) stems of woody dicotyledons and gymnosperms, (2) monocotyledonous stems, (3) stems of herbaceous plants, and (4) variously modified stems.

2. The plant body of the seed plant is composed of two principal systems, the shoot and root. The shoot system is composed of two kinds of organs, stems and leaves (foliage leaves, scale leaves, floral leaves).

3. While all stems may be divided into nodes and internodes, these features may not be readily apparent in some gymnosperms and palms.

4. The buds and leaves are attached at the nodes, their conducting tissue joining that of the stem at these points.

5. Buds may be classified as to their *arrangement on the stem* (alternate, opposite, whorled); as to their *position on the stem* (terminal, lateral or axillary, accessory, adventitious); and as to the *nature of the organs into which they develop* (leaf, flower, mixed).

6. Woody dicotyledonous twigs and gymnosperm stems have characteristic markings caused by the fall of leaves, bud scales, and fruits or cones.

7. Herbaceous plants, both monocotyledons and dicotyledons, whether annuals or perennials, have naked active buds and their stems are not marked by leaf and bud scale scars.

8. Woody monocotyledons, such as palms, do not branch and have only primary growth.

INTERNAL CHARACTERISTICS OF BUDS

A longitudinal section of a single leaf bud is shown in Fig. 6.7. We see that the bud is essentially a **miniature shoot,** with nodes and very short internodes, with leaf primordia at each node, and primordial buds in the axils of the more advanced leaf primordia. Note (Fig. 6.10A) that the shoot tip is composed of cells and that the cells are not all alike. Figure 6.10B, C, D, E is an enlargement of selected areas and shows more distinctly the different kinds of cells that occur. Such groups of cells are known as **tissues.** A given tissue or cell group has definite functions to perform. For instance, some cells are constructed and grouped to protect, others to support, or to conduct. If we have one cell type performing but a single function we have a **simple tissue.** Frequently, however, several cell types will be closely associated into a tissue performing more than one function, support and conduction for instance. In this case we may speak of a **complex tissue.**

Let us examine the cells and tissues of the bud. At the apex of the shoot within the terminal bud, and also at the apices of shoots of axillary bud primordia, there are dome-shaped masses of cells, the **apical meristem.** The cells of the apical meristem have large nuclei, a compact cytoplasm, and small vacuoles (Fig. 6.10*B*). While the bud is dormant these cells are relatively quiescent, but when conditions are favorable they divide rapidly and the daughter cells increase in size, becoming in some instances larger than the cell from which they originated. This increase in number and size of cells results in the elongation of the young shoot. But, in conjunction with increase in number and size of cells, **differentiation** occurs; that is, the cells change morphologically and physiologically from the meristematic cells from which they arose. Thus, a short distance (usually a few millimeters) below the apical meristem we recognize three fairly distinct **primary meristematic tissues,** namely **protoderm, ground meristem,** and **procambium** (Fig. 6.7). These three tissues are derived directly from apical meristem.

The term **shoot tip** is applied to the youngest part of the shoot and includes apical meristem cells, together with those immediately below, of which some are elongating and others are in early stages of differentiation. The rapid elongation of stems results from the formation and growth of thousands of new cells in the shoot tip. It is in the shoot tip that we see the origin

of **leaf primordia, bud primordia,** and the **primary meristematic tissues.**

We have noted that stems may be classified conveniently as woody stems of dicotyledons and gymnosperms, stems of monocotyledons, stems of herbaceous dicotyledons, and variously modified stems. All of these stems possess buds and every bud contains a shoot tip from which the shoot and all of its parts arise. Let us consider first the shoot tip and the development of a young woody twig from it.

DEVELOPMENT OF TISSUES OF THE PRIMARY PLANT BODY OF A WOODY STEM

The Primary Meristems

The process of stem development is gradual. The youngest cells are those of the apical meristem, and they are similar morphologically. But, in the process of differentiation, different cell types and tissues are formed. Thus, as seen in Fig. 6.10*A*, and as mentioned previously, we recognize three different tissues, protoderm, ground meristem, and procambium. These three primary meristematic tissues differentiate into the **primary tissues.**

The **protoderm** (Fig. 6.10*C*) is the outermost layer of cells. It develops into the **epidermis**—that special primary tissue which covers and protects all underlying primary tissues. The epidermis prevents excessive water loss and yet allows for the exchange of the gases necessary for respiration and photosynthesis.

The **ground meristem** (Fig. 6.10*A, C*) comprises the greater portion of the meristematic tissue of the shoot tip. The ground meristem cells are relatively large, thin-walled, and isodiametric. The primary tissues forming from the ground meristem are (1) the **pith,** in the very center of the

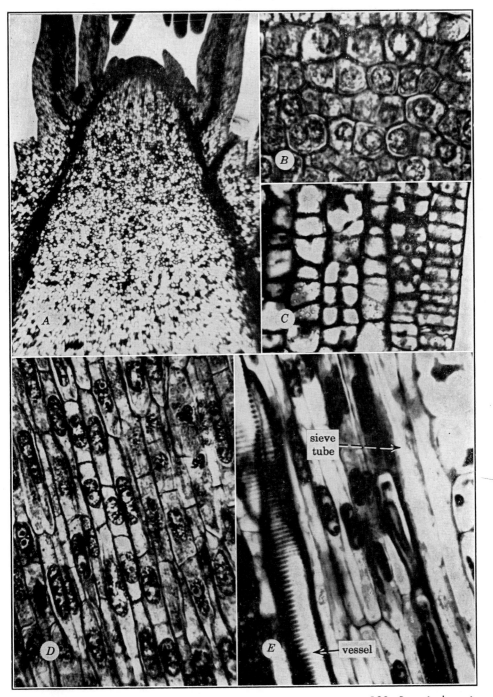

Fig. 6.10. Primary tissues of a young stem. *A,* primary meristems, ×100; *B,* apical meristem, ×500; *C,* protoderm and ground meristem, ×500; *D,* procambium strand, ×500; *E,* first sieve tube and vessel members, ×500. (Slide courtesy of Gifford.)

stem, and (2) the **cortex,** in a cylinder just beneath the epidermis and surrounding the vascular tissues. Sometimes the pith and cortex are connected by (3) **pith rays,** also

formed from the ground meristem (Fig. 6.11*C*).

   Procambium cells usually appear first as strands among the ground meristem cells

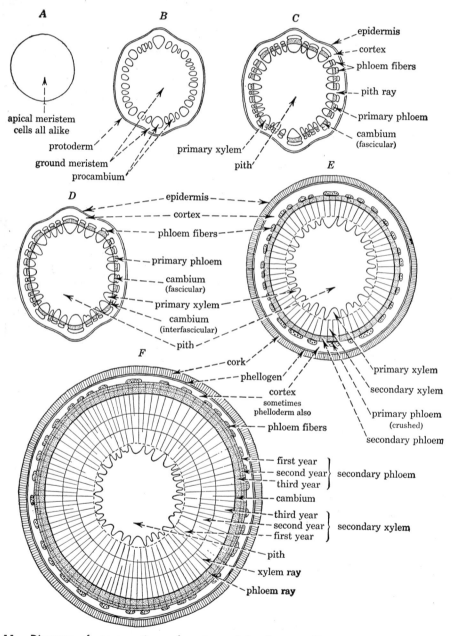

Fig. 6.11. Diagram of cross sections of a stem of *Sambucus.* (From Holman and Robbins, *A Textbook of General Botany,* John Wiley & Sons. Courtesy of Esau.)

(Fig. 6.11*B*). In cross section (Fig. 6.11*B*), the strands appear as isolated groups of cells arranged in a circle. Sometimes a continuous **procambium cylinder** is formed. As seen in transverse section (Fig. 6.12) the procambium cells are smaller than those of the surrounding ground meristem, and in lengthwise section they are much longer and some of them may be pointed at the ends (Fig. 6.10*D*). The procambium cells give rise to the **primary vascular tissues** (Figs. 6.10*E*, 6.11, 6.12, 6.13). These primary tissues carry out several functions and are divided rather rigidly into three groups according to these functions. The food is conducted in the outer group of primary vascular cells, which is the **primary phloem.** Water and mineral salts are conducted in the inner group of primary vascular cells, which, together with strengthening cells, constitute the **primary xylem.** In many stems a meristematic region remains between the primary xylem and the primary phloem. This region is the **vascular cambium** (Figs. 6.11*C*, 6.13).

It is well to repeat here that the **primary tissues** of the stem are those differentiated from the three primary meristematic tissues—protoderm, ground meristem, procambium—and that these three are derived from the apical meristem of the shoot tip. In woody plants, we must look for primary tissues of the stem a very short distance behind the stem tip. Even before the end of the first season's growth, the differentiation of these primary tissues from primary meristematic tissues is completed, and **secondary tissues** may be formed in abundance. Whereas primary tissues are derived from the primary meristematic tissues of the shoot, secondary tissues are the result of the production of new cells by **vascular cambium** and by **cork cambium.** The origin and nature of these two types of cambiums are discussed farther on.

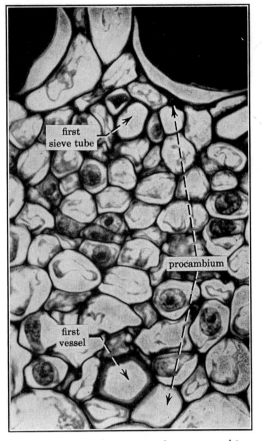

Fig. 6.12. Cross section of a procambium strand of *Sambucus* at level shown in Fig. 6.11 B. ×500. (Slide courtesy of Triarch Products.)

A Summary of Primary Development

Apical meristem	Protoderm	Epidermis		
	Ground meristem	{ Cortex { Pith and pith rays		
	Procambium	{ Phloem { Vascular cambium { Xylem	}	Primary vascular tissues

The term **stele** is applied to that part of the stem which includes the primary vascular tissues, the pith, and the pith rays. The so-called **primary plant body** is composed of the above primary tissues.

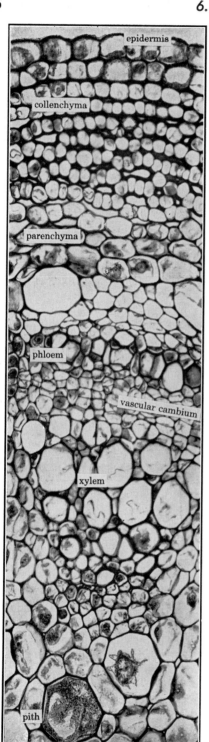

The main functions of these primary tissues may be summarized as shown below.

Epidermis: Protection of underlying tissues.
Vascular tissues:
  Phloem: Conducts foods.
  Vascular cambium: Produces secondary phloem and secondary xylem.
  Xylem: Conducts water and mineral salts, and gives strength to stem.
Cortex: Stores food and, in young stems, manufactures food, strengthens, and protects.
Pith: Stores food.
Pith rays: Store food, and conduct water, mineral salts, and foods radially.

PRIMARY TISSUES

The primary structural organization in the stems of most gymnosperms and dicotyledonous angiosperms consists of several tissues, possessing different cell types. The different kinds or types of cells described in the following few pages may be more or less isolated or they may be grouped to form a tissue.

The Epidermis

The epidermis is usually a single superficial layer of cells covering all other primary tissues and protecting them from drying out and to some extent from mechanical injury. It is the limiting layer of cells between the plant and its environment. In surface view (Fig. 6.14) epidermal cells are elongated in the direction of the stem's length; in transverse section they are usually isodiametric. The protoplasm forms a thin layer lining the cell cavities and normally retains its living properties for a long time. Such substances as oils, tannins, and anthocyanin pigments occur.

Fig. 6.13. Cross section of *Sambucus* stem showing complete sector of primary plant body at level of Fig. 6.11 C. ×200. (Slide courtesy of Triarch Products.)

The outer tangential wall of cells exposed to the air is usually thicker than other walls of the cells, and its surface layer is usually coated with a waxy substance called **cutin.** This superficial layer of cutin is termed the **cuticle.** By means of certain stains and chemical tests the cutin can be readily distinguished from the cellulose of the rest of the wall. The cuticle is quite impermeable to water and gases. The inner walls, parallel to the stem surface, are the thinnest and the radial walls, at right angles to the surface, often taper in thickness toward the inner wall.

Young stems usually possess specialized epidermal cells called **guard cells** (Fig. 6.14). Between each pair of guard cells is a small opening, the **stoma,** by which gases enter and leave the underlying stem tissues. Guard cells, unlike ordinary epidermal cells, possess chloroplasts. They also differ from ordinary epidermal cells in their crescent shape, as seen in surface view. Guard cells are usually thought of as structures peculiar to foliage leaves. While they are much more common in the epidermis of leaves, they may occur also in the epidermis of young stems, of floral structures, and of fruits.

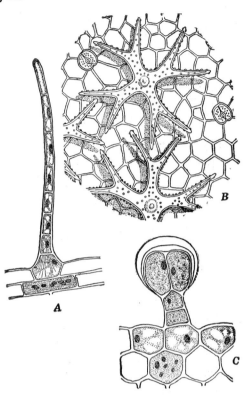

Fig. 6.15. Epidermal hairs. A, simple; B, star-shaped; C, glandular. ×50.

Epidermal appendages, such as hairs, may occur on young stems (Fig. 6.15).

The Cortex

This complex tissue, derived from ground meristem, forms a cylindrical zone beneath the epidermis extending inward to the primary phloem (Fig. 6.11C). The following simple tissues or cell types may be found within it: **parenchyma, collenchyma, sclerenchyma,** and **secretory tissue.**

Parenchyma. The principal tissue of the cortex is parenchyma (Fig. 6.13). It usually consists of isodiametric cells, with thin walls, mostly of cellulose, and with protoplasts that remain alive for a long time.

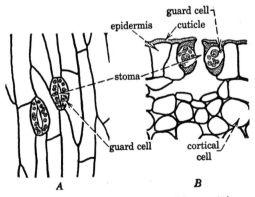

Fig. 6.14. Epidermis of stem of bean (*Phaseolus*). A, surface view; B, cross section. ×40.

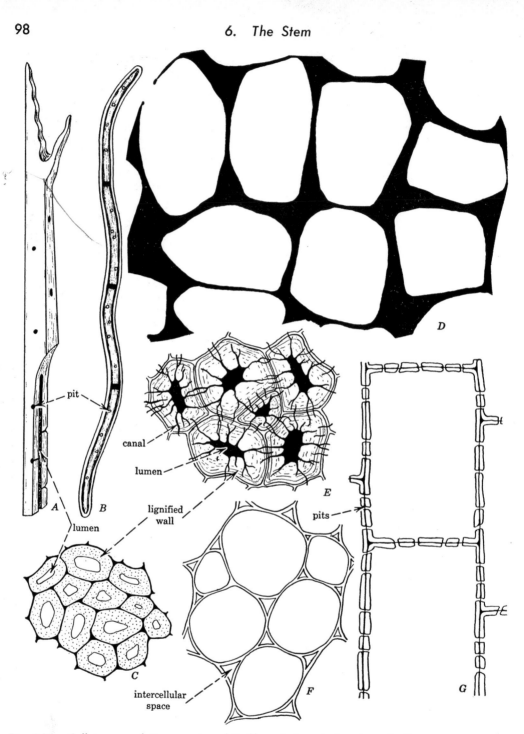

Fig. 6.16. Cell types and tissues.   A and B, fibers in lengthwise view; C, fibers in cross section; D, collenchyma; E, sclereids (stone cells); F and G, parenchyma.   (A and B redrawn from Forsaith.)

We may speak either of a parenchyma tissue or of a parenchyma cell, one of the units composing the tissue.

This tissue is characterized by the presence of intercellular air spaces. The air spaces vary greatly in size; in some parenchyma tissues they are difficult to find while in others they are very apparent (Fig. 6.16*F*). Because parenchyma cells retain active protoplasts, they function in the storage of water and food, or in photosynthesis, and sometimes in secretion. The green color of many stems is due to the presence of chloroplasts in the parenchyma cells, **chlorenchyma,** of the cortex.

Parenchyma tissue is not confined to the cortex of the stem but occurs in practically all parts of the plant: flowers, fruits, seeds, leaves, and roots.

Collenchyma. The outermost cells of the cortex of young stems, those cells lying just beneath the epidermis, often constitute a tissue known as **collenchyma.** This tissue may form a complete cylinder or it may occur in separate strands. The cells are elongated, rather than isodiametric as are those of parenchyma, and have pointed, blunt, or oblique ends. In the most common type of collenchyma the cell walls are thickened at the corners where the cells meet (Figs. 6.13, 6.16*D*). Because of these thickenings, collenchyma serves as a strengthening tissue. The walls are composed of pectin and cellulose. As in parenchyma, cells of collenchyma have long-lived protoplasts. Chloroplasts are often present.

In addition to the cortex of the stem, collenchyma cells may occur in other plant parts comprised of primary tissues. For instance, collenchyma is frequently associated with the veins of leaves.

Sclerenchyma. The main functions of sclerenchyma tissue are support and, in many cases, protection. Their shape and the thickness and toughness of their walls

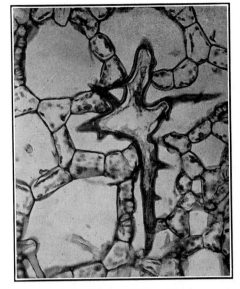

Fig. 6.17   Sclereid.   ×200.   (Photo courtesy of Foster.)

contribute to the ability of these cells to support and protect the young stem. The thickness and toughness of the walls are increased by the deposition, within the original cellulose wall, of a substance known as **lignin.** The process of deposition is called **lignification.** The lignin is elaborated by the protoplast, and when deposition ceases the protoplast usually dies. There are two types of sclerenchyma cells, (1) **sclereids** and (2) **fibers.**

Of the various types of **sclereids,** the most common are the so-called stone cells (Fig. 6.16*E*), which are more or less isodiametric. Other types of sclereids are much branched, resembling very irregular stars (Fig. 6.17). Some sclereids are derived from parenchyma cells by pronounced thickening of the cell walls; others arise from separate meristematic cells. Minute canals, the so-called pit canals, extend outward through the thickened walls, being separated only by the primary walls from the ends of similar canals in the walls of adjoining cells (Fig. 6.16*E*).

Sclereids occur not only in the cortex of stems but also in the hard shells of fruits, seed coats, and bark, in the pith of stems, and in certain leaves.

Fibers are elongated, thick-walled cells, usually pointed at the ends (Fig. 6.16A, B, C). They give strength to the tissue in which they occur. Each fiber is **one cell.** The walls may or may not be lignified. When lignified, the walls may be so thick that the cavity, **lumen,** of the cell almost disappears. Fibers are usually very elastic and can be stretched to a great degree without losing their ability of returning to their original length. Various types of fibers occur in vascular tissue of stems as well as in the cortex. The protoplasts of fibers often disappear as they attain maturity.

Secretory Cells. Secretory cells are parenchyma-like, with dense, protoplasmic contents that secrete various substances, such as resinous materials (Fig. 6.39) and nectar. Many epidermal hairs are secretory cells (Fig. 6.15C).

Summary of the Cortex. Thus, we may find in the cortex of woody stems several kinds of tissues and of cell types. Usually it is not possible to find all kinds in the cortex of any one species of plant. Parenchyma and collenchyma occur in most species and usually predominate. Sclereids may occur singly or in groups. Cortical fibers and secretory cells are more rare.

The Primary Vascular Tissues

The term vascular pertains to tissues that conduct various substances in liquid form. For example, the veins and arteries that carry blood in higher animals are vascular tissues. In vascular plants, water and different water-soluble inorganic salts from the soil, as well as food substances, are conducted throughout the plant in well-defined vascular tissues.

In a young dicotyledonous stem, very near the bud (Figs. 6.11C, 6.28C), the vascular tissues occur as separate bundles, the **vascular bundles.** Each vascular bundle is differentiated from a procambium strand. Between the vascular bundles are parenchyma cells of the **pith rays,** and internal to the vascular bundles is the **pith,** also of parenchyma.

Except for many small herbs, each vascular bundle of dicotyledonous plants and gymnosperms is composed of three tissues: (1) **phloem,** (2) **cambium,** and (3) **xylem.** A radius through a bundle, from the cortex inward, cuts these three regions in the order: phloem, cambium, xylem. In some herbs, there is no cambium.

The Primary Phloem. The phloem in angiospérms may possess four types of cells: **sieve-tube members, companion cells, fibers,** and **parenchyma.** In gymnosperms companion cells are lacking; there are sieve cells rather than sieve-tube members, and in the primary phloem of many species there may be no fibers. The important role of phloem is the conduction of organic solutes. It is probably through the sieve tubes, rather than through other types of phloem cells, that organic substances move rapidly.

A sieve tube refers to a vertical row of elongated cells, each cell being known as a **sieve-tube member** (Fig. 6.20). Among angiosperms a sieve-tube member (one cell) and a companion cell are sister cells; that is, they originate by division of a common procambial mother cell. The young sieve-tube member is rich in cytoplasm and possesses a normal nucleus. As the member matures, the nucleus disintegrates, although the cytoplasm remains. The sister cell (companion cell), however, has a nucleus at maturity.

A characteristic structural feature of mature sieve tubes is the **sieve plate** (whence the term sieve tube). It may occur in end walls (Figs. 6.18, 6.19, Plate I, 6.20) or in side walls. In end walls, sieve plates are seen to the best advantage. The end wall between two adjacent sieve-tube members is thickened and strands of cytoplasm pass through pores in it. Hence, the protoplasts of adjoining sieve-tube members are connected. As the sieve plate matures, a substance known as **callose** is deposited as a cylinder about each cytoplasmic strand (Fig. 6.19); later the amount of callose may increase to form a rather continuous deposit of the material on the plate. The walls of companion cells, sieve tubes, and phloem parenchyma are of cellulose.

The fibers of phloem have the same general characteristics as those described as occurring in the cortex. In most plants the development of fibers is greater in the phloem than in the cortex (Fig. 6.21).

The Vascular Cambium. Xylem and phloem elements that have differentiated from procambium cells cease to be meristematic. Certain cells derived from procambium, however, do not lose their meristematic character. They form a narrow tissue, between xylem and phloem, known

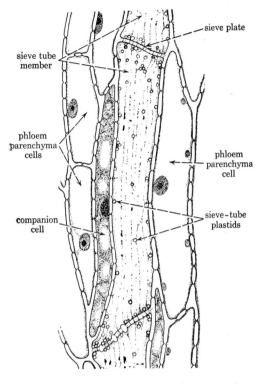

Fig. 6.18. Phloem tissue from the stem of tobacco (*Nicotiana*). ×500. (From Holman and Robbins, *A Textbook of General Botany*, John Wiley & Sons, Inc. Courtesy of Crafts.)

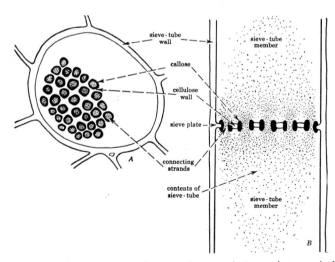

Fig. 6.19. Phloem tissue showing sieve-tube members and sieve plates. A, in cross section; B, in lengthwise section. ×100.

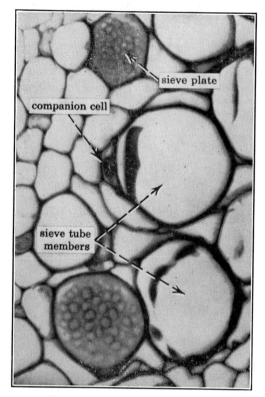

Fig. 6.20. Cross section of phloem tissue of squash (*Cucurbita*). ×100. (Slide courtesy of Triarch Products.)

lar or oval areas called **pits** (Fig. 6.22). There are two types of pits in xylem cells, **simple pits** and **bordered pits**. A **simple pit** is shown in Fig. 6.16G. Here it will be observed that, where two cells lie side by side, the pit (depression or recess) in the wall of one cell is opposite the pit in the wall of the adjacent one. The term **pit-pair** is used to designate this condition. A pit-pair is *not* a hole in the wall; the two cells are separated by a membrane, the so-called **pit membrane**, comprised of the primary wall of each of the two cells and the intercellular cementing substance between these walls. Pits of this type commonly occur in the walls of parenchyma cells, also in collenchyma cells and vessel members. The type of pit known as **bordered pit** occurs in tracheids, vessel mem-

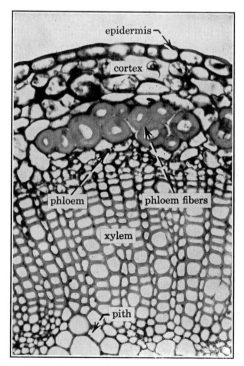

Fig. 6.21. Cross section of stem of flax (*Linum usitatissimum*). ×100. (Photomicrograph courtesy of Esau.)

as **vascular cambium** (Fig. 6.13). Procambium and cambium may be regarded as two developmental stages of the vascular meristem.

The Primary Xylem. The conducting cells that occur in the primary xylem of vascular plants are **tracheids** and **vessel members**. These cells conduct water and mineral salts. Associated with them may be **fibers** (xylem fibers) and **parenchyma** (xylem parenchyma).

The **tracheid** is a single elongated cell more or less pointed at the ends (Fig. 6.33B). Functioning tracheids are not alive. The tracheid wall may not be the same thickness throughout. All the wall may be thickened except for numerous small, circu-

bers, and xylem fibers. Sometimes the thickening in tracheids is in rings, spiral bands, or bars, and sometimes it forms a network.

A **vessel member** is a *single cell* with oblique, pointed, or transverse ends. A **vessel** is a *series of vessel members,* end to end, most of whose end walls are perforated or dissolved. Thus a vessel is a long tube. Vessels are often several centimeters long and in some vines and trees they may be many meters in length. A row of procambium cells becomes transformed into a vessel. Before the protoplasts disappear, the vessel walls become thickened forming a secondary wall (Fig. 6.23A), the thickening material being laid down on the primary walls in various patterns so that parts of the secondary walls are thick and others thin. The material deposited is cellulose; later the layers of cellulose become ligni-

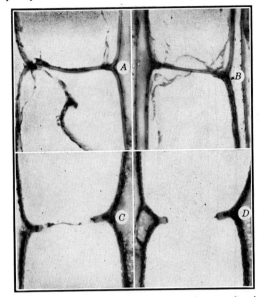

Fig. 6.23.   Photomicrograph of longitudinal section showing stages in development of vessels in *Cucurbita. A,* transverse wall between vessel members intact; *B,* transverse wall beginning to dissolve, whereas thickening material is being laid down on longitudinal walls; *C* and *D,* transverse walls dissolved.   ×150. (Photo courtesy of Esau.)

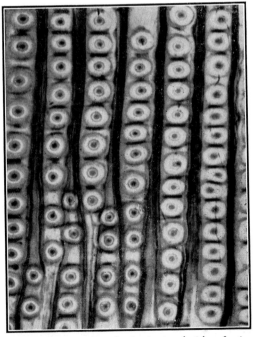

Fig. 6.22.   Bordered pits in tracheids of pine wood *(Pinus).* ×85. (Photo courtesy of Artschwager.)

fied. The dissolution of end walls of vessel members also takes place before the protoplasts disappear (Fig. 6.23B, C, D). Thus, the deposition of thickening material forming the secondary walls and the dissolution of end walls are functions of living cells. Following these processes, the protoplast dies. Therefore, functional vessels have no living contents.

The secondary walls of vessels are deposited in several different patterns (Fig. 6.24). **Annular vessels** have the material in the form of separate rings, much like barrel hoops in a sack. In **spiral vessels** the material is in the form of spiral bands. **Scalariform vessels** have the thickenings as transverse, interconnecting bars. In **reticulate vessels,** the material forms a network on the wall. And, in **pitted vessels,** the walls are

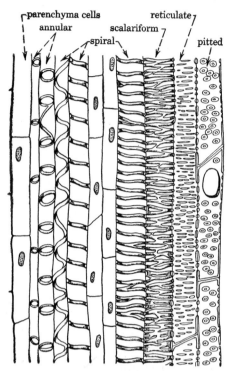

Fig. 6.24. Different types of vessels. (Redrawn from Eames and MacDaniels, *Introduction to Plant Anatomy*, McGraw-Hill Book Co.)

pitted. The ends of the vessel members (Fig. 6.33*C*, *D*) are generally on a slant, and although open, they may have bars of wall material across them.

Xylem parenchyma cells outlive vessels, tracheids, and most xylem fibers. They function in the storage of water and foods, which, as we have learned, is one of the principal functions of parenchyma wherever it occurs in the plant. Parenchyma may also conduct materials for short distances.

Xylem fibers are similar to the fibers described elsewhere.

Pith and Pith Rays

Pith is composed of large-celled parenchyma with numerous intercellular spaces

(Fig. 6.16*F*). The storage of food is its principal function. In some stems primary vascular bundles are separated by wide strips of parenchyma, which extend from the pith to the cortex. Such strips of parenchyma are called pith rays and may be considered radial extensions of the pith (Fig. 6.28). Like the pith, one of their functions is food storage; they also conduct materials short distances radially. They merge with the parenchyma of cortex so that no line of separation is visible. In many woody species the primary vascular bundles are separated by very narrow rays of perhaps two to four cells in width (Fig. 6.25).

THE PRIMARY PLANT BODY

We have seen how the apical meristems differentiate the various tissues that form the primary plant body of a woody gymnosperm or dicotyledon stem. We have learned that primary growth is responsible for the growth and the distribution of the tissues which form a pattern that is characteristic for each kind of stem.

While this pattern shows almost as many variations as there are species of plants all of them have certain features in common. Figure 6.25 shows the arrangement of the various tissues in a cross section of a *Sambucus* stem when the development of the primary body is completed in a woody dicotyledonous stem.

THE MONOCOTYLEDONOUS TYPE OF STEM

In stems of dicotyledonous plants, both herbaceous and woody types, and in those of gymnosperms, the procambium strands, and hence vascular bundles, are usually arranged *in the form of a single ring*. With but few exceptions the procambium strands, and hence the vascular bundles, in stems of monocotyledonous plants are *scattered* throughout the ground meristem or at least through the outer region of it (Fig. 6.26). In the rhizomes (underground stems) of *Clintonia* and certain other monocots, however, the vascular bundles are in a definite ring. In most monocotyledonous stems, *all* the procambium cells differentiate into primary xylem and primary phloem elements; there is no vascular cambium and, as a consequence, no production of secondary tissues. Bundles of this sort which are "closed" to further growth are called **closed bundles** (Fig. 6.27). As has been observed, bundles of other seed-bearing plants that possess a vascular cambium are "open"

to further growth; they are known as **open bundles.**

In transverse sections of the internodes of most grasses (barley, rye, wheat), the following tissues are evident (Fig. 6.26): (1) a single layer of epidermal cells, (2) strengthening tissue variously arranged beneath or near the epidermis, (3) ground parenchyma, and (4) vascular bundles. The limits of cortex and pith are indistinct. Stomata occur in the epidermis. The strengthening tissue consists of elongated fibers with thick lignified walls. In some grasses the vascular bundles are arranged in two rings near the periphery of the stem, and in such there is usually a continuous ring of fibers some distance from the epi-

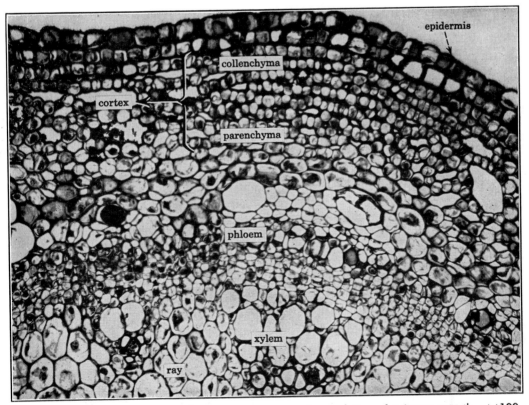

Fig. 6.25.   Cross section of *Sambucus* stem at stage of completion of primary growth.   ✕100. (Slide courtesy of Triarch Products.)

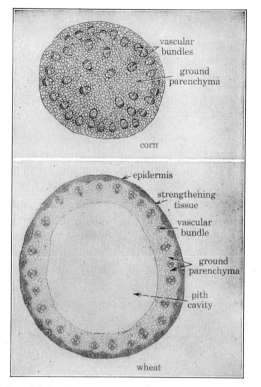

vascular bundles

ground parenchyma

corn

epidermis

strengthening tissue

vascular bundle

ground parenchyma

pith cavity

wheat

Fig. 6.26. Cross sections of monocotyledonous types of stems. The corn (*Zea mays*) stem is a much younger one than that of wheat (*Triticum*). (Wheat, photo courtesy of Esau.)

dermis, with the small bundles of the outer row embedded in it. On the outer sides of the small bundles of the outer ring occur strands of fibers that reach to the epidermis. Bands of chlorophyll-bearing ground parenchyma are enclosed between these strands. Ground parenchyma may extend to the center of the stem, as in corn (Fig. 6.26), sorghum, and sugar cane, or its central portion may become destroyed during the growth of the stem, leaving a hollow pith cavity, as usually happens in wheat (Fig. 6.26), oats, barley, and rye.

The bundles of monocotyledonous stems have no true vascular cambium and, as a result, no secondary xylem and phloem. In herbaceous monocots, increase in diam-

eter of the stem is due wholly to increase in number and size of the cells composing primary tissues. In treelike monocotyledons, however, such as *Aloe* and *Yucca*, there is secondary growth of a special type. A cambium arises in the cortex. This cambium produces groups of cells on the inner side which develop into typical closed vascular bundles, and on the outer side a relatively few parenchyma cells. Thus vascular bundles are developed which may be arranged to some extent in rows. Outside of and between the rows is newly differentiated parenchyma.

The vascular bundle of the corn stem is an example of a common type of bundle occurring in monocotyledonous stems (Fig. 6.27). The large pitted vessels of the xylem are prominent features. There are usually two of these, and one or two smaller annular or spiral vessels may also be present. In addition, older bundles invariably contain a large air space or intercellular passage. Close examination of this space is likely to reveal within it a lignified ring or portion of a ring. This is evidence that the air space was originally an annular vessel which, due to growth of the young stem, has been stretched and broken, thus giving rise to the relatively large air space. These vessels together with the intervening fibers, tracheids, and parenchyma cells comprise the xylem tissue which is always located on the side of the bundle toward the center of the stem. The cells of the phloem form a regular pattern of thin-walled cells exterior to the xylem. Sieve plates may usually be seen. The companion cells are small, generally square or rectangular in cross section and, because of their cell contents, stain more heavily than the sieve tubes. The bundle is generally surrounded by lignified fibers forming a tissue called the **bundle sheath.**

In grasses, a tissue at the base of each

internode usually remains meristematic long after the tissues in the rest of the internode are fully differentiated. Thus, such plants contain a meristem at the apex of the shoot and also a meristem at the base of each internode. Each internode has its own growing zone. These internodal meristems are called **intercalary meristems,** and growth of the cells derived from them is termed **intercalary growth.** The flowering stems of such cereals as wheat, oats, barley, and rye shoot up very quickly. This rapid elongation results not only from the growth of cells derived from the apical meristem but also from the growth of cells derived from intercalary meristems at the base of each internode.

THE HERBACEOUS DICOTYLEDONOUS TYPE OF STEM

The stems of herbaceous dicotyledons differ from the woody stems to be described in the section that follows chiefly in the fact that their growth quite generally stops when the primary plant body has been laid down. Essentially then, the internal organization of an herbaceous stem has been described in detail on pages 92 to 104. The tissues of both herbaceous and woody stems originate in the same fashion. The primary tissues are arranged in bundles in alfalfa (Fig. 6.28) as they are in *Sambucus.* Slightly different arrangements occur in other species.

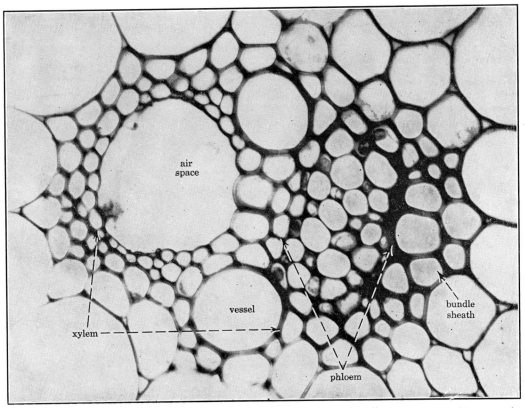

air space

vessel

xylem

phloem

bundle sheath

Fig. 6.27. Photomicrograph of cross section of closed vascular bundle in corn stem (*Zea mays*). ×125.

These primary tissues are, from the epidermis inward: the epidermis; the cortex composed of collenchyma, groups of fibers, and parenchyma; the phloem with sieve tubes, companion cells, fibers, and parenchyma; the xylem with vessels, tracheids, fibers, and parenchyma; the pith and pith rays composed of parenchyma cells. The outermost cells of the primary phloem in alfalfa develop into fibers.

Alfalfa is an herbaceous plant and as such its growth essentially stops when the primary plant body is completed. However, alfalfa is a perennial herbaceous plant and, as in certain other herbs, secondary development may be initiated and a small but definite secondary plant body may be formed. This occurs in the following manner. Not all of the procambium between

the primary xylem and primary phloem is used up, some remains and proceeds to divide to form phloem toward the exterior of the stem and xylem toward the interior. It has become a vascular cambium and is forming secondary xylem and secondary phloem thus causing the stem to increase in girth. Since it has formed within vascular bundles it is called a **fascicular cambium.** What happens between the vascular bundles? In stems such as alfalfa, in which the vascular bundles are separated by strips of parenchyma, the pith rays, certain of these cells may become meristematic. Thus cambium within the bundles (fascicular cambium) may be joined by cambium between the bundles with the result that a complete cambium ring is formed. Cambium formed between bundles is called

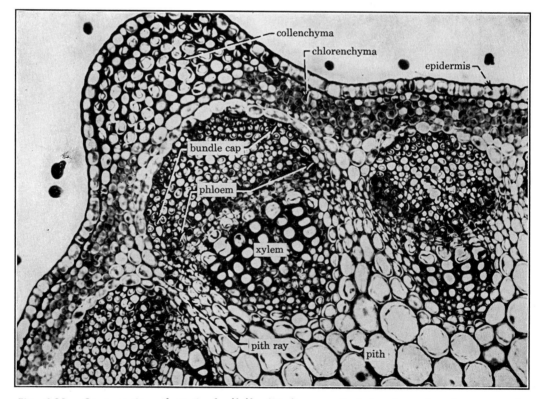

Fig. 6.28. Cross section of stem of alfalfa (Medicago sativa) showing only primary growth. ×100. (Slide courtesy of Triarch Products.)

interfascicular cambium. The circle of vascular cambium thus formed in herbaceous stems is not active for long. As we shall see, in woody stems it remains active as long as the tree lives, over a thousand years in the case of the redwoods.

SUMMARY OF PRIMARY GROWTH IN STEMS

1. All primary growth originates in shoot tips.

2. Primary growth brings about the elongation of the stem and lays down the basic pattern of cells and primary tissues characteristic of the particular stem and upon which the functioning and future growth of the stem depend.

3. The primary meristematic tissues are: apical meristem, protoderm, ground meristem, and procambium.

4. The primary plant body is composed of the following different kinds of cells and tissues: (a) the epidermis, with possibly three cell types, epidermal, guard cells, and epidermal hairs; (b) the cortex, composed of collenchyma, sclerenchyma (fibers and sclereids) and parenchyma; (c) the vascular tissue composed of xylem (fibers, tracheids, vessel members, parenchyma) and phloem (fibers, sieve-tube members, companion cells, parenchyma); (d) pith composed largely of parenchyma with occasional fibers; (e) pith rays composed of parenchyma cells.

5. The functions of these cells and tissues are as follows: The functions of parenchyma are the storage of water and food and the conduction of materials short distances. Collenchyma, sclereids, fibers, and tracheids are strengthening or mechanical tissue elements. Tracheids and vessels (series of vessel members) conduct water and mineral salts. Sieve tubes (series of sieve-tube members) conduct foods. Vascular cambium is a meristematic tissue, the cells of which are capable of division.

6. Collenchyma and sclerenchyma may occur in patches or completely surround the stem just underneath the epidermis. Sclerenchyma is frequently associated with vascular bundles.

7. In woody and herbaceous stems the vascular tissues are arranged in bundles generally forming a definite circle. In monocotyledonous plants the bundles are irregularly distributed throughout ground parenchyma.

8. In woody dicotyledonous plants some procambium together with parenchyma cells of the pith rays unite to form a continuous cylinder of vascular cambium which proceeds to lay down the secondary plant body.

SECONDARY PLANT BODY OF GYMNOSPERMS AND OF WOODY ANGIOSPERMS

Whereas primary growth is responsible for increase in stem length and laying down the basic tissue pattern, secondary growth is responsible for the development of new secondary vascular tissue, increasing the girth of the stem and providing a continuous connection between the newly formed primary tissues of the developing shoots and roots.

This immediate discussion is concerned with perennial woody stems like those of common shrubs and trees, including pines and their allies; but even some herbs, as alfalfa, may develop some secondary tissues before the end of their relatively short lives. We may be quite certain, however, that all the tissues of seedlings are primary growth.

Cambium

So-called **secondary tissues** are not derived directly from the three primary meri-

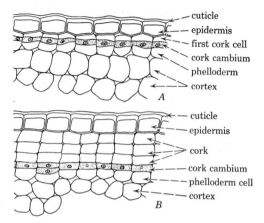

cuticle
epidermis
first cork cell
cork cambium
phelloderm
cortex

A

cuticle
epidermis
cork
cork cambium
phelloderm cell
cortex

B

Fig. 6.29. Cross section of portions of a stem. A, origin of cork cambium; B, development of secondary tissues from it. (Redrawn from Holman and Robbins, *A Textbook of General Botany*, John Wiley & Sons.)

stematic tissues (protoderm, ground meristem, and procambium). They are the result of the production of new cells by (1) **cork cambium (phellogen)** and by (2) **vascular cambium.**

Cork Cambium. The first-formed **cork cambium** or **phellogen** originates from certain cells of the cortex or, rather rarely, as in the apple, from epidermal cells. As a rule, this first-formed cork cambium is short-lived, but that formed later may be derived from tissues as deep as phloem and be long-lived (Fig. 6.29). The activity of the cork cambium will be discussed in more detail after the discussion of the vascular cambium.

Vascular Cambium. We have seen that the vascular cambium is derived from (1) the procambium of primary vascular bundles and (2) certain parenchyma cells between the bundles. There are differences between cells of procambium and cambium as well as between the cells of vascular tissues that originate from them. In the differentiation of tissues from

meristematic cells of the shoot tip young cells similar in general appearance and activity change morphologically and physiologically, they become differentiated. Ordinarily a differentiated cell does not divide. In the development of interfascicular cambium as already described for alfalfa certain differentiated parenchyma cells of the pith rays resume meristematic activity. Interfascicular cambium thus formed joins the fascicular cambium to form a complete ring of vascular cambium. It should be noted that fascicular cambium cells are derived from procambium cells that have never ceased to behave as a meristem; interfascicular cambium originates from cells that had differentiated into a parenchyma tissue.

This development results in a circular sheet of vascular cambium completely surrounding the xylem and protected on the outside by the phloem. In cross section these cambial cells are uniformly bricklike with thin walls (Fig. 6.30*C*). However, all cells of the vascular cambium thus formed are not alike as reference to the longitudinal view (Fig. 6.30*B*) of the *Robinia* stem will show. The small cells packed in regular groups will develop into vascular rays; they are **ray initials.** The elongated cambial cells will develop into fibers, tracheids, vessel members, companion cells, or sieve-tube members; these cambium cells are called **fusiform initials.**

In most woody species, the interfascicular cambium differentiates typical secondary xylem internally and typical secondary phloem externally, so that a solid cylinder of xylem and phloem is formed. In many vine types of stems the interfascicular cambium continues to produce parenchyma cells only; thus these stems are composed of a number of well-formed vascular bundles separated by distinct pith rays.

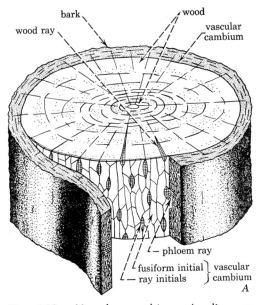

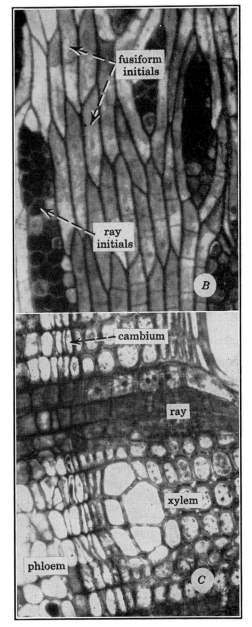

Fig. 6.30. Vascular cambium; A, diagrammatic, showing relation of cambium, and cambial initial to stem; B, tangential section; C, cross section. ×100. (B and C, *Robinia*, slides courtesy of Cheadle.)

Sections of Woody Stems

A woody stem may be viewed in three different planes (Fig. 6.31). A cross-wise view is logically termed a **cross section.** There are two types of longitudinal sections; a section cut in a plane passing through both the center of the stem and the circumference is cut along a radius and is termed a **radial section.** The other longitudinal section is one which is cut at right angles to a radius and is therefore called a **tangential section.**

Differentiation of Phloem and Xylem from Vascular Cambium

Figure 6.32 shows stages in the differentiation of vascular cambial cells to form secondary phloem and secondary xylem.

Cambial cells divide most frequently by a tangential wall, forming two daughter cells. As a rule, the inner daughter cell, next to the xylem, develops into a secondary xylem member, and the outer daughter cell, next

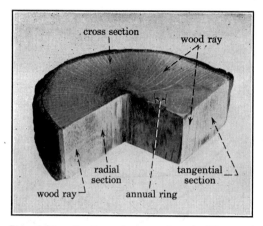

Fig. 6.31. Portion of stem of oak (*Quercus*) to show cross, radial, and tangential sections and their gross characteristics. ×½.

to the phloem, remains meristematic and again divides. When new phloem elements are produced, the inner daughter cell retains the power of division, and the outer daughter cell gives rise to one or more secondary phloem members. Generally, more secondary xylem is produced during the season than secondary phloem. The cambium cells continue thus to divide throughout the growing season, adding secondary xylem on the *outside* of the old xylem, and secondary phloem on the *inside* of the old phloem. Thus, secondary xylem is superimposed upon primary xylem, and secondary phloem tends to exert pressure on primary phloem and cortex and to push them outward. Although cambial cells by repeated divisions are differentiating into xylem and phloem elements, some daughter cells remain meristematic, and so a cambium is always between the xylem and the phloem. In addition, as the stem increases in circumference the cambium keeps step with this increase by radial divisions of cambial cells, thus increasing the number of cells and the circumference of the cam-

bium cylinder. During the winter season the cambium is inactive, only to begin divisions again in the spring.

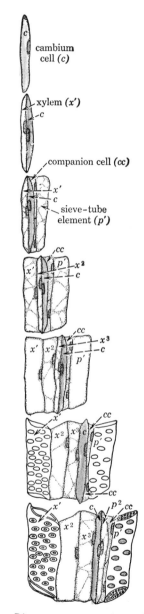

Fig. 6.32. Diagram as seen in radial section showing stages in differentiation of vascular cambium cells. c, cambium; cc, companion cell; p^1, p^2, phloem; x', x^2, x^3, xylem.

The resulting cellular composition of the secondary xylem (Fig. 6.33) and phloem is in general quite similar to that of the primary vascular tissues. It differs generally in that annular and spiral vessels are usually lacking, and secondary phloem contains more fibers.

The Tissues of a Young Woody Stem. In a section of a young woody twig such as that of the basswood shown in Fig. 6.34 the relationships and arrangements of the various secondary and primary elements may be distinctly made out. Note the layers of cork cells on the exterior of the stem. The collenchyma of the cortex (primary tissue) is intact, but there appears to be some crushing of the cortical parenchyma. The primary phloem is the outermost tissue of the phloem region; it is not distinguishable in this figure. There are

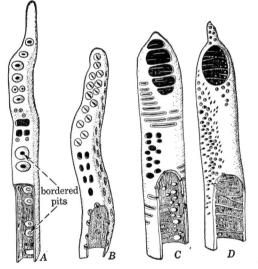

Fig. 6.33. Tracheids and vessel members from secondary wood. A, tracheid from spring wood of white pine; B, tip of tracheid from wood of oak; C, tip of vessel member from wood of *Magnolia*; D, tip of vessel member from wood of basswood. (Redrawn from Forsaith.)

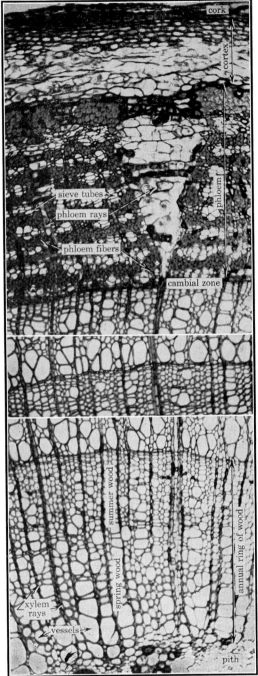

Fig. 6.34. Cross section of 3-year-old stem of basswood (*Tilia*). ×85. (Slide courtesy of Triarch Products.)

two types of **phloem rays,** and the sieve tubes and companion cells are sandwiched between masses of fibers. Individual cambium cells are difficult to distinguish but a cambial zone is apparent. The secondary xylem is well differentiated into **spring wood** and **summer wood** which together form a year's growth or an **annual ring.** Spring wood is frequently characterized by cells having larger lumens and thinner walls than those found in summer wood. Vessels are prominent, but in cross section the distinction between tracheids and fibers is difficult to see. Xylem rays, composed of parenchyma cells, are conspicuous, although none occur which are as large as the larger phloem ray in the illustration. Points of primary xylem may be distinguished adjacent to the parenchyma cells of the pith (primary tissue).

Tissues of an Old Woody Stem. As the woody stem increases in girth the primary phloem and tissues external to it are completely lost as will be described below. The primary xylem, on the other hand, together with the pith remains in the center of the stem but both are reduced to insignificance by the great accumulation of secondary xylem. The possible variations in size, shape, and arrangement of the vessels, tracheids, fibers, and parenchyma cells composing secondary xylem are so great that individual species may generally be identified by the structure of their wood. The secondary phloem, formed in lesser amount and continuously sloughed off, constitutes a complex tissue.

Xylem. The cell types of the xylem have already been described in the discussion of primary xylem, and though detailed differ-

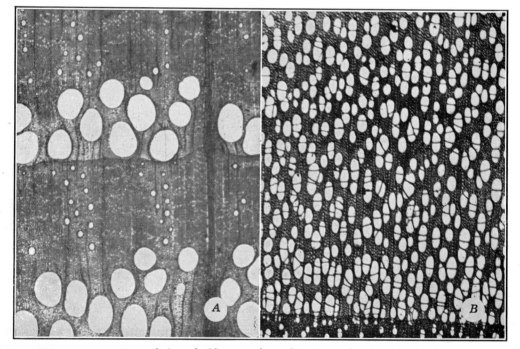

Fig. 6.35.   Cross sections of A, oak (*Quercus borealis*); B, poplar (*Populus deltoides*).   ×30. (Slides courtesy of Triarch Products.)

ences do occur between the cells of the primary and secondary xylem we shall not consider these differences. Thus in the following description of secondary xylem, the fibers, tracheids, vessels, and parenchyma cells, unless otherwise specified, will be considered as having the same characteristics as those of primary xylem.

A comparison of the cross sections of oak and poplar (Fig. 6.35) shows how differences in the size and distribution of the vessels may be responsible for important characteristics of wood. Note that summer and spring wood are present in both cases. In oak the vessels are of two distinct sizes and less numerous than in poplar. Furthermore, the larger vessels of oak are grouped in the spring growth. The character of the rays and grouping of the fibers are also different in each species. Because of the distribution of the vessels in rings in the oak it is said to be **ring porous**, while poplar is **diffuse porous.**

Under higher magnification the cellular detail of the oak wood becomes more apparent (Fig. 6.36A). Note the large vessels in the spring wood and the compact summer wood. The rays are of two sizes, one

but a single cell in width and the other massive. The radial view (Fig. 6.36C) shows the rays, a cell in width, lying perpendicular to a group of fibers. Note the intertwining fibers and the parallel rows of wood parenchyma interspersed among the fibers. A single large vessel is present in this section and as it was not perfectly parallel with the section the cut passes through it. Note the pits here, and the overlying parenchyma cells. One complete vessel member and portions of two others are visible. The locations of the original end walls are indicated by projections into the lumen of the vessel. The tangential section (Fig. 6.36B) shows again the intertwining fibers and the vertical rows of parenchyma cells. The two types of rays are strikingly evident. Note that the vessel present in this section is smaller in diameter than that of the vessel seen in the radial section, but it is composed of members of comparable length as indicated by the projections of the original end wall. The presence of the large rays, in radial section, is one of the characteristic features of quarter-sawed oak (Fig. 6.50B).

As a tree grows older the wood in the

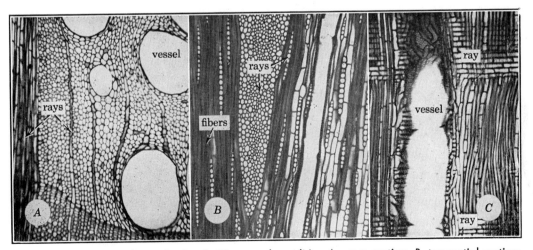

Fig. 6.36. Sections of wood of oak (*Quercus borealis*). A, cross section; B, tangential section; C, radial section. ×85. (Slide courtesy of Triarch Products.)

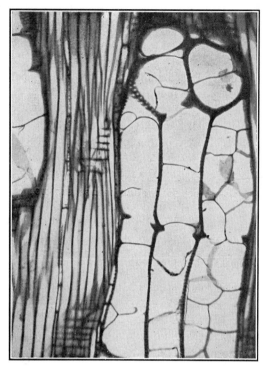

Fig. 6.37. Tyloses in vessels of walnut (*Juglans cinerea*). ×150. (Slide courtesy of Triarch Products.)

rays or **wood rays** composed of parenchyma cells and the occasional small square cells with dark staining contents. These latter are also parenchyma cells. The radial view

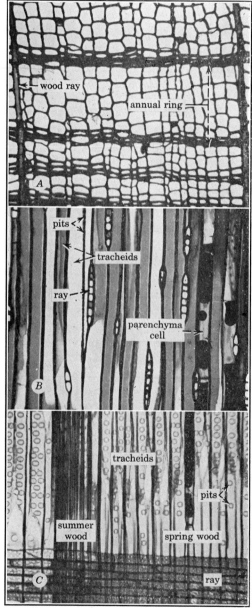

Fig. 6.38. Sections of wood of *Sequoia*. A, cross section; B, tangential section; C, radial section. ×100. (Slide courtesy of D. Graham.)

center of the stem changes in character; it becomes known as **heartwood** and it no longer serves to conduct. The outer unchanged conducting wood is called **sapwood** (page 120, Fig. 6.43). Parenchyma cells adjacent to the vessels may grow into the lumen of the vessel through the pits and completely plug the vessel. Such cells form **tyloses** (Fig. 6.37).

The wood of gymnosperms, with few exceptions, has no vessels. A cross section from a small piece of *Sequoia* is shown in Fig. 6.38A. It is extremely regular, almost like a wire netting. The tracheids appear in cross section as square hollow cells. Those formed in the spring are the largest in diameter; as the season progresses newly formed tracheids are smaller in diameter with thicker walls. The heavy-walled cell is called a **fiber-tracheid.** Note the xylem

(Fig. 6.38*C*) shows mainly tracheids, with a small strand of fiber-tracheids. Pits are present in the radial walls of tracheids. An elongated parenchyma cell is made apparent by its dark staining contents. Note that an adjacent, lower, parenchyma cell appears to be empty. A horizontal ray lies perpendicular to these cells. Pits occur between ray cells and the tracheids. The ends of the rays are apparent in the tangential section (Fig. 6.38*B*). Here the fiber-tracheids have pits in their tangential walls. The pits in the radial walls of the tracheids are just visible. In this view several parenchyma cells with heavily stained contents are present.

Sequoia does not produce resin as do many other gymnosperms. This substance occurs in specialized cavities which are surrounded by groups of parenchyma cells. Together they are called **resin ducts** and occur in many gymnosperms where they may be continuous over considerable distances. One is shown in Fig. 6.39.

We have learned that water and mineral salts are conducted upward in the xylem (in tracheids and vessels), and that foods are conducted upward or downward in the phloem (in the sieve tubes).

Radial conduction occurs in *vascular rays*. These are composed of relatively long-lived parenchyma cells which are somewhat elongated radially.

Vascular rays in the xylem are spoken of as wood or xylem rays, and those in the phloem as phloem rays. Phloem rays are always contiguous with xylem rays. They both originate from the ray initials of the cambium.

The parenchyma cells in vascular rays may differ in detail from the parenchyma cells of the pith and the cortex. The parenchyma cells of the cortex, pith, xylem, and phloem form a living network extending throughout the stem, at least until the formation of heartwood.

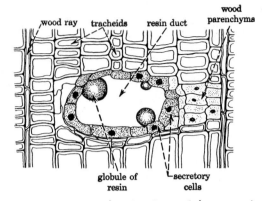

Fig. 6.39. Resin duct in pine wood as seen in cross section. (Redrawn from Holman and Robbins, *A Textbook of General Botany*, John Wiley & Sons.)

Phloem. Sections of grape phloem are shown in Plate I (Chapter 15). The sieve tubes may be recognized by the presence of the blue-staining callose which is deposited on the sieve plates. Note in *A* that the callose forms on both sides of the sieve plate and in the lower right-hand cells there are strands passing through the sieve plate connecting the two deposits of callose. The stains used give the protoplasm and its contents a reddish brown color; this shows to advantage in the cross section of *A*. Note that the brown-stained protoplasm does not fill the cell, the vacuole remaining colorless. The parenchyma cells at the top of the print contain yellow-brown tannin bodies. Note the thickness of the cell walls and compare the appearance of the cell walls of the parenchyma cells in the upper portion of the print with the walls of the phloem fibers in the lower portion of the print. *B* is a longitudinal section and again the sieve-tube members are apparent because of their length and the oblique sieve plates with their blue-staining callose. Note the difference in the protoplasmic contents of the various sieve-tube members as indicated by the staining. There are two types of parenchyma cells

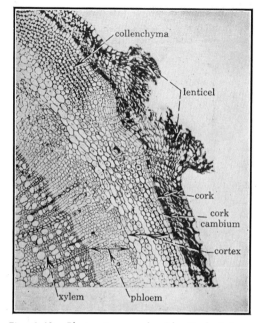

Fig. 6.40. Photomicrograph of lenticel of *Sambucus.* ✕40. (Photo courtesy of Triarch Products.)

present, ray parenchyma on the two margins of the print and phloem parenchyma cells arranged in rows between the sieve tubes.

Formation of Cork

Cork Cambium. Figure 6.29 shows the origin of cork cambium and the development of secondary tissues from it. Cork cambium in most plants arises from outer cortical cells. Cortex cells divide by tangential walls, producing daughter cells. The outer daughter cells generally differentiate into cork cells, thus forming a layer of **cork** beneath the epidermis. Should the outer daughter cells remain meristematic the inner daughter cells may give rise to a tissue known as **phelloderm,** which is composed of parenchyma-like cells. Cork cambium may originate also from epidermal or phloem cells.

Cork. This tissue (Figs. 6.29, 6.34) is composed of flattened, thin-walled cells with no or small intercellular spaces. A fatty substance, called **suberin,** is deposited in the walls, rendering the cells almost impermeable to water and gases. Hence, cork tissue provides protection for the stem against excessive loss of water and also against mechanical injury. The protoplasts of cork cells are short-lived. When cork tissue with its impermeable cell walls is formed, the epidermis and other tissues outside of it are cut off from water and food supplies and soon die. In woody stems cork replaces epidermis as a protective tissue.

In a young stem the bark is made up of the following tissues, in order from the *outside* to the *inside:* cork, cork cambium, phelloderm (if present), cortex, and phloem (Figs. 6.11F, 6.34). Microscopic examination may reveal the presence of epidermal cells still clinging to the cork. In old stems the epidermis, cortex, and primary phloem become separated from the adjacent inner tissues by successive deeper layers of cork formation. As this happens the tissues outside of newly formed cork die for lack of water and nutrients. They dry up and eventually weather away.

Lenticels

An impervious layer of cork would effectively cut off the oxygen supply of the living tissues beneath, if it were not for the development here and there of groups of parenchyma cells called **lenticels** (Fig. 6.40), through the intercellular spaces of which gases can move freely. Stomata occur in the epidermis of very young stems. Gases may enter and leave through these openings. A lenticel is usually formed just beneath a stoma and takes its place as an aerating organ in older stems. Beneath a stoma, cork cambium cells differentiate into parenchyma rather than into cork. These masses of parenchyma tissue enlarge and finally break through the epidermis. The shape and other characters of lenticels are usually quite distinctive in different genera or species. They are especially conspicuous in cherries, plums, birches, maples, dogwoods, and hazelnuts.

ANATOMY OF THE STEM AT NODES

Buds occur in the axils of leaves and this whole region is called the node. Now since both buds and leaves are joined by vascular tissue to the conducting tissue of the stem, anatomically the node must be characterized as a region where vascular bundles are connected to bring about a continuity of vascular tissue in leaves, buds, and stem. It is often a rather complex region. The bundles leading to the leaves and buds are referred to as **leaf traces** and

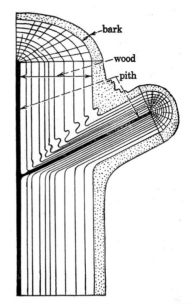

Fig. 6.42. Relation between wood and bark in main stem to these in a branch. (Redrawn from Eames and MacDaniels, *Introduction to Plant Anatomy*, McGraw-Hill Book Co.)

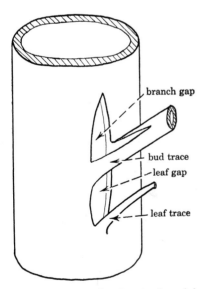

Fig. 6.41. Diagram showing leaf and branch traces and gaps. (Redrawn from Eames and MacDaniels, *Introduction to Plant Anatomy*, McGraw-Hill Book Co.)

bud traces, respectively. The xylem of the traces is continuous with the xylem in the leaf and stem and the phloem of the trace is continuous with the phloem of the leaf and stem.

Where vascular tissue leaves the vascular cylinder of the stem, a gap exists in the cylinder immediately above the point where the trace departs. This is called a **leaf gap** or a **bud gap**. They are shown diagrammatically in Fig. 6.41 and as they appear in the primary plant body of a cabbage stem in Fig. 7.10. Now as secondary development of the branch and trunk proceed both will increase in diameter and new vascular tissue of the stem must be laid down in such a manner as to bury the younger portions of the branch in the trunk. Furthermore there must be a crowding of the new tissue in the upper acute angle formed by the branch and the stem. This is shown diagrammatically in Fig. 6.42. This entire process re-

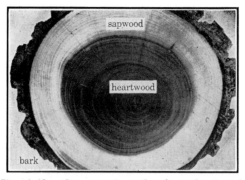

Fig. 6.43. Cross section of a branch of mulberry (*Morus*). $\times \frac{1}{2}$.

sults in a knot. Can you explain why it is that in some gymnosperm lumber the knots are held firmly in place while in others they fall out?

A SUMMARY OF SECONDARY GROWTH

1. Vascular cambium originates from the procambium and adjacent parenchyma cells in the rays between vascular bundles.

2. Vascular cambium lying between xylem and phloem produces new secondary xylem and secondary phloem each year: fusiform initials differentiate into elongated conducting and strengthening cells and ray initials differentiate into ray cells.

3. Primary xylem (next to the pith) becomes more and more widely separated from primary phloem (next to the cortex) as secondary xylem and phloem are produced.

4. Vascular cambium persists as a meristem between the last-formed xylem and the last-formed phloem.

5. Cork cambium is short-lived; new cork cambiums may arise each year producing new layers of cork.

6. Cork cambium may originate in successively deeper tissues from epidermis, cortex, and phloem.

MACROSCOPIC APPEARANCE OF AN OLD WOODY STEM

If we look at the end of a several-years-old stem that has been cut across, or at the end of a log, two prominent regions are distinguished—the bark and the wood (Fig. 6.43). Pith may be evident in certain species or in young stems. In old stems, it may be impossible to find even a trace of pith, and, also, it may be very difficult to find primary xylem, which is at the very center of the stem just outside the pith. The vascular cambium can be seen only by microscopic examination.

Bark

The bark (Fig. 6.43) includes all of the tissues outside of the vascular cambium and its exact cellular composition will depend upon the age and species of the twig or tree trunk being examined. In this discussion we shall consider only bark as it occurs on an old woody tree trunk in which all of the epidermal and cortical tissues have disappeared and the activity of the cork cambium has resulted in the formation of considerable cork tissue. Bark as such may easily be separated from the woody cylinder or trunk, especially in the spring or early summer, because the walls of the cells in the "cambial zone" are thin and easily ruptured. When the bark is peeled from the wood, some of the cells of the "cambial zone" adhere to the bark, some to the wood. Examination of a piece of bark of incense cedar (Fig. 6.44) shows that it is made up of a series of layers of two different appearing tissues. Recalling that the vascular cylinder of a tree is increasing in diameter, let us examine the manner of formation of this bark.

We have seen that through the activity of the vascular cambium new xylem cells are laid down internally to the cambium and new phloem cells externally to it. As this takes place what will happen to the epidermis? The cells composing it are fully differentiated and except in rare cases (apple) do not divide. As the stem increases in diameter through the activity of the vascular cambium the epidermis must be stretched and torn. When this happens the delicate underlying cells would be exposed to drying out and weathering were it not for the development of a cork cambium and a layer of cork as previously described.

As the stem continues to grow in girth the cylinders of cork, in their turn, will be ruptured. Exposure of underlying tissue is prevented by generation each spring, or sometimes more frequently, of a new cork cambium. Finally even the parenchyma

Fig. 6.45. Bark of three species of trees. A, western yellow pine (*Pinus ponderosa*); B, cork oak (*Quercus suber*); C, plane tree (*Platanus orientalis*).

Fig. 6.44. Bark of incense cedar (*Libocedrus decurans*). ×½.

cells of the secondary phloem may produce a new cork cambium. This is why bark from some old tree trunks is layered (Fig. 6.44). This layering is brought about by the formation of successive layers of cork cutting off exterior phloem tissue. The tissue is thus deprived of water by the impervious nature of the cork cells. Now with further increase in circumference the dead exterior sheets of phloem and cork cells are stretched and torn resulting in bark patterns characteristic of many trees (Fig. 6.45). Weathering causes a continual wearing away of the surface of the bark and in regions where sand particles are carried by the wind the trees have a beautiful polished appearance. Cork of commerce is the bark of an oak (*Quercus suber*) (Fig. 6.45B). It is not layered, because it develops in a somewhat different fashion, the cork cambium never developing within phloem tissue. Thus the outer bark of the cork oak may be comprised almost entirely of cork cells.

Wood

The commercial product, **wood**, is xylem. It occurs in all vascular plants, even the tenderest herbs, but only trees that have lived for a number of years and gradually built up a large trunk capable of being converted into lumber furnish us with commercial wood (secondary xylem).

Annually, the vascular cambium forms a new layer of wood which is usually many cells thick. As seen on the end of a log, these layers appear as concentric rings (Fig. 6.43), the so-called **annual rings**. It should be kept in mind, however, that the vascular cambium in a tree like the pine, for example, has the form of a hollow cone; consequently, the wood produced annually has the same form (Fig. 6.46). The wood produced in any one year is laid down over that of the preceding year.

Annual rings of wood are particularly conspicuous in woody plants of temperate climates, where a season of active growth alternates with a season of inactivity. In

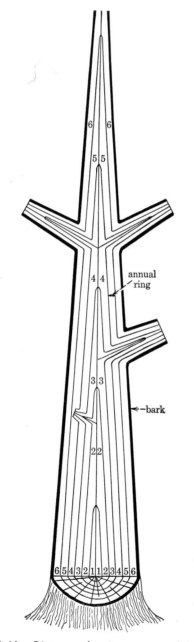

Fig. 6.46. Diagram showing cross and longitudinal sections of a 6-year-old tree.

such plants, the wood elements formed in the spring and early summer are quite different from those produced in late summer and fall. That portion of the ring formed in the early part of the season is known as **spring wood.** That of angiosperms has larger and more numerous vessels than does the so-called **summer wood,** produced later in the season (Figs. 6.34, 6.36). Also, tracheids and fibers of spring wood are less abundant and thiner-walled than those of summer wood. As viewed with a hand lens, or even with the naked eye, summer wood appears darker and denser than spring wood. Of course, in any annual ring, summer wood lies outside of spring wood, and the summer wood of any year is bounded on the outside by the spring wood of the following year. Therefore, small, thick-walled elements of summer wood of one year stand out in contrast to the adjoining, relatively large, thin-walled wood elements of the spring growth of the following year (Fig. 6.34). Thus a sharp line of demarcation lies between them.

Annual rings or growth increments are just as conspicuous in gymnosperms, which possess no vessels, as they are in woody angiosperms. In gymnosperms, the tracheids of spring wood are radially larger and have thinner walls than those of summer wood.

In the moist tropics, where there are no marked seasonal changes, growth rings are almost completely absent or, at best, poorly defined. If they occur, they do not necessarily represent annual growth increments and hence could not be used in determining the age of a tree.

Examination of the cut end of a log shows that in the individual tree annual rings vary greatly in thickness. In other words, the amount of wood produced each year is not the same. As a rule, the first few rings produced in the early life of the tree are thicker than those formed later. Also, the thick-

ness of rings, or, to state it differently, the amount of wood added during any season, is influenced by many factors, such as the age of the tree, light, temperature, moisture, leaf area, and competition both above and below ground. As would be expected, naturally fast-growing tree species have thicker annual rings than slow-growing species living under the same environmental conditions.

The **age of a woody stem** can be determined by counting the annual rings of wood. It is obvious that the true age of a tree can be ascertained only by counting the rings at the very base of the main trunk. As shown in Fig. 6.46, the number of annual rings decreases from the base of the trunk to its apex.

Infrequently, two or more rings of growth may be formed during one season. For example, in irrigated apricot orchards an application of water may stimulate cambium activity, resulting in the differentiation of wood elements resembling those of spring growth. Then, as the soil dries out, the wood elements formed may be smaller and thicker-walled. A second irrigation again stimulates the vascular cambium to greater activity, and thus a line of demarcation is formed between two rings of growth, both made in one season. Sometimes a drought or an insect attack may destroy the foliage and thus interrupt the activity of the cambium. Later, a new crop of leaves may be produced, the cambial activity renewed, and another ring of wood produced. Under these conditions two (or more) growth rings of wood will be formed in one season.

The forester is primarily interested in the amount and quality of wood laid down in the main trunks of commercial timber trees. It is of practical value to know in terms of board feet the volume of wood formed by a certain species, say over a 10-year period. The volume may be determined by counting the annual rings on cross cuts of tree

Fig. 6.47. Collecting latex from the sapodilla tree (*Achras sapota*) for the manufacture of chewing gum. (Courtesy of American Chicle Company.)

performs only the function of mechanical support. Sapwood is gradually transformed into heartwood. In this transformation, various substances infiltrate into the cell walls and even accumulate in cell cavities. The substances include tannins, gums, resins, pigments of various sorts, salts of organic acids, and other materials. These depositions may impart a characteristic color to the heartwood, and they also may increase its weight, hardness, and durability and decrease its permeability. In some species the vessels and even tracheids may

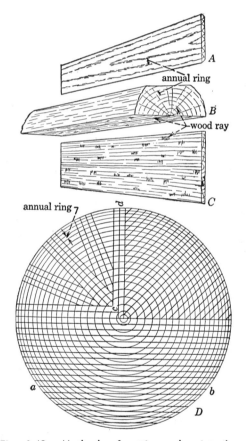

Fig. 6.48. Methods of cutting a log into lumber. A, tangential section, *a-b* in *D*; C, quarter-sawed or radial section, *c-d* in *D*. (A–C redrawn from *U. S. Dept. of Agriculture Misc. Circ. 66*.)

trunks, or on stumps of a considerable number of trees, or by using an instrument known as the increment borer to determine the age of a number of standing trees. This borer has a hollow bit that bores out a "core" of wood, on which the rings may be counted. The hole that it makes does not seriously injure the tree.

Sapwood and Heartwood. The end of a log usually shows the presence of two zones of wood: (1) a light-colored outer zone, the **sapwood,** surrounding a generally darker-colored zone, the **heartwood** (Fig. 6.43). The sapwood functions in sap conduction and food storage, whereas the heartwood

be plugged by protrusions from adjacent living parenchyma cells. These plugs are called **tyloses** (Fig. 6.37). The penetration of wood preservatives is rendered difficult by the presence of tyloses.

INDUSTRIAL PRODUCTS FROM TREES

The most obvious use of wood is as lumber. Trees are, however, grown in many countries for other purposes, some of which do not involve the destruction of the trees. For instance, turpentine, natural rubber, and chewing gum are derived, respectively, from the sap exudates of south-ern pine, particularly the long leaf pine (*P. palustris*) and the slash pine (*P. cubensis*), the rubber tree (*Hevea brasiliensis*), and the sapodilla tree (*Achras sapota*) (Fig. 6.47). In all three cases gashes are cut in the trunks of the trees and the sap is collected in buckets or on sticks after which it is processed in factories into the well-known articles of commerce.

When the wood itself is utilized the trunk may be sawed into lumber or completely disintegrated into the fibers and tracheids of which it is composed. In the manufacture of ordinary lumber the log moves against the saw so that tangential cuts rip each board from the log. The large rays of

Fig. 6.49. Preparation of plywood. View of lathe from veneer side; sheet of veneer being peeled from slowly revolving log. (Courtesy of Canadian Western Lumber Co. and Crown Zellerbach Corporation.)

oak wood give boards cut from these trees a characteristic pleasing appearance if they are cut in a radial plane. This is more difficult to accomplish on a commercial scale; the manner of manufacturing this lumber, known as quartersawed oak, is shown in Fig. 6.48. Sheets for plywood manufacture are produced in a different manner. The logs are steamed and then placed on a large lathe and made to turn against a large and sharp knife which literally peels off thin sheets of wood from the slowly revolving log (Fig. 6.49). Note (Fig. 6.50) the different appearances that these processing procedures give to wood. Can you account for the "grain" in A and B, in terms of spring and summer wood? Compare B with Fig. 6.31.

For other industrial uses wood is not sawed into boards but placed into machines which tear it apart, breaking it down in some instances into fibers and tracheids. The paper you have in your hands is the end product of such a process (Fig. 6.51), and if examined under a microscope will reveal the presence of the cellular elements of the trees from which it was manufactured. Rayon shirts may have started as trees, although other cellulose products may have been the original raw material. To make such fibers the cellulose is dissolved in various solvents to produce one of several modern man-made fibers. In paper making the lignin is undesirable and must be removed from the fibers and tracheids. It is a waste product and huge piles of it accumulate outside of paper mills. To find a use for it has been a major research project of a number of the large paper companies. It is now being marketed and used among other things as a soil conditioner, as an aid in drilling oil wells, and as an adhesive in the manufacture of plywood and linoleum.

SUMMARY OF STEM STRUCTURE

1. From a structural viewpoint there are four general types of stems: (1) woody

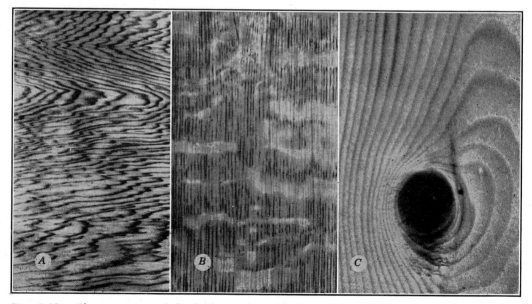

Fig. 6.50. Characteristics of finished woods. A, plywood, a perfect tangential section; B, quarter-sawed oak; C, knotty pine. ✕ 1.

stems belonging to the dicotyledons and the gymnosperms; (2) herbaceous dicotyledons; (3) the stems of the monocotyledons; and (4) modified stems.

2. Stems grow in length only at their tips and only from buds.

3. Growth in length is accomplished through the development of a basic pattern laid down as primary tissues (xylem, phloem, cortex, pith, and epidermis) by the primary meristems (ground meristem, procambium, and protoderm) at the shoot tip.

4. Stems increase in girth through the activity of the vascular cambium, which lays down the secondary xylem internally and secondary phloem externally.

Fig. 6.51. Manufacture of paper. The "wet" end of a Fourdrinier paper machine. A thin suspension of pulp flows onto a moving endless wire screen from the head box in the background. The water drains through the screen leaving behind a mat of fibers in the form of a sheet of paper shown in the foreground. (Courtesy of Crown Zellerbach Corporation.)

5. Increase in girth results in the tearing of the protective epidermis and cortex. This is replaced by cork developing from a cork cambium.

6. The activity of vascular cambium and cork cambium means that a tree is composed of a series of cones of wood and bark. A new cone of wood is formed each year and deposited upon the wood formed the preceding year. A new cone of bark is deposited beneath the old cone of bark.

7. In cross section these cones appear as rings. They are from the outside in: (1) alternating layers of cork and old phloem (also phelloderm, if present); (2) cork cambium (not visible to naked eye); (3) secondary phloem; (4) vascular cambium; (5) secondary xylem composed of annual rings of summer and spring wood; (6) primary xylem (if present); (7) pith (if present).

8. Secondary xylem forms the wood of commerce. It has different appearances in cross, radial, and tangential sections.

9. Trees, other than furnishing wood, are the source of many additional commercial products, such as natural rubber, turpentine, chewing gum.

10. Fewer industrial products are obtained from bark. Notable products are cork from *Quercus suber* and linen from flax.

UNUSUAL TYPES OF STEMS

In the preceding pages it was stated that the ordinary type of stem is a cylindrical organ growing more or less erect and aboveground. There are, however, types of stems that are not cylindrical, others that grow horizontally rather than upright, and others that are subterranean. Examples are such stems as the **rhizomes** (rootstocks) of iris, the **tubers** of the Irish potato, the **bulbs** of onions, the **corms** of gladiolus, the

runners of strawberry, and several other unusual types.

Casual observation of such organs may not lead to the conclusion that they are stems; it may be necessary to study them carefully. We should recall that the seed plant body contains two systems: shoot and root. The shoot is an axis (which may assume any position relative to the earth's surface), composed of a *stem* (with its branches), from which at regular intervals arise *leaves*. It has nodes and internodes, the nodes being the regions from which leaves and buds originate. Roots may resemble stems, particularly certain types that grow underground, but roots do not have nodes and internodes. Moreover, the internal structure of roots and stems differs, and whereas stem branches normally originate at the surface of a main stem and near its tip, branch roots arise from meristematic tissue, situated some distance below the surface of a larger root. Thus, stems, no matter what their form, their direction of growth, or medium in which they grow, have certain external and internal characteristics which distinguish them from roots. Although some few plants may be propagated by means of pieces of roots, most plants may be propagated by means of pieces of the stems, provided that these pieces include one or more nodes with their buds.

Rhizomes (Rootstocks)

The two preceding terms are synonymous. Rhizomes are more or less cylindrical stems growing horizontally underground; they may be slender or fleshy, but in either event are generally rich in stored food. Rhizomes have stem characteristics: nodes, internodes, and scale leaves at the nodes; the buds, which give rise to aerial shoots, originate in the axils of the scale leaves. Whereas the aerial stems of false Solomon's seal die back to the ground each autumn, the underground stems (rhizomes) live throughout the winter, and send up new shoots the following spring. Such plants are perennials. Many weeds are of this type. With these it is not sufficient to kill the top growth, for new shoots are sent up repeatedly, utilizing reserve food stored in the rhizomes. To effect eradication, it is necessary to destroy the rhizomes as well as the top growth. Plants with the habit of wild morning-glory (bindweed or creeping Jenny), quack grass, horse nettle, and many others are pernicious weeds because they possess rhizomes. They spread by means of these underground stems as well as by seeds. Often they are spread in fields by tillage implements that break the rhizomes, distributing the pieces throughout the area cultivated. Any piece of the rhizome that has one or more nodes, with a bud in the axil of each scale leaf at the nodes, is capable of producing a new plant.

Many economic plants may be propagated by means of rhizomes. Among such are iris, asparagus, rhubarb, Jerusalem artichoke, lily-of-the-valley, and most ferns.

Tubers

A splendid example of a tuber is the Irish potato (Fig. 6.52). The potato plant possesses three types of stems: (1) ordinary **aerial stems**, (2) slender rhizomes underground, which become enlarged at the tips and form (3) **tubers**. The tuber is a greatly enlarged, short, underground stem, replete with stored food. In the mature potato the scar left where the tuber was broken from the rhizome is clearly visible.

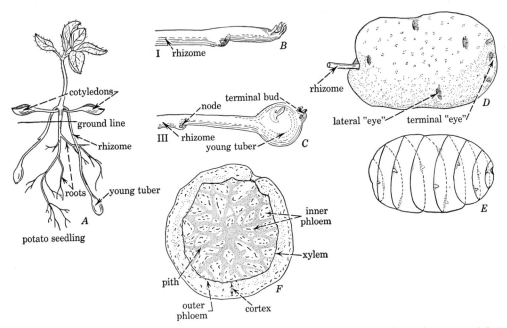

Fig. 6.52. Morphology of potato tuber (*Solanum tuberosum*). A, seedling showing origin of first tubers at tips of rhizomes, which arise in the axils of the cotyledons; B, C, stages in development of a tuber at tip of rhizome; D, external view of mature tuber; E, tuber showing the spiral arrangement of the lateral buds; F, cross section of tuber. (A, redrawn from Percival, *Agricultural Botany*, Henry Holt and Co., B, C, D redrawn from Artschwager.)

Fig. 6.53. Sprouting potato tuber showing the development of stems from terminal and lateral eyes. ×½.

all of these regions, except the periderm and xylem bundles, there is a great quantity of storage parenchyma. The phloem elements, both internal and external, are in numerous groups.

The principal food stored in potato tubers is starch. In addition to starch, there are small quantities of protein and sugar.

If the potato tuber is a stem, we should expect to find nodes and internodes, lateral buds, and a terminal bud. The buds develop into stems (Fig. 6.53). The "eyes" of the tuber are groups of buds; each group along the sides represents a lateral branch with undeveloped internodes; and at the unattached "seed end" of the tuber the "eye" is in reality a terminal branch on which only one bud is strictly terminal. In an elongated potato, it is possible to make out the spiral arrangement of the eyes, for there is only one eye at a node. Beginning at one end of a tuber and proceeding toward the other end, at the same time turning the tuber, usually enables one to follow the spiral arrangement (Fig. 6.52E).

Not only in its external morphology but also in its internal structure does the tuber have stem characteristics (Fig. 6.52F). A very young tuber has an epidermis that is later replaced by a layer of cork cells; this layer is the **periderm** (the "skin" of the potato). Beneath the periderm is the cortex; then, in order, are (1) a region of external phloem, (2) a ring of disconnected xylem bundles, (3) internal phloem and, in the center, (4) the pith (Fig. 6.52G). In

Fig. 6.54. Bulb of onion (*Allium Cepa*). A, median lengthwise section; B, cross section. ×½.

Bulbs

The common onion (Fig. 6.54) is a typical example of a bulb. As seen in a lengthwise section through the center, there is a small disk-shaped stem upon which are borne the numerous fleshy scale leaves. Thus, a very small proportion of the bulb is stem tissue, and a bulb is a modified shoot rather than a modified stem. A single terminal bud is usually visible, and lateral buds occasionally may be found in the axils of the fleshy scale leaves. Both terminal and lateral buds may develop into aerial shoots.

The bulb is a storage organ, the reserve carbohydrate being sugars rather than starch. The characteristic flavor and odor of onions is due to an oil-like organic compound of sulfur, allyl sulfide.

The bulbs of garlic are composed of several small, egg-shaped bulbils called "cloves," all of which are enclosed by a whitish skin.

In "top," or "tree," onions, clusters of bulblets are produced at the top of the flower stalk. Some primordia develop into flowers and others into bulblets. Each bulblet has essentially the structure of a bulb.

Among ornamental plants, those producing bulbs or bulblets include hyacinth, lilies, and tulips. Tiger lilies grow from bulbs and produce bulblets in their leaf axils.

Corms

Typical examples of corms are the underground stems of crocus, gladiolus (Fig. 6.55), and cyclamen. These stems are short, solid, vertical, and contain stored food. As contrasted with bulbs, corms have much more stem tissue and relatively fewer scale leaves. The corm differs from the tuber in

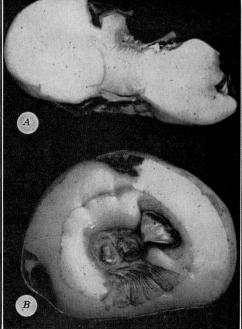

Fig. 6.55. Corm of *Gladiolus*. A, median lengthwise section; B, surface view. ×¾.

that it is the enlarged base of a stem rather than the swollen tip of a stem. On the upper surface of the corm are several lateral buds and a terminal bud.

Runners (Stolons)

A runner or stolon is a slender stem that grows horizontally along the ground surface. As a rule, the internodes of runners are long, and leaves, flowers, and roots are produced at certain nodes. These characteristics are well exemplified in the strawberry plant. In Fig. 6.56, note that there is a scale leaf at each node. New shoots and roots, however, develop only at every other node. Daughter plants become separated from the original plants by the death of runners.

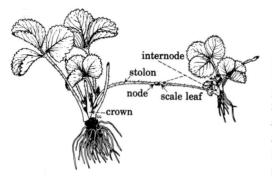

Fig. 6.56. Runner of strawberry (Fragaria).
×⅛.

Stem Tendrils

Tendrils are slender, coiling structures that are sensitive to contact stimuli and attach the plant to a support. Tendrils of plants, morphologically, are of two sorts: leaf and stem. In the sweet pea, for example, several of the uppermost pairs of leaflets have no blades but instead form very slender cylindrical tendrils (Fig. 8.13A). Obviously, these are leaf tendrils. In grapes and Virginia creeper, the tendrils are modified stems (Fig. 6.57B). This is evidenced by the fact that they arise at nodes in leaf axils and sometimes bear small leaves or flowers.

In Virginia creeper each tendril ends in a knob which flattens out when it comes in contact with a surface, and it adheres to that surface by a mucilaginous disk-shaped structure.

Cladophylls (Cladodes)

These are stems which are leaflike in form, are green, and perform the functions of stems. They may bear flowers, fruit, and temporary leaves. Examples of plants with cladophylls are *Ruscus* (Fig. 6.57D), asparagus (Fig. 6.57E), smilax, and various species of cactus (*Opuntia*).

Stem Spines and Thorns

Most spines and thorns of plants are modified stems or outgrowths of the stems. Leaf spines, however, occur in certain plants, e.g., barberry and black locust, and in a few cases even roots become modified as spines. Good examples of stem thorns are those of *Pyracantha* (Fig. 6.57F) and honey locust (Fig. 6.57G). They are borne in the axils of leaves as ordinary branches are. Sometimes thorns bear leaves (Fig. 6.57F), which is further evidence that they are stems. In the honey locust the stem thorns may be branched (Fig. 6.57G).

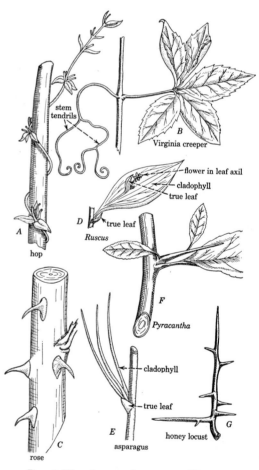

Fig. 6.57. Types of stem modifications.

FUNCTIONS OF STEMS

The functions of different cell types and tissues were mentioned earlier in this discussion of stems. It is rather obvious that the principal functions of stems are **support** and **conduction.** They support the leaves, flowers, and fruits. They conduct water and mineral salts for food manufacture *to* the leaves, and food *from* the leaves. In addition to these primary functions, young stems manufacture food if they possess chlorophyll, and stems of all ages may store food.

Support by Stems

In herbaceous dicots, collenchyma located in the outer cortex lends strength to the stem. It may be augmented by fibers in cortex, phloem, and xylem and also by the turgor of all living cells. It is a common observation that tender herbs, those with very little strengthening tissue, may droop if they do not have an adequate water supply. The mechanical tissue they possess is not sufficient alone to keep them erect; the combined turgor of all living cells is chiefly responsible for their erectness. In woody plants, on the other hand, rigidity of the stems is due to the relatively large amount of mechanical tissues. Secondary xylem (wood) constitutes the bulk of the stems of trees and shrubs. The cells of which wood is composed are closely fitting, and the walls are thick and lignified. The stem system is capable of supporting a heavy load of leaves and fruit.

Conduction in Stems

The movement of materials short distances through the plant is accomplished by diffusion from cell to cell. Such movement is very slow. But the transfer of materials long distances, as from roots to leaves, or from leaves to roots, occurs in the vascular tissue and is comparatively rapid.

The substances conducted in stems are water and mineral salts from the soil, and foods which are manufactured principally in leaves but also in chlorophyll-bearing tissues of other organs. In angiosperms the vessels are the chief carriers of water and mineral salts, although tracheids may also play a minor role. Gymnosperms possess no vessels; in this class of plants, tracheids are the only elements that conduct water and mineral salts longitudinally. The movement of foods takes place chiefly in sieve tubes. Lateral (radial) movement of water and solutes occurs in vascular rays. We will consider the mechanism of conduction in plants in more detail after we have studied the structure of roots and leaves (Chapter 10).

Storage in Stems

Stems may serve as **storage** places for water, food, and various other substances, such as mucilage, resins, tannins, and latex.

Water. The so-called "succulent plants" are the best examples of those whose stems may store large quantities of water. In various cacti, for example, water storage tissue constitutes a large proportion of the stem, and the water stored therein may be as much as 90 per cent of the weight of the entire plant (Fig. 6.58). This water reserve may be used during drought.

Food. The principal food stored in stems is starch. Even in herbaceous stems, starch will be found as a temporary storage product in parenchyma cells, especially those of the cortex and pith. In woody plants, starch usually occurs in stems of all ages, even in the main trunk. Starch is found in abundance in vascular rays, including those which are many years old and still living. Studies of food reserves in twigs of fruit trees show that starch accumulates toward the end of the growing season, remains in parenchyma cells throughout the winter season, but largely disappears when growth is resumed in the spring. A very large part of the food used by any individual bud in its early spring growth comes from the storage tissues in the immediate neighborhood of that bud.

In addition to starch, other foods, such as sugar, fats, and proteins, are stored in stems. For example, the stems of sugar cane are about 80 per cent juice, the sugar content of which is quite high.

Fig. 6.58. An Arizona cactus. (Courtesy of Ansel Adams.)

Although some reserve foods usually occur in all types of stems, subterranean stems, such as tubers, rhizomes, and corms, are especially adapted for food storage.

Mucilaginous substances (complex carbohydrates very similar to gums) accumulate in the stems of some plants, such as many ferns, cacti, and other succulents.

Tannins, substances that impart an astringent, bitter taste to tissues in which they are present, occur in the bark and wood of many plants. They are derived commercially chiefly from the bark of hemlock, tan oaks, mangrove, and wattle (certain *Acacia* species), and from the wood of chestnut, and from "Quebracho" (the heartwood of a South American tree).

Latex is a milky secretion that occurs in many different families. It is a very complex mixture containing such materials as water, resin, oil, proteins, gums, tannins, sugars, alkaloids, and salts of calcium and magnesium. Latex may occur in special cells or in tubes (**latex tubes**), which are distinct from the vascular system. Common latex-producing plants are the fig, dandelion, spurge, and milkweeds. Of particular economic importance is the latex of those plants from which crude natural rubber is obtained. The most important rubber-yielding species are as follows:

(1) *Para rubber tree* (*Hevea brasiliensis*), a native of the tropical forests of the Amazon and Orinoco river valleys in South America, but since 1929 grown in large plantations, chiefly in Ceylon, Malaya, Java, and Sumatra; (2) *Panama rubber tree* (*Castilla elastica*), a native of Mexico and Central America; (3) *Manihot glaziovii*, a native tree of Brazil, yielding "ceara rubber"; (4) *guayule* (*Parthenium argentatum*), a native American shrub which, during World War II, was grown in large plantations in western United States; and (5) *kok-saghyz* or Russian dandelion (*Taraxacum koksaghyz*), a plant grown quite extensively in Russia, and to some extent, experimentally, in the United States during the period of rubber shortage.

Resins are complex substances, secreted by glands into special ducts, known as resin ducts (Fig. 6.39). Crude resins contain, in addition to resinous materials, a considerable amount of essential oils. The principal product derived from resin is turpentine, obtained exclusively from coniferous trees.

7

The Root

The roots of a plant, considered collectively, form the **root system**. The two principal functions of roots are **anchorage** and **absorption**. In addition, the roots of all plants usually **store** a certain amount of food, at least for a short time; and the roots of such plants as sugar beet, carrot, sweet potato, and others are specialized food storage organs. Besides anchorage, absorption, and storage, roots perform the function of **conduction**. Water and mineral salts absorbed from the soil, and foods that may be stored in roots, are conducted by the roots to the stems, and thence to the leaves and other organs aboveground. Foods manufactured in the leaves are conducted by the stems to the main roots, and then by the latter to branch roots, so that these foods are carried to the extremities (growing tissues) of all the smallest roots.

BALANCE BETWEEN SHOOT AND ROOT SYSTEMS

In a normal, healthy plant there is a balance between the shoot system and the root system. Of particular importance is the relation of total leaf surface to total root surface; or, to state it differently, total surface exposed to the sun, from which energy is absorbed and used in the manufacture of carbohydrates, in relation to the total root surface in contact with the soil solution, from which the plant absorbs water and mineral nutrients. The root system must be able to supply the shoot with sufficient water and mineral nutrients, and the shoot system to manufacture enough food for maintenance of the root system. Thus is the balance physiological rather than one involving actual weights or dimensions of root and shoot systems.

The balance may be disturbed in several ways: (1) by fungous diseases or insect pests that attack either the roots or shoots; (2) by destruction of roots during transplanting or through improper cultivation; (3) by pruning of branches. When a young tree is transplanted, some destruction of roots is unavoidable; consequently, the absorbing surface of the plant is reduced. In this event it is advisable to cut back or remove branches and thus attempt to reestablish the balance between the root system and shoot system. If the shoot is severely pruned, thus reducing the food-making tissue, the relatively large root system, incapable of making food, may suffer because of a lack of food. In the pruning of orchard trees, attention is given to the balance between carbohydrates (manufactured by the leaves) and nitrogen (absorbed from the soil solution); or, more strictly, between available carbohydrates and available nitrogenous compounds. This carbohydrate-nitrogen relationship is somewhat complicated, but suffice it to say here that severe pruning of the shoot stimulates the development of new shoots and discourages fruitfulness. It reduces the amount of tissue that manufactures carbohydrates. Thus, there will flow into the branches the usual amounts of nitrates from the soil, with the result that the amount of nitrogen in proportion to carbohydrates will be high. Under these conditions shoot development is stimulated, and fruit development discouraged. On the other hand, an excess of carbohydrates over nitrates may encourage fruitfulness. But it should be kept in mind that plants are both vegetatively weak *and* unfruitful if the proportion of available carbohydrates to available nitrogen is either *very high* or *very low.*

EXTENT OF ROOT SYSTEMS

Although it is not generally known, the root system of a plant may equal or exceed the shoot system—that part of ordinary plants which grows aboveground and is usually referred to as "top growth." Specifically, the total number and extent of root branches may equal or exceed the total number and extent of stem branches, and in some plants the total weight of the root system greatly exceeds that of the top growth. For example, in the sugar beet (Fig. 7.1), at the end of the first season's growth, the root system may penetrate to a depth of 5 or 6 feet and have a lateral spread of about 6 feet in diameter, thus

Fig. 7.1. Tap root system of the sugar beet (*Beta vulgaris*). (Photo courtesy of the Great Western Sugar Co.)

occupying a volume of soil equal to approximately 170 cubic feet. The top growth at the end of the first season is much smaller. Moreover, the total weight (dry as well as fresh) of the root system of the sugar beet at the end of the first season greatly exceeds that of the top.

Other studies emphasize the importance of roots. A quantitative study of the number, length, and total surface area of the roots and root hairs of *one rye plant* has been made. Seed was sown in wooden containers, and, when the plants were 4 months old, the soil was washed from the roots and the entire root system removed intact. *One 4-month-old rye plant* had a total of nearly 14 million roots, with a surface area of 2500 square feet. Living root hairs on the plant numbered over 14 billion and had a total surface area of about 4300 square feet. This latter figure, combined with that of the roots, gave a total area of contact with the soil of approximately 6800 square feet. The total external surface of the 80 shoots with their 480 leaves was but 51 square feet. It is surprising to note that in the one rye plant the combined length of all its roots was 387 miles.

Similar studies show that in many plants the total absorbing surface of roots, that is, the surface of contact with the soil, is very much greater than one would suspect.

Various factors influence the number and distribution of roots. Worthy of mention is the fact that when plants grow very closely together competition between overlapping root systems begins long before the tops begin to shade one another. For example, when weeds occur in a cereal crop, the yield of the crop is reduced. Also, studies of the root systems of the cereal at different stages of development show that the presence of competing weeds greatly reduces their absorbing area. This reduction in yield is undoubtedly due in part to root competition as well as to competition of top growth for light. The root system of a wheat plant grown without competition is usually many times larger than that of one grown in drill rows several inches apart and in competition with its close neighbors.

"Intercropping" is not an uncommon agricultural practice but is one of doubtful economy. It means the planting of annual crops, such as beans or corn, between rows of young orchard trees or other perennials. Although little competition of the top growth may be apparent, not infrequently root competition results and both crops suffer.

It is important from the standpoint of practical agriculture to have knowledge of the root systems of orchard, garden, and field crop plants. To what depth do the roots penetrate? What is their horizontal spread? From what soil zones do they absorb water and mineral nutrients? Answers to these questions are available for many crop plants. The known facts are a guide in irrigation practices, in fertilizer applications, and in cultural operations. As one example, a study of the root system of corn at different stages in its development has led to the adoption of improved tillage machinery and methods. According to estimates, an improper system of deep cultivation of corn in certain parts of the Corn Belt, resulting in root injury, decreased the average yield of corn 2 to 8 bushels per acre.

ROOT CROPS

Many plants are cultivated for their roots. Such plants are known as "root crops." They include beets (garden beet and sugar beet), carrots, parsnips, radishes, turnips and rutabagas, sweet potatoes, yams, and cassavas. The cassava (*Manihot esculenta*) is the most important of the tropical root crops, and in the tropics it furnishes a staple food of the natives. Tapioca is made from raw cassava, the supply for the United States being imported chiefly from Brazil, formerly from the East Indies also.

KINDS OF ROOT SYSTEMS

If we pull up wheat, oats, rye, or some other cereal "by the roots," we observe a mass of roots arising at the base of the stem. The *main roots* of the cluster are approximately of the *same size;* each gives off numerous side roots, or roots of the second order; these, in turn, bear branches of the third order, and these, in turn, roots of the fourth order. All the roots are slender and fiberlike; no one root is more prominent than the others. Such a root system is spoken of as a **fibrous root system** (Fig. 7.2). It is characteristic of all the cereals (wheat, oats, rye, corn, sorghum, rice, etc.) and other grasses, and many other monocotyledons. The rye plant referred to on page 138 had 143 main roots, 35,600 of second order, 2,300,000 of third order, and 11,500,000 of fourth order. All of these roots, with over 14 billion root hairs, had an enormous area of soil contact. Plants with a fibrous root system of the type described are used as sand and soil binders on ditch banks, levees, or other steep slopes in order to prevent erosion, either by wind or water.

Contrasted with the fibrous root system is that of such plants as carrot, beet, radish, turnip, and parsnip. These plants have one main root that grows directly downward, from which branch roots arise. A root system of this kind is called a **tap root system** (Fig. 7.1). The main or tap root of the examples cited is a fleshy, food-storing organ. In other plants, the main or tap root may not be fleshy but more or less woody, as exemplified in oak, red clover, flax, lettuce, cotton, kohlrabi, etc.

In general, fibrous root systems are relatively shallow, whereas tap root systems may penetrate the soil to considerable depths. For example, the fibrous root system of cereals seldom penetrates the soil to a depth greater than 5 or 6 feet. The tap root system of alfalfa, on the other hand, may grow downward to depths of 12 to 15 feet or more.

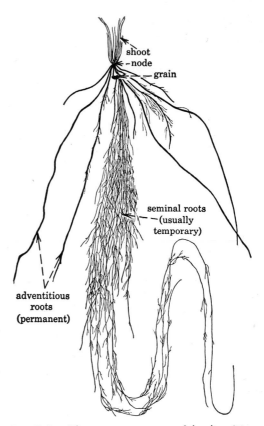

Fig. 7.2. Fibrous root system of barley (*Hordeum vulgare*). (After Jackson.)

KINDS OF ROOTS

A seed contains a young plant, the **embryo.** By soaking a seed, such as the bean, in water so as to remove the seed coat more easily, the entire embryo may be observed. It will be seen that certain rudimentary organs are already in evidence. One of these organs is the **radicle** or **rudimentary root** (Fig. 4.1). When the seed germinates the radicle is usually the first structure to appear; it becomes the *first* root and is called the **primary root.** It has branches and subbranches, all of which are called **secondary roots.** In many plants, such as beet, radish, and carrot, the primary root remains the principal root throughout

Fig. 7.3. Adventitious roots from a tomato (*Lycopersicon esculentum*) stem cutting. ×½.

wheat usually consists of five roots (sometimes six) (Fig. 7.2). In most grasses the seminal root system is usually temporary, although under some conditions it may function throughout the life of the plant. Within a short time after the seminal root system is formed, permanent roots arise from that portion of the stem of the young plant which extends from the germinating seed to the surface of the ground (Fig. 7.2). These roots are not branches of the primary root. They are **adventitious roots.** It is customary to speak of all roots that arise from organs other than roots as adventitious roots. Good examples of adventitious roots are the "prop roots" of corn, which grow out from the lower nodes of the stem and enter the soil obliquely, serving as braces for the plant. Also, the roots that grow out from planted tubers, bulbs, and rhizomes are adventitious; and, when stem cuttings of such plants as tomato, pear, blackberry, geranium, and rose are placed in moist soil or sand, adventitious roots are developed at the lower end (Fig. 7.3).

Summarizing, according to origin there are three main kinds of roots: (1) **primary,** which develop from the radicle (rudimentary root) of the seed; (2) **secondary,** which are branches of other roots; and (3) **adventitious,** which originate from other organs of the plant.

STRUCTURE OF ROOTS

The root, like the stem, grows, conducts water and nutrients, and stores food. Unlike the stem, it absorbs nutrients and water from the soil and anchors the plant. Accompanying similarities and dissimilarities in function are corresponding variations in structure. We shall find, in the root, meristematic and vascular tissues similar to those found in the stem. Both primary and secondary growth occur. There are three tissues in the root (root cap, endodermis

the life of the plant. The tap root system is usually the primary root and its branches.

The development of a fibrous root system, like that of a cereal, is quite different from that of the tap root system. In the embryo of barley or wheat, for example, a primary root (Fig. 13.29) is evident. When the grain germinates, this root takes the lead. Soon it is followed by two pairs of threadlike roots, which, however, are not branches of the primary root; that is, they are not strictly secondary roots. The primordia of the two pairs of roots can be detected by microscopic examination of the ungerminated grain. Therefore, we may speak of the primary root and the two pairs of roots which follow it as **seminal (seed) roots,** because the primordia of all these roots are evident in the embryo of the seed. Thus, the seminal root system of barley or

and pericycle) that are not present in the stem, and the arrangement of vascular and meristematic tissues is slightly different.

Primary Plant Body

External Features. The general structural features of roots can best be studied by means of seedlings that have been grown either in sand or on filter paper in a moist atmosphere. Figure 7.4 shows such a seedling. Observe here the portion of the root that is clothed with root hairs; this region is usually known as the **root-hair zone.** Note that root hairs do not extend to the very tip of the root. The root-hair zone and the hairless tip constitute a region of especial interest. It is in this part of the root where take place: (1) growth in length, (2) most of the absorption of materials from the soil, and (3) development of the primary tissues.

Figure 7.4 (right) is a diagrammatic lengthwise section of the root tip, including only a part of the root-hair zone. Observe the following regions, beginning at the very end: (1) **root cap,** (2) **apical meristem,** (3) **region of elongation,** and (4) **region of root hairs** (**region of differentiation**).

In stems the apical meristem is either naked or protected by rudimentary leaves and bud scales. In contrast, the apical meristem of roots is protected by a thimble-shaped mass of cells, the **root cap.** Cells of the root cap are constantly being sloughed off at the very tip, but at the same time new cells are being added to it by apical meristem cells. In the **apical meristem** the cells are actively dividing, adding new cells to the root cap and others to the region of elongation. When an apical meristem cell divides in a plane at right angles to the length of the root, and when the daughter cells enlarge, some length is added to the root. Rapid growth in root

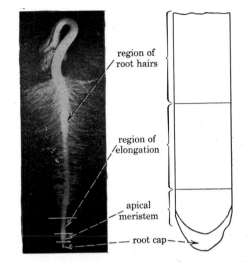

region of root hairs

region of elongation

apical meristem

root cap

Fig. 7.4. Root tip of radish (*Raphanus sativus*) showing principal growth regions. ×4. Compare with Fig. 7.5.

length, however, is largely the result of elongation of cells back of the apical meristem. This is the **region of elongation.** Thus, it is seen that a very short portion of the root at the tip, usually from 2 to 5 millimeters in length, is constantly being forced through the soil. The method of growth in length of the root just described explains the protective function of the root cap; the delicate cells of the apical meristem are protected from mechanical injury as they are pushed through the soil.

It is significant that elongation of cells does not occur in the root-hair zone. If elongation did occur in this zone, root hairs that wrap around and adhere to soil particles would be torn loose. The root-hair zone is also spoken of as the **region of differentiation,** for it is here that cells differentiate into primary tissues.

Anatomy. The root cap is composed of short-lived parenchyma-like cells. Since new cells are continually being added to it, the root cap persists throughout the growing life of the root. It is present in all

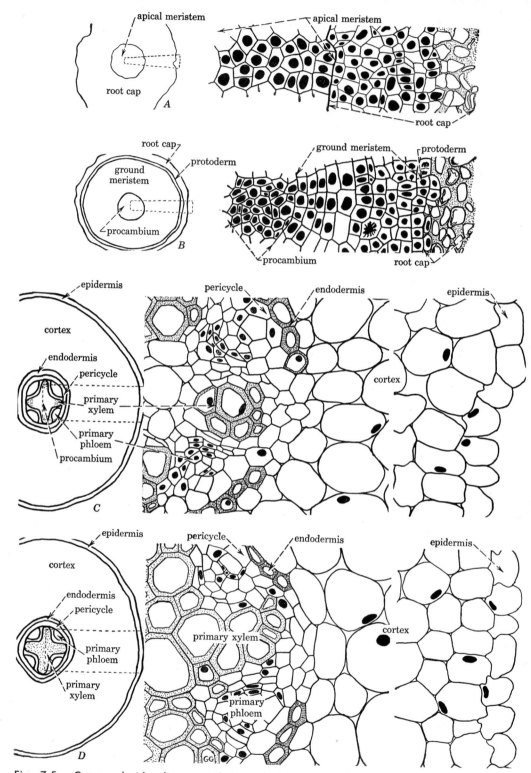

Fig. 7.5. Camera lucida diagrams (left) and drawings (right) of stages in development of root primary tissues. Dashed areas (left) are shown in detail (right). In C and D, primary xylem is stippled and a portion of cortex is omitted. (Illustrations by Girolami.)

common land plants but is lacking in many aquatic plants and certain other specialized types.

The apical meristem is composed of thin-walled cells, which are very much alike and practically without intercellular spaces. Sections in this region usually show many cells in which the nuclei are in some stage of mitosis.

In the region of elongation, there is less uniformity in the appearance of cells than there is in the apical meristem. Some differentiation has taken place. As in the corresponding region of the stem, three primary meristematic tissues are evident although the exact sequence of their development may vary in different plants: (1) the **protoderm,** (2) the **procambium,** and (3) the **ground meristem.** These three meristematic tissues differentiate into the primary tissues of the roots.

In the section through the root-hair zone, or region of differentiation, the following primary tissues can be seen (Fig. 7.5C).

(1) The **epidermis,** with its root hairs— a single layer of cells derived from the protoderm.

Root Hairs. A single 4-month-old rye plant was found to have a total of over 14 billion living root hairs with a total surface area in excess of 4000 square feet. Most land plants, with some exceptions which will be mentioned later, possess root hairs, which are important absorbing organs of the plant. Root hairs are usually most abundant on very young roots and, as a rule, are limited to the root-hair zone very near the tip (Fig. 7.4). In some plants, however, root hairs have been found to cover a large proportion of the surface of young roots. The surface of the old parts of roots is often covered with a layer of cork cells which when intact is impermeable to water and mineral salts.

Figure 7.6 shows stages in the development of a root hair. Essentially, it is a

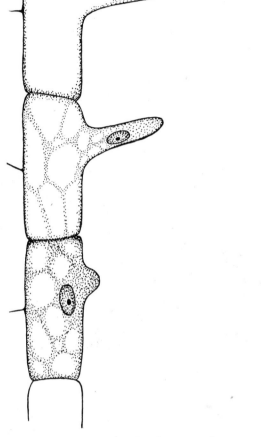

Fig. 7.6. Stages in the development of a root hair. ×1500.

lateral outgrowth of an epidermal cell. When grown in moist air each root hair has the form of a slender tube, but in the soil it may be greatly contorted in its growth between and around soil particles. The root hair and the epidermal cell from which it grows constitute a single cell. The walls are thin, composed principally of cellulose and pectic substances, and lined with a thin layer of cytoplasm. The nucleus is usually near the end of the hair, and there is a large central vacuole.

In most plants, the life of any one root hair is short; it functions only for a few days or weeks. New hairs are constantly forming at the anterior end of the root-hair zone, while those at the posterior end are dying. Thus, as the root advances through the soil, fresh, actively growing root hairs are constantly coming into contact with new soil particles. In the rye plant mentioned above, it is estimated that new root hairs develop at an average rate in excess of 100 million per day. *Root hairs do not become roots.*

The root hairs of such plants as redbud, honey locust, and a number of others may persist for several years.

Although nearly all ordinary land plants possess root hairs, a few, such as the firs, redwoods, and Scotch pine, are devoid of them. Also many aquatic plants have no root hairs. Moreover, land plants (corn, for example) that normally develop root hairs when the root system grows in the soil, or in moist air, develop no root hairs when the roots grow in water. In plants devoid of root hairs absorption is through the thin-walled epidermal cells. Root-hair development is often inhibited by a concentrated soil solution and by high or low soil temperatures. Root hairs develop in the light and dark about equally well, providing that moisture and oxygen are adequate.

(2) The **cortex,** a region relatively thicker than that in stems, derived from the ground meristem. The cortex is composed chiefly of storage parenchyma with large intercellular spaces (Fig. 7.7). In many species secretory cells and resin ducts are present. The innermost layer of the

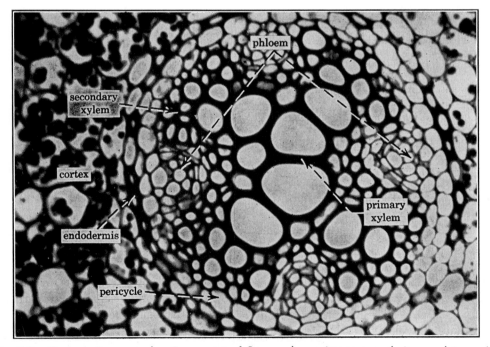

Fig. 7.7. Cross section, vascular tissue, root of *Ranunculus;* primary growth is complete and a small amount of secondary xylem has formed. ×100. (Slide courtesy of Triarch Products.)

cortex is a single row of cells, the **endodermis**, which is usually a conspicuous feature of roots. As a rule, in the primary state the endodermal cell walls are thin except for a bandlike thickening running around the cell on the radial and transverse walls. This thickened strip, known as the **Casparian strip**, is suberized or cutinized (Fig. 7.8). Frequently, in older root regions, the inner, radial, and transverse walls of endodermal cells are thickened.

(3) At an early stage of development a special layer of parenchyma cells is differentiated from the outer region of the procambium cylinder. This is the **pericycle** (Figs. 7.5, 7.7). It persists as a rather unspecialized type of meristematic tissue until secondary development interferes with its activity. It gives rise to lateral roots, certain of its cells develop into vascular cambium, others give rise to cork cambium and it perpetuates itself by cell division. In roots without secondary growth it may eventually form a sclerenchyma tissue.

(4) The **vascular cylinder** (Figs. 7.5, 7.7) originates from the remaining internal portion of the procambium. Since there is generally no internal ground meristem as occurs in the tip of shoots, pith does not usually develop in dicotyledonous roots, although it may occur in the roots of monocotyledons.

In some treatments of root structure, the pericycle and vascular cylinder, which both originate from the procambium, are considered a single general region called the **stele.**

It will be recalled that in stems, xylem and phloem groups of a vascular bundle occur in such a manner that a radial line cuts through both groups (see Fig. 6.11). In roots, in contrast, the primary xylem and phloem groups occur in such a manner that a radius passing through the xylem arms does not pass through the phloem. The primary xylem usually consists of a cen-

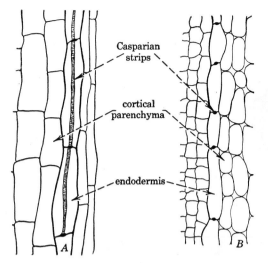

Fig. 7.8. Endodermis of root showing Casparian strips. A, radial section; B, cross section. ×100.

tral mass or "core" of xylem elements, with several radiating arms, between which are groups of phloem elements. Between these two groups are one or more layers of procambial cells. In roots with secondary growth, these cells give rise to vascular cambium; in roots without secondary growth they often mature into sclerenchyma. Many roots have no pith, but in most monocotyledons and some herbaceous dicotyledons, the central core of the stele is parenchyma that resembles the pith of stems. Whereas the pith of stems is derived from ground meristem, that of roots is derived from procambium.

The tissues that occur in the primary xylem of stems may be found also in the primary xylem of roots, although spiral and annular vessels are relatively rare in roots. The primary phloem of roots does not differ essentially from that of stems. It consists of sieve tubes, companion cells, and parenchyma.

Origin of Lateral Roots. It will be recalled (page 92) that lateral or branch

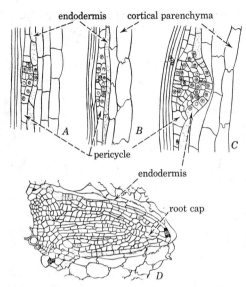

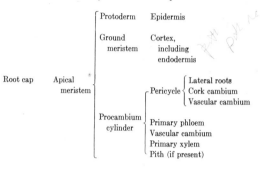

Fig. 7.9. Stages in the development of a branch root in carrot (*Daucus carota*). ×50. (Redrawn from Esau.)

trates that portion of cabbage xylem where root and shoot merge.

A Summary of Primary Tissues

The Secondary Plant Body

If we examine old roots of woody plants, some of which may attain a diameter of stems originate from superficial cells or cell layers at or near the shoot tip. In contrast, lateral or branch roots in gymnosperms and angiosperms originate from cells of the pericycle. Figure 7.9 shows the manner of origin of branch roots. Often the point of origin of a branch root is opposite a primary xylem strand. For example, in the beet root, there are two primary xylem strands and two vertical rows of branch roots. It is seen from Fig. 7.9A–D that the tip of the branch root must penetrate the cortex and the epidermis in order to reach the surface. These tissues are stretched and finally ruptured as a result of the mechanical pressure of the growing root. It has also been suggested that cells of the branch root secrete substances which digest the tissues ahead of it. This method of root formation leaves the xylem portion of the vascular cylinder intact, in contrast with the stem where leaf and bud gaps result in openings in the xylem cylinder. This difference is shown in Fig. 7.10 which illus-

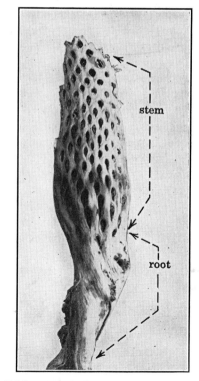

Fig. 7.10. Xylem framework of rotted cabbage (*Brassica oleraceae*) showing junction of stem and root. ×¾.

many inches, we observe annual rings of growth resembling those in stems (Fig. 7.11). At the completion of primary growth, procambium remains between the radiating arms of the primary xylem separating it from the primary phloem. No procambium remains at the points of the radiating primary xylem arms so a continuous band of procambium is not present. In this early stage of development no vascular cambium is present, but it is soon formed in the following manner: (1) A curved band of vascular cambium forms from the procambium remaining between the primary xylem and primary phloem, and (2) parenchyma cells of the pericycle on the outside of the radiating arms of primary xylem become meristematic. Thus a continuous layer of vascular cambium is formed and, as in the stem, it has developed from procambial cells that have not lost their meristematic character, and from parenchyma cells that had become differentiated and returned to a meristematic condition. As seen in cross section (Fig. 7.12A), this layer has the form of a wavy band; it passes inside each primary phloem group and outside each of the arms of the star-shaped primary xylem. This vascular cambium gives rise internally to secondary xylem and externally to secondary phloem, with initial production of secondary xylem being more rapid between the arms of primary xylem. This development soon results in a continuous smooth circle of vascular cambium (Fig. 7.12B). With continued secondary growth, the epidermis and cortex are usually ruptured and finally sloughed off.

The cambium thus formed gives rise to secondary xylem and phloem after the manner of the vascular cambium of stems. Annual rings are generally formed and macroscopically the wood of an old root cannot be distinguished from that of a stem. However, microscopic examination shows that, in general, the secondary xylem of the root contains fewer fibers, more storage

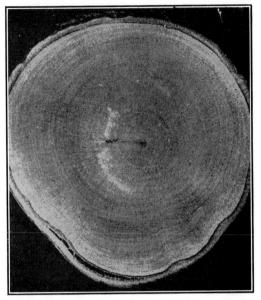

Fig. 7.11.   Cross section of an old root of cherry (*Prunus avium*). $\times \frac{7}{8}$.

parenchyma, and larger and more numerous thin-walled vessels than does that of the stem. The secondary phloem of the root as compared with that of the stem has more storage parenchyma and less mechanical tissue.

The formation of cork cells accompanies the development of the secondary xylem and phloem. They are derived from a cork cambium which in most cases originates first in the pericyclic cells (Fig. 7.13E). As the root increases in diameter this first-formed cork is stretched and torn as in stems. Cork cambium forms anew from deeper lying cells, generally in the phloem. This results, as in stems, in the development of a thick protective layer.

SUMMARY OF SECONDARY GROWTH IN ROOTS

A vascular cambium originates from the procambium cells between the primary xylem and phloem and from the pericyclic cells exterior to the radiating points of the primary xylem. From this, secondary xylem develops internally and secondary phloem externally. The resulting increase in diameter stretches and tears the endodermis, cortex, and epidermis. A cork cambium develops from the pericycle and forms cork. Woody roots, consequently, are very similar in structure to woody stems.

THE FUNCTIONS OF ROOTS

The functions of the root system are **absorption, anchorage, conduction,** and

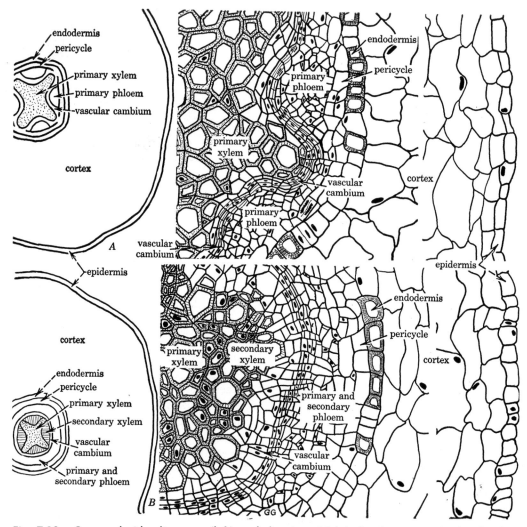

Fig. 7.12. Camera lucida diagrams (left) and drawings (right) showing stages in the development of secondary tissues of a root. Primary xylem stippled, secondary xylem lined. A portion of cortex is omitted. *A*, formation of vascular cambium; *B*, development of secondary xylem and phloem. (Illustrations prepared by Girolami.)

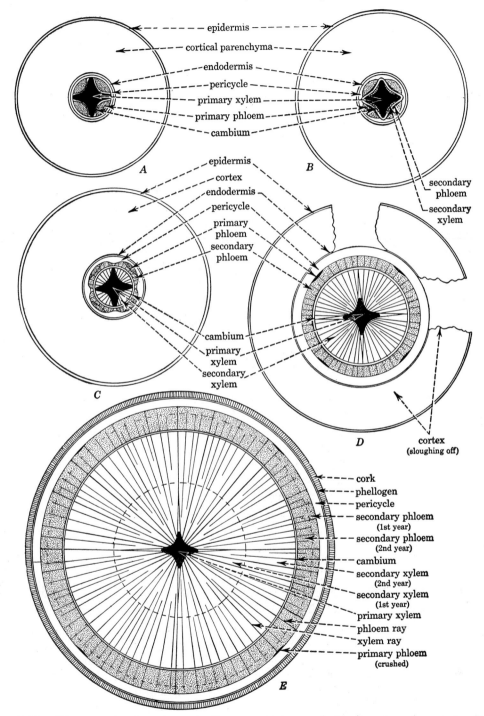

Fig. 7.13. Diagrams showing stages in the secondary growth in diameter of a root. (From Holman and Robbins, *A Textbook of General Botany*, John Wiley & Sons; drawing prepared by Esau.)

storage. From the soil, roots absorb water, mineral salts, and oxygen. They anchor the plant firmly in place. They conduct water, mineral salts, and sometimes foods, previously stored, *to* the stems and leaves aboveground, and they conduct foods *from* the leaves to all parts of the system underground. Most roots usually store foods at least for a short period and in small quantities, and special storage roots accumulate rather large amounts of foods.

Absorption by Roots

Absorption of Water. In land plants, large amounts of water are absorbed by the roots and lost from the leaves. Most of the water that is absorbed moves upward to the leaves and passes out as *water vapor* through stomata in the epidermal layers of the leaves.

Water constitutes a large percentage of protoplasm; all vacuoles are chiefly water; all walls are wet with water (imbibed water); substances moving in the conducting elements are in solution in water; and water serves as a raw material for food manufacture. As a matter of fact, in ordinary plants, a large proportion (75–95 per cent) of the total weight of the plant is water. In spite of this, during any period in the plant's life, the amount of water retained by the plant is but a small part of the total amount absorbed and transpired. For example, it has been determined experimentally that approximately 400 units of water for every unit of dry matter produced may pass through a wheat plant during its life.

A part of the water absorbed by most land plants enters through the root hairs (Fig. 7.6); some enters through the thin walls of ordinary epidermal cells. We have learned that the area of contact of the root system with the soil may be enormous; that the numerous rootlets are constantly elongating and exploring new soil areas; that root hairs are being formed anew just back of the growing tip of the root; and that these young, thin-walled root hairs are flattening out and surrounding soil particles, and thus coming into very close contact with the film of water that surrounds the soil particles.

Separating the vacuole of a root hair and the soil solution is the cell wall and a thin layer of cytoplasm. The wall itself is chiefly of cellulose and pectic substances. There is usually a pectic coating on the outside of the wall. Due to the gummy nature of this coating the root hairs adhere closely to the soil particles.

If a molecule of water in the soil is to reach the cell vacuole, it must penetrate the cell wall of the root hair and a layer of cytoplasm (Fig. 7.6).

As seen from Fig. 10.6, the pathway of water from the root hair is through several layers of thin-walled cortical cells, then through the endodermis and one or more layers of cells of the pericycle, to the vessels of the xylem. Once in the vessels, the water moves from the very small root branches to larger roots, finally to the stem, and on upward to the leaves and other organs of the plant. From the leaves and young stems, the water passes off to the atmosphere as water vapor. Thus there is a continuous stream of water through the plant.

The mechanism of the absorption of water and its movement through the plant will be discussed in Chapter 9.

Absorption of Solutes. Land plants derive their inorganic salts from the soil. Usually every kind of chemical element found in the soil can also be found in plants. Certain mineral elements, such as potassium, sulfur, phosphorus, calcium, magnesium, and silicon, constitute a relatively large proportion of the inorganic components of plants. Other elements, such as iron, manganese, boron, zinc, copper, iodine, and selenium, occur in small quantities or as mere traces.

At present there is no reason for believing that every element found by chemical analysis in plants has an essential role in the plant's life. Although a number of elements are known to be essential, others are apparently carried into the plant but are of no particular use. Certain elements, however, such as boron, zinc, copper, and manganese, formerly regarded as nonessential, now are known to be indispensable. Some elements are absorbed in considerable excess of the plant's actual needs. It is very likely that most salts of the soil enter chiefly in the form of ions.

The process of the absorption of solutes by roots will be discussed in Chapter 9.

Anchorage by Roots

We have seen (pages 137–139) how extensive are the root systems of ordinary plants and how completely they may occupy the soil. Thus, the roots function as very effective anchorage organs. Within recent years our attention has been drawn to the enormous losses of the agricultural wealth of our country as a result of soil erosion. Owing to action of wind and water on hilly lands and on lands from which the original plant covering has been destroyed or disturbed by cultivation, by overgrazing, and sometimes by burning, there may be a very great loss of topsoil and with it the mineral nutrients required for crop growth.

The principal methods employed to check erosion by wind and water include **terracing, contour tillage, strip cropping,** and **growth of a vegetative covering.** One of the values of plants in preventing soil erosion resides in the efficient living anchorage system of the roots, which holds the soil in place. The hold that roots have on the soil is well shown in sand dunes, where the sand is constantly shifting except where it is held in place by the roots of plants.

Some plants develop special types of aerial (air) roots. For example, the Indian banyan (*Ficus indica*) may send out aerial roots from the horizontal branches, and these roots grow downward, become attached to the soil, and serve as "props" as well as absorbing organs. In corn, adventitious roots arising from nodes just above the ground line grow downward, penetrate the soil, and act as "props." Other plants that develop supporting roots aboveground are *Pandanus* (a tropical plant), the red mangrove, and certain figs. Aerial roots also occur on the stems of many vines, such as English ivy, trumpet creeper, and Virginia creeper, and enable the trailing, slender stems to cling to trees and other supports. Aerial roots also develop on certain plants that have no connection whatever with the soil; these plants, such as some orchids and ferns, known as **epiphytes,** live on the branches of trees and develop aerial roots that both anchor and absorb.

Storage by Roots

All roots, even slender ones whose primary function is absorption, may have a small amount of food stored temporarily in them. For example, when sugar moves into the roots more rapidly than it can be utilized by the growing cells, it may be converted to starch and as such be stored for a time, particularly in cortical cells. During the dormant season rather large quantities of starch are stored in the woody roots of orchard trees. This food constitutes a reserve that is called upon when active growth is resumed in the spring. The roots of the wild morning-glory (bindweed) and other perennials store large quantities of food. This stored supply enables the plant to send up new shoots when the "tops" of

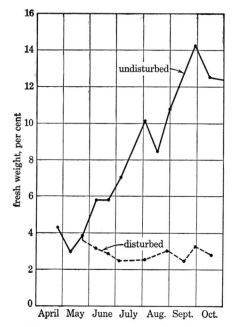

Fig. 7.14. Seasonal trend in the storage of reserve carbohydrates in the roots of wild morning-glory (*Convolvulus arvensis*). (From Barr.)

Food storage in roots may occur in the cortex, phloem, and xylem.

Such crops as beet, carrot, radish, parsnip, etc., are examples of plants that store large quantities of foods, chiefly sugars and starch, in the roots. The sugar beet, for example, usually contains from 15 to 20 per cent of sucrose. In 1954, farmers of the United States harvested 27.6 billion pounds of sugar beets, yielding 3.8 billion pounds of sugar. This amount of food was manufactured in the leaves of the sugar beet plant and stored in the roots.

The sweet potato, turnip, parsnip, and many other fleshy roots have considerable quantities of stored starch. Among our native plants, the most striking examples of fleshy-rooted plants occur in arid regions. Such roots generally contain a large quantity of stored water that can be used by the leafy shoots during periods of drought.

Reproduction by Means of Roots

Ornamental crab apple, cherry, plum, quince, hawthorn, and a number of other plants are usually propagated by root cuttings. The shoots that arise from the cuttings are from adventitious buds (Fig. 7.3). Injury of roots may induce the development of such buds. Many weeds, such as wild morning-glory and Canada thistle, propagate by means of roots. The roots of these plants, broken off by tillage implements, may strike root and grow into new plants if located in moist soil. The roots of wild morning-glory often penetrate to depths of 10 to 20 feet. If cut pieces of roots are taken at any depth and placed under suitable conditions, they will develop new plants. The tap root of a dandelion may be cut into many small pieces, and each section be capable of producing new shoots. In the propagation of sweet potatoes, the usual practice is to place whole, small,

the plants are destroyed; it is this habit that makes such plants pernicious weeds. Control of deep-rooted perennial weeds by tillage is dependent on exhausting the food reserves in the roots, and other organs underground, through continued cutting of the top growth. The seasonal trend in the storage of foods in the roots of wild morning-glory is seen in Fig. 7.14. It will be noted that, in undisturbed plants, readily available carbohydrates rapidly build up during the summer, whereas, in plants cultivated at 2-week intervals, food storage is greatly hindered. This example is cited to show an application to a practical problem of a knowledge of food reserves, particularly their seasonal trends, in roots. A study of food reserves in the roots, as well as the stems, of orchard trees has been made, especially in its relation to pruning practices.

fleshy roots ("potatoes") in the hotbed. Shoots arise from adventitious buds. Or, sections of the fleshy root also may be used. The roots of many plants, however, will not develop adventitious buds, even though they are placed under good growing condi-tions. For example, sections of a carrot root will not grow. In growing carrot seed, the roots are set in the ground, care being taken that the "crown" (stem tissue) is intact. Buds arise from the crown, not from the root.

8

The Leaf

Green plants play a singular and important role in the world; they alone of all living things are able to absorb and store energy. The energy of sunlight is changed into a form that can be utilized in the life processes of both plants and animals. By far the greater part of the energy used in transportation and industry was absorbed by green plants from sunlight and stored in wood, coal, or petroleum, which directly or indirectly are plant products.

The green plant has been aptly called the great *"converter of solar energy."* This process of energy conversion by green plants is called **photosynthesis** (Greek, *photos,* light, and *synthesis,* putting together). One of the striking characteristics of a green plant is the continuous accumulation within it of **organic compounds** (sugars, fats, proteins, etc.). These compounds are not absorbed from outside the plant but are built up within the plant out of simple inorganic compounds, such as water, carbon dioxide, and various mineral salts derived from the soil or air. One of the steps in this process is photosynthesis. We shall see that nongreen plants (bacteria, fungi, and a relatively few flowering plants) absorb organic compounds (their foods) directly.

The dominant color in the plant world is green. The green color in most plants is due to a mixture of two pigments— **chlorophyll a** and **chlorophyll b.** Most of the chlorophyll of ordinary plants is in leaves, although young stems and young fruits may also possess chlorophyll. Except in a few lower forms of plants, chlorophyll is localized in **plastids**—specialized parts of the cytoplasm. The energy-converting process takes place within those plastids that possess chlorophyll. Green plastids are called **chloroplasts.** The chloroplast is in reality the food laboratory of the world. Thus photosynthesis is a primary function of the leaf. In other words, most of the carbohydrates required by the plant are manufactured in leaves.

Another important leaf activity is **transpiration**—the loss of water as vapor. The form and anatomy of the leaf are such that it is peculiarly adapted to carry on the two primary functions of photosynthesis and transpiration. The blade provides a large surface for the absorption of light energy and carbon dioxide needed in photosynthesis; it is thin, and hence none of the cells lie far from the surface. These characters facilitate the absorption of light, carbon dioxide, and oxygen by the cells inside the leaf, and also the outgo of gases, including water vapor, oxygen, and carbon dioxide from the cells inside the leaf. Moreover, the soft tissues of the leaf are strengthened by the veins, which also carry water, mineral salts, and foods.

Man utilizes commercially the leaves of a great variety of plants. Vegetables grown for their leaves include spinach, lettuce, cabbage, kale, rhubarb, celery, and endive. The leaves of certain plants are aromatic and are used for flavoring; among such are peppermint, sage, spearmint, parsley, and others. Fully one-half of the population of the world uses tea, a caffeine beverage made from the dried leaves of *Thea sinensis*. Maté or Paraguay tea, a drink of many millions of South Americans, is made from the leaves of several species of holly (*Ilex* species). A number of important drugs are derived from the leaves of *Aloe, Atropa belladonna* (belladonna), *Erythroxylon coca* (cocaine), *Digitalis purpurea* (digitalis), and *Datura stramonium* (stramonium). The leaves of a few plants yield commercial quantities of textile fibers; among such are Manila hemp, sisal, Mauritius hemp, and New Zealand hemp. Important dyestuffs, such as indigo, chlorophyll, henna, and woad, are secured from leaves. And the leaves of *Nicotiana tabacum* supply the tobacco of commerce.

EXTERNAL MORPHOLOGY OF THE FOLIAGE LEAF

Leaves are varied as to their arrangement on the stem, their form, the distribution of their veins (venation), their structure, and many other characters. Leaf characters are used extensively in the description of species. It is often possible to distinguish certain species of the same genus by a glance at the leaves. For example, in Fig. 8.1, note the marked differences in the leaves of several common species of *Populus*. On the

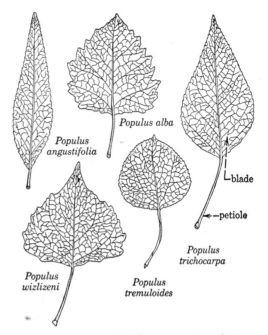

Fig. 8.1. Leaves of different species of *Populus*. Leaf characters alone often enable one to identify a species.

other hand, plants distantly related may have leaves that are quite similar. Thus, reliance cannot usually be placed on leaf characters alone in identifying plants. As a rule, a combination of plant characters needs to be taken into consideration.

Dicotyledonous Leaves

The leaves of dicotyledons are generally distinctly different from those of monocotyledons. A typical foliage leaf of a plant belonging to the dicotyledons is composed of two principal parts: (1) blade or lamina and (2) petiole or stalk (Fig. 8.2). The blade is thin and expanded, the petiole slender. The thin blade is supported by the very distinct network of veins which are composed of vascular tissues and fibers or collenchyma. The veins collect at the base of the leaf into several strands and passing through the petiole join the leaf blade with all parts of the plant. In addition to thus forming a supporting framework for the softer tissues of the blade they carry water and mineral salts and food to and from the leaf.

Venation. The arrangement of the veins of a leaf is called **venation**. There are two principal types of venation: (1) **parallel venation,** characteristic of monocotyle-

donous leaves (Fig. 8.3A, B) and **netted venation** characteristic of dicotyledonous leaves (Fig. 8.3C, D). In this latter case there are one or more prominent veins from which the smaller veins branch off, to join with other small veins, thus forming a conspicuous net. When there is a single midrib from which branches diverge like the pinnae of a feather, the leaf is **pinnately netted-veined** (Fig. 8.2A). When several

Fig. 8.2. Different kinds of leaves. A, poplar (*Populus deltoides*); B, castor bean (*Ricinus communis*); C, oak (*Quercus lobata*); D, rose (*Rosa odorata*); E, Virginia creeper (*Parthenocissus quinquefolia*); F, Zinnia. $\times \frac{1}{2}$.

Fig. 8.3. Leaves to show parallel and netted venation. A, Canna leaf about $\frac{1}{5}$ natural size; B, portion of similar leaf about 16 times; C, maple (Acer) leaf about $\frac{1}{2}$ natural size; D, portion of similar leaf about 16 times.

principal veins diverge from the base of the blade, each of which branches, the leaf is **palmately netted-veined** (Fig. 8.2*B*).

Parallel venation, characteristic of mono-cotyledons, is discussed below.

The Blade. The chief variable features of the leaf blade are its overall shape, its apex, its margin, and its base. This range of variation is great and many terms are employed by taxonomists to describe leaf shape accurately. A few of these terms are given below; those starred are illustrated in Figs. 8.2 and 8.3.

Shape. The leaf may be long and slender * (linear), or oval,* or heart-shaped (cordate), or triangular * (del-toid).

Apex. The apex of a leaf may be pointed,* rounded, or flattened.

Margin. The margin may be entire,* that is, with no indentations whatsoever; the margin may be toothed,* or scalloped,* or wavy,* or cut into a number of lobes.* The marginal indentations may be shallow, or they may be deep clefts extending almost to the midrib. Lobed leaves that are pin-nately veined are said to be pinnately lobed (Fig. 8.2*C*); those that are palmately veined are palmately lobed (Fig. 8.2*B*).

Base. The base of the leaf may be rounded,* heart-shaped (cordate), or flat-tened * (truncate).

The Petiole. Some leaves, as those of peas, beans, roses, tulip-trees, and many others, have two small, leaflike outgrowths at the base of the petiole, known as **stipules** (Fig. 8.2*D*). The petiole itself may be long or short, rounded, or occasionally flat. It is usually attached to the base of the leaf, but in some plants, such as nasturtium and castor beans, it is attached, not to the edge of the leaf, but to its underside. This leaf is called a **peltate** leaf (Fig. 8.2*B*). The petiole is sometimes absent, as in *Zinnia,*

the blade being mounted directly on the stem. Such a leaf is said to be **sessile** (Fig. 8.2*F*).

Simple and Compound Leaves. As to configuration of the blade, there are two kinds of leaves: (1) **simple** and (2) **com-pound.** A simple leaf is one in which the blade is all in one piece (Figs. 8.1, 8.2*A, B, C*). A compound leaf is one in which the blade is composed of a number of separate leaflike parts, the **leaflets** (Fig. 8.2*D, E*). Inasmuch as leaflets have the characteristics of a simple leaf, one may be in doubt at times as to whether the structure is a simple leaf or a leaflet, especially if the leaflets are large. The distinctions are as follows: (1) buds occur in the axils of leaves, not in the axils of leaflets; (2) leaves stand in different planes on the stem, whereas leaf-lets lie in a single plane; (3) in trees and shrubs that shed their leaves, the leaf as a whole usually falls, being cut off at the base of the petiole, whereas leaflets seldom fall separately. Since individual leaflets pos-sess, in common with simple leaves, apices, margins, bases and shapes, the leaflets may be described in the same terms used to describe the simple leaves.

When the leaflets of a compound leaf arise from the **rachis** (continuation of the petiole), as do the pinnae of a feather, the leaf is said to be **pinnately compound,** sweet pea and rose (Fig. 8.2*D*); when the leaflets diverge from a common point at the tip of the petiole, the leaf is said to be **palmately compound,** horsechestnut and Virginia creeper (Fig. 8.2*E*). Compound leaves may be once, twice, or thrice compound.

Monocotyledonous Leaves

The leaves of members of this subclass generally have parallel veins, corn and canna (Fig. 8.3*A, B*). As contrasted with netted venation, the veins in leaves with parallel venation are all of about equal size, usually very numerous, and all parallel with each other. They are sparsely joined by inconspicuous cross veinlets. In many monocotyledonous leaves the veins run from the base to the apex of the leaf; in other monocotyledonous leaves they extend from a prominent midrib outward to the margin; they quite generally join at the leaf margin.

Leaves of the monocotyledons show as great a diversity of form as do those of the dicotyledons. In onions they are tubular, in palms they are large and fanlike. The grasses have a very characteristic type of leaf. Corn and crabgrass (Fig. 8.4) may be taken as examples. The grass leaf is divided into two parts, the **sheath** and the **blade**. The blade is the typical thin expanded portion. The sheath is green, perhaps nearly as large as the blade, but it is not a flat expanded structure. Instead it completely sheaths the stem, extending in many species, corn (Fig. 8.4B) for example, over at least one complete internode. In crabgrass (Fig. 8.4A) the sheath covers only about one-half of an internode. If the region of union between the blade and the sheath be examined carefully a small flap of delicate tissue extending upward from the sheath may be seen, closely investing the stem. This is called the **ligule** (Fig. 8.4B). It may, in some cases, serve to keep water and dirt from sifting down between the stem and the sheath. In many species, of which barley (Fig. 8.4C) is a good example, the base of the blade, at its union with the sheath, is carried around the stem in two earlike points. These points are called **auricles**. Ligule and auricles may both be present or one or the other may

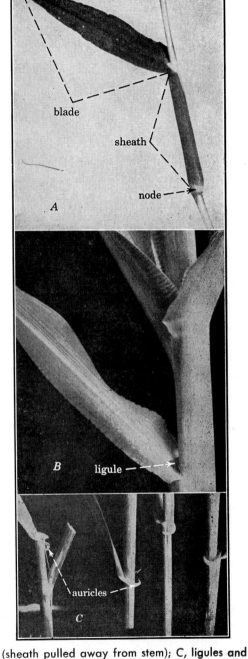

Fig. 8.4. Leaves of various members of the grass family. A, crabgrass showing sheath and blade; B, corn (*Zea mays*) showing ligules (sheath pulled away from stem); C, ligules and auricles of barley (*Hordeum vulgare*). ✕ ½.

**Table 8.1. Ligules and Auricles in Several
Important Grasses**

Grass	Ligule	Auricle
Corn	+	−
Zea mays		
Rice	+	+
Oryza sativa		
Barley	+	+
Hordeum vulgare		
Oat	+	−
Avena sativa		
Wheat	+	+
Triticum vulgare		
Watergrass	−	−
Echinochloa crusgalli		

be absent. The situation is given for several important grasses in Table 8.1. These characters may be used to identify some grains in their seedling stage.

Gymnosperm Leaves

The leaves of all gymnosperms native to the United States and Europe are either needle- (Fig. 24.19) or scalelike (Fig. 24.26). The Ginkgo tree, a primitive gymnosperm, native to China, has broad leaves that are deciduous (Fig. 24.17). The leaves of many gymnosperms from the Southern Hemisphere have expanded blades.

ANATOMY OF THE FOLIAGE LEAF

The anatomy of a leaf blade is best shown in a cross section (Figs. 8.5, 8.6A). In these figures we observe three principal tissues: (1) **epidermis**, (2) **mesophyll** (middle of leaf), and (3) **veins** or **vascular bundles**. The **epidermis** usually consists of a single layer of cells that covers the entire leaf surface. It protects the tissues within from drying out and from mechanical injury. The **mesophyll** is composed of parenchyma cells, most or all of

which contain chlorophyll and thus are able to carry on photosynthesis. The **veins** possess xylem and phloem elements and hence conduct water, inorganic salts, and foods. Fibers and collenchyma may be associated with the conducting elements of the midrib and larger lateral veins.

The **petiole** has its own specialized structures enabling it to support the leaf blade, to conduct food, water, and inorganic salts, and to disconnect itself from the stem at the close of the growing season without exposing living stem tissue to drying out or to infection.

Let us now consider each of these regions in detail.

The Epidermis

The epidermis covers the entire surface of the leaf and is continuous with that of the stem to which the leaf is attached. In most leaves, the epidermis is a single layer of cells. It may consist of several kinds of cells: (1) **ordinary epidermal cells**, (2) **guard cells**, (3) **hair cells**, (4) **glandular cells**. The ordinary epidermal cells show a variety of shapes depending upon the species. One form is shown in Fig. 8.7A.

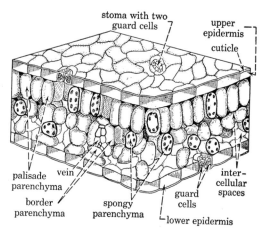

Fig. 8.5. Three dimensional diagram of a section of a foliage leaf. ×35.

They are similar in shape to an irregular pavement block, whose depth is usually less than its breadth or length.

Guard Cells. Guard cells occur in pairs, and each is crescent-shaped or semicircular in form, as seen in surface view (Fig. 8.7*B*). Chloroplasts occur in guard cells but are lacking in ordinary epidermal cells. Both kinds of epidermal cells have long-lived protoplasts. The outer wall of epidermal cells, including guard cells, has a cuticle (Figs. 8.5, 8.7*B*) like that of the epidermis of stems. It is effective in limiting the movement, either inward or outward, of water vapor and other gases. The cuticle is usually thicker on the upperside of the leaf than on the underside.

A guard cell is a special type of epidermal cell. Guard cells occur in pairs, and between them is an opening or pore. This opening is called a **stoma** (plural, **stomata**) (Fig. 8.7). The stomata are the only openings in the leaf epidermis, and it is chiefly through them that gases pass into or out of the leaf. Although the cuticle is nearly impermeable to gases, small amounts of gases pass directly through the outer wall and the cuticle of epidermal cells.

Stomata vary considerably in size in different species of plants, and even on any one plant. Some representative measurements in microns * are as follows (length $\times$ breadth): bean, 7×3; geranium, 19×12; corn, 19×5; oat, 38×8; sunflower, 22×8. The number of stomata per unit area varies widely, depending upon the species of plant and the environmental conditions under which it is growing. Usually more stomata are on the lower surface than on the upper. Table 8.2 gives the average number of stomata per square centimeter on the upper and lower surfaces of some common plants.

* A micron is 1/1000 millimeter. Since there are about 25 millimeters in an inch, 1 micron equals about 1/25,000 inch.

Table 8.2

Average Number of Stomata
Per Square Centimeter

Name of Plant	Upper Epidermis	Lower Epidermis
Alfalfa	16,900	13,800
Apple	0	29,400
Bean	4,000	28,100
Cabbage	14,100	22,600
Corn	5,200	6,800
English oak	0	45,000
Nasturtium	0	13,000
Oat	2,500	2,300
Potato	5,100	16,100
Tomato	1,200	13,000

Opening and Closing of Stomata. Stomata may open and close, and thus they tend to regulate the entrance and exit of gases. Usually stomata are open when the **turgor** of guard cells is greater than that of adjacent epidermal cells and are closed when the turgor of guard cells is less than that of adjoining epidermal cells. Changes occur in the osmotic pressure of guard cells, usually making it higher during daylight than at night. On the other hand, other epidermal cells do not manifest these diurnal changes. When the cell sap in the guard cells has a greater osmotic pressure or concentration than that in adjoining epidermal cells, and hence the diffusion pressure of water in guard cells is less than in epidermal cells, water moves from adjacent cells into the guard cells. The guard cells swell, the turgor increases, and the stomatal aperture enlarges. When the osmotic pressure of the cell sap in the guard cells decreases, they lose their turgor and the stomatal aperture diminishes in size.

Let us inquire now as to the conditions that cause an increase or decrease in the osmotic pressure of the sap of guard cells. Guard cells may contain starch in chloroplasts and sugar dissolved in the cell sap. When the starch content is high, the sugar

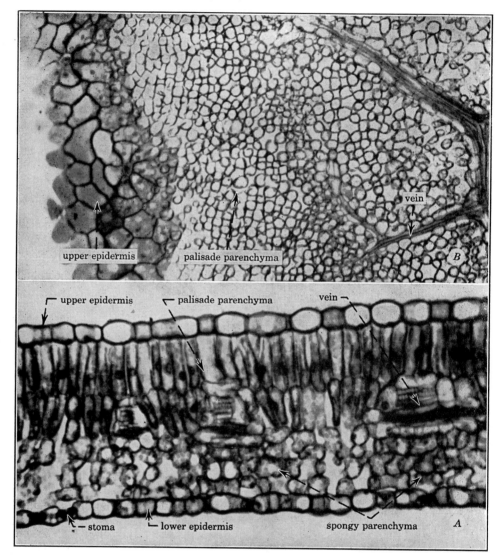

Fig. 8.6. Photomicrograph of sections of a *Syringa* leaf. A, cross section of leaf; B, section cut parallel to surface of leaf (completed on opposite page). ×75. (Slides courtesy of Triarch Products.)

content is low; when the starch content, because of its conversion to sugar, is low, the sugar content of the cell sap is relatively high. The changes of starch to sugar and sugar to starch result from the action of cellular enzymes. When the concentration of sugar in the cell sap in guard cells increases, as it usually does during the

daytime, the osmotic pressure of their sap *increases,* water diffuses *in* from adjacent cells, turgor pressure of guard cells *increases,* and the stoma *opens.* On the other hand, when the concentration of sugar in the cell sap in guard cells *decreases,* owing to its transformation to starch in guard cell chloroplasts or its diffusion into adjacent

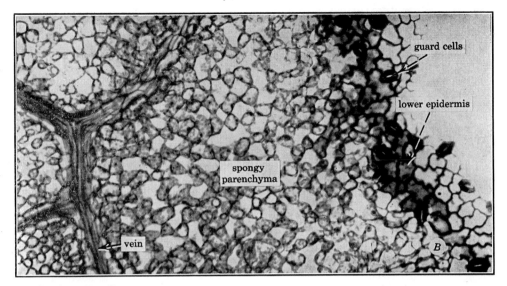

Fig. 8.6 (continued).

cells, as usually occurs during *nighttime,* the osmotic pressure of guard cells *decreases,* movement of water is *from* guard cells to adjoining cells, the turgor pressure of guard cells *lessens,* and the stoma closes.

Studies have shown that the changes within guard cells that seem to control their change in shape are affected by light, temperature, and relative humidity. In most instances, these investigations have analyzed the separate effects of these three factors, whereas it is important to know their interrelations. Of the various theories that have been offered to explain how environmental factors affect guard-cell movements, the one briefly given in the foregoing paragraphs is probably most widely accepted. This theory, it will be noted, lays stress on enzyme activities in guard cells, which in turn modify osmotic values in these cells, thus changing their turgor pressure and causing movement. Other theories propose that light, temperature, and relative humidity influence guard-cell movement, chiefly as a result of their direct effect on the permeability of the cell membranes of these cells. And still other the-

ories emphasize the influence of external factors upon the hydration of the colloidal materials in the guard cells. A detailed discussion of these theories is out of place in this book.

From Fig. 8.7B it is seen that in certain plants the wall of a guard cell next to the stoma is thicker than the opposite wall, that is, the one farthest from the stoma. The thinner wall has greater elasticity. When the guard cells become turgid the thinner wall of each cell bulges, *drawing with it* the wall adjacent to the stoma, with the result that the stomatal aperture widens.

Epidermal Hairs. Several different types of hairs grow out from the epidermis of leaves. They resemble those from the epidermis of stems. They may be unicellular or multicellular, simple or branched, scale-like or glandular. The unicellular hair is the simplest kind. It may be an extension of an epidermal cell, or it may be provided with a basal cross wall. Unicellular hairs are sometimes branched. Multicellular hairs may consist of a single row of cells, or they may be branched. Glandular hairs bear at the upper end a single large cell

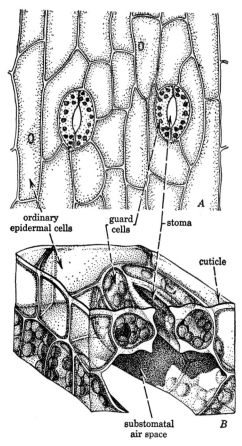

ordinary   guard
epidermal cells   cells — stoma

                                                    cuticle

                                         A

                          substomatal   B
                          air space

Fig. 8.7. Epidermal cells of leaf. A, lower surface, ×60; B, diagram showing surface view and cross section, ×150. (B redrawn from Holman and Robbins, A Textbook of General Botany, John Wiley & Sons, Inc.)

or a group of cells; such cells excrete ethereal oils. The excretion from glandular hairs often imparts a stickiness to leaves.

The Mesophyll

The mesophyll is the photosynthetic tissue between the upper and lower epidermal layers. It is parenchyma tissue, traversed by veins. The chloroplasts are present in the mesophyll cells, which may be divided in two distinct layers: **palisade parenchyma** and **spongy parenchyma** (Figs. 8.5. 8.6A).

The palisade parenchyma is adjacent to the upper epidermis and usually consists of from one to several layers of narrow cells with their long axes at right angles to the leaf surface. The spongy parenchyma extends from the palisade parenchyma to the lower epidermis. Cells of the spongy parenchyma are irregular in shape and loosely arranged. Large air spaces, or stomatal chambers, are generally present above each stoma.

A section cut obliquely through the leaf shows essentially cross sections of the leaf tissues. Such a view is given in Fig. 8.6B. The cells of the upper epidermis may be seen to the left (page 162) with the cuticle at the extreme edge of the section. The palisade parenchyma cells in this section have a circular outline and fit together very loosely. The impression one obtains indicates a greater amount of air space in the palisade tissue than is apparent in the cross section of leaf. The anastomosing veins with their occasional endings are very apparent. The palisade parenchyma is in general found above the veins and the spongy parenchyma below them. Note also that in this plane the cells of the spongy parenchyma fit together so as to form an open network. The lower epidermis is at the right of the section (page 163) and guard cells may be seen within it.

Intercellular spaces are prominently developed in the mesophyll but are much larger in the spongy parenchyma than in the palisade parenchyma. The air spaces between cells of the mesophyll are interconnecting, and many cells are in contact with an intercellular space. Thus, most food-making cells have free access to carbon dioxide and oxygen.

Veins of the Leaf

The veins or vascular bundles form a network extending throughout the leaf. The conducting elements are xylem and phloem and sometimes associated with these are fibers and collenchyma. Hence, veins conduct water, mineral salts, and foods and also mechanically support the mesophyll tissue. In addition to the midrib and larger lateral veins that are visible to the naked eye, innumerable minute branch veins occur that can be seen only with the aid of a microscope. The large veins contain vessels, tracheids, sieve tubes, and companion cells and also some mechanical tissue (Fig. 8.8). Such veins may have both primary and secondary vascular elements. The smaller veins have few vascular elements and little or no mechanical elements. The very end of a vein is usually a single tracheid of the spiral type (Fig. 8.9C). The free ends of veinlets are usually surrounded by one or more layers of parenchyma cells, **border parenchyma,** which may or may not possess

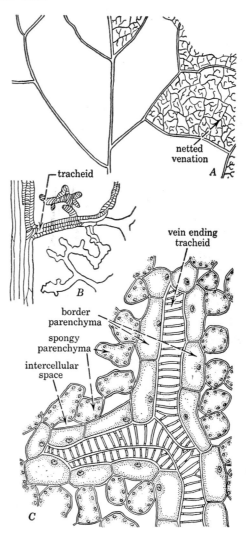

Fig. 8.9. Venation. A, portion of "skeletonized leaf"; B, portion of vein system; C, veinlets and adjacent mesophyll parenchyma.

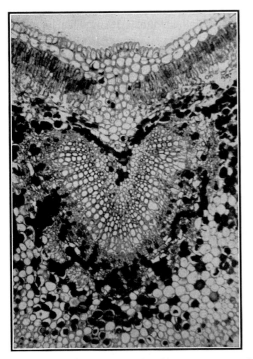

Fig. 8.8. Photomicrograph of cross section of midrib of *Photinia* leaf. ×50.

chloroplasts. Through these cells, water and solutes must pass from the conducting elements of the veinlet to cells with chloroplasts. The smallest veinlet has an unbroken connection with the vascular elements of the midrib, the petiole, and the stem to which the leaf is connected.

In larger veins that have both xylem and phloem elements, the xylem is toward

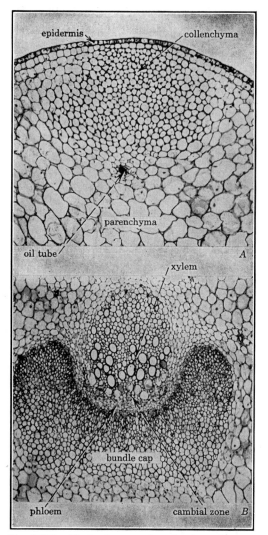

Fig. 8.10. Photomicrographs of celery (*Apium graveolens*) petiole. A, outer tissues; B, vascular bundle (vein). ×50. (Courtesy of Esau.)

(and leaf blade) and xylem on the upperside. One or more vascular bundles are embedded in parenchyma. Fibers may be associated with the vascular tissues of the bundles, and not infrequently groups of collenchyma cells occur beneath the epidermis (Fig. 8.10A).

LEAF FALL

The separation of plant parts from a parent plant is a normal, continually occurring phenomenon. Leaves fall, fruits drop, flower parts wither and fall away, even branch tips or whole branches may be separated normally from the parent plant. The autumn fall of leaves from woody dicotyledons is the most common example of this. In practically all cases separation or **abscission** is the result of the formation of definite, specialized cell layers, known as the **abscission zone,** at, or close to, the base of the petiole (Fig. 8.11). In some instances the abscission zone is formed early in the development of the leaf; in other species it does not appear until the leaf is fully developed. The parenchyma cells comprising the abscission layer may be smaller and lack the lignin which may occur in significant amounts in the cells of adjacent tissues. Even the vascular elements may be shorter and fibers absent from the bundle in the abscission zone. These anatomical features definitely make this zone an area of weakness.

Previous to leaf fall changes may normally occur in the zone. Cell divisions, though apparently not necessary, frequently take place. When they do occur, a layer of brick-shaped cells is formed across the petiole. Actual separation of the leaf may be brought about in a number of ways. In some species the middle lamella is dissolved away and the cells simply fall apart. In other plants, the cells themselves are dissolved and thus the separation is affected.

the upper surface of the leaf, the phloem toward the lower surface (Fig. 8.8).

The Petiole or Leaf Stalk

In the vascular tissue of the petiole, the phloem and xylem maintain their relative positions, as in the stem (Fig. 8.10B); thus, phloem is on the underside of the petiole

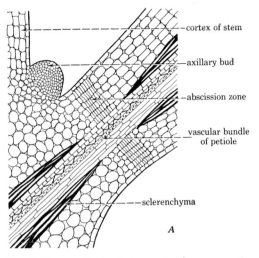

Fig. 8.11. Leaf abscission. A, diagrammatic; B and C, photomicrographs of cotton (*Gossypium*) petioles from leaves treated with 2,4-D; B, abscission layer still intact; C, abscission layer parting. ×10. (A courtesy of Addicott; B and C courtesy of Hall.)

In a third small group of plants a layer of cork forms across the petiole so that the leaf simply withers in place and is blown away. If a cork layer has not formed previous to leaf fall it develops immediately afterward. Furthermore, the vessels are likely to become plugged with tyloses or gums. Thus the fall of a leaf does not leave an open wound, or point of entrance for organisms that might cause disease.

The function of the abscission zone is two-fold: (1) to bring about the fall of the leaf or other plant part, and (2) to protect the region of the stem from which the leaf has fallen against insect damage or rot caused by lower plants.

The development of the abscission zone can be controlled in some plants, and is of importance in some types of agriculture. Certain hormones may retard, others accelerate, the development of the zone. Indoleacetic acid or 2,4-D will inhibit or delay its development. Used in the correct manner, these substances will prevent the premature drop of apples. Cotton can be picked mechanically only after the leaves have been removed. This may be done by a number of defoliants. In cotton (Fig. 8.11B, C) the abscission zone slowly develops from the lower side of the petiole toward the top. It appears to cut across the vascular bundles so that when completed the leaf hangs by a thin strip of tissue at the top of the petiole. Certain defoliants stimulate this development and bring about the early fall of the cotton leaves.

DEVELOPMENT OF THE LEAF

When a leaf bud opens in the spring, the very young leaves have the general shape characteristics of the adult leaf. Growth is very rapid; in fact, within 10 or 12 days they may have attained their adult size.

Reference to Fig. 8.12 shows that the leaf originates from the outer layers of cells at the side of the shoot tip. During the very early stages of differentiation a leaf consists entirely of actively dividing meristematic cells. Soon a central procambium strand is differentiated, which becomes the midrib. Then a row of epidermal and subepidermal cells on each side of the strand becomes active; these cells constitute a marginal meristem, which gives rise to the leaf blade. True apical growth is of short duration in the leaves of most angiosperms; growth in length is largely the result of cell divisions and enlargements between the base and the apex. The tip of most leaves matures first, and usually there is a decrease in the age of cells from the tip to the base. Cell division ceases first in the epidermis, next

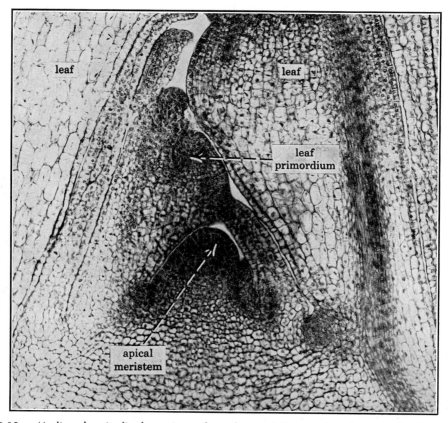

Fig. 8.12. Median longitudinal section of a shoot of *Ranunculus* showing development of leaves. ×100. (Courtesy of Tepfer.)

in the spongy parenchyma, and last in the palisade parenchyma. Epidermal cells, however, continue to increase in size for some time after enlargement of mesophyll cells has ceased. Lateral veins, both large and small, originate in the middle of the young leaf from procambium strands.

In grasses and other monocotyledonous plants, cells at the base of the leaf remain meristematic for a long period and growth in length is due to activity of these cells. The upper portion of the leaf may there-fore be removed without permanent injury to the leaf as a whole. This fact is well shown in the rapid recovery of the leaves of lawn grass after mowing, and of pasture grasses after grazing.

SPECIAL TYPES OF LEAVES

In the foregoing pages we have discussed **foliage leaves,** which are the ordinary kind with which we are familiar. The two prin-

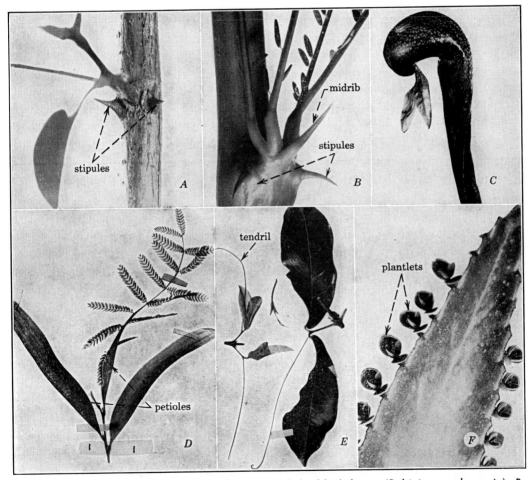

Fig. 8.13. Leaf modifications. A, stipular spines of the black locust (*Robinia pseudoacacia*); B, spines from stipules and midrib in *Parkinsonia;* C, insect-capturing leaf of *Darlingtonia;* D, modified petioles of *Acacia;* E, tendrils from leaflets of *Bignonia;* F, plantlets on leaf of *Bryophyllum.* Between ×¼ to ×1.

cipal functions of foliage leaves are photosynthesis and transpiration. There are special types of leaves, so different in form and structure from the foliage type that we scarcely recognize them as leaves at all. These highly **modified leaves** may be bud scales, spines, tendrils, thick and fleshy storage organs, or peculiar and fantastic structures that are adapted for catching insects.

Why are these structures considered leaves? (1) They arise in regular order at nodes on the stem; (2) they may bear buds in the axil; and (3) they have the essential structure of leaves.

Bud scales have been described (page 86). These scale leaves are short, thick, sessile, often covered with dense hairs on the outer surface, and sometimes waxy or resinous. When present, they protect the delicate meristematic tissue of the shoot tip, and the rudimentary leaves, from drying out.

The **spines** of various species of cacti and those of the *Fouquiera* represent entire transformed leaves. In the black locust (Fig. 8.13A) the stipules are spines and in *Parkinsonia* the stipules and midrib are spines.

In some species of *Lathyrus*, the **tendrils** are transformed leaflets; in others, the whole leaf is transformed into a single tendril and leaflike stipules perform the normal functions of the leaves. In *Bignonia carpreolata* the third leaflet is transformed into a tendril (Fig. 8.13E). Tendrils, whether they be leaf tendrils or stem tendrils, serve to attach the plant to a support. In certain species of *Acacia,* the petiole is leaflike (Fig. 8.13D).

Leaves are sometimes modified as food or water **storage organs.** The thick, fleshy

Fig. 8.14. Sundew (*Drosera*). ×1. (Courtesy of P. Jones.)

bases of leaves that make up much of the onion bulb (Fig. 6.54) accumulate large quantities of food. The so-called "succulents" of deserts and of saline soils have thick, fleshy leaves with special water-storage tissue. This tissue consists of large, parenchyma cells that usually lack chloroplasts. During the short period when water is available, water accumulates in the special storage tissue, and the plant draws upon it during periods of drought. Examples of plants bearing water-storing leaves are stonecrop (*Sedum*), species of *Mesembryanthemum*, Russian thistle, *Sempervivum*, and *Bryophyllum*.

A striking adaptation of leaves to a special function occurs in the so-called **insectivorous plants.** In these plants the leaves have taken on forms and various structural features that enable them to capture insects and obtain food from their bodies. The best-known insectivorous plants are the Venus's-flytrap (*Dionaea muscipula*) (Plate II, Chapter 15); sundew (*Drosera*) (Fig. 8.14); pitcher plants (*Nepenthes, Sarracenia,* and *Darlingtonia*) (Fig. 8.13C); and bladderwort (*Utricularia*) (Fig. 8.15).

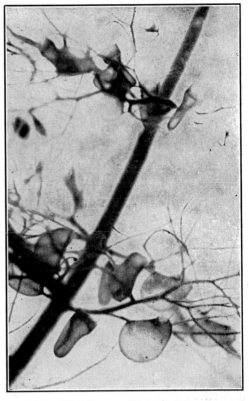

Fig. 8.15. Bladderwort (*Utricularia*), an aquatic insectivorous plant. Insects are trapped in the modified bladder leaves. ×6.

Leaves generally do not function effectively in vegetative reproduction. However, African violets are regularly reproduced vegetatively by placing leaves in moist sand. In certain species of *Bryophyllum* (Fig. 18.13F) patches of tissue in notches along the leaf margins remain meristematic. In time this tissue will develop small new plants while the parent leaf is still active. The little plants eventually drop from the leaf to the ground where under favorable conditions they may develop into new individuals.

9

Soil and Mineral Nutrition

We have been studying the morphology of seed plants: the structure of their organs, tissues, and cells. With this knowledge to help us, we are now ready to consider in more detail the physiology of the plant, how the various parts function together in the processes of absorption, conduction, transpiration, photosynthesis, and respiration.

SOIL—THE ENVIRONMENT OF ROOTS

Soil is the natural medium in which the roots of most plants grow. From the soil the plant absorbs the water and solutes necessary for its continued well being. If a soil is fertile, it contains in a readily available form all the chemical elements essential for plant growth. It is through the soil that the agriculturist can effectively alter the environment of the roots and thus control plant growth, at least partially. The time and method of fertilizer application, the kind of fertilizers used, cultivation and irrigation practices are all directed toward increasing the production of plant products through the effects that these practices have on the soil and root relationships and ultimately on the growth and development of the plant. There are many kinds of soils and many different soil conditions. The character of the natural plant covering and the behavior of crops depend upon soil conditions as well as upon climatic conditions. Environmental factors that operate through the soil are called **edaphic factors;** those that act upon the plant through the atmosphere are called **climatic factors.**

The soil is a complex system. Its components are (1) **mineral (inorganic) matter,** (2) **organic matter,** (3) **soil water and its dissolved substances,** (4) **soil air,** and (5) **soil organisms.** Also to be considered is the factor of **soil temperature.**

Mineral Matter of the Soil

The mineral matter is derived from fragmented rock. The kind of parent rock (granite, feldspar, sandstone, limestone, shale, etc.) and the degree of weathering determines the nature of the mineral or inorganic components of the soil. Some phosphorus and sulfur, and most of the nitrogen, come from organic sources during the process of decay.

In referring to the size of the mineral fractions of a soil, it is customary to speak of **coarse sand, fine sand, silt,** and **clay.**

Table 9.1. Classification of Soil Mineral Matter According to Size of Particles

Type of Particles	Range in Diameter of Soil Particles in Millimeters
Coarse sand	2.0 –0.2
Fine sand	0.2 –0.02
Silt	0.02–0.002
Clay	0.002 and smaller

The size of soil particles decreases in the order given (Table 9.1). The smallest particles, clay, are of colloidal dimensions.

From the standpoint of plants, an important difference among these four types of soil is their **water-holding capacity.** It is greatest in clay, least in coarse sand. If water is applied to a soil in the field the spaces between the soil particles (**pore spaces**) become filled only for a short time to the depth wetted. With drainage the water begins to move downward under the influence of gravity. After a while this movement downward stops; the soil particles hold a certain amount of water against the pull of gravity. The amount of water held by the soil after drainage is called the **field capacity** of that soil. When a soil is at field capacity, or even at a moisture content well below this amount, a film of water completely surrounds each soil particle, and, also, water exists in the form of wedges between the soil particles. Clay particles in the soil constitute a colloidal system, and such particles hold water by imbibition. Water imbibed by soil particles is much more difficult to remove from the soil than that which exists as a film or as wedges. Water is held less tenaciously by sand and silt soils than it is by clay soils. It percolates downward the most rapidly in sandy soil, the least rapidly in clay soil; and it is raised much higher by capillarity in clay soil than in sandy soil but rises more rapidly in the latter.

In general, soils are not entirely sand or silt or clay but contain each of these components in different amounts. Such mixtures are called **loams.** Depending upon the relative amounts of each component, we speak of clay, clay loam, silt loam, loam, sandy loam, loamy sand, and sand according to the relative amounts of clay, silt, and sand that the soils contain (Table 9.2). Soil texture and the suitability of a soil for plant growth are greatly influenced by its sand, silt, and clay content.

Organic Matter of the Soil

The organic matter of the soil is derived from plants and animals. Through the centuries of soil formation, the plants and animals that lived in and on the soil have left their residues. Annual herbs die each year; the whole plant, including the roots and tops, contributes to the organic matter of the soil. Also, trees and shrubs shed their leaves, twigs, bark, and fruits, and roots die. All this plant material decomposes, and thus, with unimportant exceptions, soils are a mixture of mineral matter and organic matter, the latter in various stages of decomposition.

We might be led to believe that during the centuries the organic material in the soil would gradually increase. This material, however, is continually decomposing, owing principally to the activity of bacteria and fungi. Cultivation hastens the loss of organic matter from a soil by increasing aeration.

Table 9.2. Composition of Three Soils According to the Size of the Mineral Particles

Soil Type	Coarse Sand %	Fine Sand %	Silt %	Clay %
A sandy loam	67	18	6	9
A loam	27	30	20	19
A clay	1	7	21	66

It is generally conceded that soils for crop growth should have considerable organic matter. Those soils naturally low in organic residues may be improved by adding barnyard manure, or other organic fertilizers, or by plowing under green manure crops. Organic matter improves the physical condition of most soils, especially those with much clay. It makes them easier to cultivate, and it may increase slightly their field capacity but may not increase the amount of water the plant is able to extract from the soil. The gradual decomposition of organic matter in the soil continually liberates mineral elements that are essential for plant growth. Sulfur, phosphorus, and nitrogen are among the most important elements thus liberated in forms available for plant growth.

In most upland soils, the organic matter constitutes from 2 to 5 per cent of the soil and inorganic matter from 95 to 98 per cent. In bogs, marshes, and swamps, on the other hand, the organic matter may be 80 per cent or more of the total.

Soil Water and Its Dissolved Substances

The soil is a reservoir of water. The water holds in solution various inorganic salts (nitrates, phosphates, sulfates, etc.) and other water-soluble substances. The composition and concentration of this solution is ever-changing, depending upon the higher plants and the microorganisms growing on and in the soil. All substances that enter the plant must be in solution. This makes possible their passage through the cell wall and the cytoplasmic membranes of root hairs. In most agricultural soils, the soil solution has a very low concentration—usually lower than that of the cell sap. As long as this relationship maintains, water will diffuse inward.

In the soil, nutrient elements may exist in a relatively unavailable form. For example, most organic nitrogen compounds are not available as such to crop plants; that is, nitrogen in the form of either plant or animal proteins cannot be utilized directly by green plants. However, these organic compounds are acted upon by soil organisms, and some of the products of decomposition do become directly available, usually as inorganic nutrients of green plants. Organic sulfur compounds are also broken down by living organisms to inorganic compounds. In general, it can be said of soils that at all times chemical changes are taking place which set free inorganic nutrient substances that will dissolve in soil water and thus assume a form that will diffuse into the roots.

The soil solution is usually very dilute. In this state, a large part of the soluble inorganic compounds are present as ions. For example, sodium nitrate, $NaNO_3$, exists as Na^+ and NO_3^- ions.

The soil particles themselves, particularly the finely divided clay and organic matter, act as giant negatively charged ions surrounded by an atmosphere of positively charged ions. Thus the colloidal soil particles, while not in solution themselves, serve as reservoirs to which many of the various ions essential for plant growth are attached and from which these ions may be released into solution.

Negatively charged ions such as nitrate, NO_3^- and sulfate, SO_4^{--}, are not held by the soil particles but are in solution. Phosphate, PO_4^{---}, presents a different picture in that these ions enter into the composition of certain clays and do not usually exist in high concentrations in soil solution.

Air of the Soil

We have spoken of the pore space in soils. The air of the soil contains the same gases as the atmosphere above the soil. The relative proportions of these gases in the soil air, however, may be somewhat different from those in the atmosphere. The air of the soil is considerably richer in carbon dioxide and poorer in oxygen than that of the atmosphere. In the latter, the average percentage by volume of carbon dioxide is .03 per cent; in soil air the percentage may go as high as 5 per cent. This high percentage of carbon dioxide in soil air is due to the respiration of soil bacteria and fungi and, to a lesser degree, the respiration of roots themselves. The soil air usually has a relative humidity near 100 per cent, a condition very favorable to the growth of soil organisms.

The living cells of roots must have oxygen to support respiration. Normally, the roots secure the necessary oxygen for respiration by absorption of oxygen through the root hairs and other epidermal cells. This inward diffusion of oxygen from the soil air ordinarily goes on readily because of the thinness of the walls of these cells and the absence of a cuticle. Roots at all levels in the soil secure oxygen directly from the air in the pore spaces and to a limited extent from the oxygen dissolved in water; in ordinary land plants there is no system of air-conducting tubes that convey oxygen from the atmosphere, through the plants, to the extremities of the roots.

The amount of air in the soil depends not only upon the pore space but also upon the water content of the soil. If water

Fig. 9.1. Effect of aeration on root growth in tomato. Left, plants growing in complete nutrient solution through which air was bubbled; right, plants growing in same solution without aeration. (Photo courtesy of Hoagland.)

Fig. 9.2. Aerial "stump roots" of bald cypress (*Taxodium distichum*). (Photo by U. S. Forest Service.)

occupies the pore space, air is forced out. A water-soaked (saturated) soil contains practically no air save that which is dissolved in water. If the soil about the roots is continuously water-soaked, plants die because of insufficient oxygen and possibly as a result of the accumulation of carbon dioxide. Most species of land plants will grow normally with their roots in a water solution, if it is well aerated by bubbling air through it (Fig. 9.1). Evidence indicates that inadequate soil aeration results in a reduction in the rate of water absorption.

Whereas most land plants, including agricultural plants, will not long survive with the root system submerged in unaerated water or surrounded by a soil that is water-soaked, some plants flourish under such conditions. Among them may be cited rice, various swamp and marsh plants, and the bald cypress (*Taxodium distichum*) (Fig. 9.2). Almost all such plants contain in the stem and roots large communicating air spaces. Thus, air absorbed into the leaves and stems may reach the living cells of the root in sufficient quantity. Bald cypress and certain species in tropical mangrove swamps develop special root branches that grow upward until their ends are above the water level. These special root branches have a central core of loose tissue through which air moves downward to the submerged organs.

In most agricultural soils air of the soil is not a limiting factor in plant growth. However, stirring of the soil (tillage) may facilitate its aeration and is especially beneficial if the supply of air is inadequate to begin with. But, as stated, it is very improbable that in ordinary agricultural soils an actual deficiency of soil oxygen ever exists, unless the soil is water-soaked; the latter condition is one that cannot be corrected by tillage. If not to improve soil aeration, what are the benefits of tillage? The student may care to explore this subject further.

Organisms of the Soil

Ordinary soils teem with living organisms, both plants and animals. These organisms are an important part of the environment of roots. The soil flora includes bacteria, fungi, and algae. Living roots of higher plants also are an important part of the soil. When the roots die they leave a considerable quantity of organic matter. The soil fauna includes protozoa, nematodes, earthworms, various insects, and burrowing animals. Most of these are beneficial in some way or another; others may be harmful. Certain bacteria are absolutely essential in the maintenance of soil fertility. This point will be pursued further in Chapter 17, but it should be indicated here that certain bacteria and fungi that live in the soil are responsible for the decomposition of organic matter (plant residues, manure, and other organic fertilizers), and for nitrogen fixation (see page 343). As a result of their activity, they keep up the supply of soil nitrogen, one of the chief factors in soil fertility. Earthworms affect soil structure, in that they move and mix the soil, and pass large quantities through their bodies. Charles Darwin, in 1885, published *The Formation of Vegetable Mold*, in which the importance of earthworms in soils is stressed. He points out that earthworms in an acre of soil may pass through their bodies annually as much as 15 tons of dry earth.

Temperature of the Soil

The rate of absorption of both water and solutes by roots may be reduced by extremes of temperature. Plants native to cool climates absorb these substances more freely at low temperatures than do plants of warm climates. A plant may wilt in a soil containing ample water if the soil temperature sinks below, or rises above, a certain degree. In cold, dry climates winter killing may be the result of a cold soil, which slows up absorption, accompanied by a high transpiration rate. It is believed that in winter killing the plant is as frequently killed by direct drying as by actual freezing.

All chemical and biological activities of a soil are influenced by soil temperature.

The soil temperature is by no means always the same as the temperature of the air above it. It may be lower or higher than the air temperature.

MINERAL ELEMENTS ESSENTIAL FOR PLANT GROWTH

For almost 100 years physiologists have been studying the mineral nutrition of plants. Extensive investigations have been carried out to determine which elements are essential for plant growth, how the plant absorbs and utilizes these elements, and what effects are produced in the plant when a particular essential element is lacking.

What methods have been employed to determine the chemical elements that are essential to plant growth? Of course, there are the accumulated experiences of agriculturists which have shown that applications of various nutrients to the soil result in healthier plants, increased yields, and better quality. But these observations have thrown little light on the specific role played by chemical elements in the plant. Plant physiologists have used more critical methods—careful weighings and measurements of quantities of elements used and results obtained. The solution-culture method has long been employed to determine what elements are indispensable in plant growth. Most kinds of plants that normally grow in soil can be grown to maturity (fruit and seed production) in water to which soluble essential nutrient salts have been added (Fig. 9.3). By growing plants in a nutrient solution containing all elements believed to be essential, except the particular element being investigated, the response of plants when this element is absent can be ascertained.

From such experiments a list of elements that are known to be essential for the growth of plants has been compiled. Long recognized as essential to the continued growth and development of green plants are the following ten elements, with their appropriate chemical symbols: carbon (C), hydrogen (H), oxygen (O), phosphorus (P), potassium (K), nitrogen (N), sulfur (S), calcium (Ca), iron (Fe), magnesium (Mg).

If the symbols are arranged in a line they can be used to remember the elements thus:

C HOPK'NS   CaFe   Mg

"See Hopk'ns Cafe, mighty good." Of these ten elements, the last seven are in the nutrient medium, that is, the various salts dissolved in the water of the soil. Relatively large quantities of nitrogen, sulfur, phosphorus, potassium, magnesium, and calcium are required; very small quantities of iron meet all plant needs for this element. These elements, with the exception of iron, have been called the **macronutrient elements,** because they are needed in relatively large amounts. More recently it has been discovered that at least six additional elements are needed by higher plants but in much smaller amounts. The **micronutrient elements** (trace elements or minor elements)

include in addition to iron (Fe), the elements boron (B), manganese (Mn), copper (Cu), zinc (Zn), chlorine (Cl), and molybdenum (Mo).

A plant growing in soil or in solution cannot distinguish between those elements that are essential to it and those that are not essential or that might be harmful. If the element or ion containing it is in solution, it will probably be absorbed by the plant. Thus we find in the plant almost all the elements present in the soil. Gold has been isolated from plants growing in gold-bearing soils. Selenium, an element poisonous to livestock, when present in soils is absorbed by certain plants in sufficient amounts to be harmful to animals grazing on them.

Macronutrient Elements

Carbon, Hydrogen, and Oxygen. The absorption of water, carbon dioxide, and oxygen brings into the plant large quantities

Fig. 9.3. Lettuce grown in nutrient solutions, without nitrogen; without potassium; without phosphorus; and in a solution containing all chemicals essential for plant growth. (Photo courtesy of Hoagland.)

of the elements carbon, hydrogen, and oxygen from which is formed the major part of each of the hundreds of organic compounds found in the plant. We have seen how in the process of photosynthesis these elements are combined into carbohydrates. Simple fats also are composed entirely of these three elements while proteins alone of the foods have appreciable amounts of other elements, particularly nitrogen and to a lesser extent sulfur and phosphorus.

Nitrogen. This element is a component of proteins which form an essential part of protoplasm. Proteins also occur as stored foods in plant cells. Nitrogen is also a part of other organic compounds in plants, such as chlorophyll (chlorophyll *a* has the molecular formula $C_{55}H_{70}O_6N_4Mg$), amino acids, alkaloids, and at least some plant hormones.

Ordinary green plants cannot utilize elemental nitrogen which represents about 78 per cent of the air. It has been estimated that above every acre of land surface there are about 145,000 to 150,000 tons of this gas. Chief sources of nitrogen for green plants are the nitrates, such as sodium nitrate (Chilean saltpeter), potassium nitrate, ammonium nitrate, and calcium nitrate. Green plants can also utilize nitrites and ammonium salts, and evidence indicates that some plants can derive nitrogen from certain organic nitrogenous compounds.

Nitrogenous fertilizers, both natural and commercial, are usually the most important fertilizers applied to growing plants. The chief commercial nitrogenous fertilizers are as follows: (1) those with nitrogen in the nitrate form; (2) those with nitrogen in ammonia or its compounds; (3) those with nitrogen in organic compounds, such as tankage, cottonseed meal; and (4) those with nitrogen in the amide form, such as urea and calcium cyanamide. Organic nitrogen in complex molecules cannot be used directly by plants but must first be converted into available forms through the action of organisms in the soil.

The rate of growth of plants is influenced to a large degree by the available nitrogen. An early symptom of nitrogen deficiency is a yellowing of leaves, particularly the older leaves, although other factors may cause this condition; then follows a stunting in the growth of all parts of the plant (Fig. 9.3). On the other hand, an excess of available nitrogen results in vigorous vegetative growth and a suppression of food storage and of fruit and seed development.

Sulfur. Sulfur forms a part of the molecules of proteins. Plant proteins containing sulfur may have from 0.5 to 1.5 per cent of this element.

Ordinary green plants cannot utilize elemental sulfur; it must first be oxidized to sulfates in which form it is normally absorbed by the roots.

Certain agricultural soils may become deficient in sulfur. The most noticeable responses to applications of sulfur fertilizers are an increased root development and a deeper green color of the foliage.

Phosphorus. This element is also a component of some plant proteins. The highest percentages of phosphorus occur in those parts of the plant that are growing rapidly, such as meristematic regions and maturing fruits and seeds.

Methods have been developed by which elements are "tagged." For example, radioactive phosphorus in the form of phosphate has been introduced into the culture solution in which tomatoes were growing. By means of the Geiger-Müller counter, or by radiograms (Fig. 15.11), the path of radioactive phosphorus through the plant has been followed. After a time, the greatest accumulation of phosphorus was found in the young developing fruit; very little occurred in the ripe fruit. Within the fruit itself the greatest accumulation of phosphorus was in the developing seed.

Applications of phosphorus to soils deficient in this element promote root growth and hasten maturity, particularly of cereals. Phosphates are the principal source of phosphorus for plants. Lettuce grown in culture solution without phosphorus is shown in Fig. 9.3.

Potassium. This element, indispensable to plants (Fig. 9.3), accumulates in those tissues that are growing rapidly. It will migrate from older tissues to meristematic regions; for example, during the maturing of a fruit crop there is a movement of potassium from the leaves into the fruit. In plants, potassium occurs both in inorganic and organic forms.

The specific functions of potassium in the plant are not clearly understood. It is known, however, that plants do not grow normally in a soil deficient in this element (Plate III*b*, Chapter 15). In fact, many plant diseases, abnormal responses, and low yields of crops are associated with a lack of potassium; they are cured or alleviated by applications of potassium. Processes in the plant that appear to require an adequate supply of potassium are: (1) normal cell division, (2) synthesis and translocation of carbohydrates, (3) synthesis of proteins in meristematic cells, (4) reduction of nitrates, and (5) development of chlorophyll.

Any water-soluble inorganic compound of potassium, such as potassium sulfate, potassium phosphate, or potassium nitrate, can be utilized by plants as a source of potassium.

Calcium. All ordinary green plants require calcium. It is one of the constituents in the middle lamella of the cell wall, where it occurs in the form of calcium pectate. Calcium affects the permeability of cytoplasmic membranes and the hydration of colloids. Calcium may be found in combination with organic acids in the plant. Oxalic acid, for example, is a by-product of protein metabolism. It is a soluble substance and is toxic to the protoplasm if it reaches a high concentration in the cell. When united with calcium, however, the soluble oxalic acid is converted into the highly insoluble calcium oxalate, which does not injure the protoplasm. There is also evidence that calcium favors the translocation of carbohydrates and amino acids and encourages root development.

Magnesium. This element is a constituent of the chlorophyll molecule. A deficiency of magnesium results in the development of pale, sickly foliage, an unhealthy condition known as **chlorosis.** This disease is a common one of economic plants, and in many instances applications of magnesium have effected a cure. However, chlorosis can be caused by deficiencies in other essential elements such as iron.

Micronutrient Elements

Until recently, it was not known that the elements boron, zinc, manganese, chlorine, molybdenum, and copper were indispensable for normal plant growth. The reasons were that they are needed only in very minute quantities (mere "traces") and that the chemicals used in culture solutions contained unsuspected traces of these elements sufficient to supply the needs of the plant's growth in the water culture. For example, a bottle of ferric sulfate labeled "chemically pure" taken from the laboratory shelf, may show on the label traces of chlorine, phosphoric acid, manganese, zinc, copper, sodium nitrate, and ferrous salts. If a culture solution containing this "chemically pure" ferric sulfate were used, most likely it would possess enough manganese, zinc, chlorine, and copper to meet the plant's requirements. In a study of micronutrient elements needed, or suspected of being needed by plants, it has been necessary to employ highly refined techniques, employing redistilled water and highly purified salts. It even may be necessary to prevent dust of the atmosphere from falling into the culture, as the dust may contain traces of critical elements.

Iron. Although iron is not a component of the chlorophyll molecule, it is essential for the synthesis of chlorophyll. Chlorosis may be caused by iron deficiency as well as by a deficiency of magnesium. The quantity of iron required is very small. As an example, chlorosis of pineapples in Hawaii, due to the unavailability of iron from the soil, is remedied by spraying the plants with iron salt solutions. Orchard trees suffering from iron chlorosis may be cured by injecting iron compounds into the trunk, or by applying various kinds of iron salts to the soil.

Boron. That plants require boron is well established. Symptoms of boron deficiency include darkening of tissues and various growth abnormalities and disturbances. Some of the physiological diseases of plants

Fig. 9.5. Disease of peach known as "little leaf" caused by a deficiency of zinc. Branch at left untreated; branch at right cured by driving in zinc-coated nails. (Photo courtesy of Proebsting.)

Fig. 9.6. Chlorosis of tomato leaf caused by a deficiency of manganese in the nutrient solution. (Photo courtesy of Hoagland.)

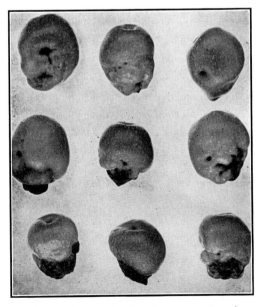

Fig. 9.4. Disease of olives known as "monkey-face," caused by a deficiency of boron. (Photo courtesy of Scott and Thomas.)

due to boron deficiency are internal cork of apples, top rot of tobacco, cracked stem of celery, browning of cauliflower, heart rot of sugar beets, and "monkey face" of olives (Fig. 9.4). Very small applications (20 to

50 pounds) of sodium tetraborate (borax) per acre may be sufficient to cure these diseases. In contrast fertilizers containing the macronutrient elements are frequently applied to fields at rates of several hundred pounds per acre.

Although plants require boron for normal development, the quantity in the soil or culture solution must be very small or injury will result. In fact, in certain agricultural sections severe injury to crops occurs be-

cause of excessive amounts of boron in the soil or in the irrigation waters. Plants vary in their tolerance of boron. Borates are used as weed-killers.

Zinc. Zinc is essential to the normal development of a variety of plants; probably it is required by all plants. As with other micronutrients, proof has come from careful water-culture experiments; also certain diseases of plants have been cured by zinc applications. Large quantities of zinc are

Fig. 9.7.   Tomatoes growing in solution with all essential chemical elements except copper. Leaves sprayed with solution containing copper (left). (Photo courtesy of Hoagland.)

toxic to plants. Two well-known diseases caused by zinc deficiency are "little leaf" of deciduous fruit trees (Fig. 9.5) and "mottle leaf" of citrus trees. These abnormal conditions are corrected by spraying the trees with zinc salts, by injecting dilute solutions of zinc salts into the trunks, or by driving zinc brads into the trunks. These corrective measures show how minute are the quantities of zinc required by plants for normal development. Zinc is a constituent of certain enzymes and plays a role in the synthesis of indoleacetic acid, an important growth hormone in plants.

Manganese. The most striking symptom of plants with a deficiency of manganese is chlorosis (Fig. 9.6), but it is a somewhat different type from that caused by iron deficiency. Whereas in iron chlorosis the young leaves may become yellow or white with prominent green veins, manganese chlorosis results in the leaf taking on a mottled appearance. Spraying or dusting crops suffering from manganese deficiency with as little as 20 pounds of manganese sulfate per acre frequently effects a cure.

Copper. Abnormalities in the growth of many plants, especially those in marsh and peat soils, have been corrected by the application of copper compounds (Fig. 9.7). Copper also is a constituent of certain enzyme systems but its exact function is not definitely known.

Molybdenum. Molybdenum is now recognized as an essential micronutrient element, at least to certain plants. For example, it was found that molybdenum is required for normal growth of tomato seedlings, that only .01 parts per million of the element in the nutrient solution is needed, and that concentrations exceeding 10 parts per million cause injury. One of the roles of molybdenum in plants appears to be associated with the reduction of nitrates.

SUMMARY

1. Soil is a complex system composed of rock particles and plant and animal remains in various stages of decay in which an abundance of soil microorganisms is growing. Throughout the soil structure there is an interconnecting system of large and small pores filled with air or with water and dissolved materials.

2. All the essential elements except carbon, hydrogen, and oxygen are absorbed through the roots generally in the form of ions from the soil.

3. The macronutrient essential elements are carbon, hydrogen, oxygen, nitrogen, sulfur, phosphorus, potassium, calcium, and magnesium.

4. The micronutrient essential elements are iron, zinc, copper, boron, manganese, and molybdenum.

5. A plant's growth can be influenced markedly by the chemical nature and physical structure of the soil.

10

Transpiration, Conduction, and Absorption

The most abundant compound in an active cell is water. It plays a varied role in the life of a plant for it serves as (1) a raw material in the synthesis of organic compounds, (2) the solvent in which vital reactions take place, (3) the medium through which solutes move from cell to cell, and it gives (4) turgor to plant cells. Plant tissues vary in water content; those actively growing have a water content equal to as much as 85 to 95% of their fresh weight, while a dormant structure such as a seed may have a water content as low as five to 10%. The entire shoot system of an herbaceous plant such as barley may be 82% water (Fig. 10.1).

A plant from which the water has been removed is made up chiefly of organic material synthesized by the plant primarily from carbon dioxide, water, and inorganic nitrogen such as found in nitrates or ammonium. Actually the mineral matter absorbed from the soil is relatively little in terms of total amount but is, nevertheless,

Fig. 10.1. Moisture content, dry weight, and ash content of fresh grass leaves; (left) 100 grams of fresh leaves yield (center) 82 grams of water and 18 grams of dry leaves; (right) the dry leaves yield on burning 1.5 grams of ash.

essential for the life of the plant. The small quantity of mineral matter contained in a plant can be readily demonstrated by burning the dry tissue. The carbon, hydrogen, and oxygen, as well as the nitrogen and some of the phosphorus and sulfur pass off in the combustion process while most of the minerals remain in the ash combined with a small amount of oxygen (Fig. 10.1). These mineral elements may have occurred in the plant as inorganic ions dissolved in the cell or may have been a part of complex organic molecules. For instance, the magnesium in the ash may come from the destruction of chlorophyll of which it is a part while the carbon, hydrogen, oxygen, and nitrogen of the chlorophyll would be lost during burning.

While minerals that are once absorbed by a plant are not generally lost again in large quantities, except during leaf fall, water is constantly being lost from the aboveground portions of the plant. Because this water loss profoundly influences the rates of water absorption and movement, it will be studied first.

TRANSPIRATION

By far the greater part of the water lost from the plant passes into the atmosphere as invisible water vapor. This loss of water in vapor form from a living plant is called **transpiration.** Although a small amount of water may be transpired directly through the cuticle, most of the water lost during the day diffuses out through the stomata. This is called **stomatal transpiration** in contrast with **cuticular transpiration.** Leaves are the principal transpiring organs.

A knowledge of leaf structure is essential to an understanding of the mechanism of transpiration. It will be recalled that the mesophyll of most leaves is a very loose tissue with large intercellular air spaces. Even within the palisade parenchyma, a large portion of the walls of most cells is exposed to intercellular air spaces (Figs. 8.5, 8.6A). These are interconnected with similar air spaces throughout the leaf and through the stomata to the outside air. The extensive intercellular surface, loose internal structure, and numerous stomata of the leaf allow for rapid gaseous exchange between the internal leaf cells and the outside air. An appreciation of this structure is gained when we consider a large leaf such as a squash leaf that may be 70% internal air space, and may have 20 times as much total internal cell surface bordering this air space as leaf surface exposed to the outside air. In addition, the squash leaf may have as many as 60 million stomata connecting this internal air with the outside environment and may have 6000 veins per square centimeter.

THE PROCESS OF TRANSPIRATION

Water permeates the living turgid leaf cells, filling the vacuoles, making up a large part of the cytoplasm, and penetrating the walls. Thus the cell walls bordering on intercellular air spaces are moist, and because of this the air in these spaces is almost saturated with water vapor. The diffusion pressure or vapor pressure of water in these spaces is then generally higher than in the outside atmosphere. When the air around a leaf is not saturated but relatively dry, water vapor molecules diffuse from the saturated air in the leaf through the stomata into the less saturated outer air where the vapor pressure, and hence the diffusion pressure of water, is lower. This loss in water results in a slight drying of the air in the intercellular spaces (Fig. 8.5). Water molecules then evaporate from the wet walls and diffuse into this drier air in the leaf. As water leaves the walls, the walls in turn become drier and imbibe

Fig. 10.2. Apparatus used in measuring loss of water by transpiration. (Photo courtesy of Veihmeyer.)

diffuses along this gradient, in liquid form within the cell, and in vapor form once it evaporates from the cell walls. Each cell, however, is in contact with several other cells and is only a few cells distant from the water-filled xylem elements of a vein.

As water is lost from a cell by outward diffusion, the cell loses some of its turgor and the concentration of solutes in it increases; hence the diffusion pressure of water within the cell sap decreases. The cell is then able to gain water by osmosis from adjacent more saturated cells. These in turn gain water from adjacent cells and eventually from the water-filled tracheid of a vein ending. A diffusion gradient soon becomes established along which water diffuses from the vein through one or several cells to a cell wall bordering an intercellular space, into and through the intercellular spaces and through the stomata to the outside air.

The Quantity of Water Transpired

Quantitative methods of measuring the loss of water by transpiration have been developed. Figure 10.2 shows the type of apparatus used in many studies. This includes a can holding sufficient soil to support the root system of large plants, even small trees. The top of the can is covered, and so all water escaping from the container must be that absorbed from the soil by the roots. This water passes up through the stems to the leaves and is transpired to the atmosphere. Provision is made for measuring accurately the amount of water that is added from time to time to the container. Also, suitable arrangements are made for weighing the whole container, including soil, water, and plant. Thus, for any time interval the transpiration loss (weight of water that passes through the plant from the soil) can be determined. Of course, some loss of weight results from respira-

water from the enclosed cytoplasm and vacuole.

Thus a diffusion gradient for water exists from the vacuole through the cytoplasm, the wall, the intercellular air spaces to the drier outer air surrounding the leaf. Water

tion, but this amount is very small as compared with that from transpiration. Also, some gain in weight occurs, owing to photosynthesis but this amount, too, is relatively small.

The amount of water transpired by plants is very great. A single corn plant (in Kansas), between May 5 and September 8, transpired 54 gallons of water. An acre of such plants (6000 plants) would transpire during the season 324,000 gallons of water, which is equivalent to a sheet of water 11 inches deep over the entire acre. It has been estimated that an acre of red maple trees, growing in a soil with ample moisture, may lose in a growing season an amount of water sufficient to cover the acre with 28.3 inches of water. A soil clothed with plants is depleted of its moisture at a much more rapid rate than one that is bare. Nearly all the water loss from a soil below the first 6 to 8 inches results from absorption and transpiration by plants.

Of the total quantity of water absorbed by the roots of plants, as much as 98 per cent of it escapes from the plant by transpiration. The small quantity of the water that is retained by the plant includes the water of vacuoles and protoplasm, that in cell walls and in the conducting elements, and that entering into chemical combination.

Using such an apparatus as shown in Fig. 10.2, the total transpiration during the life of the plant (or any part of its life) has been determined for many crops. This quantity has then been compared with the dry matter produced during the same period of time. For example, it was found that an alfalfa plant transpired 900 units of water for each unit of dry matter produced and that a millet plant transpired 248 units of water for each unit of dry matter. Although these values vary with the environmental conditions under which the plants are grown, it is evident that plants differ in their water economy.

Factors Affecting Transpiration Rate

The factors influencing the rate of transpiration include two principal groups, **environmental factors** and **morphological factors**. The former include conditions external to the plant, whereas morphological factors include structural features and habits of growth of the plant, sometimes referred to as internal factors.

Environmental Factors. The important environmental factors that influence transpiration rate are (1) relative humidity of the atmosphere, (2) air movements, (3) air temperature, (4) light intensity, and (5) soil conditions. These factors affect transpiration through their effect on the vapor pressure of water in the intercellular spaces or of water in the air.

Atmospheric Humidity. The humidity of the air surrounding the plant is an important external factor determining the rate of transpiration. The "drier" the air above the plant the greater the transpiration rate. For example, air with a relative humidity of 20 per cent is considered "dry" because it has the capacity for holding a great deal more water; air with a relative humidity of 80 per cent is regarded as "moist" because its capacity for holding more water is not great. A dry atmosphere has a low concentration of water vapor, a moist atmosphere a high concentration.

The air in intercellular spaces of a turgid leaf is very moist, in fact, usually almost saturated. A diffusion of water vapor from intercellular spaces through stomata to the air surrounding the leaf takes place as long as the diffusion pressure of water in the intercellular spaces exceeds that of the air outside. Diffusion becomes more rapid as the difference between these two pressures increases. When the difference is great, we say the **diffusion gradient** is steep. If the relative humidity of the air surrounding the plant is low, the diffusion gradient between the moist intercellular spaces and the outside air is steep, and hence transpiration is rapid.

Air Movements. As transpiration occurs there is a tendency for a moist layer of air to form next to the leaf surface, particularly in still air. This will decrease the diffusion gradient between the leaf and the atmosphere and transpiration will consequently decrease. On the other hand, air movement carries away this layer of humid air, replacing it with drier air, resulting in an increase in transpiration. The more rapid the air movement the faster the moist air will be carried away and the faster the rate of transpiration. If the wind is quite strong, stomata may close, probably as a result of excessive water loss, and transpiration is then reduced.

It is a common observation that on a warm, bright, windy day plants may lose water to the point of wilting. On a cool, cloudy day with little wind movement, however, seldom is the water loss sufficient to result in wilting. Even though plants may wilt during the hottest part of the day, this may be but a temporary condition, as is shown by the fact that the next morning the leaves are again fresh and turgid. Return to the turgid condition indicates that available water in the soil is not exhausted.

Air Temperature. In direct sunlight the temperature of a leaf is usually higher than that of the air about it; the difference may be as much as $10°$ C. About 80 per cent of the radiant energy of sunlight that falls upon green leaves may be absorbed by them. Part of this absorbed energy is changed to heat and raises the temperature of the leaf, part is utilized in vaporizing water, and another small part is used in photosynthesis (Fig. 11.4). When the leaf temperature rises, the vapor pressure in intercellular spaces becomes greater than that in the air surrounding the leaf; as a result, the diffusion gradient becomes steeper, and the rate of transpiration increases.

Light Intensity. As the light intensity increases, the internal temperature of the leaf is raised, with the result that water loss is accelerated. Another effect of illumination upon transpiration is that it stimulates, at least in many species of plants, the opening of stomata. When the stomata are closed, transpiration virtually ceases. Thus light, through its effect upon the opening of stomata, influences the rate of transpiration.

Soil Conditions. Any soil condition that influences absorption of water by the roots affects the transpiration rate. When the soil becomes very cold, absorption of water is retarded, even though soil water may be available. An increase in the concentration of the soil solution, as often occurs in alkali soils, reduces the rate of water intake. Poor aeration of the soil may result in diminished absorption. And the availability of soil water also determines (see page 195) the rate of intake. The rate at which water is absorbed by the roots greatly influences the rate of transpiration. If water loss exceeds water absorption, wilting will occur. Under these conditions the mesophyll cells do not give up water vapor as freely as when they are well supplied with water. Consequently, the rate of transpiration is reduced.

Morphological Factors. On days when water loss is high, various kinds of plants growing side by side, exposed to the same environmental conditions, respond differently as regards wilting. Some may be severely wilted; others may show no signs of distress. It is apparent that some plants have better provisions for transpiration regulation than do others. Thus, there are certain structural features of plants, and habits of growth, which influence the rate of transpiration. They may be referred to as morphological factors, that is, conditions in the plant itself.

Certain plants are able to survive in extremely dry habitats, whereas certain other plants succumb. Such surviving plants undoubtedly maintain a balance between water outgo and water intake, whereas in those plants that fail to survive the dryness, the loss of water, at least for a period, exceeds the absorption of water. Plants of dry habitats often possess roots that penetrate deeply into the soil; or, like many desert annuals, they may have an extensive surface root system that can rapidly absorb limited rainfall from spring or summer showers. Many desert plants possess special water storage tissue, as is well shown in so-called "succulents," i.e., plants with fleshy stems or leaves (Figs. 2.14, 6.58).

The anatomical features that are advantageous from the point of view of prevention of water loss are (1) the cuticle of leaves, young stems, and fruits, (2) sunken stomata, (3) distribution of stomata, and (4) reduction of the transpiring surface. In addition, stomatal behavior is an important factor in controlling water loss.

Cuticle. Most of the water lost from a plant passes out through the stomata. Some water, however, is lost through the cuticle. Various modifications in leaf structure reduce cuticular transpiration, e.g., thickening of the outer wall of the epidermal cells and the presence of a waxlike material, cutin, in this wall. Most plants of arid and semiarid climates have a thicker cuticle than do those of humid climates.

Stomatal Behavior. We have seen (page 161) that a stoma may open and close as a

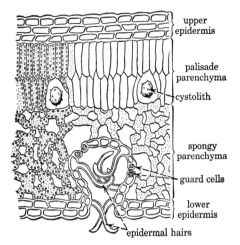

Fig. 10.3. Cross section of leaf of rubber plant (*Ficus elastica*). (Redrawn from Van Tieghem and Constantin.)

result of changes in the turgor of guard cells. When guard cells become turgid, the stomatal aperture widens; when they become flaccid, the aperture narrows or completely closes. Often after a period of rapid transpiration, there is a deficit of water in all leaf cells, and stomata close, thus reducing the water loss due to transpiration. This is an advantageous behavior. But, from the standpoint of photosynthesis, the stomata must serve also as entrances for carbon dioxide. If they close during the daytime because of excessive transpiration, the diffusion inward of carbon dioxide, as well as the diffusion outward of water vapor, is restricted. Stomatal closure, in this event, works to the disadvantage of the plant by decreasing photosynthesis, although it is a favorable behavior in that it limits water loss.

Although light is a factor that stimulates stomatal opening, in many plant species stomata may remain closed throughout the day if the water deficit in leaf cells is pronounced. On the other hand, there are species in which stomata are open all night, and in some instances stomata may remain open even though transpiration is proceeding at a high rate.

Sunken Stomata. In some plants (Fig. 10.3) the stomata are below the general level of the leaf surface. When this condition occurs the water vapor must diffuse through a relatively long passageway, which is sometimes tortuous, with the result that the diffusion rate is lessened.

Distribution of Stomata. The leaves of many plants have stomata only on the undersurface, or, if on both surfaces, mostly on the lower. This distribution is shown in Table 8.1, page 161. Hence, the loss of water from leaves that have stomata only on the lower surface, or fewer on the upper than the lower, is usually less than the loss from leaves that have an equal number on both the upper and lower sides.

Reduction of Transpiring Surface. In most plants the principal organs of transpiration are leaves. Therefore, any decrease in leaf surface will reduce transpiration and conserve water absorbed by roots. In corn and other grasses, also in oleander, the leaves roll up during drought, thus exposing less surface to the air than do fully expanded leaves. Cacti and some euphorbias have no foliage leaves; in these plants

Fig. 10.4. Guttation. A, from tips of barley (*Hordeum vulgare*) leaves; B, from the margin of rose (*Rosa odorata*) leaflets. (B photo courtesy of Armer.)

the transpiring surface is restricted to the stem surface (Fig. 6.58).

Epidermal Hairs. The leaves of many plants are clothed with epidermal hairs (Fig. 6.15). In some plants, such as common mullein and dusty miller (*Centaurea cineraria*), the hairs may form a dense, cottony covering. There is no clear evidence that surface hairs reduce transpiration; in fact, experiments with some plants have shown that water loss from the leaves is greater when the hairs are present than when they are lacking.

Guttation

The loss of liquid, as contrasted with the loss of vapor, from leaves of *intact plants* is termed **guttation.** This will occur especially in herbaceous plants when conditions favor rapid absorption of water and low transpiration. For instance, when a well-watered, vigorously growing tomato plant is placed under a bell jar, transpiration ceases as the atmosphere in the jar becomes saturated. Continued water absorption then results in a slow exudation of water from the tips of the leaves (Fig. 10.4). Many plants have specialized openings called **hydathodes** at the tips of their leaves through which the liquid passes outward. Experiments with barley plants show that, when the roots are immersed in distilled water, guttation is very slight or ceases altogether. This is true, even though the water is aerated amply. In dilute salt solution, but without aeration, guttation is also slight. On the other hand, if the roots are immersed in a dilute salt solution and the aeration is good and the temperature favorable, guttation is ample and continues for a long period in a humid atmosphere. Guttation is associated with salt absorption and salt movement into the xylem. The liquid of guttation is not pure water but a dilute salt solution (Fig. 10.5).

Fig. 10.5. Deposit on blades of grass following the evaporation of guttation fluid. Deposit composed largely of glutamine with a small amount of potassium chloride and undetermined organic matter. (Photo courtesy of Curtis.)

SUMMARY OF TRANSPIRATION

1. Transpiration is the loss of water vapor from plant surfaces, largely those of leaves.

2. Evaporation removes the water vapor from the external surface of the leaf.

3. The amount of water transpired during the life of a plant is large, from 200 to 1000 times its dry weight.

4. The rate of transpiration is affected by the relative humidity of the air, air movements, air temperature, light intensity, and soil conditions.

5. Morphological details such as the cuticle, epidermal hairs, and location and dis-

tribution of the stomata also influence the rate of transpiration.

6. Water, in liquid form in which solutes are dissolved, leaves the leaf surface by guttation when the relative humidity is high.

CONDUCTION OF WATER

Water in the plant moves upward from the roots to the stems and thence into leaves, from which it escapes into the atmosphere. That the path of movement is the xylem is shown by "ringing" or "girdling" the stem, that is, removing a complete ring of bark. This procedure has little immediate effect on the movement of water; the plant does not wilt. The path of movement of water may also be demonstrated by placing a leafy branch that has been cut underwater into an aqueous solution of a dye, such as eosin. If after a short period the stem is split, it can be observed that the walls of vessels and tracheids are stained by the dye, whereas other tissues are not stained.

Frequently not all of the xylem vessels or tracheids function in the conduction of water and mineral salts at any one time. In trees particularly, the heartwood (Figs. 6.37 and 6.43) ceases to play a role in conduction (page 116). In some instances only the outer layers of sapwood contain xylem elements filled with water.

The rate of movement of water in stems depends in large measure upon the rate of transpiration. If plants are growing in a very humid atmosphere, the movement of water through the xylem is very slow; if they are in a dry, warm atmosphere, which heightens the rate of transpiration, the movement may be as rapid as 32 inches per minute. In the tobacco plant, water conduction was found to go on at a rate of about 4 feet an hour. In the larch tree, the rate of water movement was found to be approximately 4.6 feet per hour at a

period of the day when water loss was highest; but in the early morning, when the rate of water loss was at the minimum, the rate of water movement was but 2 or 3 inches per hour.

PROCESSES CONCERNED IN ASCENT OF WATER

It is estimated that a force of 20 atmospheres (Fig. 5.13), almost 300 pounds per square inch, is necessary to lift water to a height of 350 feet through the xylem of a tree. This estimate takes into consideration the resistance to water movement offered by the xylem, as well as the weight of the water column. How does water get to such a height in a tree? What are the forces involved? Although plant physiologists are not agreed on the relative importance of the various processes, the explanation that is now most generally accepted as most plausible will be described here. It is spoken of as the **transpiration-pull** and **water-cohesion theory**.

Evaporation. When evaporation of water occurs from the cell walls in a leaf during transpiration, forces are brought into play that result eventually in the movement of water through the plant. The diffusion of water molecules from the wet cell-wall surfaces into the intercellular spaces of the leaf mesophyll results in a partial drying of the walls.

Imbibition. The walls of a leaf cell, losing water as a result of evaporation, imbibe water from the enclosed cell contents or from adjacent cell walls with a higher water content. The forces of imbibition that hold the water in the walls (see page 64 and Fig. 5.11) are very great. Although the first water that is lost from a saturated mesophyll wall is held loosely, the forces holding the remaining water in the wall are stronger. Thus, during transpiration the diffusion pressure of water in the wall gradually decreases because some of the imbibitional forces are not satisfied.

This decrease in the diffusion pressure of water in the wall results in the movement of water from the protoplast into the wall and a disturbance in the water equilibrium. This disturbance is transmitted from cell to cell through both cellular contents and walls. Water moves into these cells from the tracheids in the veinlets of the leaves. Thus a force equivalent to the imbibitional force created in the leaf cell walls, as a result of the loss of water from them during transpiration, is pulling on the water in the tracheids.

Water Continuity and Cohesion. Water in the tracheids of leaf veinlets is continuous from the leaves to the roots. This continuity exists throughout the life of the plant. In a sense the water columns "grow" with the plant. However, the living cells of the root, the xylem elements themselves, and the living leaf cells offer resistance to the free flow of water. This resistance and the gravitational pull on the water itself is overcome by the forces developed in the leaf when water is moving up in the plant. The question now arises: Do these unbroken columns of water have sufficient tensile strength to prevent them from being broken by the forces acting on them? Experiments using both water and plant sap indicate that this requirement is met. As a matter of fact, plant sap in vessels and tracheids may withstand tensions greater than 300 atmospheres without being broken. Thus, it is evident that the attractive forces of the water molecules for each other, **cohesion,** and of cell walls for the water molecules, **adhesion,** are very great. It is because of these attractive forces that the liquid columns possess tensile strength.

The columns of water are raised by the force of evaporation of water from the leaf cell walls and the imbibitional forces that develop here.

Action of Living Cells. We have stressed the importance of continuity of water from the bottom to the top of the plant. There is some evidence that the presence of living cells adjoining the nonliving conducting xylem elements may play a role in the maintenance of this continuity by preventing the formation of obstructions in the entire system.

SUMMARY OF THE TRANSPIRATION-PULL THEORY

1. The evaporation of water from the walls of mesophyll cells of leaves results in a decrease in the diffusion pressure of water in these walls.

2. This disturbance in the water balance of the cells causes a series of changes that set in motion the entire train of water through the plant.

3. The living leaf cells next to the tracheids in veinlets eventually lose water to neighboring cells.

4. Water moves from the veinlets into the adjacent cells. This results in the upward movement of water in the continuous liquid columns in the xylem.

5. Continuity of water is maintained even under conditions of considerable strain because of the strong cohesive forces between water molecules.

ABSORPTION

ABSORPTION OF WATER

The large quantities of water moved through the plant body and lost by transpiration, then, must be replaced continually if the plant is to live.

In the absorbing region of the root (Fig. 7.5), the phloem does not lie outside the xylem but occurs in groups of cells that alternate radially with xylem masses or with

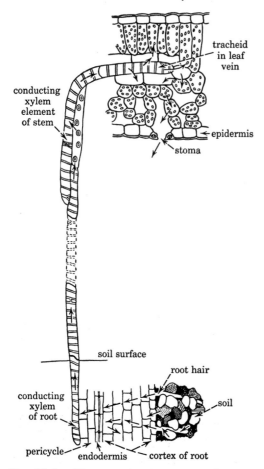

Fig. 10.6. Diagram showing entry of water from the soil to the root hair and its path of movement through the plant to parenchyma leaf cells, thence escaping as water vapor into intercellular spaces, from whence it passes to the atmosphere, mainly through stomata.

elements of the xylem to the stems and leaves is called xylem sap.

Mechanism of Absorption

The uptake of water by roots involves two mechanisms, which may or may not act simultaneously.

(1) When transpiration is slow and water is available in the soil, absorption of water may exceed transpiration. This condition results in setting up a pressure in the xylem and may lead to guttation. If the shoot of a plant is cut off a few inches above the soil level, absorption of water by the roots will often force the sap out of the cut ends of vessels and tracheids, a phenomenon known as **bleeding.** It appears that this type of absorption depends upon the *activity of living root cells.* It is termed **active absorption** and the pressure developed in the xylem is called **root pressure.**

The mechanism of active absorption of water by roots is generally explained as resulting from the osmotic movement of water into the root. As a result of the activities of the living root cells, soil solutes are absorbed and accumulate in the cell sap in high concentrations (page 198). The total concentration of the cell sap of the root hairs, as well as of the other root cells, is thus normally greater than that of the soil solution. The total amount of solutes present in the xylem elements of the root is also generally higher than that of the soil solution. The greater amount of solutes in the cell sap reduces the diffusion pressure of water in the cell sap below that of the water in the soil solution. Under this condition movement of water is inward. The rate of movement inward depends upon the difference in the diffusion pressure in the water of the two solutions.

(2) When transpiration exceeds absorption, no root pressure can be demonstrated.

the radiating arms of a single central mass of xylem. Hence, it is possible for the water and mineral salts to be absorbed by epidermal cells or root hairs, pass through the cortex, endodermis, pericycle into the primary xylem, and move upward without traversing the phloem (Fig. 10.6). This dilute solution of water and mineral salts that moves upward through the conducting

In the xylem elements of plants in this condition, the water is under tension, and the pressure on the water in the vessels is lower than atmospheric pressure. Under these conditions a high rate of transpiration results in a water deficit in the plant tissues. Water then moves into the roots passively; this process is termed **passive absorption.** In fact, under such conditions, water may even be absorbed by dead roots. **Active absorption** is a result of forces originating in the roots; **passive absorption** is a result of forces that originate in the leaves, that is, forces set in motion by the loss of water in transpiration.

Factors Affecting Absorption

We have seen that roots grow in a very complex environment—the soil. The activities of roots are influenced in a marked degree by this environment. Many factors of the environment determine the nature and extent of the root system, the rate of growth of roots, the rate at which they absorb water and mineral nutrients, in fact, all their activities.

Unavailable Soil Moisture. Plants cannot absorb all the water in a soil. Thus, there is always some water in the soil which is not available to the plant; it is held so tightly by the soil particles that the roots cannot absorb it rapidly enough to prevent wilting. To illustrate this relationship, we shall describe a simple, direct method of determining the **unavailable moisture** in a soil (Fig. 10.7). The container used here is a standard No. 2 tin can, with a tight-fitting lid in which there is a hole. The can is filled with soil which is wet to field capacity (see page 173). Several seeds are planted in the soil, and after they have germinated the best seedling is selected and led through the hole in the lid; the other seedlings are discarded. The space between the stem and the edges of the hole

Fig. 10.7. Direct method of determining the available water in the soil. It also shows the narrow range of soil moisture contents within which wilting takes place. Percentage of moisture in cans is as follows: plant 97, 3.3; 105, 3.6; 101, 3.7; 94, 3.9; 102, 4.1; 104, 4.1. Plants 104 and 102 are turgid, 94 shows slight drooping of first leaves, 101 is in a more advanced stage of wilting, 105 is permanently wilted, and 97 has passed this stage. (Photo and data courtesy of Veihmeyer.)

is filled with cotton to prevent evaporation from the soil. The roots penetrate the volume of soil in the can. It is apparent that all the water lost from the soil is that absorbed by the roots and transpired to the atmosphere. After a time, if no water is added, the plant begins to wilt, as is evidenced by drooping of the lower leaves. A degree of wilting known as **permanent wilting** is soon attained from which the plant will not recover if placed in a darkened moist chamber; the only way of bringing about its recovery is to add water to the soil. At the time that the plant has permanently wilted, the percentage of water left in the soil is determined. This percentage (based upon the dry weight of soil) is called the **permanent wilting percentage of the soil.** This water represents that which the plant cannot absorb readily from the soil. Only that part of the total soil moisture which is above the permanent wilting percentage is available for plant growth.

Influence of Soil Types. *Different kinds of ordinary plants* growing in the *same soil* reduce it to the same permanent wilting percentage. To illustrate, let us take a dozen containers like the one described above, fill them with the *same kind of soil,* and wet each to field capacity. In each can, seed a different kind of plant (tomato, wheat, flax, buckwheat, etc.). Place all the plants under the same growing conditions, and allow each soil to come to the permanent wilting point. The time required to reach this point will not necessarily be the same for each plant. Then determine the permanent wilting percentage of the soil in each can. It will be found that this percentage is essentially the same. This result means that the plants do not differ in their ability to extract water from a given soil.

Different kinds of soils, however, differ in their permanent wilting percentage. Let us cite another experiment to illustrate this point. Fill one container with a clay soil, and another with a sandy soil. Then wet each soil to field capacity. We know the clay soil will hold more water than the same volume of sandy soil. In each grow the *same kind of plant.* Allow each to reach permanent wilting, and then determine the permanent wilting percentage of the two types of soil. It will be found that the permanent wilting percentage of clay soil is much higher than that of sandy soil.

Moisture Content of Soil. From the standpoint of plant growth, the readily available water of a soil is the important consideration. This is really of more significance than a knowledge of the water-holding capacity of a soil.

It has been determined experimentally for many crop plants, including orchard trees, that if a soil has a moisture content *above* the permanent wilting percentage, there is no optimum moisture content, that is, a content at which the plants grow best. For example, if the percentage of water in a soil at field capacity is 30 per cent, and its permanent wilting percentage is 15 per cent, the plant growing therein will do equally well with the moisture at 16, 17, 18, or any other percentage up to 30 per cent.

Under field conditions, soon after a rain or irrigation, followed by drainage, the soil to a certain depth (depending upon the amount of rain or irrigation water applied) is up to its field capacity of moisture. The roots of plants begin to absorb the water, and soon the soil is below its field capacity. The soil moisture constantly decreases in the zones occupied by roots. Moreover, the movement of water by capillarity from moist soil to that which is drier immediately surrounding the roots is so slow that it may be regarded as negligible in influencing water available to the roots. As the soil moisture is reduced there is no sign of wilting in the plants until the permanent wilting percentage of the soil is approached.

Root Growth and Soil Moisture. Since the capillary movement of water in soils is too slow to meet the requirements of growing plants, it means that roots must penetrate the body of soil if they are to utilize the water which it holds. The total root elongation of a plant may be very great. Root extensions and the formation of new root hairs are constantly bringing about new contacts with moist soil.

There seems to be no reliable evidence that the roots of ordinary crop plants are able to penetrate more than a fraction of an inch of dry soil, that is, a soil at or below the permanent wilting percentage. Some evidence, however, indicates that certain drought-resistant plants, such as occur in deserts, are able to push their roots considerable distances into a dry soil.

The erroneous impression is sometimes held that roots "go in search of water." A more accurate statement is that they grow only in moist soil (soil above the permanent wilting percentage). In practice this would mean that if the upper foot of soil is moist and dry soil lies below it, the roots of plants will be confined to the upper, moist soil. In irrigation practice, this relationship of soil moisture and root growth is of importance. In irrigating a garden or lawn with a hose, one is easily misled into believing, because the soil surface is "wet," that sufficient water has been applied. Examination may reveal that at depths of 5 or more inches the soil is very dry—too dry for the growth of roots. In growing plants it is nearly always desirable to stimulate maximum root growth and a root system that attains its normal depth and spread. This may be accomplished in part by keeping the soil moist to the proper depth.

It may be possible for a plant to obtain sufficient moisture to keep it alive, even though only a part of the root system is in moist soil. In early spring or after an irrigation, when the soil is moist from the surface to deep levels, the roots may develop in the surface foot of soil and continue to penetrate to greater depths. Later, the loss of water by direct evaporation from the superficial soil layers and the removal of water by transpiration may bring the moisture content of the top layers of soil below the permanent wilting percentage; but the plant may continue to survive from water absorbed by the deeply penetrating roots.

The loss of water from soils at levels below the first few inches is essentially that due to transpiration from plants. Soils are dried out because of the presence of absorbing roots. One of the principal reasons for removing weeds from a growing crop is that they deplete the soil of water. In an orchard, weeds, as well as cover crops which may be allowed to grow too late in the season, compete with the trees for moisture. Cultivation of all kinds of crops has as one of its principal objects the removal of weeds.

Solute Concentration of Soil Solution. As the concentration of the soil solution approaches that of the cell sap, rate of water absorption declines. When the concentrations of the two solutions are the same, water intake ceases. And, if the soil solution becomes more highly concentrated than the cell sap, owing to excessive applications of fertilizers or of saline water, water will be withdrawn from the root cells. Moreover, root growth is inhibited at high salt concentrations, and the roots are not able to extend into new soil areas.

Transpiration and Absorption. Within limits, if a plant is placed under conditions that cause it to transpire rapidly and if soil water is available, the rate of water intake will increase. At times when transpiration

is very rapid, absorption lags behind transpiration to a point which causes wilting,
even though the water in the soil is ample.

ABSORPTION OF SOLUTES

Inorganic Solutes.   In the discussion of
absorption by the plant cell, the principle
of diffusion of water and solutes was discussed.   Diffusion of a solute was described
as a movement of solute particles from a
point where their diffusion pressure is
higher to a place where their diffusion pressure is lower.   Also, it was pointed out that
the different solutes diffuse independently
of the movement of each other, and of
water.   Investigations indicate that the intake of solutes by the roots cannot always
be explained as being the result of simple
diffusion.   For example, it has been shown
that the root cells of higher plants absorb
nutrients and build up within their vacuoles
a concentration of certain ions many times
that of the external solution.   This process
is called **accumulation** or **active solute absorption.**   There is a movement of ions
from a region of the lesser concentration of
any particular ion to a region of its greatest
concentration.   This movement *against* a
concentration gradient is accomplished by
an expenditure of energy and may constitute much of the work the plant cells are
required to perform.   It appears that high
absorption rates are usually attended by
high respiration rates, and it seems logical
to conclude that respiration provides the
energy required for active absorption and
accumulation of solutes.

SUMMARY OF ABSORP-
TION

1. Absorption of water by roots when
transpiration is low or absent is called ac-

tive absorption of water; it occurs only in
living root systems.

2. Active absorption of water results
when the solute concentration of the xylem
sap is higher than that of the external solution.

3. Root pressure, guttation, and bleeding
are expressions of the active absorption of
water by roots.

4. Passive absorption of water is a result
of the transmission to the roots of forces
that originate in the leaves; it may even
take place if the roots have been killed.

5. A plant is said to be permanently
wilted when it will not recover in a saturated atmosphere but only when water is
added to the soil.

6. The per cent moisture remaining in
soil in which a plant is permanently wilted
is called the permanent wilting percentage
of that soil.

7. Only that part of the total soil moisture which is above the permanent wilting
percentage is available for plant growth.

8. The rate of water absorption is influenced by the available water in the soil,
the air in the soil, the soil temperature, the
concentration of the soil solution, and the
rate of transpiration.

9. The absorption of ions by root cells
may occur against a concentration gradient.
This process is called accumulation and is
dependent upon energy released by the
living cells during respiration.

CONDUCTION

CONDUCTION OF MINERAL SALTS

The mineral (inorganic) salts that are
absorbed from the soil and conducted in
roots and stems are in solution.   The solvent is water.   Experiments indicate that
salts move upward past a girdle in the stem
and that girdling may or may not decrease

this upward movement, depending upon the species and other factors. This fact would serve to indicate that normally the greater amount of salt translocation in the stem is in xylem elements. An especially convenient method of studying the path of movement of salts in stems is now being used: Certain ions, such as potassium, phosphate, and bromide, are rendered radioactive and added to the solution in which the plants are growing. By appropriate means the path of movement of these radioactive "tracers" has been followed accurately, even for short periods of time, both in girdled and ungirdled stems. The results of these experiments seem to show that inorganic solutes move upward chiefly in xylem tissues. As the salts move upward, however, they may transfer radially from xylem through vascular rays into phloem tissues; and, also, they may accumulate in living cells along their path of movement. When radioactive phosphorus was supplied to the nutrient solution in which tomato plants, 6 feet high, were growing, it could be detected throughout the plant after 40 minutes. There is also evidence that certain minerals carried upward in the xylem to the leaves may be "exported" from the leaves and conducted downward via the phloem.

Absorption of inorganic salts by roots is *not proportional* to the absorption of water. Some increase in salt absorption accompanies an increase in water absorption, but not in the same ratio. Moreover, the different ions are not absorbed at the same rate. Thus, the amount of water moving through the plant is not the only factor that determines the amount of salts or of any particular ion which is absorbed and conducted through the plant to the leaves. Other factors, such as the photosynthetic activity of leaves, respiration, and other chemical processes in the plant, determine to a degree the quantity and kind of ions absorbed and transported.

CONDUCTION OF FOODS

The formation of carbohydrates (sugars and starch) and some proteins takes place principally in the leaves. These foods move from the leaves to the stems and thence to various parts of the plant.

Phloem. Conduction of foods from leaves and in stems takes place principally in the phloem, and it is quite generally agreed that this movement occurs mostly in sieve tubes. That phloem is the path of transport of foods is borne out by the results of ringing experiments followed by chemical analyses of tissues and cells. When the stem is ringed, the carbohydrate content and the sugar concentration of the sap in the leaf, bark, and wood *above* the ring increases after a few hours. And *below* the ring, the carbohydrate content and sugar concentration in the sap of bark and wood are decreased. It appears that these two conditions would not prevail if the foods were carried downward in the xylem tissues.

Both carbohydrates and nitrogenous substances move to tissues that are utilizing them. This means that foods may move upward or downward in the phloem. The direction of food movement is usually from a region of the shoot where excessive food is present to a region where a lesser amount is present. Food may move from the place of manufacture (leaves) to a storage place (roots, fruits, seeds) or to a region of growth (buds, cambium). It may also move from storage tissue to a region of growth.

Vascular Rays. There is transverse (radial) movement of foods in stems along the vascular rays, bringing the foods into close contact with conducting elements of both phloem and xylem. Thus the rays carry foods from sieve tubes radially into the cambium and xylem.

In some plants, such as the sugar maple, the xylem parenchyma cells serve as places where large quantities of carbohydrates are stored. In the spring, the presence in the xylem of soluble carbohydrates results in a high osmotic concentration. This, in association with cold nights and warm days, is responsible for the bleeding from wounds made for collecting maple sap in the spring of the year.

A SUMMARY OF CON-DUCTION OF SOLUTES

1. Normally the greater amount of mineral salt translocation in the stem is in the vessels and tracheids of the xylem. The movement is usually upward.

2. Salts also may be conducted in the phloem.

3. The major path of food movement is the phloem.

4. Food movement is from a region of high food content, place of manufacture or storage, to a place of food utilization, or from a point of manufacture to storage tissues.

5. Rapid lateral movement of solutes takes place along the vascular rays.

6. The mechanics of food movement are not well understood and much information still needs to be obtained before a detailed explanation of food movement can be given.

CLASSIFICATION OF PLANTS ACCORDING TO THEIR WATER NEEDS

In many agricultural sections of the country, and particularly in semiarid and arid regions, water is the principal limiting factor in crop production. Water is a most important factor in determining both the distribution of plants over the earth's surface and the character of the individual plant. Probably no single factor is so largely responsible for the diversity of plants in various habitats as is the difference in supply of water. So important are the water relations of plants that various attempts have been made to classify plants on the basis of these relations. One such classification is as follows: (1) **xerophytes** (Figs. 2.14, 6.58), plants that are able to live in very dry places, (2) **hydrophytes** (Fig. 2.3), plants that live in water or in very wet soil, and (3) **mesophytes,** plants that thrive best with a moderate water supply.

Plants with xerophytic characteristics, which limit transpiration or in other ways balance water outgo and water intake, occur in different climatic zones, but those of deserts are most typical. Xerophytic species do not necessarily have a lower transpiration rate than do mesophytes when water is ample, but they do possess one or more characteristics that enable them to survive periods of drought. The most effective of these are thick cuticle, stomatal closure, reduction of the transpiring surface, and water storage.

It should be kept in mind that all plants which fall in any one of the above three classes cease active growth when the soil moisture reaches the permanent wilting percentage. Xerophytes and mesophytes alike, growing side by side, reduce the soil to the same permanent wilting percentage. Mesophytes may not be able to survive the drought, whereas plants with xerophytic characteristics will. If the permanent wilting percentage of the soil is reached early in the season, because of low rainfall or unusually dry atmospheric conditions or a heavy "stand" of plants with its accompanying large transpiring surface, then individual plants will be stunted and production decreased. On the other hand, the active period of growth will be prolonged and the plants will be bigger if the amount of water stored in the soil is large, if atmospheric conditions are such that transpiration is not excessive, or if the number of plants per unit area is limited.

11

Photosynthesis and Respiration

The maintenance of life, whether in a plant or animal cell, requires the continual use of energy. Of all the many energy-consuming reactions going on in a living plant only two, transpiration and photosynthesis, are not regulated through the release of energy by respiration. During transpiration, energy from the sun is used to evaporate the water from the cell walls. Although this results in a movement of the water in the xylem, this energy is neither stored nor used to bring about the vital reactions involved in the synthesis of foods, in assimilation, growth, and reproduction. On the other hand, photosynthesis (Chapter 5) is a process in which energy from the sun is used to unite carbon dioxide and water into complex sugar molecules. During this process there is a liberation of oxygen. In this process the energy from the sun is changed into the energy which holds the atoms together in the sugar molecule. When sugar is broken down (oxidized during burning or during respiration in the cell), this energy is released and can do work. All energy-consuming reactions in the living cell, except transpiration and photosynthesis, are driven along by the continual release of energy from carbohydrates,

fats, and proteins, plant and animal foods. Photosynthesis stores the energy in these molecules. Respiration releases it, enabling the cells to perform the work of living.

PHOTOSYNTHESIS

"Photosynthesis by green plants alone prevents the rapid disappearance of all life from the face of the earth." This is a statement by a prominent physicist (Rabinowitch) in a review of photosynthesis. The principal characteristics of this process have been briefly discussed (page 72). It will be recalled that green plants are able to combine carbon dioxide and water to form a carbohydrate, a sugar. Neither carbon dioxide nor water will burn, nor would they make a very good meal. Carbohydrates (sugars, starches, cellulose), on the other hand, burn easily and release considerable energy in the process. Furthermore, many carbohydrates are excellent foods. The great importance of photosynthesis lies in the transformation of low-energy compounds, carbon dioxide and water, to high-energy compounds (sugars). This transformation occurs in the chloroplasts of green plants, which have the ability to convert the energy of sunlight into the chemical energy of the sugar molecule.

Photosynthesis is the largest single chemical process on earth; 200 billion tons of organic carbon are produced each year. This is about 100 times as much as the total annual output of all the chemical, metallurgical, and mining industries in the world; about 90 per cent of the energy used in industry is derived from coal and oil, which are composed of organic carbon compounds.

THE CHEMICAL REACTION

In spite of intensive investigation into the nature of photosynthesis, the actual chemical reactions as they occur in plant cells are still not completely understood. In the course of these studies sugars have been artificially synthesized; carbon dioxide and water have been combined to form a simple carbohydrate, and simple sugars have been united to form more complex carbohydrates. Necessarily, these laboratory experiments have been carried out under conditions very different from those existing in living cells. Furthermore, they require large expenditures of energy and their yields are very low, and so they are not as yet of any commercial importance.

The process of photosynthesis is the formation of high-energy organic compounds (sugars) from two low-energy inorganic compounds (carbon dioxide and water) in the presence of light and chlorophyll. Oxygen is liberated in the process. The overall reaction describing photosynthesis may be written as follows:

$$6CO_2 + 6H_2O \xrightarrow[\text{chlorophyll in living cells}]{\text{light energy}} C_6H_{12}O_6 + 6O_2$$

carbon dioxide + water → sugar + oxygen

Many steps and intermediate products are involved between the raw materials and the final products of this reaction. A knowledge of these intermediate steps is gradually being gained through the intensive research in photosynthesis. Some of the principal aspects of photosynthesis in living cells follow:

1. The raw materials for the process are carbon dioxide and water.

2. The products of the reaction are oxygen and sugar; the oxygen evolved comes from water, not from carbon dioxide.

3. Light energy is utilized to bring about the transformation of the low-energy raw materials into the high-energy product, sugar; definite amounts of light energy are required for definite amounts of sugar formed.

4. Chlorophyll, a green pigment present in the chloroplasts, absorbs the light energy and aids in the splitting of the water molecule.

5. The hydrogen of the water molecule is transferred to organic compounds and eventually to carbon dioxide; enzymes are responsible for some of these transfers. Light is not required for the action of enzymes.

6. Phosphorus is essential to the formation of sugars in plants; one of the intermediate compounds in photosynthesis is the phosphorus-containing phosphoglyceric acid.

Let us consider these aspects of photosynthesis in more detail.

The Raw Materials for the Process

Carbon Dioxide. The carbon dioxide utilized by land plants is absorbed by the leaves from the atmosphere. About 78 per cent of the atmosphere is nitrogen, about 21 per cent oxygen, the remaining small percentage being composed of carbon dioxide, argon, and traces of hydrogen, neon, helium, and other gases. Surprisingly, only about 0.03 per cent of the atmosphere is carbon dioxide.

Carbon dioxide in the air surrounding the leaves ultimately reaches the chloroplast. Its inward diffusion path is through the stomata to the intercellular spaces, through walls of palisade and spongy parenchyma cells, to the hyaloplasm, and thence into the chloroplasts. The walls of palisade and spongy parenchyma cells contain water. Carbon dioxide is readily soluble in water; hence, carbon dioxide passes through the cell walls in aqueous solution.

In the process of photosynthesis, the cells remove carbon dioxide from solution in the cell sap. As a result, there is diffusion of that gas inward from the wet cell walls. This loss of carbon dioxide from the cell wall allows the water in the wall to dissolve more carbon dioxide from the air in the intercellular spaces, which thus has its carbon dioxide content lowered below that of the outside atmosphere. Diffusion of carbon dioxide inward through stomata tends to make up this deficiency. Thus, during active photosynthesis in the chloroplasts, a diffusion gradient for carbon dioxide is set up between the outside atmosphere and the chloroplasts. At the same time, oxygen liberated in photosynthesis is used in respiration, or it diffuses outward in aqueous solution through the cell walls to intercellular spaces and thence through stomata to the atmosphere surrounding the leaf (Fig. 8.5).

We may rightly consider the problem: If all the chlorophyll-bearing cells of the plants of the world are constantly taking carbon dioxide from the atmosphere during daylight, the quantities of this gas used must be enormous, and there must necessarily be processes in nature that are continually replenishing this supply. It is known that the amount of carbon dioxide in the air is low (0.03 per cent) and that it remains fairly constant. It has been esti-

mated that an acre of corn (10,000 plants) during a growing season of 100 days will accumulate 5585 pounds of carbon; all this carbon is derived from the carbon dioxide of the atmosphere. It would require 20,480 pounds of carbon dioxide to furnish this quantity of carbon. These estimates serve to emphasize the fact that enormous quantities of carbon dioxide are used in the photosynthetic process of green plants.

Obviously, the amount of carbon dioxide is limited. The present atmospheric supply would be used up in about 22 years were it not constantly being renewed. Several natural processes are continually releasing carbon dioxide to the atmosphere. They are as follows: (1) The living cells of all plants (both green and nongreen) and of all animals release carbon dioxide in the respiratory process. (2) The dead bodies of plants and animals, and the excretions of animals, contain large quantities of carbon and other elements in the form of organic compounds; in the decay of these compounds, resulting from the activities of bacteria and fungi, large quantities of carbon dioxide are released to the atmosphere. (3) Carbon dioxide is also added to the atmosphere when wood, coal, oil, gas or any other carbon compound burns. (4) Carbon dioxide is released to the atmosphere from mineral springs and volcanoes. (5) The oceans are important reservoirs of carbon dioxide, and carbon dioxide probably escapes from the oceans whenever its concentration in the atmosphere decreases.

Water. In land plants, the soil is the source of water. The water used by the green cells enters the roots from the soil and is conducted upward through the xylem of the roots and stems to the leaves. It moves through the xylem of the petiole and veins of the leaf blade to the finest veinlets. Then it passes from the tracheids of the veinlets to the mesophyll. Although the water content of an actively photosynthesizing cell is high and large amounts of water are lost from the cell by transpiration, only about 1 per cent or less of the water absorbed by the roots is actually used in photosynthesis.

The Products of the Reaction

Oxygen. The evolution of oxygen during photosynthesis can be readily demonstrated. If an inverted glass funnel is placed in water over a mass of green water plants and the funnel is completely filled with water and then closed, the gas bubbles given off by the plants may be collected in the funnel tube. If a glowing splinter is inserted into the tube, it will glow more brightly, showing that the gas contains oxygen.

The volume of oxygen liberated in photosynthesis is approximately equal to the volume of carbon dioxide absorbed. This ratio, $O_2/CO_2 = 1$, is known as the **photosynthetic quotient.** Under like conditions of temperature and pressure, equal volumes of different gases have the same number of molecules; hence for every molecule of carbon dioxide absorbed during photosynthesis one molecule of oxygen is liberated. Thus the equation

$$6CO_2 + 6H_2O \xrightarrow[\text{green plant cell}]{\text{light energy}} C_6H_{12}O_6 + 6O_2$$

is supported by experimental data. This equation, however, does not indicate whether the oxygen evolved comes from the water or from the carbon dioxide. In order to answer this question, plants were exposed to carbon dioxide in which the oxygen was heavier than ordinary oxygen, having an atomic weight of 18 rather than 16. When this was done, the oxygen evolved during photosynthesis was found to be composed of oxygen atoms with an atomic weight of 16. However, when a photosynthesizing plant was placed in water

made with O^{18}, the oxygen evolved contained the O^{18}. This indicated that the process of photosynthesis involves a splitting of the water molecules and a liberation of oxygen from them.

A more complete equation for photosynthesis that indicates this fact is

$$6CO_2{}^{16} + 12H_2O^{18} \xrightarrow[\text{green plant cell}]{\text{light energy}}$$

$$C_6H_{12}O_6{}^{16} + 6O_2{}^{18} + 6H_2O^{16}$$

Sugar. The demonstrations that carbon dioxide and water are the raw materials and that oxygen is one of the end products of photosynthesis are easy to make and may be carried out in any botany laboratory. Proof that sugar is the other end product of photosynthesis is more difficult.

It has been pointed out that the photosynthetic quotient, O_2/CO_2, is equal to 1; in other words, the amount of carbon dioxide taken up by the leaf is equal to the amount of oxygen given off. This condition is met by the elaboration of a carbohydrate as is seen from the overall equation.

A chemical analysis of leaves in order to determine the compounds formed during photosynthesis is an obvious but not a simple procedure. Not only is photosynthesis very rapid but also the first products are quickly changed to other substances. Furthermore, changes may occur in preparing the leaves for analysis.

J. H. C. Smith, in 1943, successfully accounted for all the carbon dioxide absorbed by a leaf during a period of several hours. The analyses were accomplished by carefully measuring the amount of carbon dioxide the plants absorbed during a definite period of illumination. Then he located the carbon assimilated within the leaves. His results showed about 70 per cent of the carbon absorbed by the leaves was in the form of sugar. The remainder was present in starch and in a compound allied to cellu-

Fig. 11.1. Photograph of model of a 6-carbon-atom sugar.

lose. All of these compounds are carbohydrates.

These results seem to indicate (1) that sugar is most likely the first-formed carbohydrate, and that (2) it is very rapidly changed to other substances.

Sugar (glucose, $C_6H_{12}O_6$) may be written as follows:

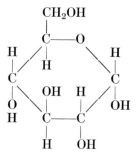

A formula like this, written with lines joining the letters representing atoms, is a structural formula and diagrammatically represents the positions of the atoms within the molecule. Actually, molecules have three dimensions with the various atoms associated with each other in definite positions. This is shown by the photograph of a model of a sugar molecule (Fig. 11.1).

Fructose is a 6-carbon atom sugar with a ring structure similar but not identical to that of glucose. Notice that 6 carbon atoms are contained in the molecule of glucose. Such sugars are known as **hexose sugars.** Sugars with 3, 4, 5, 7, and 8 carbon atoms in the molecule are also known. Furthermore, there are 24 possible different hexose sugars, 8 of which occur in nature. It seems likely that the first sugar in the photosynthetic process is a **hexose sugar.** Sucrose, ordinary table sugar, is composed of glucose and fructose.

Sugar molecules, attached in chains, form more complex carbohydrates, such as cellulose and starch. Only glucose molecules occur in starch, and they are united to form an irregular chain. Starch grains occur only in the chloroplasts of the higher plants and if leaves containing starch are kept in darkness for some time the starch grains will disappear (Fig. 11.2); then if these leaves are exposed to light, starch reappears in the chloroplasts. Starch is the *first visible product* of photosynthesis.

Fig. 11.2. Starch test. Right, leaf from plant kept 24 hours in darkness; middle, in light; left, leaf exposed to light but center portion covered. All leaves subsequently tested for the presence of starch. Dark areas indicate starch. $\times \frac{1}{2}$.

We have emphasized that photosynthesis involves the transformation of two low-energy inorganic compounds to a high-energy organic compound. We know that oxidation usually involves the union of oxygen with some other element or some compound and that energy is released during oxidation. Note that in photosynthesis oxygen is given off and that hydrogen combines with carbon dioxide to form a carbohydrate. This type of reaction is **reduction,** and requires energy. This energy requirement can be measured. We know, for instance, how much energy is needed to separate the oxygen from the hydrogen in the water molecule. The oxygen-hydrogen bonds in water are among the strongest known. The bonds that hold together carbon and oxygen in carbon dioxide are also quite strong, but in sugar or starch they may be easily broken. Carbon dioxide and water do not burn, but sugar does. In other words, the heat of combustion of carbon dioxide and water is zero, the heat of combustion of glucose is 673 kilocalories for each gram molecule of glucose.

It is interesting to note that the plant is able to rearrange the elements carbon, hydrogen, and oxygen which compose sugar to form compounds of even higher energy content. For instance, sugar may be transformed into fats—compounds also containing carbon, hydrogen, and oxygen.

Light—the Energy Used in Photosynthesis

Composition of White Light. It can be demonstrated that photosynthesis does not go on in the absence of light. If leaves are kept in the dark (or both surfaces covered with black paper or tinfoil), they do not increase in dry weight. But during exposure of green leaves to light, they increase in dry weight, owing chiefly to the production of sugar and starch using the carbon dioxide of the surrounding atmosphere.

White light, as it comes to us from the sun, is composed of waves of different lengths, ranging from the relatively long waves of red light, through successively shorter waves, to violet light. When passed

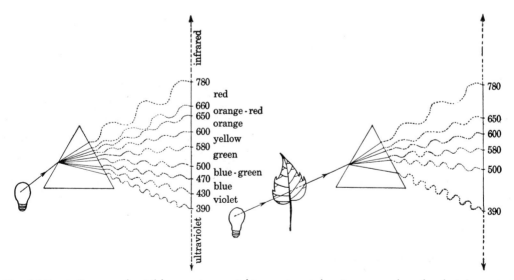

Fig. 11.3. Left, normal, visible spectrum; right, spectrum showing wave lengths that have not been absorbed by chlorophyll. Absorbed light does not enter prism.

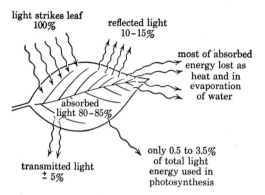

Fig. 11.4. Diagram showing what happens to light that strikes a leaf.

through a glass prism, white light is resolved into these colors. The band of colors is the **visible spectrum.** The complete visible spectrum is composed of the following colors (starting with the longest rays): red, orange, yellow, green, blue, indigo, and violet. Wave lengths exist that we are unable to perceive with our eyes. Beyond the red are still *longer,* invisible rays, the infrared; and beyond the violet are *shorter,* invisible rays, the ultraviolet. Thus, the visible spectrum represents only a part of the radiant energy that comes to the earth from the sun. But only a part of the visible spectrum is effective in photosynthesis (Fig. 11.3).

Efficiency of Photosynthesis. The green leaf is not particularly efficient in utilizing the sun's energy. We speak of the efficiency of a machine, such as a Diesel engine, a gasoline or electric motor. We calculate the energy value of the fuel used and compare it with the energy output of the machine. We know that much of the energy is lost. The ratio of energy outgo to the energy intake represents the efficiency. Of the total radiant energy that falls upon green leaves, about 80 per cent is absorbed (Fig. 11.4). Of the remaining 20 per cent, a part is reflected from the leaf surface and a part passes through the leaf. Part of that

absorbed is changed to heat and raises the temperature of the leaf; a large part of that absorbed is used up in transpiration; the remainder is utilized in photosynthesis and stored in the carbohydrate molecules. Thus only about 0.5 to 3.5 per cent of all the light energy that falls on a leaf is used in the process of photosynthesis. By standards of machine efficiency, this is a very low percentage. But the supply of solar energy is continuous and abundant. However, if we consider only the light reaching the chloroplasts, where photosynthesis actually occurs, an efficiency of 85 to 95 per cent may be obtained. This is a remarkably high efficiency.

Chlorophyll

The Chloroplast as the Place of Photosynthesis. Chlorophyll is almost universally confined to chloroplasts. The first visible product of photosynthesis is generally starch, and starch grains first appear in the chloroplasts of most plants when they are exposed to light.

Chloroplasts may be isolated from cells. Such chloroplasts will absorb light energy and bring about the splitting of water into hydrogen and oxygen when a suitable chemical that will combine with the hydrogen is present. In carefully controlled experiments such isolated chloroplasts may actually cause the synthesis of sugar from carbon dioxide and water. The structure of chloroplasts is still not fully understood. It appears that they are composed of a colorless background material called the **stroma** and that the chlorophyll is confined to small green structures, the **grana,** which are embedded in the stroma (Fig. 11.5). Some of the chemical reactions going on in photosynthesis are directly associated with the structure of the chloroplast.

Chlorophyll as an Aid in the Energy Transformations. The fact that chlorophyll is green to the eye is evidence that certain wave lengths of white light are absorbed by chlorophyll, while others are transmitted. It is this absorbed light that is used in photosynthesis. The part of the white light that is absorbed by chlorophyll can be determined if the light is passed through a solution of chlorophyll in alcohol and then caused to fall upon a glass prism so that it is broken up into its component colors. The spectrum thus formed is different from the spectrum of white light that has not passed through a chlorophyll solution. In the chlorophyll spectrum, the wave lengths that are absorbed appear as dark bands, the absorption bands (Fig. 11.3). Thus, the positions of dark bands in the chlorophyll spectrum indicate which wave lengths are absorbed. They show that much of the red, and much of the blue, indigo, and violet are absorbed; these are the wave lengths that are utilized the most in photosynthesis. Part of the red and most of the yellow, orange, and green are scarcely absorbed at all unless the chlorophyll solution is very concentrated.

Only absorbed light can be utilized in photosynthetic reactions. If a green leaf, instead of a chlorophyll solution, is placed between a light source and a prism, the absorption bands are quite similar though not identical with those from the chlorophyll solution (Fig. 11.3). The leaf contains the yellow carotenoid pigments that absorb blue light; also the chlorophyll in the leaf is probably in association with protein and fatlike materials while the chlorophyll in the solution is not. These factors contribute to the difference between the absorption spectra of a green leaf and of a chlorophyll solution.

Some plants, such as certain varieties of geranium and of *Coleus*, have variegated leaves, that is, leaves with white bands or blotches. Microscopic examination of the mesophyll cells of the white areas shows them to be devoid of chloroplasts. These

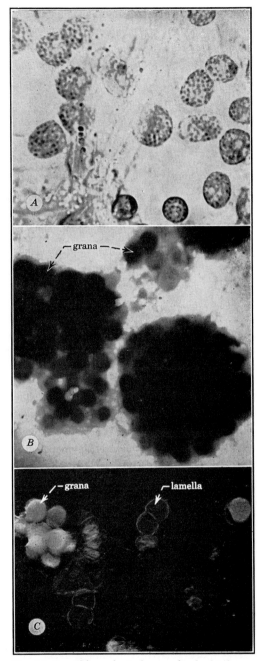

Fig. 11.5. Chloroplasts from a leaf of tobacco (*Nicotiana tabacum*). A, isolated chloroplasts showing grana and stroma, ×1000; B, portions of plastids showing grana, ×8000; C, grana and lamella of grana, ×8000. (B and C courtesy of Granick.)

Fig. 11.6. Variegated leaves of *Coleus* showing green and nongreen areas. A, chlorophyll extracted, leaf subsequently tested for
presence of starch; B, untreated. Dark area
in A indicates starch; in B, chlorophyll. $\times \frac{1}{2}$.

cells, however, are living and functioning.
If a variegated leaf is given the starch test
after several hours' exposure to light, starch
will be found only in those cells that contain chloroplasts (Fig. 11.6), demonstrating that photosynthesis and starch storage have occurred in association with the
chloroplasts.

Enzymes Are Necessary for Photosynthesis

Photosynthesis will not go on in the absence of light yet many of the steps in the
process are controlled by enzymes and are
not sensitive to light. This can readily be
shown by comparing the rate of photosynthesis by a plant exposed to a bright light
at 20° C and then exposed to the same
light at 5° C. It is known that photo-
reactions (reactions brought about by light
energy) are relatively unaffected by temperature in contrast with enzyme reactions
that are temperature sensitive. When one
takes pictures on a hot beach or in the snow,
one makes the same exposure for the same
light conditions irrespective of the tem-

perature. This is because the reaction of
light on the film is a photo-reaction and
not particularly sensitive to temperature.
Likewise if photosynthesis were only a light
reaction or series of light reactions it should
not be influenced by a change in temperature. In our example above, however, it
would be found that the rate of photosynthesis would be several times faster at 20° C
than at 5° C, as long as the plant was in
bright light.

This means that some of the intermediate
reactions in the process of photosynthesis
are temperature sensitive and hence controlled by enzymes rather than by light. As
we have seen, the splitting of water is a
light sensitive photo-reaction that goes on
in the chloroplast. Other steps in the reduction of carbon dioxide are, however,
controlled by enzymes.

Phosphorus and Photosynthesis

Much knowledge of the process of photosynthesis has been gained in recent years by
using carbon dioxide that has been tagged
with radioactive carbon and studying the
utilization of this carbon dioxide by plants.
If photosynthesis proceeds for an hour or so
in an atmosphere containing tagged carbon
dioxide, most of the labeled carbon will be
found in carbohydrates (sugar). If photosynthesis is stopped after only a few seconds, most of the labeled carbon is found
in a compound called **phosphoglyceric acid.**

Phosphoglyceric acid, formed during photosynthesis, is thus an intermediate between
carbon dioxide and sugar. This compound
contains three carbon atoms as well as one
phosphorus atom, while glucose and fructose, characteristic plant sugars, are 6-car-
bon atom sugars and contain no phosphorus.
Evidence indicates that a further step in the
formation of sugar is the joining together
of two 3-carbon molecules derived from
phosphoglyceric acid. Indeed it has been

found that the first sugars formed during photosynthesis are sugar phosphates and only at a later step are free sugars produced (Fig. 11.7).

CONDITIONS AFFECTING THE RATE OF PHOTOSYNTHESIS

The rate of photosynthesis is of great importance in agricultural production. The rate at which sugar or other carbohydrates is formed will affect the yield of any given crop.

Internal Factors

The rate of photosynthesis is influenced by a number of **internal factors,** that is, conditions inherent in the plant itself. Chief of these are: (1) the structure of the leaf and its chlorophyll content; (2) accumulation within the chlorophyll-bearing cells of the products of photosynthesis; and (3) protoplasmic influences, including enzymes. Considering the interplay of these various internal factors, it is evident that different species of plants vary considerably in their photosynthetic efficiency, even when growing under the same environmental conditions.

Leaf Structure. The structural features of the leaf influence the amount of carbon dioxide that reaches the chloroplasts. These features include size, position and behavior of the stomata, and the amount of intercellular space. Also, the intensity and quality of the light that reaches the chloroplasts are influenced by thickness of the cuticle and epidermis, by presence of epidermal hairs, arrangement of mesophyll cells, position of chloroplasts in the cells, etc.

Products of Photosynthesis. With an increase in the concentration of the products of photosynthesis in mesophyll cells, there is a decrease in the photosynthetic rate. Starch may accumulate in chloroplasts during the day, when sugar is manufactured at a more rapid rate than it is transferred from the cell; a result of this accumulation may be a retardation in the rate of photosynthesis.

Protoplasm. The rate of photosynthesis is affected by conditions associated with the protoplasm itself. If the cells lack water and the protoplasm is dehydrated, photosynthesis slows down. Moreover, a disturbance of certain enzyme activities, influences the photosynthetic rate.

External Factors

These factors as they influence the rate of photosynthesis are, to a degree, under the control of the plant grower. Crop yields can be influenced by modifying these factors. The principal external conditions that affect the rate of photosynthesis are (1) temperature, (2) light—its intensity, quality, and duration, (3) carbon dioxide content of the air, (4) water supply, and (5) mineral elements in the soil.

Temperature. Plants of cold climates carry on photosynthesis at much lower temperatures than do those of warm climates. The process is known to occur in certain evergreen species of cold regions, even at temperatures below 0° C. Algae in the water of hot springs may carry on photosynthesis at a temperature as high as 75° C. Most ordinary temperate-climate plants, however, function best between temperatures of 10° and 35° C. If there is adequate light intensity and a normal supply of carbon dioxide, the rate of photosynthesis of most ordinary land plants increases with an increase in temperature up to about 25° C; above this range there is a continuous fall in the rate as the temperature is raised. At these higher temperatures the time of exposure is of importance. At a given constant high temperature (e.g., 40° C), the rate of photosynthesis decreases with time.

Under conditions of low light intensity an

increase in temperature will not produce an increase in photosynthesis. These conditions may occur in the winter time in greenhouses. If the temperature is raised too high the plants will suffer because the rate of photosynthesis has not been changed but respiration has been increased by the higher temperature.

Light. In discussing the effect of light upon the rate of photosynthesis, three elements must be considered: (1) intensity, (2) quality (wave lengths), and (3) duration. With temperature and carbon dioxide sufficient, carbohydrates produced by a given area of leaf surface increase with increasing light intensity up to a certain point (optimum light intensity), after which they decrease. It is not the intensity of light that falls upon the leaf surface that is of importance as much as it is the intensity to which the chloroplasts are exposed. The light intensity diminishes from the leaf surface to the chloroplasts, owing to surface hairs, thick cuticle, thick epidermis, the shading of deeper-lying chloroplasts by superficial chloroplasts, and other structural features.

Intense light appears to retard the rate of photosynthesis. Many plants that live in deserts and other places where the light is very bright often have structural adaptations which tend to diminish the intensity of light that reaches the chloroplasts. The usual light intensity in arid and semiarid regions is well above the optimum for photosynthesis in many plants, especially introduced crop plants. In these regions on days when the sky is overcast, the light intensity is probably nearer the optimum for photosynthesis than on clear, sunny days. Leaves on the surface of plants receive light of greater intensity than those beneath that are shaded. Therefore, some of the leaves receive light of optimum intensity, whereas others may receive light either above or below the optimum.

So-called smother crops or competitive crops are used to suppress weed growth. Such crops as rye, winter barley, rape, hemp, millet, and Sudan grass make a rapid growth and soon produce a shade, shielding the young weeds underneath from sufficient light so that photosynthesis is greatly retarded. Of course, in addition, smother crops compete with weeds for water and mineral nutrients.

Carbon Dioxide. The atmosphere has approximately 0.03 per cent carbon dioxide by volume. If light intensity and temperature are favorable, the carbon dioxide of the atmosphere limits the rate of photosynthesis. This may be particularly true in greenhouses kept closed in the winter time. Under these conditions the carbon dioxide in the air may be reduced much below the 0.03 per cent average.

It has been determined experimentally that at usual temperatures and light intensities an artificial increase of carbon dioxide up to a concentration of 0.5 per cent may give an increased rate of photosynthesis, but only for a limited period. It appears that after 10 to 15 days' exposure to these higher concentrations of carbon dioxide the plants show injury.

Water Supply. As we know, water is an essential chemical component in photosynthesis. Although but a small fraction (approximately 1 per cent) of the water absorbed by a plant is used in photosynthesis, the rate of this process may be changed by small differences in water content of the chlorophyll-bearing cells. In some instances the rate of photosynthesis is increased by mild dehydration (15 per cent water loss) and retarded by vigorous drying (45 per cent water loss). Since stomata tend to close when the plant is deprived of water, conditions of drought tend to reduce the rate of photosynthesis. Thus, though water is one of the raw materials in the process, it rarely, if ever, is directly a **limiting** factor in photosynthesis.

Minerals. The chemical formula of chlorophyll *a* is $C_{55}H_{72}O_5N_4Mg$ and, of chlorophyll *b*, $C_{55}H_{70}O_6N_4Mg$. Thus it is seen that the manufacture of chlorophyll depends upon a supply of nitrogen and magnesium, both derived from salts in the soil. Moreover, chlorophyll is not formed unless iron is available, although this element is not a component of the chlorophyll molecule. Leaves of plants deficient in nitrogen, magnesium, or iron are pale and yellow, a condition termed **chlorosis.** This abnormal condition may be caused also by other factors, but when it occurs the rate of photosynthesis is lowered.

SUMMARY OF PHOTO- SYNTHESIS

Some of the important points that have been mentioned concerning photosynthesis are summarized in the schematic diagram shown (Fig. 11.7).

1. Photosynthesis is the major energy-storing process of life in which light energy is stored as chemical energy in organic compounds.

2. Carbon dioxide and water are the raw materials.

3. The products of photosynthesis are sugar and oxygen.

4. Light energy is absorbed by chlorophyll in the chloroplasts and drives the reaction of photosynthesis along by splitting water, releasing oxygen.

5. The hydrogen of the water is transferred to organic compounds and eventually reduces the carbon dioxide.

6. Phosphorus is essential to the formation of sugars in plants and is found in some of the intermediate products, one of which is phosphoglyceric acid.

7. Many steps in the process of photosynthesis are controlled by enzymes.

8. Both external and internal factors affect the rate of photosynthesis.

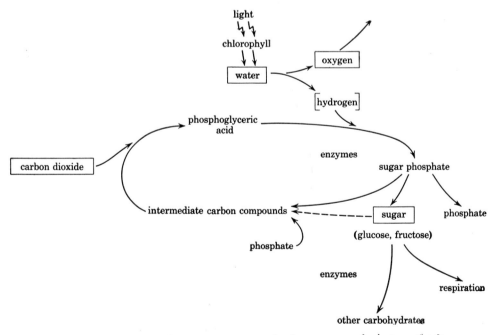

Fig. 11.7. Diagram showing some steps in the process of photosynthesis.

RESPIRATION

The term respiration was first used to indicate the exchange of gases between an organism and its environment. Even today respiration and breathing of animals are often popularly considered to be synonymous. Nevertheless, breathing is only an outward indication of the fundamental chemical reactions going on in the animal cells and characteristic of all life. Every living cell, in order to stay alive, must break down complex organic molecules, foods, and obtain energy from them. This breakdown process, as we have seen (page 74), is brought about through oxidation reactions and often, though not always, yields carbon dioxide and water as end products. Today the term respiration has come to have a wider and more fundamental meaning than mere gaseous exchange or breathing. *Respiration is defined as the oxidation of organic substances within cells, and is accompanied by the release of energy.*

THE CHEMICAL REACTION

A knowledge of the process and effects of respiration in plant cells is of paramount importance to growers and handlers of fruits and vegetables. For example, let us consider the storage of a ton of apples. Every apple contains thousands of living cells each of which is respiring. If sufficient oxygen is available to the cells, each cell will be using oxygen to break down some of its sugar and will be producing carbon dioxide, water, energy, and in addition, various other products in low concentration. Much of the energy is not used by the cells but is lost as heat.

If the fruit has been packed tightly together in a closed storage room, the environment around the apples will change. The air will be depleted of oxygen and become richer in carbon dioxide. The apples will begin to warm up. Such changes will affect the storage life of the fruit and must be controlled if the fruit is to be held in storage with a minimum of loss.

Respiration involves a whole series of chemical reactions, each of which is controlled by a particular enzyme and each of which proceeds more slowly at low temperatures than at high temperatures. Cold storage slows down respiration and reduces the changes in fruit during storage. Refrigeration is needed not only to cool the fruit but to prevent the release and accumulation of heat by the fruit itself as a result of respiration. How much ice would be required to prevent the heat released during respiration from heating the fruit? For example, if we desired to keep in storage a ton of apples at 0° C, it would require between five and six pounds of ice every day to prevent the heat released by respiration from raising the temperature of the apples above 0° C. It is apparent that shippers of fruits and vegetables must know how much refrigeration should be supplied to keep the produce at the proper temperature. Likewise they must know how the products of respiration affect the stored plant material. Carbon dioxide at high concentrations can be toxic. If allowed to accumulate, injurious effects may result. Various gases, such as ethylene, are given off by some cells during respiration and affect the ripening processes of certain fruits. These and many other problems make a knowledge of plant respiration essential to agriculturists.

The Overall Process of Respiration

The process of respiration is summarized by the following equation which represents the oxidation of a simple hexose sugar in the presence of oxygen from the atmosphere:

$$\text{sugar} \quad + \text{ oxygen} \rightarrow \text{ carbon dioxide} + \text{water} + \text{energy}$$
$$C_6H_{12}O_6 + 6O_2 \quad \rightarrow 6CO_2 \quad\quad\quad + 6H_2O + 673 \text{ kcal}$$

The equation for respiration indicates the two reacting substances, sugar and oxygen, and the two usual end products, water and carbon dioxide; it tells nothing of the intermediate steps or of other possible end products.

In our brief consideration of this process, all of the detailed steps whereby sugar is completely oxidized will not be discussed. Rather the process of respiration will be considered as consisting of several general phases, each of which represents a whole series of individual reactions. Further, although these reactions have been studied in some organisms it is not necessarily true that the course of respiration follows the same pathway in all plant cells.

When a cell uses sugar in the process of respiration, the sugar first undergoes a series of changes and is broken apart. No atmospheric or molecular oxygen enters into these first reactions, but small amounts of energy

tion by the addition of phosphorus—**phosphorylation.**

2. The splitting of the sugar into two fragments—**sugar cleavage.**

3. The oxidation of the fragments to form an intermediate product of respiration—**pyruvic acid formation.**

The final reactions of respiration are influenced by the presence or absence of oxygen. If oxygen is present, as is usual, the intermediate product formed by glycolysis is oxidized to carbon dioxide and water. This process that requires molecular oxygen is called **aerobic respiration.** If oxygen is absent, a state that prevails under certain conditions, the intermediate compounds of glycolysis are usually broken down to form carbon dioxide and alcohol. This process, that does not involve molecular oxygen, is termed **anaerobic respiration.**

We may summarize respiration as follows:

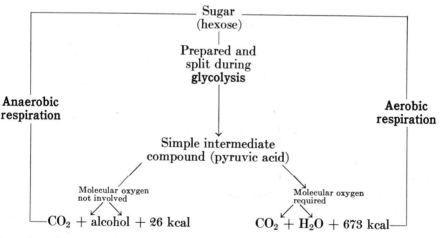

are released and intermediate compounds are formed. This series of reactions is usually referred to as **glycolysis** and consists of the following three steps:

1. The preparation of the sugar for reac-

Preparation of Sugar for Reaction. Sugar itself does not combine readily with oxygen at temperatures at which life reactions proceed, nor is it easily broken down into intermediate products. You will recall that phosphorus compounds serve as intermediate steps in photosynthesis and that sugar phosphates are formed. So also in respiration, before sugar can be broken down and its stored energy released, it must be combined with phosphorus to form sugar phosphate. This preparation of sugar in the process of respiration is called **phosphorylation** and like the other steps in respiration is controlled by enzymes. The phosphorus that combines with the sugar molecule comes from an organic phosphorus compound, **adenosine triphosphate (ATP)**, that gives up one of the three phosphate groups that it contains. Two ATP molecules are involved in the complete phosphorylation of the sugar molecule. Adenosine triphosphate and similar organic phosphorus compounds are formed during the later stages of respiration and are very important as carriers of energy in cell metabolism. They might be likened to cogs in the respiration wheel that mesh with other wheels of cell metabolism and through which the energy of respiration can be directed to turn the other reaction wheels.

Sugar Cleavage. After sugar has been prepared by phosphorylation, enzymes can now act on it to break the molecule into two parts. The original 6-carbon atom sugar becomes changed into two 3-carbon atom fragments that are each still combined with phosphorus. You will recall that photosynthesis also involves a 3-carbon atom intermediate compound containing phosphorus. In some of its stages, respiration appears to be a reversal of photosynthesis.

Pyruvic Acid Formation. The sugar fragments containing phosphorus lose their phosphorus, some of their hydrogen atoms, and a small amount of energy in a series of reactions that result in the formation of the 3-carbon atom intermediate compound called **pyruvic acid.** During the changes that have so far been described, molecular oxygen has played no part. Oxidation of

the sugar has occurred through a rearrangement of the atoms within the molecule and the removal of some of its hydrogen. The fate of the final product of glycolysis, the final intermediate compound common to both aerobic and anaerobic respiration, now will depend upon the presence or absence of molecular oxygen.

Anaerobic Respiration. Normally, higher plants are not able to live long in the absence of oxygen. Under this condition, insufficient energy is available for life processes, and certain products formed may be poisonous. By contrast some fruits, notably apples, may be held for long periods in an atmosphere containing very small amounts of oxygen and continue to give off carbon dioxide. Other plants, such as yeast, may live actively in an atmosphere with very small amounts of oxygen and produce relatively large amounts of carbon dioxide and alcohol. Still other microorganisms will live in an atmosphere completely devoid of oxygen.

Under completely anaerobic conditions the products of glycolysis are most frequently converted into carbon dioxide and ethyl alcohol. This process is often called alcoholic fermentation. In this process the original sugar is only partially oxidized and only a small amount of its energy is released; the rest remains unavailable to the organism. This energy is still locked in the molecular structure of the alcohol. Alcohol and carbon dioxide are not the only possible products of anaerobic respiration. There is a great variety of microorganisms that respire anaerobically and many produce other products besides alcohol (see page 340).

Aerobic Respiration. Although some cells of higher plants are capable of living under anaerobic conditions, such conditions are harmful to the majority of the tissues and to the entire plant. Anaerobic respiration that results only in a partial breakdown of the foods either does not yield sufficient energy for the life processes of these cells or the partially oxidized products may injure the cells. Aerobic respiration is the common way in which these cells obtain energy.

When oxygen is dissolved in the cell fluid and the sugar has been prepared, as explained, the oxygen itself is still unable to combine directly with this intermediate compound (pyruvic acid). Rather, a whole series of reactions must occur before the final products, carbon dioxide and water, are formed. These reactions can be summarized in two main steps:

1. *The organic acid cycle of respiration.* This involves the gradual breakdown of pyruvic acid. Other organic acids in the plant combine with pyruvic acid, carbon

dioxide is lost, and hydrogen is removed in several stages (Fig. 11.8).

2. *Terminal oxidation, the final stage of aerobic respiration.* The hydrogen that has been removed from the substance being respired is transferred by a series of enzymatic reactions to molecular oxygen, and water is formed (Fig. 11.8). Let us briefly look at these final two stages of aerobic respiration.

The Organic Acid Cycle of Respiration. Sometimes this is called the Krebs cycle after a physiologist whose research contributed a great deal to our knowledge of respiration. It has been found that, after glycolysis has broken down sugar into pyruvic acid, the hydrogen in this compound is removed by a series of reactions. One

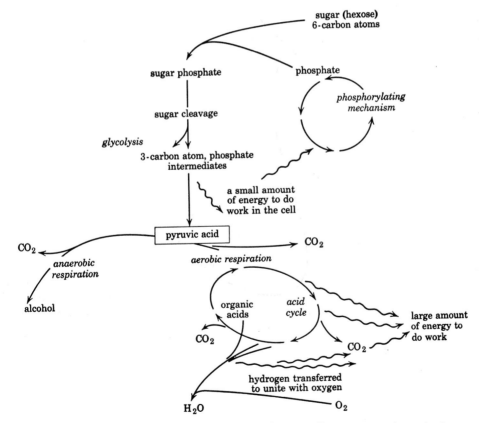

Fig. 11.8. Diagram showing some steps in the overall processes of respiration.

of the ways in which this may occur in the cell is that pyruvic acid combines with another organic acid (oxaloacetic acid) that is present in the cell. In this process a larger molecule (also an acid) is produced and a molecule of carbon dioxide is lost. Now the new acid is gradually broken down a small piece at a time. Hydrogen is removed and transferred to other substances, carbon dioxide is evolved, and finally a new molecule of oxaloacetic acid is formed which in turn can combine with more pyruvic acid to keep the cycle going, as shown in Fig. 11.8.

Because this is a repeating process and because organic acids are involved in the process, it has been called the organic acid cycle of respiration. It is believed that in many plants, animals, and microorganisms such a cycle is a part of aerobic respiration. In this stage, some of the energy contained in the pyruvic acid being oxidized is lost as heat, but much of it is stored in energy-rich compounds, such as adenosine triphosphate (page 216), that are produced during this oxidation. These energy-rich compounds can be broken down by the plant cell and some of the energy that they contain is used to do work in the cell, such as the phosphorylation of sugars (page 216).

The Final Stages of Oxidation. We have seen how in the presence of oxygen sugar may be broken down and the hydrogen of its molecule removed and carbon dioxide produced. The final stages of aerobic respiration involve a transfer of this hydrogen by means of a series of enzyme reactions to molecular oxygen; thus, water is produced and respiration is complete.

SUMMARY OF RESPIRATION

We may summarize the process of respiration as shown in Fig. 11.8.

1. Sugar is prepared for oxidation through the process of phosphorylation during which phosphorus is transferred from an organic phosphorus donor to the sugar molecule. Sugar cleavage then occurs resulting in the production of two 3-carbon atom phosphate intermediates. These in turn are oxidized to the common intermediate pyruvic acid.

2. If molecular oxygen is absent, pyruvic acid is changed to ethyl alcohol and carbon dioxide in the final stages of anaerobic respiration. Only small amounts of energy are released in this process.

3. If molecular oxygen is present the pyruvic acid becomes further oxidized to carbon dioxide and water through the organic acid cycle. In this process, aerobic respiration, large amounts of energy are stored in energy-rich compounds that are used when work is done in the cell.

12

The Flower

The rapid progress in the improvement of useful plants has been made possible by the knowledge gained through fundamental studies as to the nature of the reproductive processes in flowers. We are familiar with the phenomenal yields of hybrid corn, a product of the plant breeder. The growing of hybrid corn, a comparatively recent commercial development, has greatly increased food production in a hungry world. The breeding of other staple crops, such as wheat, oats, barley, sugar cane, and sugar beet, is based upon an understanding of flower structures and the reproductive processes associated with these structures.

In Chapter 2 where the plant body was discussed the importance of the flower was pointed out. Flowers are the reproductive organs of the common plants we see about us. The flower itself is a group of specialized leaves called **floral leaves** adapted for (1) the development of reproductive cells, (2) the correct functioning of these cells, and (3) the ultimate development of the seed. These floral leaves grouped together on a stem form the flower.

In the chapter "The Plant Cell" it was stated that the chromosomes carry the determiners of inheritance, that there are two critical stages of chromosome behavior associated with sexual reproduction: **fertilization** and **meiosis**. In fertilization two protoplasmic bodies, usually from different individual plants, unite to form one body of protoplasm, thus combining factors that determine characters from two different parents. In meiosis, four cells are formed, each containing sets of chromosomes that differ somewhat from each other. Thus character-determining factors within a single individual are sorted out.

Just what is the structure of the reproductive organs that makes possible the combining of the hereditary characters of two parents and the sorting out of the characters of one parent? In this chapter, we shall discuss the structure and development of the organs of the flower, the transportation of pollen, and the process of fertilization. The transfer of pollen is called **pollination;** the fusion of two protoplasmic bodies is termed **fertilization.** Following fertilization, the **seed** develops. In flowering plants, the seed or seeds are enveloped by tissues of the parent plant, the whole constituting the **fruit.** The seeds are scattered by various agencies and, if conditions are suitable, germinate to form new individual plants.

Thus the steps involved in the reproduction of flowering plants are: (1) the pro-

219

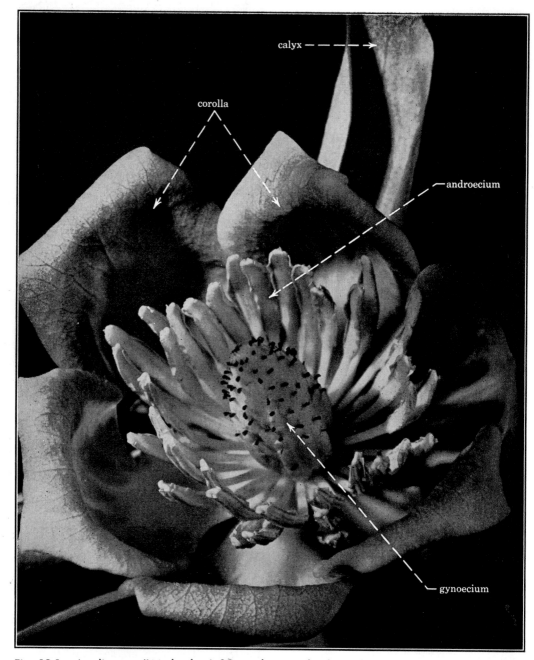

Fig. 12.1. A tulip tree (*Liriodendron*) flower showing the four whorls. Only one sepal of the calyx is apparent. $\times \frac{3}{4}$. (Courtesy of Russell.)

duction of special reproductive cells, (2) pollination, (3) fertilization, (4) seed and fruit development, (5) fruit and seed dissemination, and (6) seed germination. In Chapter 4 we called attention to the fact that all plants have a life cycle. These six steps constitute the essential steps in the life cycle of a flowering plant.

THE MORPHOLOGY OF THE FLOWER

Flowers are of many different forms. They also vary greatly in size, color, number of parts, and arrangement of parts. There are flowers so small that their organs are scarcely visible to the unaided eye; such are the flowers of the duckweeds, free-floating plants common in ponds throughout the world. Then there are the flowers of a plant (*Rafflesia*), growing on the floor of dark tropical forests of the Malay archipelago, which are 3 to 4 feet in diameter.

A typical flower is composed of four main parts: (1) **sepals**, (2) **petals**, (3) **stamens**, and (4) a **carpel** or **carpels**, all attached to the **receptacle**, the modified stem end that supports these structures (Figs. 12.1, 12.2, 12.3).

The **sepals** enclose the other flower parts in the bud. Generally, they are green. All the sepals taken collectively constitute the **calyx**; that is, the calyx of a flower is composed of more or less distinct parts, the sepals.

The **petals** are usually the conspicuous, colored, attractive flower parts. Taken together, the petals constitute the **corolla**.

The **stamens** form a whorl, lying inside of the corolla. Each stamen has a slender stalk or **filament**, at the top of which is an **anther**, the pollen-bearing organ. The whorl or grouping of stamens is called the **androecium**.

The **carpel** or **carpels** comprise the central whorl of modified floral leaves. Collec-

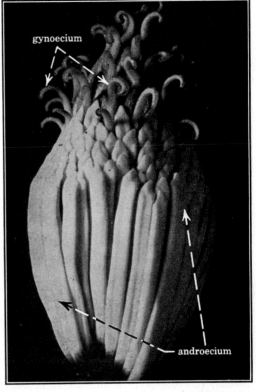

Fig. 12.2. The essential organs of a *Magnolia* flower. ×1.

tively the carpels are spoken of as the **gynoecium**. Each individual structure in the gynoecium is commonly referred to as a **pistil**. As will be shown later a pistil may consist of one or more carpels and an individual flower may have one or more pistils. This name is ancient and is derived from the resemblance of numerous commonly occurring pistils to the pestle of the mortar-and-pestle set always present in the medieval pharmacy where it was frequently used to compound medicines from floral parts. The term is a convenient one but modern concepts of flower structure have rendered its meaning somewhat inexact.

There are generally three distinct parts to each pistil: (1) an expanded basal portion, the **ovary**, in which are borne the

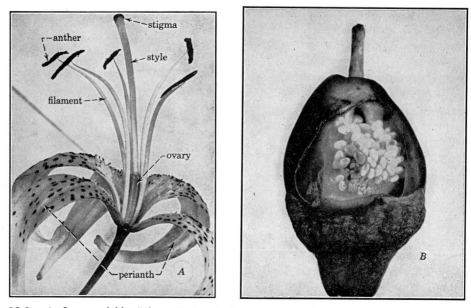

Fig. 12.3. A, flower of lily (*Lilium tigrinum*) showing perianth, stamens, and pistil. Petal facing camera has been removed; B, pistil from a flower of pepper (*Capsicum frutescens*), ovary opened to show ovules.

ovules, (2) the **style** a slender stalk supporting (3) the **stigma** (Fig. 12.3A). The pollen is deposited on the stigma.

The **receptacle** is the enlarged end of the flower stem or stalk to which the sepals, petals, stamens, and pistils are attached.

The term **perianth** is applied to the calyx and corolla collectively. It is frequently used to describe those flowers, such as the tulip, in which the two outer whorls, though present, are morphologically indistinguishable.

Sometimes individual flowers or compact clusters of flowers will have a whorl of small leaves or **bracts** standing close below them. Such a collection of bracts subtending flowers is called an **involucre.**

The parts of the flower in outline are as follows:

Receptacle
Calyx, consisting of sepals ⎱ Perianth
Corolla, consisting of petals ⎰

Androecium, consisting of stamens
Gynoecium, consisting of carpels

ESSENTIAL ORGANS OF THE FLOWER

The essential floral organs are the androecium (stamens) and gynoecium (carpels) (Fig. 12.2). They are essential in that they produce reproductive bodies. The perianth, composed of calyx and corolla, is a protective covering of the stamens and pistil.

The Androecium *STAMENS*

Each stamen consists of an anther supported on a stalk, or filament (Figs. 12.3, 12.4, 12.5). The anther usually has two longitudinal lobes united by a band of tissue. Each lobe has two longitudinal pollen sacs, within which the **pollen grains** are produced. Before the distribution of pollen, the tissue separating the two pollen sacs in each lobe of the anther breaks down. In most species a longitudinal slit then develops in the wall of each anther lobe. The edges of the slit separate and the pollen escapes through the opening thus formed.

The anther consists at first of a small mass of meristematic cells. Early differentiated in this mass are four separate groups of cells, called **pollen mother cells** (Fig. 12.4A, B). Each pollen mother cell by two successive divisions forms four cells, each with a single nucleus. These cells are commonly called **spores** and since they are smaller in size than cells formed in a similar manner (by meiosis) in the ovules

(page 287), they are known as small spores or **microspores** (Fig. 12.4C, D). Shortly after they are formed the single nucleus divides mitotically so that a two-celled body results. This body eventually forms a heavy cell wall and is the **pollen grain**. The two nuclei are called the **generative** and **tube nuclei**, respectively (Fig. 12.4E). At this stage the pollen is generally shed and in some manner transferred to the stigma of adjacent flowers. This process is **pollination**. On the stigma the pollen grain germinates to form a **pollen tube**. Within the pollen tube the tube nucleus degenerates and the generative cell divides to form two **sperms** (Fig. 12.4F).

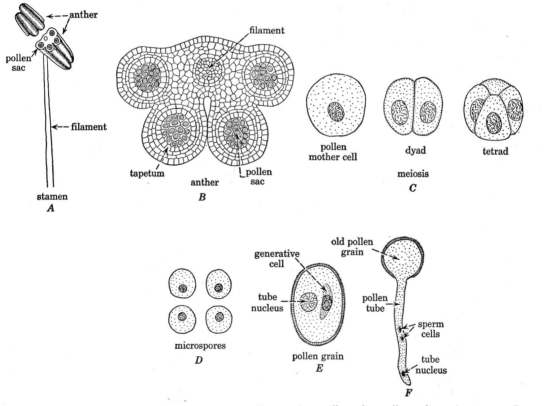

Fig. 12.4. Development of pollen from a pollen mother cell to the pollen tube. A, stamen; B, cross section of anther; C, development of tetrad of cells from the pollen mother cell by meiosis; D, four microspores; E, pollen grain; F, germination of pollen grain into pollen tube. Diagrammatic.

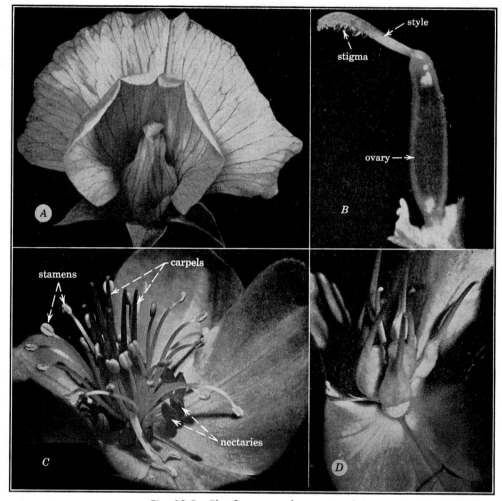

Fig. 12.5.   The flowers and gynecia of A, B, pea (*Pisum sativum*);

The Gynoecium PISTILS

The structure of the gynoecium depends upon the number and arrangement of carpels comprising it (Fig. 12.5). In the pea flower (Fig. 12.5A) there is a single carpel forming the gynoecium (Fig. 12.5B). It consists of three parts, (1) the **ovary**, an expanded basal portion, (2) the **style**, a slender stalk which ends in (3) a hairy irregular portion, the **stigma**. In the flower of the Christmas rose (Fig. 12.5C) there are five separate and distinct carpels comprising the gynoecium, and each carpel has its own ovary, style, and stigma (Fig. 12.5D). In the flower of *Cotyledon* (Fig. 12.5E, F) there are again five carpels, which while not actually fused together, grow so compactly as to appear on casual observation to form a single central organ. Now in the tulip (Figs. 12.5G, H) there are three carpels so completely fused that only a single structure is present to represent the central whorl of floral leaves. This flower

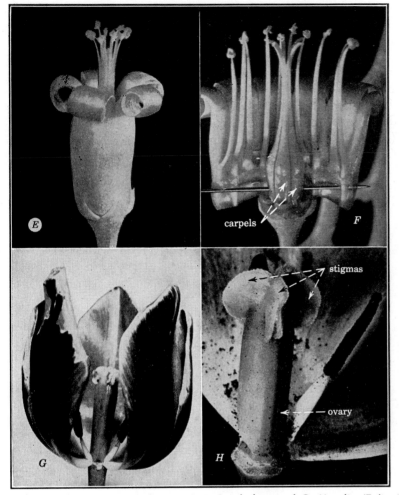

C, D, Christmas rose (*Helleborus*); E, F, Cotyledon; and G, H, tulip (*Tulipa*).

has a single ovary, divided, however, into three sectors, a single short style and three stigmas.

The term pistil refers to the arrangement of carpels in these examples in the following manner:

Plant	Carpels	Pistil
Pea	1 carpel	1 simple pistil
Christmas rose	5 single and separate carpels	5 simple pistils
Cotyledon	5 distinct but closely appressed carpels	5 simple pistils
Tulip	3 fused carpels	1 compound pistil

In all of these cases the term gynoecium refers to the carpels taken collectively without reference to their number or their manner of association with each other. The term simple pistil refers to a single carpel, while a compound pistil denotes the union of several carpels to form a single structure.

The Carpel as a Modified Leaf. The question arises as to why a carpel is considered to be a modified leaf. There are two main reasons for so considering it. One of these is its manner of development, which in early stages resembles that of a foliage leaf. After this early leaf development the two edges of the carpel grow together (Fig. 12.6).

Starting as a mere enlargement of meristematic tissue, the carpel becomes a hollow structure (ovary) from the top of which is an extension, the style, bearing at its tip the stigma. In the development, the two edges of the carpel (floral leaf) grow together (Fig. 12.6). This line of union is called the **ventral suture,** and the line corresponding to the midrib of the carpel is called the **dorsal suture.** In the carpel along the ventral suture, **ovules** (which after fertilization, develop into seeds) arise. The special tissue from which ovules develop is called the **placenta** (Figs. 12.7D, 12.9), and to which they eventually are attached by a short stalk known as the **funiculus.**

The compound pistil of violet is first evident as a shallow depression at the summit of the floral apex (Fig. 12.7). This depression is deepened by the upward growth of

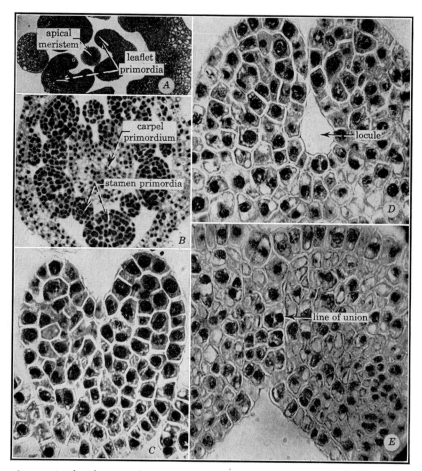

Fig. 12.6.   Stages in development of a pea carpel. A, cross section of vegetative bud showing leaflet primordia; B, cross section of flower bud (compare carpel primordium with leaflet primordia); C, cross section of young carpel, showing area where marginal growth occurs; D, margins of carpel in contact; E, margins of carpel grown together, line of union still evident. (Photos courtesy of Spurr.)

its margins, resulting in a hollow cup (Fig. 12.7B, C). The carpels are not separate at any stage of development. In some plants, such as heath (Fig. 12.7E), the individual carpels may be evident at first, but subse-

quently they fuse along their margins. In both types the hollow cup gradually narrows at the top and elongates to form the slender style (Fig. 12.7D). In the great majority of flowers any opening into a

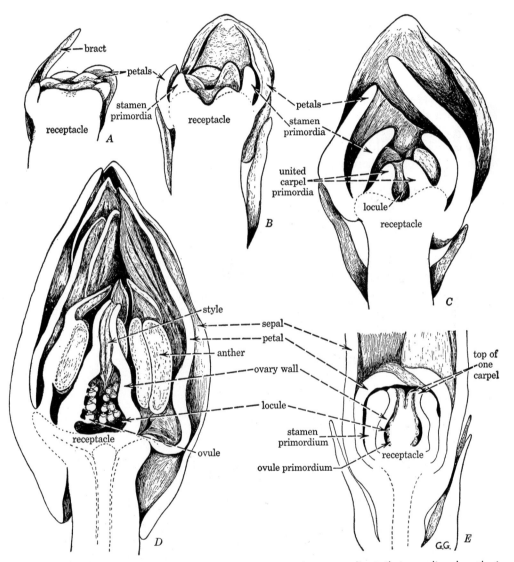

Fig. 12.7. Stages in the development of a syncarpous (compound) pistil, in median lengthwise section. A to D, violet; E, heath. In violet, the three carpels are not separate at any stage of development (A to D) but arise simultaneously as a cup. In heath, the four carpel primordia are at first evident as separate structures and later, by marginal growth, fuse to form a single organ. In violet the placentation is parietal; in heath it is axile. (Redrawn by Girolami from Church, *Types of Floral Mechanism,* The Clarendon Press.)

locule, a chamber in the ovary in which ovules are found, is finally closed. Ovules appear at an early stage within the cup, which finally forms the ovary (Fig. 12.7D). In compound pistils the number of locules and of carpels is usually the same; sometimes, however, the carpels of a compound pistil may be fused along their edges so that a single locule is enclosed. External characters of a compound pistil may sometimes indicate the number of carpels of which it is composed. For example, the lily or onion pistil, with three carpels, has a three-lobed ovary and a three-cleft stigma. The compound pistil of the apple flower has five united carpels, and although the ovary is not clearly five-lobed, there are five distinct styles.

The second reason for considering the carpel to be a modified leaf concerns the evolutionary development of the flower. Primitive fern leaves frequently bear new spores or specialized reproductive cells resulting from meiosis on their margins or along veins (Fig. 2.5). If a young pea pod, which is a single carpel, is opened care-

fully along its ventral suture, the margins may be folded back showing the seeds, which have developed from ovules, along the margin of a leaflike carpel (Fig. 12.8A). The situation is even more striking in *Sterculia platanifolia* for in this plant there are five simple pistils, united only by their stigmas which, when mature, open to show five very leaflike carpels bearing seeds on their margins (Fig. 12.8B, C). Carpels may thus be compared with the leaves of ferns which are not only photosynthetic organs, but are reproductive structures as well. The evolutionary steps in the transition of leaves like those of the fern to the carpel of the flowering plants will be discussed in a later chapter.

Placentation. The tissues within the ovary to which the ovules are attached are called **placentae** (singular, **placenta**). The manner in which the placentae are distributed in the ovary is termed **placentation** and its determination is helpful in classification. When the placentae are on the ovary wall, as in the violet, currant, gooseberry, and bleeding heart (*Dicentra*) (Fig. 12.9D),

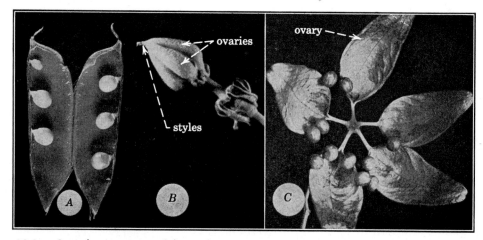

Fig. 12.8. Carpels suggesting foliage leaves. A, pea pod (*Pisum sativum*); ×½; B and C, *Stericula platanifolia*; B shows the young gynoecium with distinct ovaries and coalesced styles. ×1. In C the ovaries have opened showing seeds attached to the margins of leaf-like carpels. ×½.

the placentation is **parietal.** When they arise on the axis of the ovary which has several locules, as in lilies and fuchsia, the placentation is **axile** (Fig. 12.9*C*). Less frequently the ovules are on the axis of a one-loculed ovary, in which event the placentation is **central,** as in the primrose family (Fig. 12.9*A, B*).

Style and Stigma. The style is a slender stalk that terminates in the stigma. It is through stylar tissue that the pollen tube grows. In some flowers the style is very short or entirely lacking; in others it is long. In Indian corn the corn "silks" are the styles (Figs. 12.10, 12.25*C, D*). As a rule, the style withers after pollination, but in some plants (for example, *Clematis*) it

Fig. 12.10. Inflorescences of corn (*Zea mays*). Left, long "silks" (styles) arising from the "kernels" (ovaries), many of which make up the "ear." Right, stamen-bearing flowers of the "tassel." $\times \frac{1}{6}$.

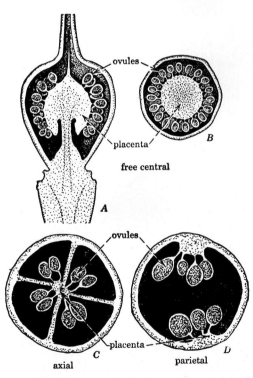

Fig. 12.9. Three types of placentation. A and B, free central (primrose); C, axial (*Fuchsia*); D, parietal (*Dicentra*). (A and B redrawn from Priestley and Scott, *An Introduction to Botany*, Longmans, Green & Co.)

persists and becomes a structure that aids in the dispersal of the fruit (Fig. 13.26). The stigmatic surface often has short cellular outgrowths that aid in holding the pollen grains; and sometimes it secretes a sugary and sticky solution, the **stigmatic fluid.** In many wind-pollinated plants, such as the grasses, the stigma is much branched, or plumelike.

Structure of Ovule. The ovule, the structure that becomes the seed, first appears as a slight dome-shaped mass of cells upon the surface of the placenta (Fig. 12.11*A*). This group of cells develops into a mass of tissue, called the **nucellus.** All

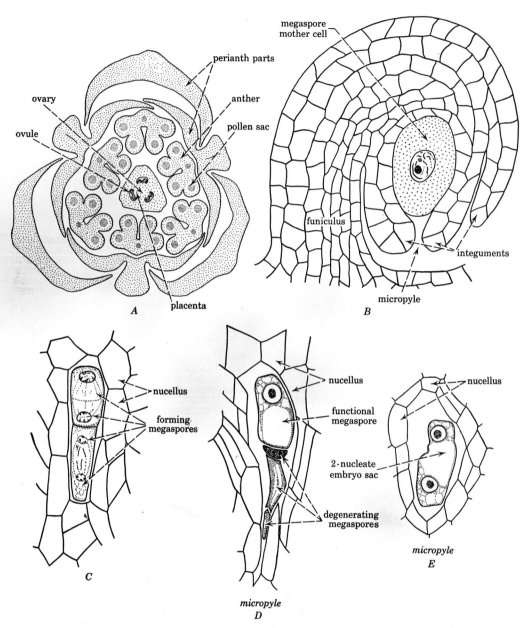

Fig. 12.11. Stages in the development of the embryo sac. *A*, cross section of a flower bud of lily; *B*, an ovule, megaspore mother cell in prophase of meiosis; *C*, late telophase of second meiotic division; *D*, four megaspores, three degenerating; *E*, two-celled embryo sac; *F*, four-celled embryo sac; *G*, eight-celled embryo sac; *H*, mature embryo sac; *I*, fertilization, synergids not present. (*A* and *B*, *Lilium*, slides courtesy of Triarch Products; *C* to *H*, *Dianthus*, redrawn from Buell; *I*, *Lilium*, slide courtesy of Cave.)

of the cells at this stage are meristematic in nature. From the sides of the nucellus usually two ring-shaped layers of tissue arise; they grow upward and enclose the apex of the nucellus, except for a narrow opening at the end, which is the **micropyle.** These two layers are called the **inner integument** and **outer integument.** The integuments become the seed coats.

Usual Type of Embryo Sac Development. In a very young ovule all the cells that compose the nucellus are alike, as far as can be discerned by microscopic examination. Soon, however, one of the nucellar cells, at the micropylar end of the sac, becomes differentiated from the surrounding cells by its larger size and the denser protoplasmic contents. This is the **embryo sac** (**megaspore**) **mother cell** (Fig. 12.11B). The nucleus of this mother cell undergoes two successive divisions (**meiosis**), and as a result a row of four cells (the **megaspores**) is produced in the nucellus (Fig. 12.11C, D). As a rule, three of the cells (the ones nearest the micropyle) disintegrate and disappear, whereas the one farthest from the micropyle enlarges greatly. This megaspore, with its one nu-

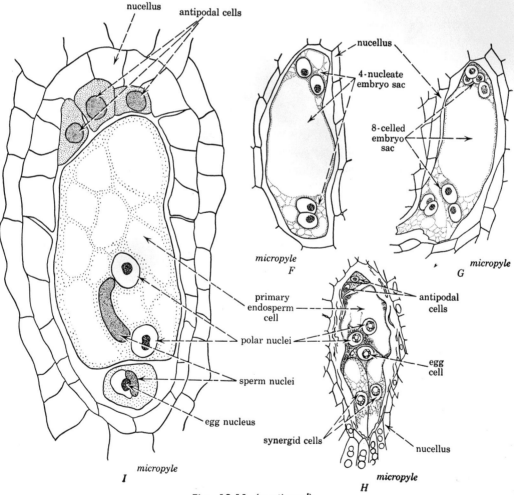

Fig. 12.11 (*continued*).

cleus and cytoplasm, now develops into the mature embryo sac. The usual stages are as follows: (1) *a series of nuclear divisions;* the megaspore nucleus divides forming a two-nucleate embryo sac, each of these two nuclei divides forming a four-nucleate embryo sac, and then each of the four nuclei divides forming an eight-nucleate embryo sac; (2) *migration of nuclei;* after the first division the daughter nuclei migrate to opposite poles of the embryo sac, after the last division one nucleus from the sets of four at the opposite poles of the embryo sac migrates toward the center; (3) *cell formation about nuclei;* the nuclei with their surrounding cytoplasm form cells. Six of these nuclei, each with its associated cytoplasm, become complete individual cells. The two polar nuclei form a single, binucleate cell. This results in a seven-celled embryo sac. These cells have names as follows: At the micropylar end of the embryo sac there is one **egg cell** associated with two **synergid cells.** Since it is frequently difficult to differentiate the egg cell from the other two, these three cells are sometimes referred to

form and are known as **sperms** and **eggs.** Fertilization is not completed until a sperm nucleus fuses with an egg nucleus to form a single nucleus. The cell resulting from the union of a sperm and egg is the **zygote** and its nucleus the **zygote nucleus.** This nucleus must have two sets of chromosomes, one contributed by the sperm and another contributed by the egg. In the higher plants, in addition to the union of a sperm and an egg, the nucleus of the second sperm cell present in the pollen tube unites with the two polar nuclei in the endosperm mother cell to form the **primary endosperm nucleus.** The cell containing the *primary endosperm nucleus* is the **primary endosperm cell.** The zygote arising from the union of egg and sperm will give rise to the embryo. The primary endosperm cell arising from the union of endosperm mother cell and sperm will develop into the **endosperm,** a food tissue of varying degrees of importance in different species. Note that the primary endosperm nucleus has three sets of chromosomes. These relationships may be outlined as follows:

sperm	+ egg	→ zygote
one set of chromosomes (n)	+ one set of chromosomes (n)	→ two sets of chromosomes $(2n)$
sperm	+ endosperm mother cell	→ primary endosperm cell
one set of chromosomes	+ two sets of chromosomes $(2n)$	→ three sets of chromosomes $(3n)$

as the **egg apparatus.** The two nuclei that migrated centerwards approach each other; they are called **polar nuclei** and form a binucleate cell called the **endosperm mother cell.** The three nuclei remaining at the end of the embryo sac opposite the micropyle form the **antipodal cells.** The embryo sac, a seven-celled structure, is now mature and ready for fertilization (Fig. 12.11*H*).

Fertilization. Fertilization is a most critical stage of development in the life cycle of all sexually reproducing plants and animals (Fig. 12.11*I*). It involves the union of two cells called **gametes.** In the flowering plants the gametes differ in size and

Development of Embryo Sac in Lily. Exceptions to this so-called normal embryo-sac development are numerous. Lily, which furnishes such excellent material for class study of embryo-sac development, is one such case (Fig. 12.12). In lily four megaspores are formed as usual, but none of them degenerates. Instead, three of the megaspore nuclei migrate to the antipodal end of the developing embryo sac, while one remains at the micropylar end. This lone nucleus divides twice, forming four nuclei. One of these four cells is the egg cell, two are synergid cells, and the fourth nucleus, in a manner similar to the normal

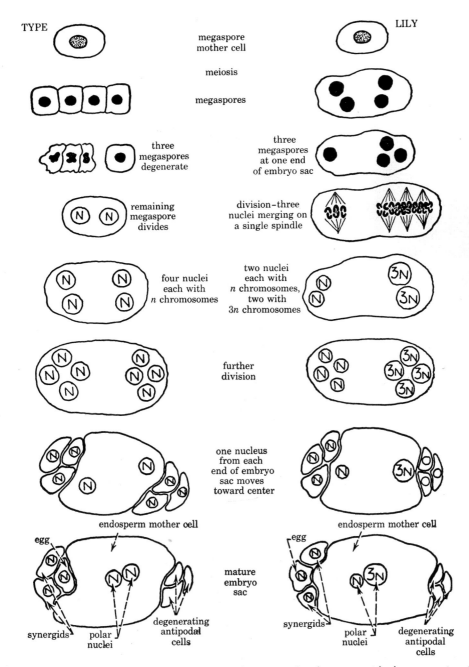

TYPE   LILY

megaspore
mother cell

meiosis

megaspores

three
megaspores
degenerate

three
megaspores
at one end
of embryo sac

remaining
megaspore
divides

division–three
nuclei merging on
a single spindle

four nuclei
each with
n chromosomes

two nuclei
each with
n chromosomes,
two with
3*n* chromosomes

further
division

one nucleus
from each
end of embryo
sac moves
toward center

endosperm mother cell

egg

endosperm mother cell

egg

mature
embryo
sac

synergids   polar
             nuclei

degenerating
antipodal
cells

synergids   polar
             nuclei

degenerating
antipodal
cells

Fig. 12.12. Comparison of the usual type of embryo sac development with that occurring in lily (diagrammatic).

type, moves to the center of the developing embryo sac, where it becomes one of the two polar nuclei.

The three megaspore nuclei that migrate to the antipodal end of the embryo sac undergo division, but the three spindles at metaphase become oriented so that eventually two nuclei are formed, each of which has $3n$ chromosomes. These two $3n$ nuclei now divide again producing four $3n$ nuclei. One of these moves to the center of the embryo sac, becoming the second polar nucleus. There are thus two polar nuclei, one having n chromosomes, the second $3n$ chromosomes. After fusion of these two nuclei with a sperm nucleus with n chromosomes, the primary endosperm nucleus will have $5n$ chromosomes. The remaining three antipodal nuclei soon disintegrate. These steps are shown in Fig. 12.12.

The mature embryo sac (Fig. 12.11H) is usually a seven-celled structure with eight nuclei. The following are the seven cells: one egg cell, two synergid cells, three antipodal cells, and one endosperm mother cell with two polar nuclei. When we say the embryo sac is mature, we mean it has reached a state of development that makes it ready for fertilization (Fig. 12.11I).

VARIATIONS IN FLORAL STRUCTURE

General Description

Complete and Incomplete Flowers. The parts of a typical flower are sepals, petals, stamens, and carpels, all attached to the receptacle. A flower with all four sets of floral leaves is said to be a **complete flower.** An **incomplete flower** is one in which one or more of the four sets are lacking. For example, there are: (1) flowers that have no perianth, (2) flowers that have a calyx but no corolla, (3) flowers with carpels but no stamens, and (4) flowers with stamens

but no carpels. The flowers of calla lily and lizard's tail are examples of those without a perianth (Fig. 12.13A, B). In the goosefoot family, which includes spinach and beet, the flowers have greenish sepals but no petals; but in *Clematis* and a number of other plants, although there are no petals, the sepals are colored and petal-like (Fig. 12.13C). Unisexual flowers (with either carpels or stamens but not both) are fairly common in the plant kingdom. Examples are Indian corn or maize (Figs. 12.10, 12.25), oak, walnut (Fig. 12.14), willow, poplar, cucumber, hemp, asparagus, hop, and date palm.

Perfect and Imperfect Flowers. Unisexual flowers are either **staminate** (stamen-bearing) or **pistillate** (pistil-bearing). Unisexual flowers are said to be **imperfect,** whereas bisexual flowers are **perfect** or **hermaphroditic.** When staminate and pistillate flowers occur *on the same individual plant,* as they do in Indian corn, pumpkin, walnut, and many other species, the species, or the plant, is said to be **monoecious.** In Indian corn (Figs. 12.10, 12.25), for example, the tassel (borne at the top of the stalk) consists of a group of staminate flowers, and the young ear is a group of pistillate flowers. When staminate and pistillate flowers are borne *on separate individual plants,* as in asparagus, willow, and many other species, the species, or the plant, is said to be **dioecious.** For example, in a commercial asparagus field, approximately half of the individual plants bear only staminate flowers, and half bear only pistillate flowers. In such circumstances, we speak of staminate or "male" plants and of pistillate or "female" plants. Only pistillate (female) plants bear fruit (berries). Another example of dioecism is the date palm (Fig. 12.15). Some individual palms are staminate, others pistillate. The edible fruit (date) is produced only by pistillate palms. In such instances there will be no fruit pro-

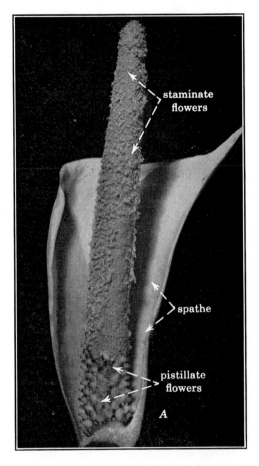

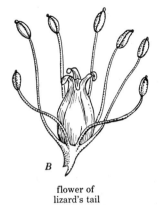

flower of
lizard's tail

Fig. 12.13. Flowers with perianth parts lacking. A, spathe of calla lily (*Zantedeschia althiopica*), sepals and calyx absent; B, flower of lizard's tail (*Saururus*), sepals and calyx absent; C, flower of *Clematis*, petals absent, sepals prominent. (B redrawn from Johnson, *Taxonomy of Flowering Plants*, Appleton-Century-Crofts.)

duction unless staminate plants and pistillate plants are growing near enough together for the pollen to be transferred. In commercial plantings of dates most of the individual palms are pistillate, that is, fruit-bearing. Dates are propagated by off-shoots, which arise chiefly near the base of the stem in the early years of the palm's life. Offshoots from a staminate palm grow into staminate palms, and offshoots from a pistillate palm into pistillate palms. In a commercial date garden it is economically desirable to have as many pistillate or fruit-bearing individuals as possible, and this is secured by vegetative propagation. A relatively few staminate palms are scattered throughout the garden—only enough to supply pollen. Pollen may be carried naturally by wind or it may be collected and dusted by hand on the pistils (Fig. 12.15).

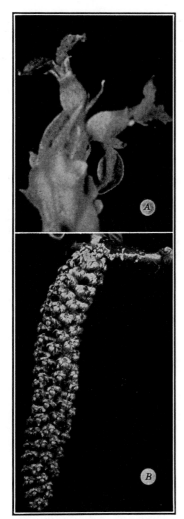

Fig. 12.14. A, pistillate flowers, ×2; and B, staminate flowers, of walnut (*Juglans regia*). ×½.

petals, stamens, and carpels are in **whorls** or circles on the axis of the flower. For example, in petunia (Figs. 12.18*C*, 12.20*B*) the sepals arise in a circle at the outer lowest level on the receptacle; slightly above this circle are the petals; above these is a circle of stamens attached to the petals; and in the center two united carpels. In contrast with this **cyclic** or **whorled** arrangement of flower parts is the arrangement in which one or more sets of flower parts are in **spirals**. Examples of flowers with spiral arrangement of certain flower parts are buttercup, magnolia (Fig. 12.2), and tulip-tree (*Liriodendron*) (Fig. 12.1).

Fig. 12.15. Artificial pollination of date flowers (*Phoenix dactylifera*); a, strands of male flowers being placed in the center of the female cluster; b, freshly opened flower cluster ready for pollination; c, flower cluster after pollination, the strands being tied to hold male flowers in place. (Photo courtesy of Nixon.)

Some species produce three kinds of flowers: staminate, pistillate, and perfect (hermaphrodite). For example, in the red maple, one may find both unisexual and bisexual flowers in the same flower cluster.

Often staminate flowers have rudiments of a pistil, and pistillate flowers the rudiments of stamens.

Whorled and Spiral Arrangements of Flower Parts. In most flowers the sepals,

Fig. 12.16. Floral symmetry. A, regular flower of *Lilium*, $\times \frac{1}{2}$; B, irregular flower of African violet (*Saintpaulia*), $\times 2$.

Floral Symmetry. In many flowers such as tulip-tree (Fig. 12.1), lily (Figs. 12.3, 12.16A) and evening primrose (Fig. 12.22C) the corolla is made up of petals of similar shape which radiate from the center of the flower and are equidistant from each other. Other flower parts have a similar arrangement. Such flowers are said to be **regular.** In these cases, even though there may be an uneven number of parts in the perianth, any line (Fig. 12.16A), drawn through the center of the flower, will divide the flower in two similar halves. They may be exact duplicates or mirror images of each other.

So-called **irregular** (Fig. 12.16B) flowers are those in which one or more members of a particular whorl are dissimilar, do not radiate from the center, or are not equidistant from each other. In most of these flowers only one line will divide the flower in equal halves. They are usually mirror images of each other. While the division of flowers into two halves as shown may generally be used to determine whether a flower is regular or irregular, it is not an infallible test for there are flowers (bleeding heart, Dutchman's breeches) which, though irregular, may be bisected by any number of lines into similar mirror images.

In the flowers of beans and peas, for example, the corolla is composed of the following (Fig. 12.17): one broad conspicuous petal (the **banner** or **standard**); two narrower petals (**wings**), one on each side; and opposite the banner two smaller petals that are united along their edges to form the **keel.** Other examples of irregular flowers are mints, violets, orchids, and snapdragons.

Union of Flower Parts. *Coalescence.* In the tulip-tree flower, illustrated in Fig. 12.1, all parts of the flower are separate and distinct; that is, each sepal, petal, stamen, and carpel is attached at its base to the receptacle. In many flowers, however, the members of one or more whorls are to some degree united with one another, or are attached to members of other whorls. The union with each other of members of a given whorl is termed **coalescence**. Partial or complete union of the sepals along their edges occurs in the flowers of mints, violets, evening primroses (Fig. 12.22C),

peas, and many other plants. This condition is referred to as **synsepaly.** Petals may also be attached to one another (Figs. 12.16B, 12.18B) and they are said to be **sympetalous** (the noun would be **sympetaly**). When the corolla is sympetalous it may have the form of a bell (Canterbury bells) or a tube (red hot poker) or a fun-

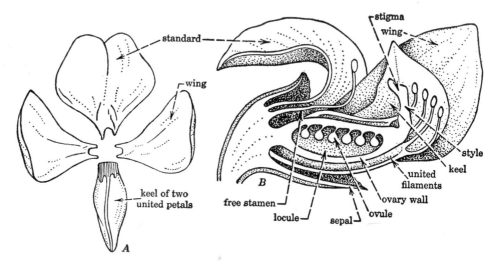

Fig. 12.17. Irregular hypogynous flower of pea. A, petals separated; B, lengthwise section.

Fig. 12.18. Coalescence, adnation, and reduction in number of floral parts. A, strawberry (*Fragaria*), numerous parts, no coalescence, no adnation, $\times \frac{3}{4}$; B, C, Petunia, few parts, syncarpy and sympetaly, stamens adnate to corolla tube. $\times \frac{1}{2}$.

nel (petunia). When the separate parts of a whorl unite to form a sympetalous corolla they are said to have coalesced.

Stamens may coalesce as is seen in the mallow or cotton family (Fig. 12.19). This coalescence is **synandry**. In the cotton flower the filaments of many stamens are united to form a sheath, whereas the anthers are separate. In the flower of orange there are 20 to 60 stamens, united at their bases to form groups. And in the thistle family the anthers are united into a tube, whereas the filaments are distinct.

When the carpels of the gynoecium coalesce, the situation is called **syncarpy** and one may say that the pistil is compound. This condition occurs in many families of plants and may be seen to advantage in such flowers as those of lily (Fig. 12.3A), petunia, (Fig. 12.18B) and quince (Fig. 12.22B).

When the parts of a flower have not joined, the prefix **apo** (separate) may be used to describe the flower, i.e., **apopetalous**. These situations may be simply outlined:

Whorl	No Coalescence	Coalescence
sepals	aposepalous	synsepalous, synsepaly
petals	apopetalous	sympetalous, sympetaly
stamens	apoandrous	synandrous, synandry
carpels	apocarpous	syncarpous, syncarpy

Adnation. We have just discussed the union of different members of the same whorl. Union of members of two different whorls also occurs, **adnation**. For example, in such flowers as petunia (Fig. 12.20), evening primrose (Fig. 12.22C), snapdragons, and honeysuckle, the stamens are attached to the corolla rather than to the receptacle. In these cases the stamens are said to be **adnate** to the corolla.

Elevation of Flower Parts. In the primitive type of flower, such as that of magnolia (Fig. 12.2), lily (Figs. 12.3, 12.20), and petunia (Fig. 12.20B), the receptacle

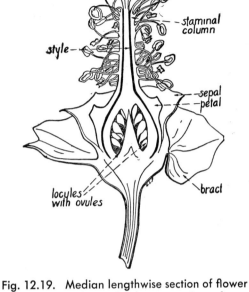

Fig. 12.19. Median lengthwise section of flower of cotton (*Gossypium*), showing union of stamens. (Redrawn from Robbins, *Botany of Crop Plants*, The Blakiston Co.)

is convex or conical and the different flower parts are arranged one above another. They occur in the following order, beginning with the lowest, sepals, petals, stamens, and carpels. A flower of this type is said to be **hypogynous** (Fig. 12.20A, B) even if the stamens are adnate to the corolla as in petunia. If the sepals, petals, and stamens appear to come from the top of the ovary, as in the flower of the evening primrose (Fig. 12.22C), quince (Fig. 12.22A, B), and sunflower (Fig. 12.27), the flower is said to be **epigynous**. Intermediate between the hypogynous and epigynous types are those flowers such as cherry and almond (Fig. 12.21), in which the sepals, petals, and stamens have their origin, not above or below the pistil, but around the ovary. This type of flower is said to **perigynous**.

The terms **inferior** and **superior** are frequently used to describe the relationship between the points of origin of the various floral parts. An inferior ovary is one that is completely or partially attached to the calyx tube, while a superior ovary is completely free from the calyx tube. Taxonomists frequently use the terms superior and inferior to explain the elevation of flower parts with particular reference to the position of the ovary. The words hypogyny, perigyny, and epigyny are employed more generally to designate the position of stamens, less frequently of petals and sepals. For instance, the ovary will be described as being superior, while the stamens may be described as being hypogynous or perigynous.

We have considered in some detail the various aspects of flower structure, as it occurs throughout the groups of flowering plants. We shall now proceed to describe the specialized flowers of two very important families, the Gramineae (grasses) and the Compositae (the sunflower family). Several members of the Gramineae are of great economic importance supplying our single largest source of food, directly in the form of flour, and indirectly as feed for cattle, sheep, and hogs. The Compositae family, while not a major source of food products, is made up of a large number of species, with a wide distribution, and has colorful flowers. Zinnias, marigolds, dahlias, dandelions, and many similar flower types belong to this family.

The Grass Flower

Grass flowers generally grow in a head or **spike** (Fig. 12.23) as in wheat or barley, or are loosely grouped in a **panicle** (Fig. 12.24) typical of oats. In all instances the

Fig. 12.20. Elevation of flower parts. Hypogyny. A, lily (*Lilium tigrinum*), B, Petunia. ×1¼.

Fig. 12.21. Elevation of flower parts. Perigyny. A, almond (*Prunus amygdalus*), ×1; B, cherry (*Prunus avium*), ×1½.

individual small flowers or **florets** are associated in groups known as **spikelets** (Fig. 12.24*B*). Each spikelet is separated from its neighbors by two small modified leaves or bracts, known as **glumes.** They are found at the base of the spikelet and in some cases (wheat, oats, barley) they may fairly well enclose it. A separation of the glumes reveals the individual florets of the spikelet attached to a slender stalk, the **rachilla.**

Each floret is in turn protected by two additional bracts, the **lemma** and the **palea** (Fig. 12.24*C*). The lemma, in wheat, barley, oats, and other grains, is large and may have attached to it a long slender **awn.** The palea is small and frequently enclosed by the lemma. The essential parts consist of the androecium composed of three stamens and the gynoecium of two fused carpels (Fig. 12.24*D*). When the flowers are mature the palea and lemma separate slightly, exposing two feathery stigmas and allowing the anthers to hang free from the spikelet on greatly lengthened filaments (Fig. 12.23). At the base of the floral parts there may be distinguished two small protuberances the **lodicules.** These are thought to be the greatly modified perianth parts and are supposed to function in the separation of the lemma and palea at pollination time.

In corn (Fig. 12.25), the flowers are imperfect, with the staminate flowers grouped in the tassel, and the pistillate flowers

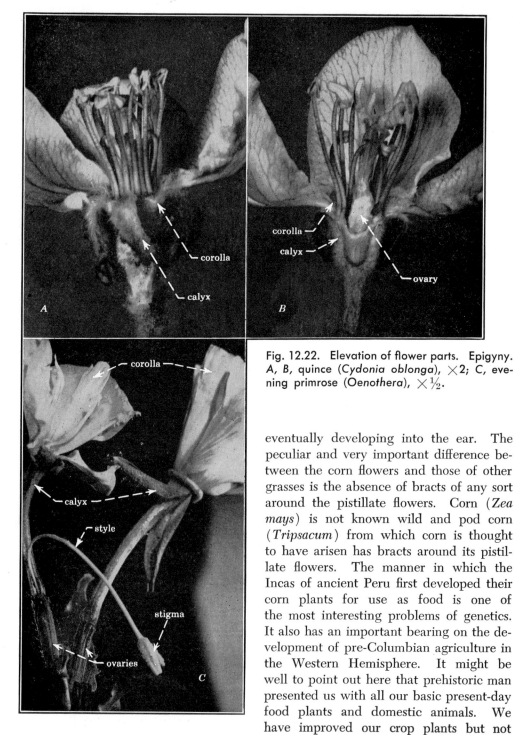

Fig. 12.22. Elevation of flower parts. Epigyny. A, B, quince (*Cydonia oblonga*), ×2; C, evening primrose (*Oenothera*), ×½.

eventually developing into the ear. The peculiar and very important difference between the corn flowers and those of other grasses is the absence of bracts of any sort around the pistillate flowers. Corn (*Zea mays*) is not known wild and pod corn (*Tripsacum*) from which corn is thought to have arisen has bracts around its pistillate flowers. The manner in which the Incas of ancient Peru first developed their corn plants for use as food is one of the most interesting problems of genetics. It also has an important bearing on the development of pre-Columbian agriculture in the Western Hemisphere. It might be well to point out here that prehistoric man presented us with all our basic present-day food plants and domestic animals. We have improved our crop plants but not greatly added to the number they handed on to us.

The Composite Flower

As the name implies the composite flower is a group of many small flowers arranged to give the appearance of a single typical flower. Several types of composite flowers are shown in Fig. 12.26. This characteristic grouping of flowers is called a **head.** In the sunflower (Fig. 12.26A) and many other composite flowers there are two distinct types of individual flowers, **ray flowers** and **disk flowers.** Some species may, however, have all ray flowers (*Dahlia,* Fig. 12.26B), others all disk flowers (globe thistle, Fig. 12.26C). Ray flowers are frequently sterile or pistillate.

The disk flower is generally complete. It is epigynous, the small tubular corolla arising from the top of the ovary (Fig. 12.27C). There are two carpels as evidenced by the forked stigma (Fig. 12.27B, C) which, when receptive to pollen, protrudes from the corolla tube. The stamens, five in number, have separate filaments but their anthers are coalesced to form a tube around the style. The stamens usually mature, in sunflower, before the stigma and protrude from the corolla tube. These details are shown in Fig. 12.27A and B. Referring to the figures, note that the flowers on the margin have been pollinated and both stigmas and stamens have withered. Adjacent flowers show protruding stigmas dusted with pollen. Next come several rows of dark anthers capped by white masses of pollen. The flowers in the center have not yet opened. A calyx is not present as such but many composite flowers are surrounded by a conspicuous tuft of hairs

Fig. 12.23. Head or spike of barley (*Hordeum vulgare*). ×2.

or otherwise modified calyx parts.   This is known as the **pappus.**   In sunflower these are simply two small sepal-like structures (Fig. 12.27C).   In dandelion the pappus is feathery and aids in the dispersal of the fruit.

Two kinds of **floral bracts** sometimes occur in composite flowers.   The whole head may be surrounded by green **involucral bracts.**   Each individual flower may have its own **receptacular bract** arising from the receptacle near the base of the flower (Fig. 12.27C).

Schematic Representations of Floral Parts

Flowers may be described conveniently and relatively simply by two shorthand methods.   These are illustrated by the diagrams and formulas shown in Figs. 12.28A, B.

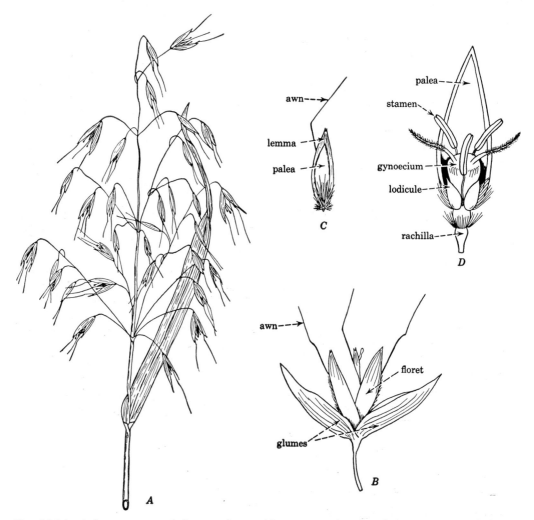

Fig. 12.24.   Inflorescence and flower of oats (*Avena sativa*).   A, inflorescence; B, spikelet; C, floret; D, opened floret.

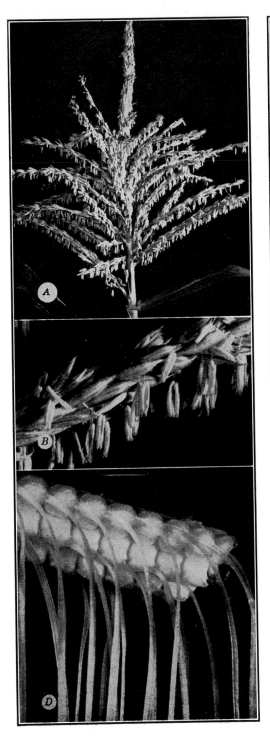

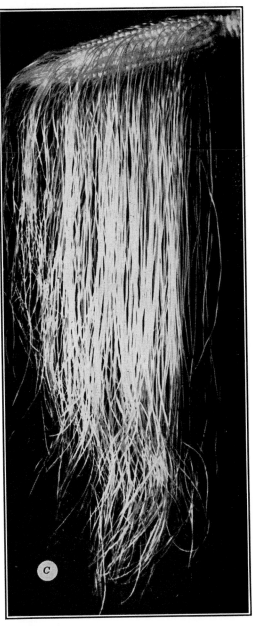

Fig. 12.25. Flowers of corn (*Zea mays*). A, the tassel, $\times\frac{1}{5}$; B, several individual flowers with anthers exerted, $\times 1$; C, pistillate flowers forming a very young "ear," $\times\frac{1}{2}$; D, several pistillate flowers with attached styles, $\times 1$.

These are but two examples. Both systems are so flexible and simple that formulas may be written or diagrams drawn for every family. A series of diagrams showing flowers in longitudinal view is given in Fig. 25.4.

Symbols for the formulas are as follows:

Ca = calyx
Co = corolla
S = stamen
P = pistil

number of parts is indicated at upper right of symbol

∞ = indefinite number
a = actinomorphic
z = zygomorphic
◯O = coalescence
◯O = partial coalescence
♂ = staminate flower
♀ = pistillate flower
═══ = receptacle
$\dfrac{\overline{\equiv}}{P}$ = inferior ovary
$\dfrac{S}{CO}$ = stamens adnate to corolla

THE DEVELOPMENT OF THE FLOWER

The meristem at the apex of the branch that will become a flower does not retain for long its meristematic activity as this tissue does in an ordinary stem; all of it eventually differentiates into floral leaves. Moreover, the floral leaves are very much crowded together, not being separated by long internodes, as are foliage leaves, and lack axillary bud primordia. Compare Fig. 8.12, which shows the shoot tip of a buttercup, with Fig. 12.29 which is a floral apex of the same plant. As a rule the sepals are in a whorl; that is, they arise on the stem axis at approximately the same level. Petals and stamens also are usually in one or more whorls; and, if there are several carpels, they too may be in one or more whorls. In some of the more primitive types of flowers, such as *Ranunculus* (buttercup) (Fig. 12.29) the stamens and pistils are in a close spiral on the receptacle. In these the distance between two successive individual stamens or individual pistils is very short; in other words, the internodes are very short.

INFLORESCENCES

In most flowering plants, the flowers are borne in clusters or groups. Morphologically, an inflorescence is a flower-bearing branch or system of branches. In manuals

Fig. 12.26.   Three types of composite flowers. A, sunflower (*Helianthus annuus*), ×¼; B, Dahlia, ×½; C, globe thistle (*Echinops exaltatus*), ×½.

Fig. 12.27. Sunflower (*Helianthus annuus*). A, top of head; B, section of head; C, flowers dissected. ×1.

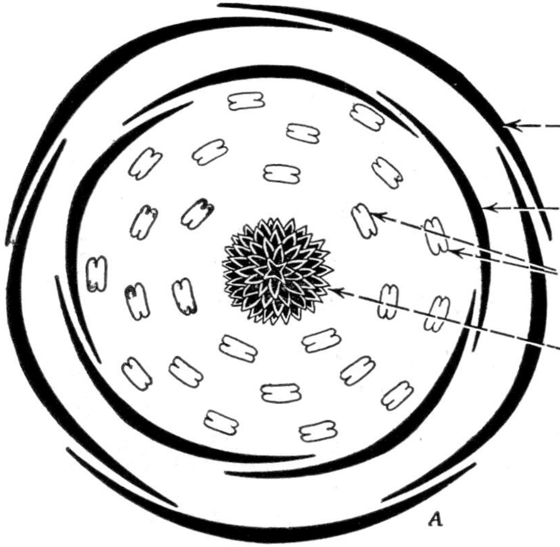

Fig. 12.28. Floral diagrams. A, Ranunculaceae; and B, Labiatae.

		Indicated in formula by	Indicated in diagram by
buttercup			
calyx sepals	present, five in number, regular, not coalesced	Ca^5	first circle
corolla petals	present, numerous, regular, not coalesced	Co^{10-20}	second circle. Note overlap in licates spiral arrangement
androecium stamens	present, indefinite in number (∞), not coalesced	S^∞	three series of circles. Note spiral order
gynoecium carpels	present, indefinite in number (∞), not coalesced	P^∞	fourth or inner circle
	hypogyny and no adnation are indicated by writing all symbols on a straight line	$Ca^\infty Co^\infty S^\infty P^\infty$	
mint			
calyx sepals	present, five in number, regular, coalesced	$Ca\,(5)$	outer circle. Note dots between sepals indicating coalescence
corolla petals	present, five in number, irregular, coalesced	$Co^Z\,(5)$	second circle. Note irregularity and union of petals
androecium stamens	present, four in number, not coalesced, adnated to corolla tube	S^4	third circle. Note stamens attached to petals
gynoecium carpels	present, four in number, coalesced	$P\,(4)$	inner circle
	adnation indicated by writing symbol for stamens above symbol for corolla	$S^{2+2(2)}$ $Ca\,(5)\,Co_Z\,(5)\,p\,(4)$	

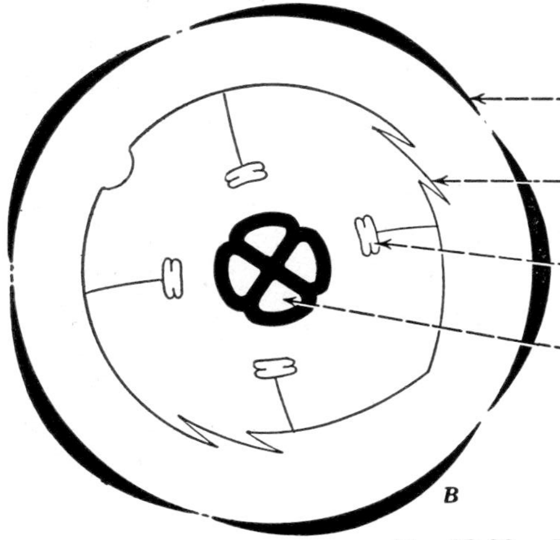

of flowering plants, one finds many different terms descriptive of the various kinds of
inflorescences.   Only the most common
ones are discussed and illustrated here
(Fig. 12.30).

Raceme Types of Inflorescence

A very simple type of inflorescence may
be found in such plants as currant, hyacinth, wild mustard, and radish.   It is

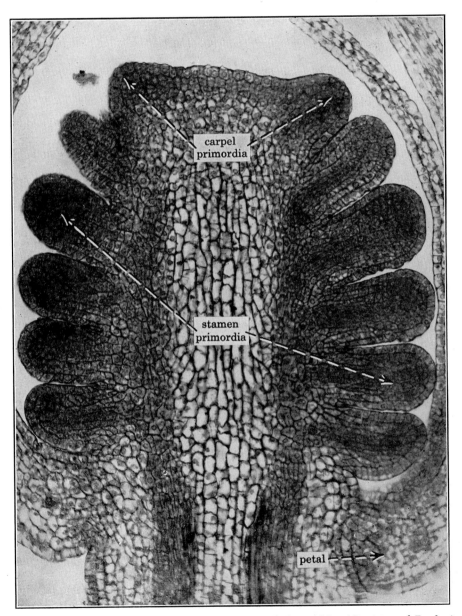

Fig. 12.29. Floral apex of buttercup (*Ranunculus*), ×100. (Courtesy of Tepfer.)

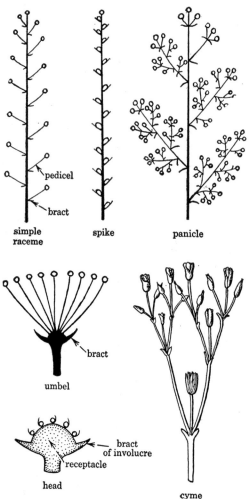

simple raceme   spike   panicle

umbel

pedicel

bract

bract

head

bract of involucre

receptacle

cyme

Fig. 12.30. Diagrams showing types of inflorescences.

base of the inflorescence and the youngest at the apex. In such an inflorescence (mustard, for example) mature fruit may be near the base, while at the upper end are minute buds containing very rudimentary flower parts. In plants like cabbage, mustard, and others with inflorescences of this type seeds may be shattering from the fruits at the base, while flowers are still forming near the tip.

In the simple raceme, the flowers are **on pedicels which are about equal in length.** In the **spike** (Fig. 12.30), the main axis of the inflorescence is elongated, but the flowers, each in the axil of a bract, are sessile (without a pedicel). The **catkin** is a spike that usually bears only pistillate or only staminate flowers. The inflorescence as a whole is shed later. Examples are willow, cottonwood, hazel, walnut.

In all the foregoing kinds of inflorescences the flowering axis is elongated; that is; the internodes are quite long. If the internodes are very short, the flowers appear to be arising umbrella-like from approximately the same level. An inflorescence of this kind, in which pedicels are of nearly equal length, is called an **umbel** (Fig. 12.30). The onion is a good example. The **head** is an inflorescence in which the flowers are sessile and crowded together on a very short axis. Members of the family Compositae, including thistle, sunflower, cosmos, dahlia, etc., have this type of inflorescence (Fig. 12.30).

Inflorescences of the raceme type may be compound, that is, branched. A branched raceme is called a **panicle** (Fig. 12.30), as in oats and rice. Compound spikes occur in wheat, rye, and certain other grasses. Umbels, also, may be compound as in carrot, parsnip, and other members of the family Umbelliferae (which family gets its name from its characteristic umbel inflorescence).

called a **raceme.** In this type, note that the main axis has short branches, each of which terminates in a flower. Thus, each flower is on a short branch stem, the **pedicel.** The main axis of a raceme continues to grow in length more or less indefinitely; the apical meristem persists. The primordia of leaves arise in the usual manner along the margin of this apical meristem, and in the axil of each leaf a flower is borne. The oldest flowers are at the

Cyme Type of Inflorescence

In contrast to the raceme types of inflorescences, just described, is the **cyme** (Fig. 12.30). In the cyme, the apex of the main axis produces a flower which involves the entire apical meristem; hence that particular axis ceases to elongate. Other flowers arise on lateral branches farther down the axis of the inflorescence, and thus usually the youngest of the flowers in any cluster occurs farthest from the tip of the main stalk. The flower cluster of chickweed is an example of the cyme.

REPRODUCTION BY FLOWERS

With the structure of the flower well in mind let us consider some of the steps involved in pollination and fertilization. These steps are not only essential to the production of fruits and seeds but of practical importance to the plant breeder and orchardist.

Pollination

Pollination is the transfer of pollen from an anther to a stigma. The mature pollen grain (Fig. 12.4) at the time it is discharged from the anther is a more or less spherical or ovoid structure with two surrounding membranes. The inner membrane is of cellulose and pectic substances, whereas the outer membrane consists largely of cutin. Ridges, spines, or other sculpturing usually cover the cell wall. Pollination may be effected by either wind or insects, and occasionally by birds. Flower structure is generally adapted to one or the other of these pollinating agents.

Pollinating Agents. *Wind.* Pollen is carried chiefly by wind and insects. Rarely, water and birds are the agents of pollination. **Wind pollination** is the common type in those plants with inconspicuous flowers,

as in the grasses (Fig. 12.23), poplars, walnuts (Fig. 12.14), alders, birches, oaks, ragweeds, and sage. Such plants usually produce pollen in enormous quantities. One worker has calculated that between 8 A.M. and 1 P.M. a single plant of ragweed sheds the amazing number of 8 billion pollen grains. In Indian corn, a single tassel may produce from 20 million to 50 million grains of pollen. The flowers of grasses are inconspicuous, and most of them lack odor and nectar and hence are unattractive to insects. Furthermore, the pollen is light and dry and easily blown, and the stigmas, in many grasses, are feathery and expose a large surface to flying pollen. In cottonwoods, alders, birches, oaks, walnuts, and hickories, the flowers are in catkins (Fig. 12.14). The staminate catkins are pendulous and move easily in the wind, and the light pollen is shaken from the anthers and readily carried away by the breezes. In many catkin-bearing trees the flowers open before the leaves unfold so that pollen movement is unhampered. In pines, the pollen grains themselves have two winglike structures (Fig. 24.31) which assist in their dispersal by wind. In pines, pollen is produced in such tremendous quantities that showers of pollen may be witnessed in a pine forest.

Insects. Insect pollination occurs in the majority of flowering plants. The principal pollinating insects are bees, although many other kinds of insects act as pollinators. In most insect-pollinated plants, the pollen is sticky and not easily blown by the wind. It adheres readily to the body of an insect visiting the flower and may be rubbed off on the stigmas of other flowers (Fig. 12.31).

It is known that French and sugar prunes, Napoleon and Black Tartarian cherries, almonds, and certain other fruit trees produce very light crops of fruit unless a large number of bees is present in the orchards at the time of blooming. Except for certain nut trees, orchard trees require

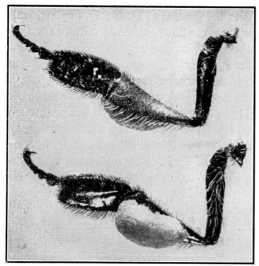

Fig. 12.31. Hind legs of bee showing pollen attached. (Photo courtesy of Vansell.)

insects for pollination. Recently, in certain western orchards, the set of fruit has been improved by artificial pollination. Large quantities of pollen are collected from mature blossoms, and the pollen blown with special equipment into the trees.

Moths and butterflies are also important pollinating agents. With their long mouth parts they are particularly adapted for securing nectar from flowers with long, tube-shaped corollas, such as larkspur, columbine, and nasturtium.

Types of Pollination. There are essentially two different kinds of pollination determined by the genetic similarity of the plants involved. If the anthers and stigmas, the essential organs in pollination, have the same genetic constitution, that is, have chromosomes bearing identical genes, whether or not they are produced on the same or different individual plants, the transfer of pollen from anther to stigma is **self-pollination.** If two parent plants, with different genetic constitutions are involved, the transfer of pollen from the anther of one to the stigma of the other is **cross-pollination.**

Self-pollination. 1. Transfer of pollen from an anther to the stigma of the same flower. This is the normal method in cereals (except rye and corn), in garden peas, and in some other plants.

2. Transfer of pollen from an anther to the stigma of another flower on the same plant. This occurs in many plants with perfect flowers and is usual in monoecious plants.

3. Transfer of pollen from an anther to the stigma of a flower on another individual plant.

(*a*) The two individual plants may be clones. For centuries many horticultural plants have been reproduced vegetatively. For example, potatoes are usually propagated by cutting the tubers into a number of sections. Obviously, all the plants grown from the tubers or sections of tubers from one plant have the same genetic composition. Such a group of asexually reproducing plants is called a **clone.** Another example: all the individual pear trees in an orchard may be parts of a single parent tree; that is, they may have been propagated by cuttings or buds from one parent tree. In this event, the individual pear trees also have the same genetic composition. Pollination among clones is essentially self-pollination.

(*b*) The two individual plants may belong to the same pure line. In wheat, for example, the stigma of a flower usually receives pollen from its own anthers. Following fertilization, the ovary of the self-pollinated flower develops into a grain. The plant that develops from this grain in turn produces many flowers. If these flowers are self-pollinated, the many individual plants that develop from the grains constitute a **pure line.** If pollen from one individual of a pure line is placed on the stigma of a flower of another individual of the same pure line, the result, genetically, is the same as when pollen is placed on the stigma of the flower that furnished the pollen.

Cross-pollination. Cross-pollination always involves two plants with different genetic constitution. The differences may involve one or many characters. The two parents may be of the same variety or of the same species; they may be of different species or even of different genera.

Fruitfulness and Sterility. Factors determining the fruitfulness, or the ability of a given plant to produce seeds and fruits, are many, frequently complicated, and not at all well understood. Furthermore they are of considerable economic importance. For instance, many orchard trees are self-sterile, that is, they will not produce fruit or seed when pollinated with their own pollen. This is complicated by the fact that trees of one variety may form a clone; an orchard of 100 Spitzenburg apple trees consists, from the practical viewpoint of fertilization, of one individual. They have all been obtained by budding; their chromosomes are all alike and since Spitzenburg apples are self-sterile, pollen from one Spitzenburg tree will not pollinate flowers on a neighboring Spitzenburg tree. It is capable of being fertilized with pollen from a number of other varieties, such as Yellow Newton, Jonathan, and Baldwin. Obviously, it would not be well to plant solid blocks of Spitzenburg. This apple should be alternated with rows of some one of the other varieties the pollen of which is capable of fertilizing it. The same phenomenon occurs in many other orchard trees, such as cherries, almonds, etc.

Other plants such as corn while not self-sterile do not produce as vigorous offspring if self-pollinated.

Artificial Pollination. Artificial methods of pollination are practiced by plant breeders in making crosses. In flowers to be cross-pollinated, the anthers are removed before pollen is shed and then emas-culated flowers are covered with a bag until the pistils are receptive. The bag is then removed, the desired pollen is placed on the stigma and the bag replaced until the stigma has passed the receptive stage.

Greenhouse tomatoes do not set fruit well unless artificially pollinated. This process may be carried out by jarring the plants when the anthers are shedding pollen, or by collecting pollen on a glass slide or small brush and removing it to other flowers.

In the date palm, staminate and pistillate flowers are borne on different individual trees. Consequently, it is necessary in a date grove that a number of staminate trees are scattered among the pistillate ones to insure pollination. Or, a grood crop of dates may be secured by cutting off the inflorescence of a staminate tree and tying it into a pistillate tree near the clusters of pistillate flowers, or by collecting large quantities of pollen and dusting the pistillate flowers when the stigmas are receptive.

It is necessary in growing Smyrna figs to resort to artificial pollination. As applied to this tree, the process is technically known as **caprification.** A wild fig, the caprifig, is indispensable to the Smyrna fig grower. When caprifig fruits are mature, there issues from them a wasp, known as the fig wasp. When the wasps emerge they are covered with pollen. In search of a place to lay their eggs, they may go to other caprifig fruits or to the partly mature figs of Smyrna. They enter the opening of the fig and scatter pollen on the stigmas, and fertilization of the ovules follows. In Smyrna fig culture the mature fruits of caprifigs, harboring fig wasps, are usually placed in small baskets or open bags and fastened in the Smyrna trees. Only caprifigs have a peculiar type of flower, the "gall flowers," in which fig wasp eggs may be laid and hatched.

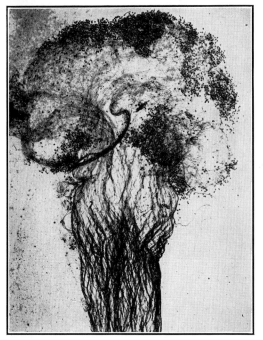

Fig. 12.32. Crushed stigma and style stained to show pollen grains and innumerable pollen tubes in the style. (Photo courtesy of Triarch Products.)

Germination of the Pollen Grain

The pollen grain adheres to the stigmatic surface. In many flowers this surface has short outgrowths to which the grains adhere; and in some species the stigma produces a sticky secretion, the **stigmatic fluid.** The presence of this fluid, which may give the stigmatic surface a shining or glistening appearance, is evidence that it is receptive to pollen. The hybridizer soon learns to recognize a receptive stigma and thus the proper time to apply pollen artificially. The pollen grain germinates on the surface of the stigma. The protoplasm of the grain absorbs water and swells, breaking the outer membrane. The inner membrane extends through the break in the outer wall and forms the limiting membrane of a protoplasm-lined tube. The pollen tube

is a slender threadlike growth; it penetrates the tissue of the stigma, grows down through the style (Fig. 12.32), and enters the ovary. The styles of some flowers are hollow, but most of them are not, and so the passage of the tube apparently involves the secretion of tissue-dissolving enzymes by the advancing tip of the tube.

In short-styled flowers the pollen tube needs to grow only a short distance. For example, in the pea and tulip, the style has a length of only 2 or 3 millimeters (Fig. 12.5*B*, *H*). On the other hand, in common corn the distance from the stigmatic surface at the end of the corn silk to the young corn grain (ovary) may be as much as 50 centimeters (Fig. 12.25*C*). In a long style, the pollen tube is not a continuous, unbroken tube extending from the grain to the ovary. It consists of a very short apical portion containing the two sperm cells, and the upper part of the tube gradually disintegrates.

The rate of growth of pollen tubes varies widely. In wheat, for example, fertilization normally occurs between 1 and 2 days after pollination. Under favorable conditions the pollen tube of corn may grow 6 inches in 24 hours. In some oaks the tube is almost a year in growing 2 or 3 millimeters.

As a rule when the pollen grain is shed from the anther it is a two-celled structure, containing a generative cell and a tube cell (Fig. 12.4*E*). Before or during growth of the pollen tube the generative cell undergoes division forming two sperm cells (Fig. 12.4*F*). The two sperms, and in some species the tube nucleus, move to the tip of the pollen tube, retaining that position as the tube grows. In other species the tube nucleus degenerates either before the tube starts to grow or shortly thereafter. The two sperm nuclei bear the hereditary characters of the male parent.

The pollen of many plants will germinate

in water. That of other plants requires a nutrient medium, such as a solution of cane sugar. For example, it was found that sugar beet pollen germinates abundantly on culture media containing 1½ per cent agar and 40 per cent cane sugar. But the pollen of some species will not germinate in any artificial medium thus far tried.

Pollen varies considerably in the length of time it will remain viable, depending particularly upon the moisture and temperature conditions surrounding the grains. Plant breeders may desire to keep pollen viable for a considerable length of time in order to make use of it in cross pollination. It is sometimes shipped long distances for special hybridizing purposes. Pollen of the date palm will retain its viability for several months, if kept dry. Experiments show that sugar beet pollen will germinate fairly well after 50 days if kept at low temperature and low humidity. Apple pollen has been successfully stored for 4½ years at 50 per cent relative humidity and at a temperature of 2° to 8° C. Dry pollen will withstand greater temperature extremes than moist pollen. However, resistance of pollen to low temperatures is a specific character. For example, pollen of apple, pear, and plum will withstand a temperature of 0.5° C, whereas as much as 50 per cent of peach and apricot pollen grains is killed by exposure to this temperature.

Fertilization

Reaching the ovary, the pollen tube grows toward one of the ovules, usually enters the micropyle, penetrates one or more layers of nucellar cells, and enters the embryo sac (Fig. 12.11), approaching, in one manner or another, the egg cell and the endosperm mother cell. These stages are not easy to study but it appears that the tip of the tube ruptures, one sperm cell enters the egg and the other sperm enters the endosperm mother cell. Within the egg the sperm and egg nuclei fuse; within the endosperm mother cell the other sperm and two polar nuclei fuse (Fig. 12.11). This double fusion of egg with sperm and polar nuclei with sperm is sometimes called **double fertilization.** The zygote and primary endosperm cell have now been formed, the antipodal cells and synergid cells have degenerated, and conditions are set for the further development of seed and fruit. (See page 257.)

Only one pollen tube functions in the fertilization of each embryo sac. If an ovary contains many ovules, each of course with one embryo sac, one pollen tube normally enters each ovule. Sometimes, however, fertilization of the egg is not effected, in which event it does not develop into an embryo. The presence of a hundred or more mature seeds in a watermelon fruit is evidence that at least just as many individual pollen tubes grew down the style of the flower and discharged their contents into separate embryo sacs. As a matter of fact, however, usually many pollen tubes disintegrate at some point along their path of growth from the stigma to the embryo sac.

The immediate external evidence of fertilization is the withering of the stigma and style and, in many flowers, the dropping of the petals. If flowers are bagged and pollination prevented, the petals usually remain fresh for a much longer time than they do in pollinated flowers.

The fusions that occur in the embryo sac initiate a number of changes in the entire ovary, which are as follows:

1. Development of zygote to form the embryo plant.

2. Development of the primary endosperm cell to form the endosperm (reserve food supply of the seed).

3. Development of the integuments to form the seed coat.

4. The absorption or disintegration of nucellar tissue. In some plants, however, a portion of the nucellus may become the storage tissue of the seed rather than endosperm. Such tissue of nucellar origin is called **perisperm.**

5. Development of ovary tissue to which ovule or ovules are attached to form the fruit.

6. Accessory flower parts, such as the receptacle, or sepals, or petals may also be stimulated to increased growth and become incorporated in the fruit.

Thus the importance of fertilization is to stimulate growth of certain floral parts and to bring about a withering of others. The net result is the development of the ovary wall into the fruit and the ovule into the seed.

Apomixis

This term refers to a type of reproduction in which no sexual fusion occurs but in which structures usually concerned in sexual reproduction are involved. Normally the egg nucleus will not start on the series of changes which result in the embryo plant unless a sperm nucleus fuses with it. In other words, in most plants, the embryo is the result of a sexual process (the union of male and female cells, gametes). Each gamete contributes n chromosomes, and hence the zygote and all the cells derived from it have $2n$ chromosomes. Rarely, however, an embryo develops from an *unfertilized egg.* This occurrence is called **parthenogenesis.** Two types of parthenogenesis are as follows: that in which the embryo develops from an n or haploid egg cell (the individuals are usually sterile) and that in which the embryo develops from a $2n$ or diploid egg cell. In the latter type meiosis is omitted in the development of the embryo sac. Another form of apomixis is that in which the embryo plant arises from tissue surrounding the embryo sac. These so-called "adventitious" embryos (diploid) occur in *Citrus, Rubus,* and other plants.

Apomixis has variations other than those given above, but all forms of this phenomenon involve the origin of new individuals without nuclear or cellular fusion.

In some plants deposition of pollen on the stigma is a prerequisite to apomictic embryo development, although no pollen tube grows down the style and no nuclear fusion takes place. In such instances, there is evidence that hormones formed in the stigma, or furnished by the pollen, are transferred to the unfertilized egg cell, initiating there those changes which result in embryo development.

13

The Fruit, Seed, and Seedling

_____

FRUIT

In everyday usage the term "fruit" usually refers to a juicy and edible structure, such as an apple, plum, peach, cherry, orange, and grape. It is unlikely that such structures as string beans, eggplant, okra, squash, and cucumbers, which are commonly called "vegetables," and the "grains" of corn, oats, wheat, and other cereals are popularly thought of as fruits. However, all of the above are fruits in the botanical sense. The term fruit as employed here in its strict botanical sense refers to a *matured ovary of a flower; sometimes other parts of the flower or inflorescence may be intimately associated with the matured ovary.*

Figure 13.1 shows changes in the appearance of an almond as it matures from the flower to the fruit. Note that the petals fall, leaving the calyx tube with attached stamens intact (Fig. 13.1A). Soon the developing ovary bursts the calyx tube, following which the ovary rapidly enlarges and differentiates into three distinct layers. Meanwhile the ovule develops into the seed. When completely mature the outer husk dries and falls away leaving the inner part of the ovary wall still surrounding the seed. Strictly, no fruits are produced in

any of the plant groups except the flowering plants (angiosperms).

Development of the Fruit

The development of the fruit (pod) of pea and bean is here described as an example of the various changes that may occur during the transformation of the ovary to fruit. The pistils of bean and pea flowers are each composed of one carpel (Fig. 13.2), that is, one ovule-bearing leaf. The ovules are attached along the ventral suture, the one along which the edges of the carpel are fused; the dorsal suture corresponds to the midrib of the carpel. At the time of fertilization, the ovary and the ovules within are very small. A cross section of the bean ovary (Fig. 13.3) shows the ovary wall, the carpellary bundles, the ovule, and the locule. The ovary wall may be divided into three distinct layers: (1) an outer epidermis, (2) an inner epidermis, and (3) a middle zone consisting of several layers of cells. There are three carpellary bundles, one on each side of the ventral suture and one on the dorsal side opposite them.

Fertilization initiates a series of changes in the embryo sac and other tissues of the ovule; these changes lead to the development of the seed which will be discussed later. The stimulus of fertilization extends not only to the ovule; other parts of the flower are also influenced. The tissues of the ovary wall undergo marked changes. The three layers of the ovary wall, however, are evident in the mature fruit. The fruit wall (developed from the ovary wall) is called the **pericarp,** and the three more or less distinct parts, named in order beginning with the outermost, are the **exocarp, mesocarp,** and **endocarp.** When the pod is mature, floral structures, such as the pedicel, the calyx, withered stamens, and sometimes even remnants of the corolla may

also be present. Quite generally withered remains of the style and stigma persist at the tip of the ovary (Fig. 13.2). Seeds have developed with the matured ovary.

In all kinds of mature fruits the various structures and tissues can be traced back to those of the ovary or ovaries, and to any other floral organs that may constitute a part of the fruit.

Mature pods usually show the presence of small, undeveloped (abortive) ovules. It is probable that these ovules were not fertilized. If none within the bean ovary is fertilized, the ovary does not enlarge. In most plants, normal fruit development takes place only if pollination is followed

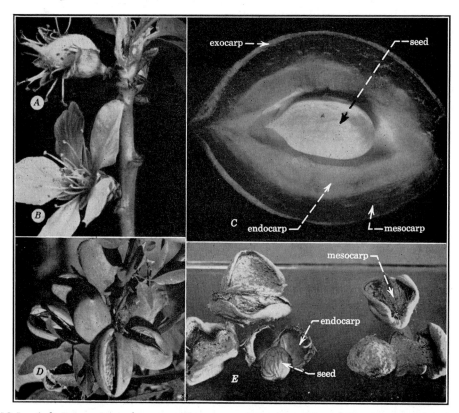

Fig. 13.1. A fruit is a ripened ovary. The ovary of an almond flower (*Prunus amygdalus*) develops into the almond. *B,* almond blossom; *A,* developing ovary bursting calyx tube; *C,* median longitudinal section of a young ovary showing pericarp; *D* and *E,* mature almonds showing split outer portion of ovary wall (shucks) and intact inner portion (shell).

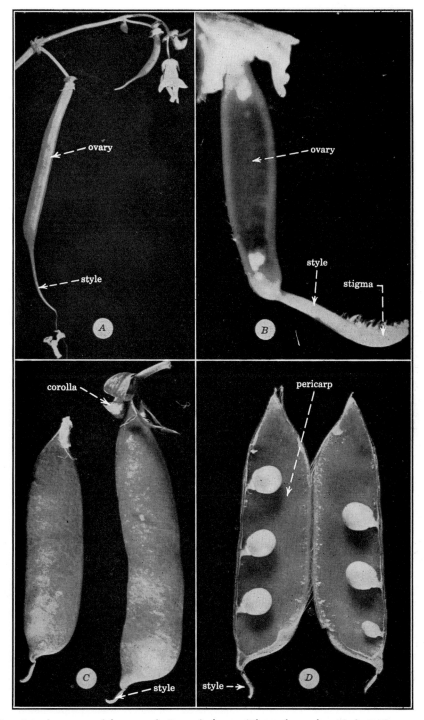

Fig. 13.2. Development of legume fruits. A, bean (*Phaseolus vulgaris*) from flower to young pod, ×1; B, pistil of pea (*Pisum sativum*) flower, ×5; C, pea pod, unopened; D, opened pea pod showing developing seeds attached to ventral suture, ×1.

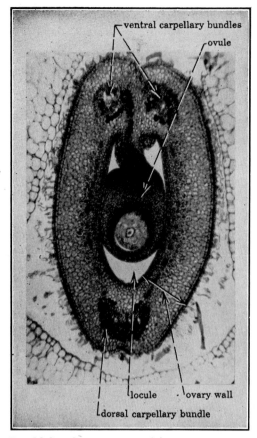

Fig. 13.3. Cross section of bean ovary after fertilization.

or may not be seedless depending upon the occurrence of parthenogenesis and the subsequent development of adventitious (page 256) embryos. On the other hand fertilization may occur, but the ovules may fail to develop into mature seeds even though fruit may form in a normal fashion. In a strict sense only those fruits that develop without

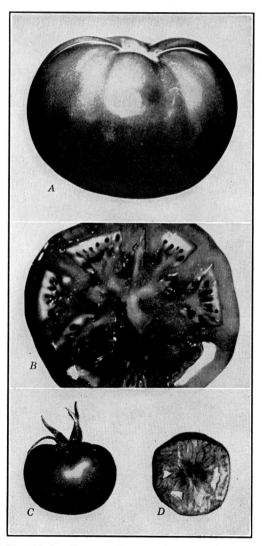

Fig. 13.4. Tomato (*Lycopersicon esculentum*) fruits. A and B, normal development after fertilization; B, cross section; C and D, parthenocarpic fruits; D, cross section. $\times \frac{3}{4}$.

by fertilization and if fertilization is followed by seed development. The fruits of tomato are sometimes distorted and irregular in form; this may be due to the lack of seeds in one or more locules and to the resultant poor development of such locules.

Parthenocarpy. The stimulus of fertilization usually exerts an influence on all parts of the flower, particularly on the ovary and its contained ovules. In Fig. 13.4 normal and seedless fruits of tomato are compared. Note the greatly increased development of the fruit that accompanies normal seed development. In some plants, *normal fruit development may take place without fertilization.* Such unfertilized fruits may

fertilization are called **parthenocarpic fruits.** Practically it is not always possible to know, without an extensive study whether or not a given fruit is parthenocarpic. For instance, Thompson Seedless grapes were thought to be parthenocarpic until it was shown that fertilization takes place and the ovules fail to mature into seeds. In many citrus fruits the seed formed by fertilization is accompanied by seeds with adventitious embryos. To complicate definitions further, the sexually formed seed is not as robust as the adventitious seeds and frequently does not develop. This situation has led to a loose use of the word parthenocarpy to mean simply seedless fruits.

Parthenocarpic (seedless) fruits are quite regularly produced in such cultivated plants as English forcing cucumber, certain varieties of eggplant, navel orange, the banana, the pineapple, and some varieties of apple and pear.

In certain plants seedless fruits may be induced by pollen that is incapable of fertilizing the ovules. For example, in some orchids, the placing of dead pollen or a water extract of pollen upon the stigma may start fruit development.

Recently, parthenocarpy has been induced in some plants by spraying the blossoms with dilute aqueous solutions of certain growth substances. Practical application of this technique is being made.

Kinds of Fruits

The flower of garden beans has a **single ovary** which is composed of one carpel. After fertilization, the seeds develop, the ovary enlarges, and the ovary wall becomes a dry, parchmentlike hull. When the fruit is mature, it splits open along both edges (sutures). The fruits of peas and beans are called **legumes** or **pods** (Fig. 13.2). Thus, the characteristics of the legume or pod are as follows: (1) derived from a single ovary, (2) ovary composed of one carpel, (3) pericarp dry, and (4) pericarp usually splitting along both sutures at maturity.

The lily type of flower has a single ovary, but, unlike that of the bean, it is composed of three united carpels (Fig. 12.3). As in the bean, the ovary wall develops into a dry structure, each locule of which splits open at maturity, allowing the seeds to escape. This type of fruit is called a **capsule** (Fig. 13.5).

These two types of fruit are discussed to point out some of the characters used in describing and classifying fruits. In classifying the different kinds of fruits, taken into account are: (1) the structure of the flower, from which the fruit develops, (2) number of ovaries involved in fruit formation, (3) number of carpels in each ovary, (4) nature of the mature pericarp (dry or fleshy), (5) whether or not the pericarp splits (**dehisces**) at maturity, (6) if dehiscent, the manner of splitting, and (7) the part that sepals or receptacle may play in the formation of the mature fruit.

The so-called **simple fruits** are those derived from a *single ovary*. They may be dry or fleshy, the ovary may be composed of one carpel or of two or more carpels, and the mature fruit may be dehiscent or indehiscent. On the other hand **aggregate** and **multiple fruits** are formed by clusters of simple fruits. The difference between these types of fruits depends upon the number of flowers involved in their formation. In the strawberry (Fig. 13.6) and blackberry (Fig. 13.7) there are many simple fruits, each derived from the individual ovaries of a *single flower*. These matured ovaries or fruits are all attached to a common receptacle. Such groupings constitute aggregate fruits and the simple fruits comprising them may be classified according to the scheme of classification of simple fruits. The mulberry, fig, and pineapple are multi-

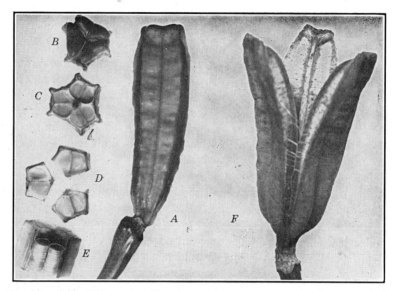

Fig. 13.5. Capsule of lily (*Lilium regali*). *A,* nearly mature capsule; *B,* view of three stigmas; *C,* section; *D,* section separated into portions of three carpels; *E,* longitudinal view showing ovules; *F,* dehisced capsule. ×1.

Fig. 13.6. Aggregate fruit of the strawberry (*Fragaria*). *A,* flower; *B,* fruits. ×1.

ple fruits. The multiple fruit consists of the enlarged ovaries of *several flowers,* more or less grown together into one mass. In some plants, mulberry, for example, associated floral structures form a part of the fruit and in the fig the receptacle enlarges to become the sweet edible portion (Fig. 13.8).

Simple Fruits. *Legume or Pod.* This type of fruit, characteristic of nearly all members of the pea family (Leguminosae), arises from a single carpel, which at maturity generally dehisces along both edges (Figs. 13.2 and 13.9). In the bean or pea pod, the "shell" is the pericarp, and the "beans" or "peas" are the seeds. Pods may be spirally twisted or curved as in alfalfa. A number of legumes such as honey locust, alfalfa, and bur clover have pods that do not dehisce.

Follicle. Typical examples of the follicle are the fruits of Christmas rose, magnolia, and milkweed (Fig. 13.10A, B, and C). The follicle develops from a *single carpel,* and opens along *one suture,* thus differing from the pod, which opens along both sutures.

Capsule. This type of fruit is derived from a compound ovary, that is, an ovary composed of two or more *united carpels.* Each carpel of the capsule produces several to many seeds. Capsules dehisce in various ways: (1) *lengthwise* (*Amaryllis, Iris,* and *Datura,* Fig. 13.11A, B, and C); (2) by *pores* toward the top of each carpel (poppy, Fig. 13.11E); (3) by a *transverse lid* (purslane, pigweed, plantain, Fig. 13.11H).

Silique. This is the type of fruit (Fig. 13.12) characteristic of the members of the mustard family (Cruciferae). One interpretation suggests that the silique is a dry fruit derived from a superior ovary consisting of four carpels; the two outer ones are sterile; the two inner are ovule-bearing

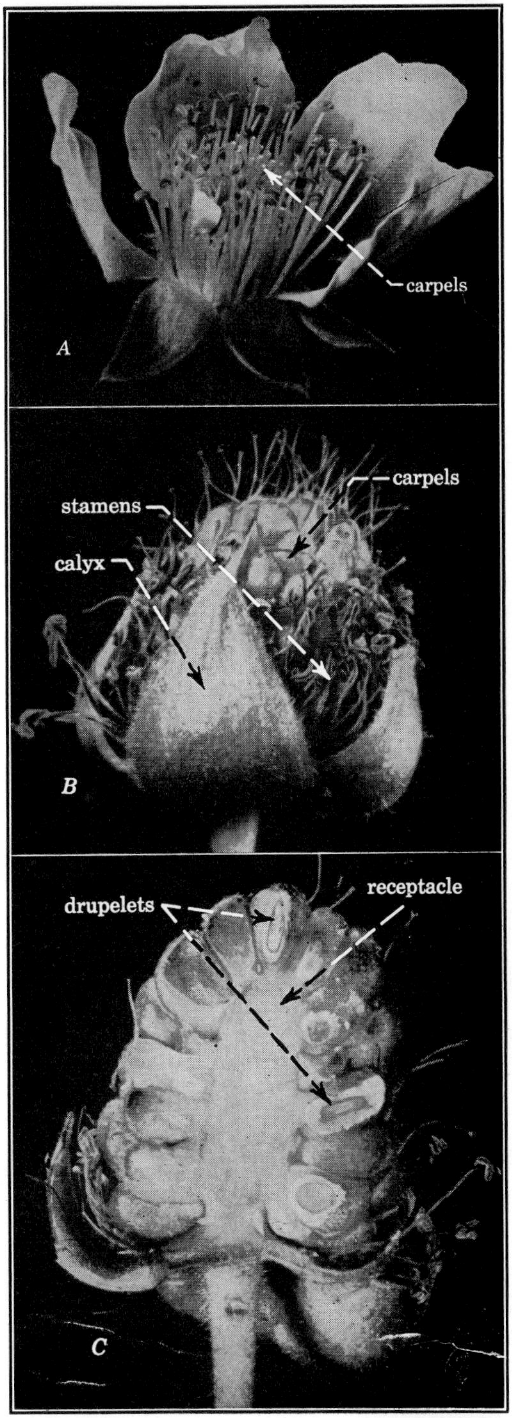

Fig. 13.7. Aggregate fruit of the blackberry (*Rubus ursinus*). A, flower; B, flower shortly after petals have fallen; C, section of fruit. ×1.

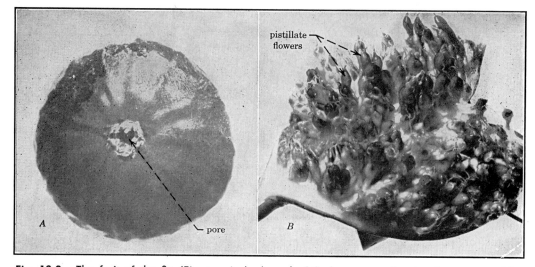

pistillate
flowers

A   pore   *B*

Fig. 13.8. The fruit of the fig (*Ficus carica*); A, end of fleshy receptacle, showing pore and location of staminate flowers; B, receptacle turned inside out showing pistillate flowers. ×1.

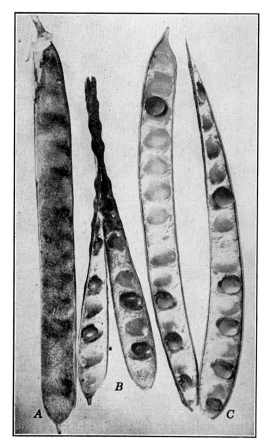

Fig. 13.9. Pod of Scotch broom. A, unopened;
B, partially split; C, dehisced down both sutures.

but very much reduced. The outer carpels of the ovary separate at dehiscence.

Achene. Examples of this type of fruit are buckwheat, strawberry (Fig. 13.6) and members of the Compositae, such as sunflower. These fruits are commonly called "seeds," but as in sunflower (Fig. 13.13), a carefully broken pericarp reveals the seed within, attached only by its funiculus to the placenta. This pericarp may be separated easily from the seed coat, that is, from the layer of cells just beneath it. Achenes are indehiscent.

Grain or Caryopsis. This is the fruit of the grass family (Gramineae), which includes such important plants as wheat, barley, oats, rye, corn, and rice. Like the achene, the grain is a dry one-seeded indehiscent fruit (Fig. 13.14). It differs from the achene, however, in that the pericarp and the seed coat are firmly united all the way around and it is difficult to separate the two except by special milling processes.

Samara. This is a dry, indehiscent fruit, which may be one-seeded, as in the elm, ash, and "tree of heaven" (*Ailanthus*), or two-seeded, as in maple (Fig. 13.15) and box elder. These fruits are typified by an outgrowth of the ovary wall which forms a winglike structure.

Schizocarp. This is the fruit characteristic of the carrot family (Umbelliferae), which includes such common plants as carrot, parsnip, celery, and parsley. The schizocarp is a dry fruit that consists of two carpels which split apart when mature along the midline into two one-seeded indehiscent halves. The carrot "seed" of commerce, for example, is the one-seeded halves of the schizocarp. The one true seed in each carpel completely fills the whole cavity and is usually grown fast to the pericarp.

Nut. The term nut is popularly applied to a number of hard-shelled fruits and seeds. A typical nut, botanically speaking, is a one-seeded, indehiscent dry fruit with a hard or stony pericarp, the shell. Examples are chestnut, walnut, hickory nut, acorn (Fig. 13.16), hazelnut, and beechnut. The chestnut develops within a bur or prickly involucre. An acorn, the fruit of the oak, is partially enclosed by a hardened involucral cup. The structure of the walnut is shown in Fig. 13.17. The husk or shuck of the walnut, which has been removed before the product reaches the market, is composed of involucral bracts, perianth, and outer layer of the pericarp; the hard shell is the remainder of the pericarp. The unshelled almond, sometimes called a nut, is, in reality, a drupe, from which the hull (exocarp and mesocarp) has been removed. Brazil nut and pinyon nut are seeds, not

Fig. 13.10. Follicles. *A, Magnolia,* each carpel shown in Fig. 12.2 develops into a follicle, ×½; *B,* Christmas rose (*Hellborus*), five follicles from one flower, ×¾; *C,* milkweed (*Asclepias*) generally has one follicle per flower, ×½. (C courtesy of K. E. Weier.)

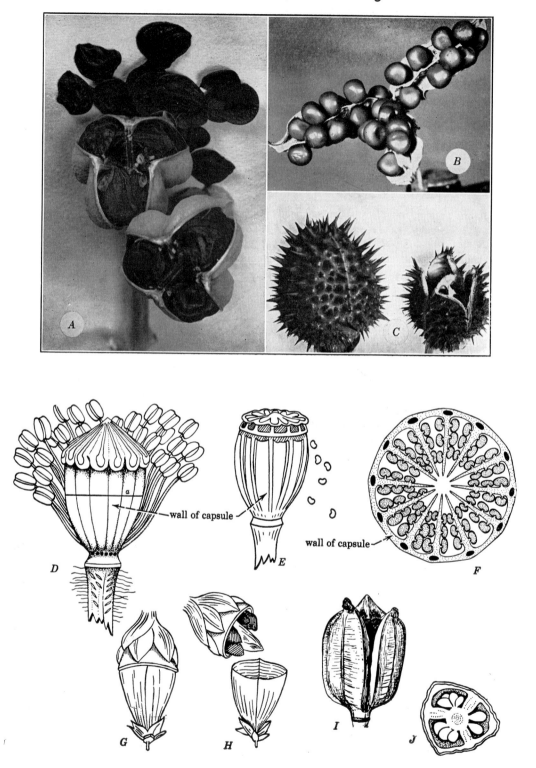

wall of capsule

wall of capsule

fruits. And the unshelled peanut is a pod, corresponding to the fruit of bean or pea; the edible portion is the true seeds within the pod.

Drupe. Examples of this type of fleshy fruit are plum, cherry, almond, peach, and apricot, all of which are members of a sub-family in the Rosaceae (rose family). The olive fruit is also a drupe. The drupe is derived from a *single carpel,* and is usually one-seeded. However, if one examines the young ovary of a flower of the almond (Fig. 13.1), cherry, plum, or other members of the group to which they belong, two ovules will be found, one of which usually aborts (fails to develop into a seed) (Fig. 13.18). The drupe has a hard endocarp consisting of thick-walled stone cells. The exocarp is thin, forming the skin, and the mesocarp forms the edible flesh. The pit or stone of a cherry, for example, is one seed, with thin seed coats, surrounded by the stony endocarp. In other words, the pit is composed of the seed plus the stony inner layer (endocarp) of the ovary wall.

In the almond fruit (Figs. 13.1 and 13.18) the mesocarp is fleshy like a typical drupe when the fruit is young, but it becomes hard and dry, as it develops, and forms the "hull." The shell of the almond is endocarp. In the coconut, also a drupe, the pericarp tissues become dry at maturity.

Berry. This fleshy type of fruit is derived from a *compound ovary.* Usually many seeds are embedded in a flesh, which is both endocarp and mesocarp, although the line of demarcation may be difficult to discern (Fig. 13.19). The tomato is a common example of a berry. The wild form of the garden tomato has a two-celled fruit; cultivated forms have several locules in the fruit, and the placentae are fleshy (Fig. 13.4).

The date is a one-seeded berry, derived from a three-carpelled ovary. After pollination one of the carpels rapidly enlarges and suppresses the other two, which soon dry up. The stone of the date is the seed, and it does not include a stony endocarp as in the drupes of peaches, plums, cherries, etc.

The citrus fruit (lemon, orange, lime, and grapefruit) is a type of berry called a **hesperidium.** It has a thick, leathery rind (peel), with numerous oil glands, and a thick juicy portion composed of several wedge-shaped locules (Fig. 13.20). The peel of a citrus fruit is exocarp and mesocarp; the pulp segments are endocarp. The juice is in pulp sacs or vesicles; they are outgrowths from the endocarp walls (Fig. 13.20*C*) and each mature vesicle is composed of many living cells filled with juice. The common sweet orange usually has ten two-seeded locules, each representing a carpel. The navel orange is a seedless variety, an example of a parthenocarpic fruit.

Another berrylike fruit is that of members of the family Cucurbitaceae, which includes the watermelon, squash, pumpkin, cantaloupe, cucumber, etc. It is called a **pepo** (Fig. 25.11*B*). The outer wall (rind) of the fruit consists of receptacle tissue that surrounds and is fused with the exocarp. The flesh of the fruit is principally mesocarp and endocarp.

Pome. This type of fruit is characteristic of a subfamily of Rosaceae, to which belong the apple, pear, and quince (Fig.

Fig. 13.11. Capsules. *A, Amaryllis; B, Iris; C, Datura; D,* poppy capsule, side view before dehiscence; *E,* mature poppy capsule dehiscing by pores at the top; *F,* cross section of poppy capsule, showing its many carpels; *G,* mature capsule of plantain; *H,* capsule of plantain opening by transverse lid; *I,* capsule of tulip dehiscing lengthwise; *J,* cross section of ovary. (*A, B,* and *C* courtesy of Russell; *D, E,* and *F* redrawn from Korsmo.) All approximately ×1.

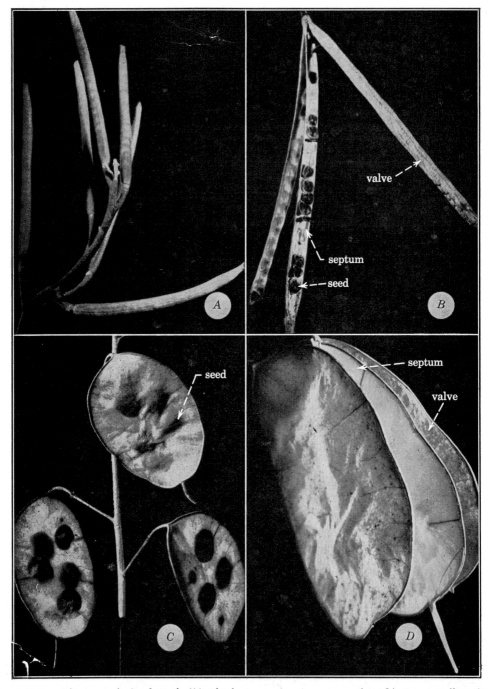

Fig. 13.12. Siliques. *A, B* of stock (*Matthiola incana*). *A,* unopened, ×¾; *B,* partially split to show orientation of valves and septum, ×¾; *C, D* of moonwort (*Lunaria annua*); *C,* unopened silique, ×¾; *D,* opened to show valves and septum, ×1. (Courtesy of Russell.)

12.22B). Cross and lengthwise sections of the mature apple fruit are shown in Fig. 13.21. Various interpretations have been given as to the morphological nature of the pome. The one accepted here is that most of the flesh is derived from the **floral tube** (fused bases of sepals, petals, and stamens) and that the five-carpelled ovary is fused with this tube; that is, the fleshy exocarp is united with the tissues of the floral tube. The so-called core line is the outer limit of the carpels. The endocarp is parchment-like, and both mesocarp and exocarp are fleshy and not easily distinguished one from the other.

Aggregate Fruit. An aggregate fruit is one formed from the numerous carpels of one individual flower. These fruits considered individually may be classified as types of simple fruits. Thus the fruits of the strawberry are achenes and the fruits of raspberry and blackberry are small drupes (Fig. 13.7). The strawberry flower and fruit are shown in Fig. 13.6. The flower has numerous separate carpels on a single receptacle. The ovary of each carpel has one ovule, and the ovary develops into a one-seeded dry fruit (achene). The receptacle to which these fruits are attached becomes fleshy; the whole structure, which we call a strawberry, is an aggregate of

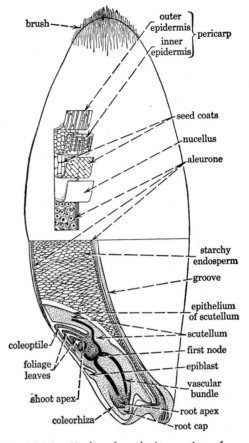

Fig. 13.14. Median lengthwise section of mature wheat grain. (Redrawn from Pope in *Extension Circular, U. S. Dept. of Agriculture.*)

Fig. 13.13. Achene of sunflower (*Helianthus annuus*), unopened, and opened to show attachment of seed. ×1.

simple fruits, each an achene. Receptacle is stem and consists of a fleshy pith and cortex with vascular bundles between them. The so-called hull of the strawberry fruit is composed of the persistent calyx and withered stamens. The achenes are usually spoken of as seeds.

The flowers of dewberry, raspberry, blackberry (Fig. 13.7), and other species of *Rubus* have essentially the same structure as those of strawberry. In these flowers, the many separate carpels attached to the one receptacle develop into small drupes (Fig. 13.7C), instead of achenes.

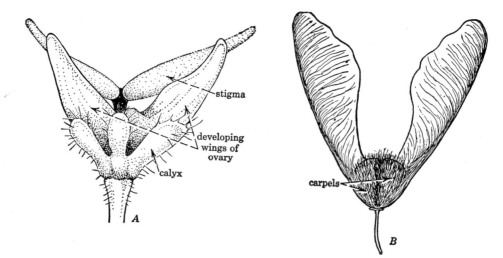

Fig. 13.15. Samara or key fruit of maple (Acer). A, flower; B, mature fruit. (Redrawn from Johnson in *Taxonomy of Flowering Plants*, Appleton-Century-Crofts.)

Fig. 13.16. Acorns of *Quercus*. Nuts; the cups are fused involucral bracts. × ¾.

An aggregate fruit is derived from a *single flower* having many simple pistils (carpels). The various kinds of aggregate fruits differ in the structure of their individual fruitlets, which may be classified as simple fruits.

Multiple Fruits. A multiple fruit is one formed from the individual ovaries of several flowers. These fruits considered individually may be classified as types of simple fruits. The fruits of the mulberry, fig, and pineapple are examples of multiple fruits and the individual fruits composing them are nutlets in the mulberry and fig and parthenocarpic berries in the pineapple.

The flowers of mulberry are of two kinds: staminate and pistillate. The pistillate flowers have a deeply four-lobed calyx, surrounding a single pistil, the ovary of which is one-seeded. The ovary develops into a nutlet and is enclosed by the persistent juicy calyx lobes. The separate fruits become very much crowded together, making up a collection of fruits that commonly goes by the name mulberry.

The fig fruit we eat is an enlarged, fleshy receptacle (Fig. 13.8). The flowers are very small and are attached to the inner wall of this receptacle. Both staminate and pistillate flowers occur and may be borne in the same or in different receptacles. The pistillate flower has a single one-celled (and one-seeded) ovary, surrounded by a two- to six-parted calyx (corolla is absent). Each ovary develops into a nutlet that is embedded in the wall of the receptacle. Thus, the "fig" is derived from many flowers, all attached to the same receptacle. Common edible figs (Mission and Kadota) are parthenocarpic. Smyrna figs and several other varieties do not mature their fruits unless fertilization and seed formation have taken place.

In the pineapple of commerce the edible portion is largely the greatly thickened pulpy central stem in which the berries are embedded.

Summary. There are *three different kinds of fruits*, classified on the basis of the number of ovaries and flowers involved in their formation:

1. **Simple fruits,** derived from a single ovary.

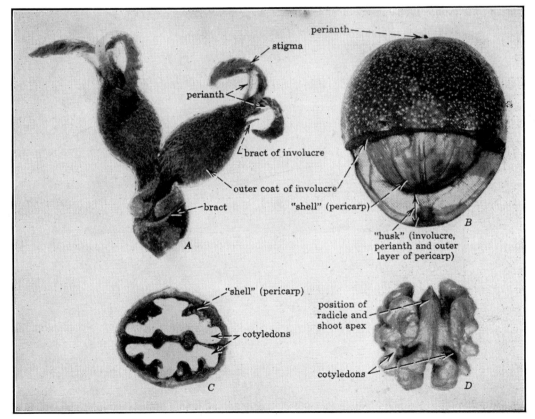

Fig. 13.17. Pistillate flowers and fruit of English walnut (*Juglans regia*). A, two pistillate flowers at time of pollination, ×3; B, mature fruit, ×1; C, cross section of nut with husk removed, ×1; D, single ovule, ×1. (Photo courtesy of Nast.)

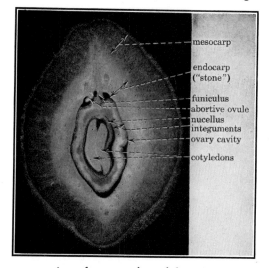

Fig. 13.18. Median transverse section of young almond fruit (*Prunus amygdalus*) (drupe).   From Holman and Robbins, *A Textbook of General Botany*, John Wiley & Sons, Inc.)

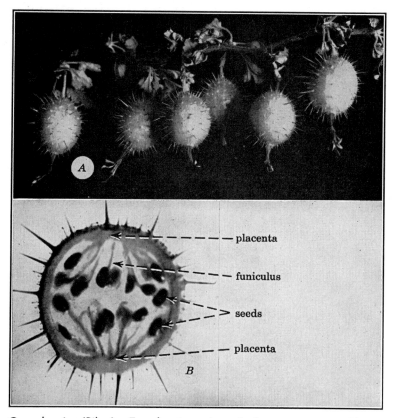

Fig. 13.19. Gooseberries (*Ribes*).   True berries.   A, typical appearance, $\times\frac{3}{4}$; B, cross section, showing parietal placentation, $\times 1\frac{1}{4}$.

2. **Aggregate fruits**, derived from a number of ovaries belonging to a single flower and on a single receptacle.

3. **Multiple fruits**, derived from a number of ovaries of several flowers more or less grown together into one mass.

Simple fruits may have a **dry pericarp** or a **fleshy pericarp**, and if the pericarp is dry it may be **dehiscent** (splitting at maturity, allowing the seeds to escape) or **indehiscent** (not splitting).

THE SEED

STRUCTURE OF THE SEED

The seed is an extremely efficient structure for reproduction and multiplication.

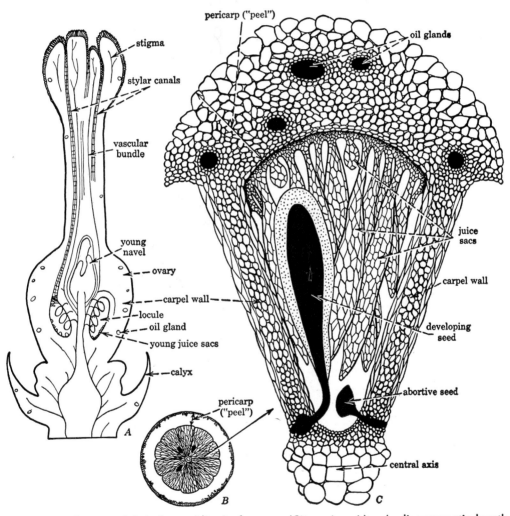

Fig. 13.20. Flower and fruit (hesperidium) of orange (*Citrus sinensis*). A, diagrammatic lengthwise section of flower; B, cross section of fruit; C, structural detail of one carpel. (Redrawn from Bartholomew and Reed in Webber and Batchelor's *The Citrus Industry*, Univ. of Calif. Press.)

Seeds of many species retain their vitality for years and are very resistant to desiccation and to extremes of temperature. Many seeds are also adapted for wide dissemination and on account of the well-advanced state of development of the young plant (embryo) within the seed and the supply of stored food associated with it, the new plant during germination is able to become well established.

As pointed out in Chapter 1, about 6000 B.C., when man first became a food producer rather than a food gatherer, he utilized such herbaceous annuals as wheat, rice, barley, rye, and peas, in other words, plants that possessed seeds with food stored in them. Today, as then, seeds furnish man with a great proportion of his food. A large part of the world's population relies on the grains of wheat and rice as principal items of diet. Other grains, such as corn, rye, and barley, and the seeds of various legumes, especially the soybean, are also important sources of food. Oils

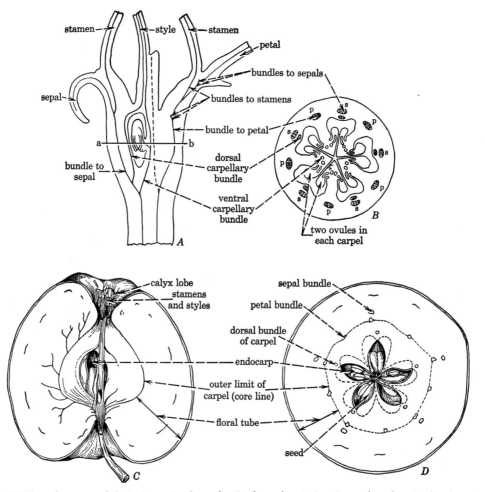

Fig. 13.21. Flower and fruit (pome) of apple (*Malus sylvestris*). A, median longitudinal section of flower; B, cross section of flower; C, median section of fruit; D, cross section of fruit. (A, B redrawn from MacDaniels; C, D redrawn from Robbins, *Botany of Crop Plants*, The Blakiston Co.)

and fats are produced from the seeds of such plants as the coconut, corn, cotton, flax, castor bean, sesame, peanut, and soybean. The oil from cotton seeds and peanuts is utilized in the manufacture of various products such as butter and lard substitutes and soap. Linseed oil from flax seed is used in the manufacture of paints, varnishes, artificial leather, oilcloth, and linoleum. The seeds of cotton bear surface fibers, the world's greatest textile product. Certain seeds are used as spices, such as cardamom, fenugreek, mustard, and nutmeg. And from the seeds of the coffee tree and the cocoa tree are prepared two of the world's most important beverages.

The seed industry is in itself an enormous one. In the United States 396,420 acres were devoted to the growing of vegetable seeds alone during 1942; the production was 333,061,425 pounds. In addition, many millions of pounds of field seeds and flower seeds were grown. The seed industry includes the growing and harvesting of the seed, often involving special climates and methods; cleaning and storing, which also requires special types of equipment and processes; seed testing; and marketing.

Development of the Seed

The seed develops from an ovule (Figs. 12.3B, 12.11). With rare exceptions, the ovule does not begin to undergo the changes that result in seed formation unless fertilization has taken place. Fertilization in the angiosperms involves the union of one sperm cell of the pollen tube with the egg cell of the embryo sac, and union of the other sperm cell of the pollen tube with the endosperm mother cell of the embryo sac (Fig. 12.11). The fertilized egg cell is the zygote, from which the embryo develops. The product of fusion of a sperm cell with endosperm mother cell is the

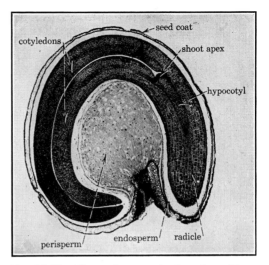

Fig. 13.22. Photomicrograph of section of beet (*Beta vulgaris*) seed in which the perisperm is the main food storage tissue. (Photo courtesy of Bennett and Esau.)

primary endosperm cell, from which the endosperm (food supply) develops.

During the development of the embryo and endosperm, part of the nucellar tissue is digested and supplies food for their growth. The nucellus in the mature seed, if present, usually consists of a thin layer of cells, called the **perisperm**. In some seeds, such as those of the beet, the perisperm is large and contains considerable stored food (Fig. 13.22); in others, such as common bean, the perisperm is used up by the developing embryo. In all cereals, the mature seed contains an abundant endosperm. The integuments of the ovule become the seed coats.

After the seed is mature, it may remain dormant for a long period, sometimes for years. Germination is a process in which the period of rest is broken and growth is resumed.

Kinds of Seeds

Seeds of different plants vary greatly as to size, form, external color and markings,

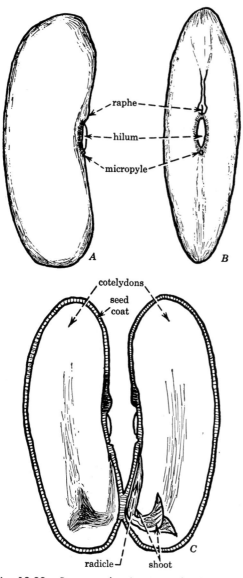

Fig. 13.23. Bean seed. A, external side view; B, external face or edge view; C, embryo opened.

(Fig. 13.26). These involve not only size, shape, and color but also surface markings. Even with different varieties of crop plants, it may be possible to identify them by seed characters.

Three common types of seeds are to be described:

1. Common bean, with two cotyledons and no endosperm.

2. Castor bean, with two cotyledons and endosperm.

3. Wheat, with one cotyledon and endosperm.

Common Bean. The fruit of bean is a pod. Within it are the seeds (beans). The external characters of the bean seed are more clearly seen after soaking it in water. The points of interest are the **hilum, micropyle,** and **raphe** (Fig. 13.23). The hilum is a large oval scar, near the middle of one edge, left where the seed broke from the stalk or funiculus when the beans were harvested. The micropyle is a small opening in the seed coat (integument) at one side of the hilum and was observed in the ovule, as the opening through which the pollen tube entered the ovule. The raphe is a ridge at the side of the hilum opposite the micropyle. It represents the base of the funiculus, which is fused with the integuments. Conducting tissue, present in the funiculus will be continued in the raphe. At the end of the raphe this conducting tissue may fan out over the ovule or seed and lose its identity as conducting tissue. This region is known as the **chalaza.** It is always present at the end of the ovule or seed opposite the micropyle. An elevation or bulge of the seed coat adjacent to the micropyle marks the position of the radicle (embryo root) within the seed.

When the seed coat of a soaked bean is removed, the entire structure remaining is the embryo; no endosperm is present. The following parts of the embryo can be ob-

internal structure, and amount and nature of stored foods. The skilled seed analyst can identify most of the species of weeds, and many other plants, by the seeds alone. Examination of seeds with a hand lens reveals many distinguishing characteristics

served: (1) the shoot consisting of (*a*) two fleshy cotyledons, (*b*) a short axis, the hypocotyl, below the cotyledons, and (*c*) a short axis, the epicotyl, above the cotyledons bearing several minute foliage leaves and terminating in a shoot tip; and (2) the root or radicle. In Fig. 13.23 the bean seed is opened out to show the relationship of some of the parts just mentioned.

Castor Bean. The external points of interest of this seed are (1) the **caruncle**, a spongy structure, an outgrowth of the outer seed coat; the (2) hilum and (3) micropyle, which are beneath the caruncle; and (4) the raphe, which runs the full length of the seed (Fig. 13.24).

The chalaza region is marked, in the castor bean, by a protuberance at the end of the seed opposite the caruncle. In contrast to the bean seed, that of the castor bean plant has a massive endosperm in which the embryo is embedded. The shoot of the embryo consists of (*a*) two thin cotyledons with conspicuous veins, (*b*) a very short hypocotyl (shoot axis below the cotyledons), and (*c*) a minute shoot tip.

The root portion of the embryo axis consists of a small radicle.

Wheat. Wheat is a member of the grass family (Gramineae). The so-called **seed** of wheat, or of any other grass, is in reality a fruit (grain), as explained on page 264. It is a one-seeded, dry, indehiscent fruit with the pericarp (ovary wall) firmly attached to the seed; the pericarp and seed coats are so firmly attached to each other and to other tissues of the grain that it is impossible to peel them off, as one can the seed coats of the common bean and castor bean. Therefore, in order to study the internal structure of the grain, it is necessary to employ sections.

A longitudinal section of the grain of wheat is shown in Fig. 13.14. Note here that the endosperm constitutes the bulk of the grain. The endosperm is composed of (1) an outermost layer (single row of cells) known as the **aleurone layer** and (2) **starchy endosperm.** The cells of the aleurone layer contain proteins and fats but little or no starch. The starchy endosperm cells are filled with starch grains

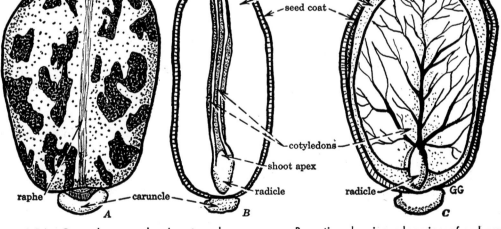

Fig. 13.24. Castor bean seed. A, external appearance; B, section showing edge view of embryo; C, section showing flat view of embryo.

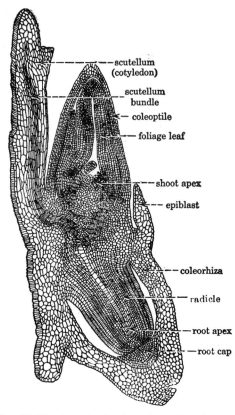

Fig. 13.25. Longitudinal section of embryo of wheat. (Redrawn from McCall.)

that are embedded in a colloidal protoplasmic matrix, containing protein granules and carbohydrates.

The embryo of grasses is quite unlike that of most other plant families. Like all embryos of seed plants, it has an axis, with a **shoot tip** and a **root tip** (Fig. 13.25). The shoot apex of the wheat embryo, and the several rudimentary leaves, are surrounded by a sheath, the **coleoptile**. The rudimentary root (radicle) is also surrounded by a sheath, the **coleorhiza**. At the juncture of the shoot and root is a very short stem structure. A relatively large part of the grass embryo is the single cotyledon, which has for a long time been called the **scutellum**. It is a shield-shaped structure that lies in contact with the endosperm. The outer cells of the scutellum secrete enzymes that digest the stored foods of the endosperm. These digested foods move from endosperm cells through the scutellum to the growing parts of the embryo. Unlike the bean and castor bean seed, the cotyledon of grasses remains within the seed during germination and never develops into a green leaflike structure aboveground.

SUMMARY

Three different types of seeds have been described. The structure of seeds in general may be summarized as follows:

Seed coat or coats (derived from the integuments).

Perisperm (remains of the nucellus).

Endosperm (sometimes lacking, derived from primary endosperm cell.

Embryo (derived from zygote) a young plant body consisting of:

1. Shoot.
   - (*a*) Epicotyl—shoot above the cotyledons; tip and foliage leaves.
   - (*b*) Cotyledons or seed leaves (two in dicotyledonous plants, one in monocotyledonous plants).
   - (*c*) Hypocotyl—part of the embryo between the point of attachment of the cotyledons and the upper end of the root.

2. Root (radicle).

The Storage of Foods in Seeds

The foods of plants are transported from their seat of manufacture (leaves, principally) either to parts of the plant that are growing rapidly or to tissues where they are stored for future use. In seed plants, with but few exceptions, the seed is an important food storage organ. In annual plants it is the chief storage organ. Thus the seed is an organ both of reproduction and of food storage. The stored foods are available to the embryo and may occur in the endosperm, the embryo, or both. Rarely, as in beet seeds, the perisperm (nucellar tissue) stores food (Fig. 13.22).

Many wild animals live on foods stored in seeds, and primitive man relied heavily upon them. As pointed out in Chapter 1, early civilizations developed in those regions of the world were wheat, corn, rice, and other cereals thrived naturally. These were annual plants which in one season stored large amounts of food in seeds—organs that could be harvested and stored easily and laid by for the winter. In our modern world, the principal plants whose seeds are utilized as food for man and beasts are wheat, corn, rice, barley, rye, oats, sorghums, millets, buckwheat, legumes (peas, beans, soybeans, cowpeas, peanuts, etc.), and nuts (Brazil nuts, coconut, pecan, walnuts, almonds, etc.).

The principal kinds of food stored in seeds are (1) carbohydrates, including chiefly starch, hemicelluloses, and sugars, (2) fats, and (3) proteins.

Starch is the commonest form of food stored in seeds. It is a polysaccharide with the formula $(C_6H_{10}O_5)_n$. In cereals it is found chiefly in the endosperm, and in legumes in the embryo.

Sugars are less common as a reserve food in seeds than are starches, fats, and proteins. When present, they are in solution in the cell sap. Sucrose (cane sugar) is the commonest sugar in seeds. The seeds of sweet corn, chestnuts, almonds, pistachios, and peas are examples of those storing fairly large quantities of sugar. Sugar content is usually a measure of the quality of green peas. Studies show that when they are of maximum marketable value, the total sugars may be as high as 35 per cent

of the fresh weight. As they ripen and develop, total sugars decrease rapidly, being changed to polysaccharides.

Fats, like carbohydrates, contain three elements—carbon, hydrogen, and oxygen. The proportion of oxygen to carbon is less in fats than in carbohydrates. Fats in the liquid state are known as oils. Fats are an important reserve food in seeds, usually more abundant in the embryo than in the endosperm. They are probably synthesized in the cells in which they occur.

In fat-storing seeds the fat content usually increases rapidly as the seeds mature. At the same time, the percentage of carbohydrates decreases, which would seem to indicate that carbohydrates are converted into fats.

Some of the most important fats (and oils) derived from seeds are those from flax, tung, cotton, soybean, olive, peanut, castor bean, coconut, sesame, and oil palm. They are used as food, in making paints and varnishes, linoleum, printer's ink, soap, artificial leather, insulating materials, and in numerous other ways. Plant fats and oils are rapidly becoming among the world's most important commercial products.

Proteins are complex carbon compounds, containing, in addition to carbon, hydrogen, and oxygen (the only three elements in carbohydrates and fats), the elements nitrogen and sulfur and sometimes phosphorus. Proteins are an important reserve food in most kinds of seeds, especially those of the legume family (peas, beans, etc.). Reserve proteins occur as solid granules.

DISSEMINATION OF SEEDS AND FRUITS

In 1886, the weed Russian thistle was introduced into the United States from Russia in flax seed sown near Scotland, South Dakota. Today, Russian thistle is an

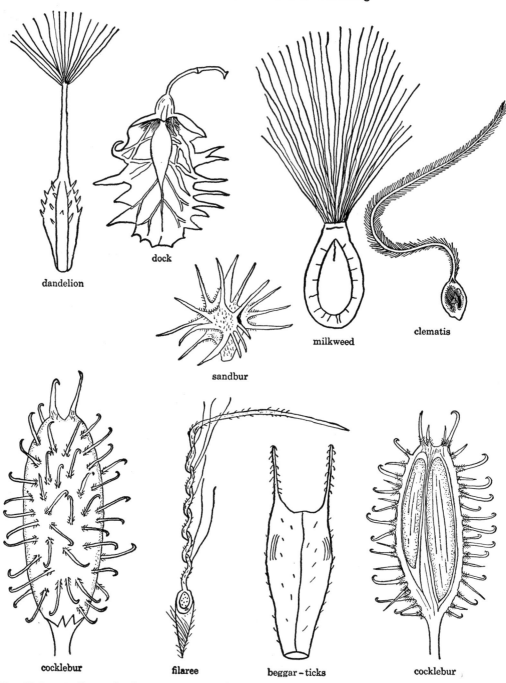

Fig. 13.26. Different kinds of seeds and fruits showing various devices that favor their dissemination. Lower right figure, cocklebur fruit in longitudinal section showing the two seeds. The lower seed usually germinates the first season after maturity, whereas there is often a delay in the germination of the upper seed. (Redrawn from Robbins, Crafts, and Raynor in *Weed Control*, McGraw-Hill Book Co.)

obnoxious weed over thousands of square miles from Illinois to the Pacific Coast. Russian thistle is an annual weed that reproduces only by seeds, and it is an example of a plant that has effective means of migrating from place to place. The whole Russian thistle plant, like witch grass, tumbling pigweed, and other so-called tumble-weeds, is carried by wind, rolling for many miles over treeless areas, scattering seeds as it travels. Many plants are weeds partly because they have effective means of disseminating their seeds. Of course, with Russian thistle, as with many other weeds, man has assisted in its distribution by disseminating the seed in shipments of crop seeds, in screenings, in hay, feedstuffs, etc.

Agents in Seed and Fruit Dispersal

The chief agents in seed and fruit dispersal are **wind, water,** and **animals,** including **man.** In weeds, as contrasted with other plants, probably no other means of dissemination is so important as the sale and distribution of farm and garden seeds and farm products containing the seeds of various weeds.

Wind. The structural modifications of seeds and fruits that aid in dissemination by wind are of several types: **winged, parachute, saccate, comate,** and **plumed** (Fig. 13.26). **Winged fruits and seeds** have expanded wings or margins. Examples are fruits of docks, tree of heaven, maple (Fig. 13.15), ash, and elm and seeds of catalpa, pines (Fig. 24.37B), and firs.

Water. Fruits with a membranous envelope containing air, as those of sedges, or with a coarse, loose, fibrous outer coat, as in the coconut, are well adapted for dispersal by water. A great variety of fruits and seeds float in water, even though lacking special adaptations to insure buoyancy, and are readily transported long distances by moving water in the form of surface runoff, natural streams, irrigation and drainage channels, and floods. In the irrigated districts, irrigation water is a very important means by which weed seeds are distributed.

Animals. Many seeds and fruits are carried by animals, both wild and domesticated. Those with beards, spines, hooks, or barbs adhere to the hair of animals (Fig. 13.26). Examples of seeds carried in this manner are wild barley, puncture vine, star thistles, sandbur, and cocklebur.

The seeds of many plants pass through the digestive tract of animals without having their viability impaired. Fleshy, edible fruits may be eaten by birds and carried by them long distances, and then the seeds regurgitated, or discharged with the excrement. Squirrels carry nuts, such as those of walnut and hickory, and the seeds of pines. The seeds of aquatic and marsh plants and those of mistletoe, which are covered with a sticky material, are carried on the feet of birds.

SEED GERMINATION

Of interest and concern to everyone who grows plants, whether it be on the farm, in the greenhouse, or in the home garden, is the germination of seeds. It is realized that seed of high vitality is desired and that external conditions essential for good seed germination and establishment of the young plant must be provided.

We have learned that the seed is a structure composed of (1) an **embryo** (young plant), (2) a **reserve food** supply, which may be in the embryo itself, or in the endosperm (if present), (3) sometimes fragments of the **nucellus,** (4) all surrounded by protective **seed coats.** We traced the development of the seed from the ovule in the ovary of the flower. The young plant developed from a zygote, the cell formed from the union of a sperm from the pollen tube with an egg in the embryo sac of the ovule. Thus did the individual plant begin its life as a **single cell,** the zygote. After fertilization and up to the stage of seed maturity, the processes of development are fairly continuous. Then, a cessation of activity ensues—a "resting period," in which the seed may remain for a long time, even years. During the resting stage there is no cell division and growth, but cells of the embryo and those in which foods are stored retain their life and undoubtedly carry on respiration at a very slow rate. When we speak of **seed germination,** we mean that certain external conditions have become favorable so that the living cells of the dormant seed can resume activity. The germination of a seed is a process of unusual activity. Cells, having been dormant, begin to divide and redivide; they increase in size; rudimentary organs, such as roots, stems,

and leaves, take form. In other words, there is **growth,** which involves (1) increase in cell number and size, and (2) differentiation with the eventual formation of a seedling.

SEEDLINGS

Ordinarily, when we speak of seedlings, we have in mind young, tender plants that emerge from the soil, having developed *directly* from the embryo of a seed. Perennials with underground stems may send aboveground young shoots that might casually be mistaken for seedlings. By digging beneath the soil surface, it will be seen that such shoots are connected to a stem. On the other hand, most dicotyledonous seedlings raise the cotyledons aboveground and these structures are a definite identifying character. If the cotyle-

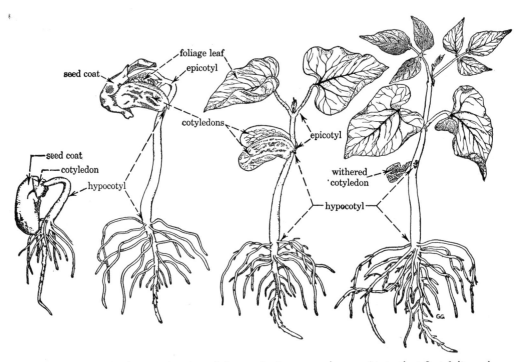

Fig. 13.27. Stages in the germination of the seed of common bean. Note that first foliage leaves are simple, whereas subsequent ones are compound.

don or cotyledons remain underground, parts of the seed persist for quite a long time at the juncture of the root and shoot.

The term seedling may be applied by propagators and horticulturists to full-grown trees. When they refer to a seedling peach tree, for example, they mean one that has been grown from seed in contrast to one that has been grafted onto the root or stem of another plant.

On pages 276–278, three types of seeds were described: (1) common bean, a dicotyledonous seed without endosperm, (2) castor bean, a dicotyledonous seed with endosperm, and (3) wheat, a monocotyle-

donous seed with endosperm. The student should refer back to the discussion of the structure of these seeds. Several stages in the germination of each type of seed are shown in Figs. 13.27, 13.28, and 13.29.

In all three types, the root is the first structure to emerge from the seed, and the young plant is for a time wholly dependent upon food stored within the cotyledons or within the endosperm. If the soil above the germinating seed should become crusted or compacted, or if the seed was planted too deeply, the seedling may exhaust its reserve of food and die before reaching the light. Large seeds with a plentiful supply of

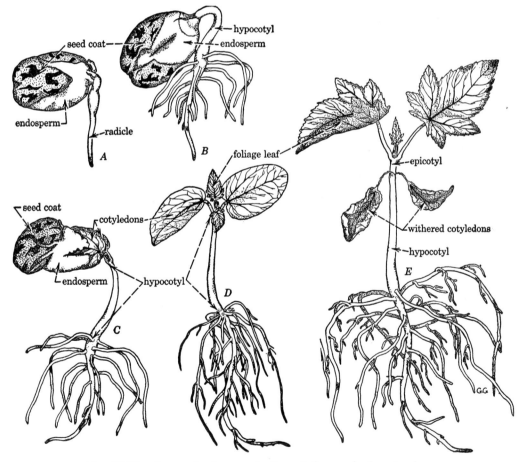

Fig. 13.28. Stages in the germination of the seed of castor bean.

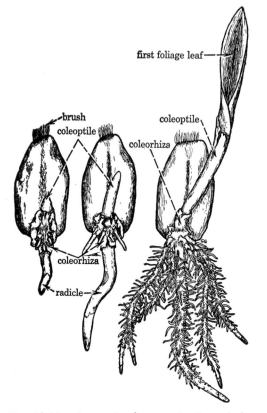

first foliage leaf

brush
coleoptile

coleoptile

coleorhiza

coleorhiza

radicle

Fig. 13.29. Stages in the germination of the grain of wheat.

stored food can be planted more deeply than small seeds with only a meager amount. Once the shoot reaches the light and is thus able to manufacture its own food, and once the root system is absorbing water and mineral salts from the soil, the young plant becomes self-supporting; it no longer depends upon the stored food.

In those plants that raise the cotyledons aboveground, these structures become green and carry on photosynthesis for some time. After a while the reserve food is exhausted and only the shriveled epidermis remains. In the castor bean seedling, the cotyledons are in close contact with the endosperm, from which they absorb food and transfer it to the growing regions.

The seedling of wheat represents a type occurring in all grasses. The one cotyledon (Fig. 13.25) remains beneath the soil. The primary root ruptures the coleorhiza. The coleoptile penetrates the soil, and soon afterwards the first foliage leaf grows through the tip.

From the descriptions of seedlings, it is seen that there are two distinct types: (1) those that raise the cotyledon or cotyledons aboveground; examples: bean, squash, castor-oil plant, alfalfa, and apple among dicotyledonous plants, and onion among monocotyledons; (2) those in which the cotyledon or cotyledons remain underground; examples: peas and scarlet runner beans among dicotyledons, and all grasses among monocotyledons.

14

Inheritance

THE LIFE CYCLE

The individuals of a single-celled species living in a pond have been multiplying by dividing in two since life started, and they will continue to divide and grow as long as they, or other species to which they may give rise, continue to exist on this earth. The simplest type of life cycle is this division of a single-celled plant to form two new plants. Most individuals, plant or animal, are not so simply constructed; specialized cells are set aside for reproductive processes. For example, in the flowering plants the flowers and seeds possess such specialized cells. Even in these plants the special reproductive cells are in a sense immortal, for one can trace their history back to the beginning of life through a series constituted mainly of meristematic cells and reproductive cells. Every plant and animal living today must have a chain of ancestors stretching back to the beginning of life. During this long period the characteristics of present-day plant and animal life have been derived. How has this happened? Are species of animals and plants constant? Do they change? How similar to each other are the individuals of a given species? If individuals of a given species vary, what are the causes of variation? Can this variation be controlled or predicted? How do the specialized reproductive cells function? What is the importance of sex? These and many other questions arise when one considers the reproductive cycle of plants and animals. Partial answers may be given, but to no question stated above is there, as yet, a final and complete answer.

Let us consider first, rather briefly, the life cycle of a flowering plant, corn, for example. Seed is planted; it gives rise to the vegetative plant, which in time produces staminate flowers in the tassels and pistillate flowers in the ears. Pollen is formed by the staminate flowers and carried to the stigmas of pistillate flowers in the young ears, either on the same individual plant or on adjacent individuals. (Self-pollination does occur but results in less vigorous offspring than does cross pollination.) The pollen tube grows down the long style and eventually penetrates the embryo sac, where a sperm and an egg eventually fuse to form the zygote, which develops into the embryo. A second sperm from the pollen tube fuses with the two polar nuclei of the embryo sac. The body resulting from this triple fusion develops

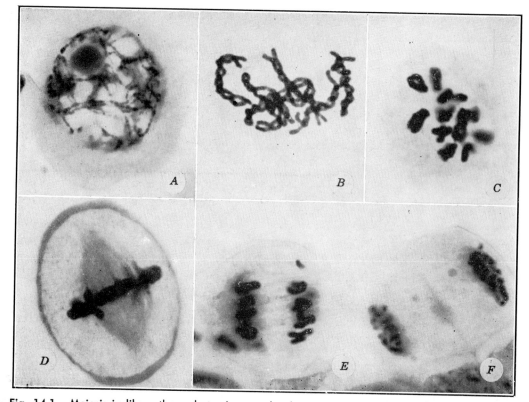

Fig. 14.1. Meiosis in lily anther; photomicrographs showing, A, early prophase I. Note paired threads; B, late prophase I. Each body represents two paired chromosomes. Note chiasmata. (Courtesy of Gankin.); C, late prophase I. Paired chromosomes; two chiasmata present. Compare with chromosomes of Fig. 14.2 D; D, metaphase I. Note tractile fibers extending from chromosomes; E, anaphase I; F, telophase I.

into the endosperm. The embryo and endosperm constitute the major portion of the corn "seed," or, more properly, the fruit. Of very great importance in this cycle is the behavior of the **chromosomes**, which are the carriers of the **genes**, the units responsible for the morphological and physiological characteristics of every individual. During the formation of the pollen and of the embryo sac the chromosomes go through two characteristic divisions, the **meiotic divisions** (**meiosis**).

At fertilization, nuclei with the gene-carrying chromosomes from two parents are generally combined to form the zygote nucleus. These two phenomena, **meiosis** and

fertilization, involving, as they do, the assortment and combination of chromosomes, form the basis of the sexual reproductive cycle. Indeed, the great diversity of plant and animal life is due largely to the changes that occur in a chromosome set during meiosis and fertilization. In many plants, asparagus and date palms, for example, two separate parents are involved in sexual reproduction; in others, such as pea and wheat, the zygotes are usually formed by sperms and eggs produced on the same parent.

Let us now consider, in some detail, chromosome behavior at these two important stages in the life history of sexually

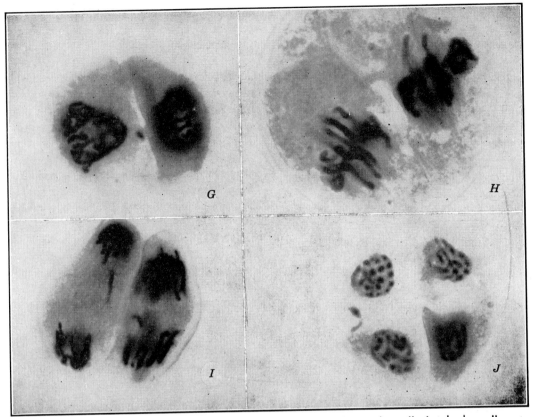

Fig. 14.1 (*continued*).   G, prophase II; *H,* metaphase II; *I,* anaphase II; *J,* telophase II.

reproducing individuals. We shall discuss first chromosome behavior during meiosis and fertilization and then follow the influence of individual genes through several generations. We shall find that chromosome behavior at these two critical stages constitutes a mechanical basis for inheritance and that inheritance itself may be placed on a firm mathematical foundation.

Meiosis

Review of Mitosis. First let us review briefly the formation and movement of chromosomes during mitosis in meristematic cells, such as occur at the apices of stems and roots (see Chapter 5). In the prophase of mitosis each nuclear thread contracts to form a chromosome possessing **two chromatids** (half chromosomes); the **kinetochores** then become aligned at the equator of the cell; during anaphase sister chromatids (half chromosomes) move to opposite poles of the cell; during telophase daughter nuclei are reconstituted; and the development of a cell wall completes the formation of two identical daughter cells. In this process there has been no change in the chromosome number, and no assortment of chromosomes; each daughter nucleus has the same complement of genes. It should be emphasized, however, that all cells containing $2n$ chromosomes have two sets of chromosomes. In corn, for instance, there are

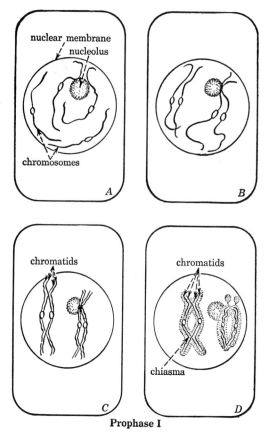

Fig. 14.2. Meiosis, prophase I. Four chromo-somes, two pairs are represented. A, very early prophase; B, beginning of pairing; C, pairing completed, each chromosome split into two chromatids; D, late prophase, showing that chromatids have broken and rejoined forming chiasmata.

twenty chromosomes, two sets of ten each. The chromosomes in corn have been num-bered from one to ten. Each nucleus of the corn plant therefore contains the fol-lowing chromosomes:

1 2 3 4 5 6 7 8 9 10
1 2 3 4 5 6 7 8 9 10

The two number 1 chromosomes are said to be **homologous chromosomes**, as are the two number 2 chromosomes, etc. Each

pair of chromosomes $(3 + 3, 4 + 4, 5 + 5,$ etc.) constitutes a pair of homologous chro-mosomes.

The term **diploid** is applied to any nu-cleus, cell, or plant having two such sets of chromosomes. Should only one set be pres-ent, as occurs in eggs and sperms, the nu-cleus, cell, or plant is said to be **haploid.** These conditions may be indicated by the symbols $2n$ (diploid) or n (haploid).

Characteristic Features of Meiosis. These features include: (1) a pairing of homologous chromosomes to form a body with four chromatids, (2) an interchange of material between chromatids of homolo-gous chromosomes, (3) the distribution of the four reconstituted chromatids to four cells or **meiospores,** and (4) chromosome arrangements, in the resulting meiospores, that may differ from each other and from those in the parent plants.

In order to accomplish the separation of the four chromatids of the originally paired homologous chromosomes, the ordinary phases encountered in mitosis (prophase, metaphase, anaphase, and telophase) occur twice, making two **meiotic divisions.** It is

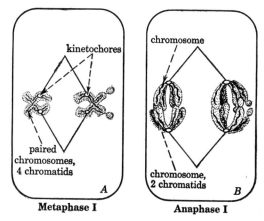

Fig. 14.3. Meiosis. A, metaphase 1; B, ana-phase I. Kinetochores move apart; associated chromatids follow.

common to designate the two divisions by the numerals I and II and the phases as prophase I, metaphase I, anaphase I, telophase I, prophase II, metaphase II, anaphase II, and telophase II.

Meiosis—First Division. *Prophase I.* During prophase of meiosis (Figs. 14.1A, 14.2) the nuclear threads of the vegetative nucleus, present in the diploid number, contract to form chromosomes each with two chromatids; in this respect the process resembles mitosis. The process is complicated, however, because before the chromatids become apparent the homologous chromosomes pair (the two number 1 chromosomes, for example). In so doing they approach and coil about each other (Figs. 14.1A, 14.2). The two chromatids of a chromosome appear only after the pairing of the homologous chromosomes is well advanced (Fig. 14.2A, B, and C). The resulting figure is composed of two paired homologous chromosomes and four chromatids (Figs. 14.1B, C, and 14.2). This stage of prophase involves two phenomena: (1) the pairing of homologous chromosomes and (2) the formation of chromo-

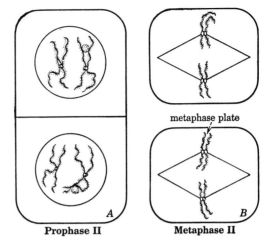

metaphase plate

Prophase II   **Metaphase II**

Fig. 14.5. Meiosis. A, prophase II; this stage passes very rapidly; each chromosome consists of two chromatids, and kinetochores have split. B, chromosomes on metaphase plate; each chromatid has its own kinetochore.

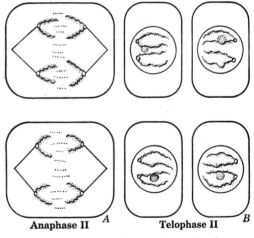

Anaphase II *A*   **Telophase II** *B*

Fig. 14.6. Meiosis. A, anaphase II; chromatids separate. B, telophase II; four cells result, each with two chromatids.

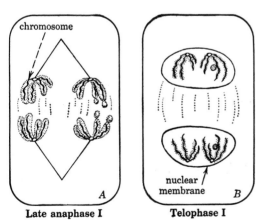

chromosome

nuclear membrane

Late anaphase I   **Telophase I**

Fig. 14.4. Meiosis. A, late anaphase I; chromosomes approaching poles of cell; B, telophase I.

somes with two chromatids each. The chromatids thus formed do not remain unchanged; they normally break at from one to ten places and rejoin in such a way that a given reconstituted chromatid may be composed of parts of several chromatids (Fig. 14.2*D*). This breaking and rejoining of the chromatids is called **crossing over,** and the cross formed by the chromatids involved in the interchange is known as a **chiasma** (**chiasmata,** plural) (Figs. 14.2*D*, 14.1*C*). Thus a third step in the prophase I of meiosis is: (3) the formation of chiasmata due to the breaking and rejoining of chromatids from homologous chromosomes. As in mitosis the nucleolus disappears, material from it probably passing to the developing chromosomes. The nuclear membrane also disappears during the later stages of prophase.

Metaphase I. At metaphase I (Fig. 14.3*A*) the kinetochores of the paired homologous chromosomes pass to the equator of the cell. Tractile fibers grow toward the poles (Figs. 14.1*D*, 14.3).

Anaphase I. In anaphase I (Fig. 14.1*E*) the kinetochores of *whole chromosomes* separate from each other (Figs. 14.3*B*, 14.4*A*) and with their associated chromosomes move to opposite poles of the cell. However, because of chiasmata formation, whole, complete chromosomes are not separated from each other, for on the side of the chiasma away from the kinetochore, sister chromatids will separate just as in mitosis. Anaphase I of meiosis is thus the separation of *two chromatids.* Since the chromatids have become variously modified, the separation involves both a separation of whole chromosomes (at the kinetochores) and a separation of sister chromatids as in mitosis (across the chiasma).

Telophase I. Following anaphase I the chromatids group together at opposite poles of the cell (Figs. 14.1*F*, 14.4*B*) and immediately prepare for the second meiotic division. While each telophase chromosome consists of two chromatids, and in this sense the *n* or haploid number of chromosomes is

present, it must be remembered that structurally the chromosome is composed of both sister chromatids and chromatids derived from homologous chromosomes.

Meiosis—Second Division. A second meiotic division now follows which separates these rearranged chromatids. During prophase II (Figs. 14.1*G*, 14.5*A*) the chromosomes again form, each with two composite chromatids. The kinetochores approach the equatorial plate, forming metaphase II (Figs. 14.1*H*, 14.5*B*). The kinetochores now split and separate. In anaphase II single chromatids move to opposite poles of the cell (Figs. 14.1*I*, 14.6*A*) and are reconstituted in telophase II into nuclei (Fig. 14.1*I, J*). Each nucleus thus formed contains one of the four chromatids that formed the tetrad of chromatids during prophase I.

Walls develop about each new nucleus and associated cytoplasm, thus forming cells with the *n* or haploid number of chromosomes. Since the chromatids within each of these four cells have been variously modified by crossing over, each of the four cells may be genetically different. In just what way do they differ and of what importance is this variance in the life cycle of plants?

Distribution of Genes. *Without Crossing Over.* In order to answer the questions raised above we shall designate one gene of each chromosome. Since we have a pair of homologous chromosomes we will have one pair of genes. In order to distinguish the genes on the different homologous chromosomes we shall use capital and small letters.

The pair of postulated homologous chromosomes at early prophase I may be diagrammed as follows:

A

During prophase the homologous chromosomes pair and coil about each other:

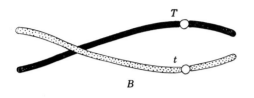

B

The next step is the formation of two chromatids within each chromosome:

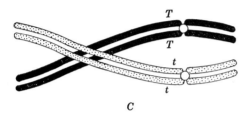

C

Since only one gene per chromosome is involved we shall, for the present, disregard chiasma formation.

At metaphase I the paired kinetochores (indicated by circles) approach the equator of the cell and the tractile fibers appear.

At anaphase I the kinetochores separate:

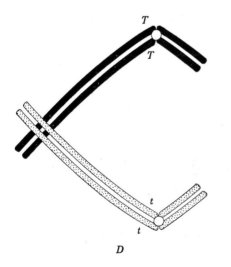

D

At telophase I the two daughter nuclei contain two chromatids each:

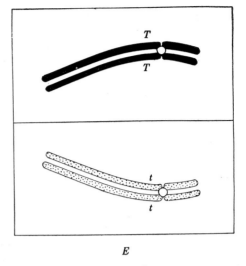

E

During prophase II chromosomes again form, and at metaphase II the kinetochores are at the equator of the cell.

The chromatids move apart at anaphase II and at telophase II, and four nuclei are reconstituted as follows:

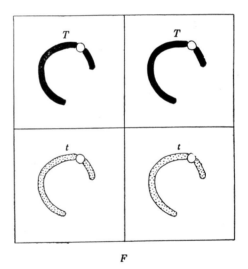

F

Notice here that two of the four cells are alike.

With Crossing Over. Now let us consider what will take place if crossing over is involved. In order to study this problem we shall need to mark two loci on the homologous chromosomes with genes, as follows:

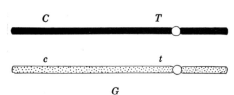

G

Pairing of homologous chromosomes with chromatid formation results in tetrad formation:

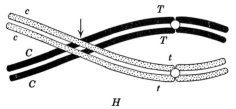

H

Let us assume that at the point indicated by the arrow one *TC* chromatid and one *tc* chromatid break and that they rejoin, not as originally constituted but with each other:

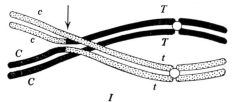

I

In order to visualize better just what has occurred, think of the four chromatids lying parallel with each other: They would appear thus:

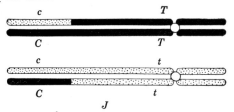

J

Notice that whereas we originally had only *TC* and *tc* chromatids we now have *Tc* and *tC* chromatids as well.

Returning to the normal course of events the chromatids will now complete prophase I and pass through metaphase I, and at anaphase I the kinetochores of whole homologous chromosomes will move to opposite poles of the cell:

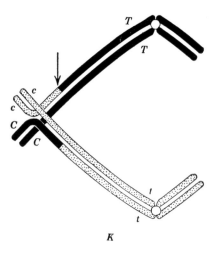

K

Notice that, at *T* and *t*, kinetochores of whole chromosomes are separating from each other, and at the opposite ends of the chromatids, at *C* and *c*, sister chromatids are separating.

The constitution of the anaphase I chromosomes will be:

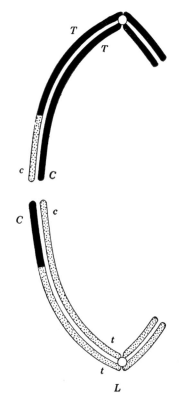

L

Skipping the details of telophase I, pro-phase II, metaphase II, and anaphase II, which are identical with those shown on page 291 the four nuclei of telophase II will be constituted as follows:

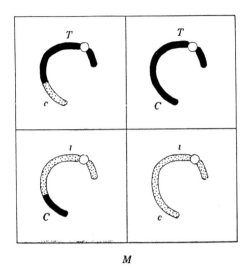

M

Notice in this stage that all four cells are different. If, however, only the gene pair *Tt* is considered the result is exactly what it should be if crossing over were disregarded; that is, there are two cells with *T* and two with *t*. *C* and *c* genes behave in a similar manner.

The importance of meiosis lies in the variety of gene combinations that arise, with the resulting variation of individuals. Two factors are responsible for this variation: (*a*) The segregation of genes and (*b*) crossing over with the resultant formation of chiasmata.

We shall now see that this variation is further increased and complicated by fertilization.

Fertilization

In our discussion of fertilization we shall disregard the effects of crossing over on chromosome segregation, but the student should remember that it is almost always present to a greater or lesser degree and

may greatly influence the results of breeding experiments.

Let us assume that the *Tt* genes occur in a cross-pollinating plant. Recall that meiosis occurs in the formation of pollen and also in the development of the embryo sac. One-half of the pollen grains and eggs formed will carry the gene *T*; the other half will carry the gene *t*. Since large numbers of both pollen and egg cells are formed and since the fusion of any two may occur we should expect the following combination:

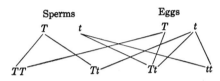

The many hundreds of sperm cells produced in pollen tubes will carry either *T* or *t* genes in approximately equal numbers. These sperms will unite with eggs carrying either the *T* or *t* gene.

Notice that there is one chance for the formation of zygote *TT*, one chance for the formation of zygote *tt*, and two chances for the formation of zygote *Tt*. If the genes *Tt* governed height, we should expect to find plants of different heights occurring in certain very definite ratios in a breeding plot. That this situation actually does take place was first discovered by the Austrian monk Gregor Mendel, whose work we shall now discuss.

GENETICS

The art of plant and animal improvement is very ancient. It has been practiced by many different races of men for thousands of years. Wheat, corn, and rice are examples of plants that have been improved by men of three different continents. The domestication of these grains was accomplished before the beginning of recorded history and ranks as an accomplishment of major importance. The task was so well

Fig. 14.7. Gregor Mendel.

While these procedures are accepted to-day as self-evident, they were so revolutionary in 1865 when Mendel's work was done that the standard scientific magazines of the time refused to publish Mendel's results. Instead, his experiments were presented before a small society of men in his home town. This society was not greatly unlike some of the present-day luncheon clubs and, like some of them, it published its proceedings. Thus Mendel's work was placed on record, where it lay unnoticed for 35 years. In 1900 it was discovered by three prominent European plant breeders and has become the cornerstone of all modern work in plant and animal genetics.

The Monohybrid Cross

Mendel selected garden peas for his experimental plants. He carefully took pollen from the anthers of a dwarf-growing variety and dusted it on the stigma of a tall-growing variety. The seeds resulting from this cross pollination were collected and planted the following season. All the plants that grew from these seeds were tall. The same results were obtained when the tall variety supplied the pollen.

Tall plant × Dwarf plant (pollen parent)

All tall plants

or

Dwarf plant × Tall plant (pollen parent)

All tall plants

The flowers on these tall plants were self-pollinated. Peas are normally self-pollinated, and so in order to obtain this seed Mendel merely had to keep stray pollen from reaching the stigmas of his experimental plants. The seeds resulting from these self-pollinated flowers were collected and planted the following spring. Upon counting the plants that grew from these

done that the tribes that grew these grains were assured of a food supply and could turn their energies to activities other than food getting. Civilization resulted. Attempts to increase crop yields and the nutritive values of plants, or to introduce new and better food plants, have been continued down through the ages to the present time. The last 50 years has seen a great increase in plant and animal improvement and in a knowledge of the mechanism of inheritance in plants and animals.

Modern **plant breeding** and **genetics** date from 1900, when Gregor Mendel's (Fig. 14.7) experiments on hybridizing garden peas were first appreciated. The importance of his experiments lies in the introduction to plant breeding of several procedures which, in 1900, were new and revolutionary. They are as follows:

1. The study of the inheritance of single or unit characters.

2. Keeping accurate records of the number of times a given unit character appears in the offspring of selected parents.

3. Maintaining the pollination of the experimental plants under the complete control of the investigator at all times.

seeds, he found that 787 were tall plants and 277 were dwarf plants. In other words, about three-fourths of these pea plants resembled one of the original pair of parents and about one-fourth resembled the other parent (Fig. 14.8).

It has been found convenient to give designations to these generations of plants. The two original parents are designated by P. The first generation, comprising only tall pea plants, is the **first filial generation,** or the F_1; the second generation of three-quarters tall and one-quarter dwarf pea plants is the **second filial generation,** or the F_2. Subsequent generations of self-pollinated plants would be consecutively the F_3, F_4, F_5, etc.

Note in the cross that, even though we are dealing with two different plants, we are concerned with only **one character**— height of growth. A cross dealing with a *single unit character* is a **monohybrid cross.**

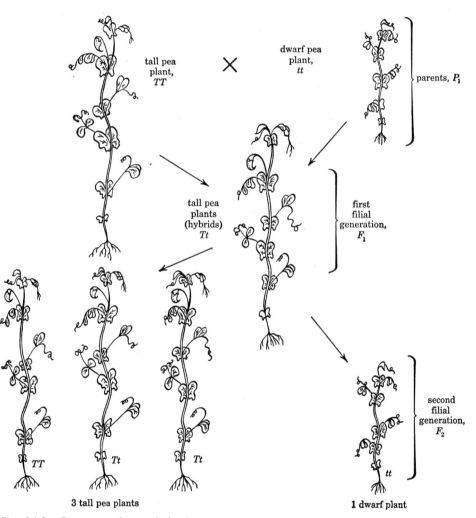

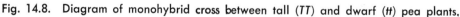

Fig. 14.8. Diagram of monohybrid cross between tall (*TT*) and dwarf (*tt*) pea plants.

Mendel studied, in all, seven monohybrid crosses. The results were similar to those just described for height. They were as follows:

1. The F_1 always resembled one of the parents: tall $\times$ dwarf gave tall; wrinkled $\times$ round seeds gave round seeds, etc. From this result, Mendel concluded that one expression of a given character was **dominant** (tall, or round seeds), whereas the other aspect of the same character was **recessive** (dwarf, or wrinkled seeds).

2. Selfing of the F_1 resulted in an F_2 generation in which the original forms of a given character **segregated** to give three times as many dominant plants as recessive plants.

Mendel further postulated a possible mechanism for this genetic behavior. He knew that the F_1 plants must contain factors, now called **genes,** responsible for both tallness and dwarfness, even though all the plants were tall, because: (1) tall and dwarf plants were crossed to produce the tall F_1, and (2) upon selfing, the tall F_1 gave rise to both tall and dwarf individuals. If we then represent the gene for tallness by T and the gene for dwarfness by t, we may diagram the genes determining height that are present in the tall F_1 by Tt.

$$Tt = \text{tall growing } F_1 \text{ pea plant}$$

Since the F_1 hybrid contains two genes, T and t, determining height, each true breeding parent plant should contain two similar genes thus:

$$TT = \text{tall growing parent}$$

$$tt = \text{dwarf growing parent}$$

Mendel assumed that the pollen would contain but one gene, and that the eggs similarly would contain but one gene. Thus, the tall parent, TT, would produce T pollen and T eggs, and the dwarf parent, tt, would produce t pollen and t eggs.

The parent plants whose nuclei contain the homologous chromosomes with the identical genes TT or tt are said to be **homozygous** for either the dominant or recessive genes. The F_1 plant with the homologous chromosomes carrying the genes Tt is said to be **heterozygous.**

Pollen produced by the heterozygous tall F_1 plant, Tt, will contain either gene, T or t. Likewise, eggs produced by this F_1 plant will contain either gene, T or t, and the sperm nuclei formed from the pollen will contain either gene, T or t. Many thousands of pollen grains, sperms, and eggs will be formed by the tall heterozygous F_1 plant. A sperm containing the gene T may unite with either a T or a t egg, as follows:

$$T \text{ sperm} + T \text{ egg} = TT \text{ zygote}$$

$$T \text{ sperm} + t \text{ egg} = Tt \text{ zygote}$$

A sperm containing the gene t may unite with a T egg or a t egg, as follows:

$$t \text{ sperm} + T \text{ egg} = Tt \text{ zygote}$$

$$t \text{ sperm} + t \text{ egg} = tt \text{ zygote}$$

These four possible combinations of genes will occur at fertilization and may be diagrammed as follows:

		Possible sperms	
		T	t
	T	Zygote 1 TT	Zygote 2 Tt
Possible eggs			
	t	Zygote 3 Tt	Zygote 4 tt

The possible types of eggs are arranged along the left of the checkerboard, and the possible types of sperms at the top. The squares of the checkerboard represent the possible zygotes, and they are derived by combining the gametes opposite the squares. For instance, zygote 1 is derived from sperm T and egg T; zygote 2 is de-

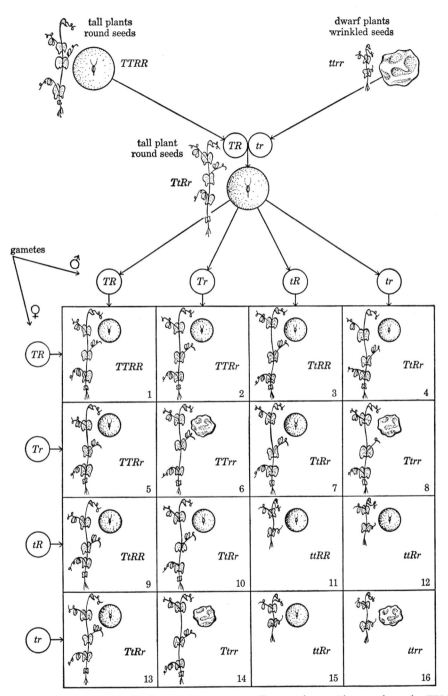

Fig. 14.9. Diagram of a dihybrid cross between a tall pea plant with round seeds (*TTRR*) and a dwarf pea plant with wrinkled seeds (*ttrr*).

rived from sperm *t* and egg *T*, etc. The genes, *Tt*, or *TT*, or *tt*, for example, present in the plant, constitute the **genotype** of the plant. Reference to the diagram will show that there are three different genotypes: *TT*, *Tt*, and *tt*. The appearance of the plant is the **phenotype**. For instance, the appearance or the phenotype of the plant *TT* is tall; of the plant *Tt* is tall, and of the plant *tt* is dwarf. Note that there are three times as many tall plants represented on the checkerboard as there are dwarf plants. Furthermore, if Mendel's assumption regarding these factors or genes is correct, the homozygous tall plant *TT* when self-pollinated should give only tall offspring; the homozygous dwarf plant *tt* when self-pollinated should give only dwarf

offspring; the tall heterozygous *Tt* plants when self-pollinated should give tall and dwarf plants in the ratio of 3 tall plants to 1 dwarf plant. This actually is what happens. A complete monohybrid cross is shown in Fig. 14.8.

The Dihybrid Cross

Let us consider a cross concerning two characters, height of the plant and form of the seeds. This is a **dihybrid cross**, that is, a cross involving *two unit characters* (Fig. 14.9). One parent plant is tall and has round seeds; the other parent plant is dwarf and has wrinkled seeds. We know that both these parent plants are homozygous for these particular characters

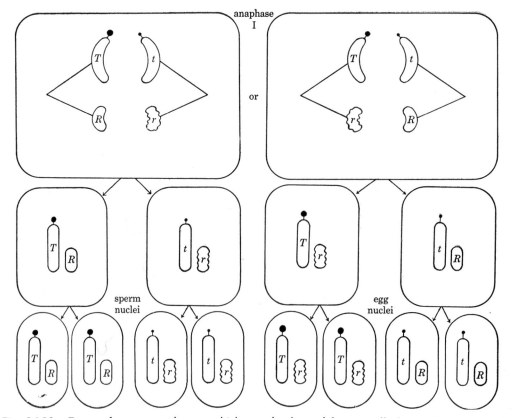

Fig. 14.10. Types of sperms and eggs which may be formed from a tall plant with round seeds and from a dwarf plant with wrinkled seeds.

because upon self-pollination they breed true. When cross-pollinated, all the resulting F_1 plants are **tall** and have **round** seeds. We know from this outcome that tallness is dominant over dwarfness and that roundness is dominant over wrinkledness. We may therefore write the genotype of the parent plant as follows:

The tall plant with round seeds, *TTRR*
The dwarf plant with wrinkled seeds, *ttrr*

Since all plants possess the characters of height and seed form, factors determining these characters must always be present in every plant.

After meiosis the pollen and eggs produced by the tall plant with round seeds will contain the genes *TR*. The pollen and eggs produced by the dwarf plant with wrinkled seeds will be *tr*. Union of sperms from a pollen grain *TR* with an egg *tr* (or a pollen grain *tr* with an egg *TR*) will result in a zygote having the genotype *TtRr* (Fig. 14.9). This plant will be tall and have round seeds. It is heterozygous for both height and seed shape.

The four possible types of eggs and sperms that may be formed during meiosis from a plant with the genotype *TtRr* are shown in Fig. 14.10. The sperms and eggs that result are:

Sperms	*TR, Tr, tR, tr*
Eggs	*TR, Tr, tR, tr*

Any one of the four types of sperms may unite with any one of the four types of eggs. The number of possible combinations is best shown on the checkerboard of Fig. 14.9. The four types of sperms are listed along the top of the checkerboard, the eggs are placed at the left. Each square represents a possible zygote. Examination of these squares will show that four phenotypes are possible:

9 tall plants with round seeds, squares numbered 1, 2, 3, 4, 5, 7, 9, 10, 13.

3 tall plants with wrinkled seeds, squares numbered 6, 8, 14.

3 dwarf plants with round seeds, squares numbered 11, 12, 15.

1 dwarf plant with wrinkled seeds, square number 16.

A dihybrid cross carried through the F_2 generation may be simply diagrammed as follows:

Parent	*TTRR*	×	*ttrr*
Plants	Tall plants with round seeds		Dwarf plants with wrinkled seeds
Gametes	*TR*		*tr*
		TtRr	
F_1	All plants heterozygous, tall with round seeds		
Self-pollination of F_1	*TtRr*	×	*TtRr*
Gametes	*TR, Tr, tR, tr*		*TR, Tr, tR, tr*
F_2	9 tall plants with round seeds		
	3 tall plants with wrinkled seeds		
	3 dwarf plants with round seeds		
	1 dwarf plant with wrinkled seeds		

In this cross it is important to note that the genes for height and seed shape separate or *segregate independently of each other* during the formation of meiospores from the spore mother cell.

Soon after Mendel's work was discovered it was noticed that his results could be explained by assuming that the genes were located in the chromosomes. It has now been well demonstrated that the genes are carried in the chromosomes, and maps have been prepared showing their relative positions in the chromosomes of many plants.

SUMMARY

Summarizing, the following important facts have been established regarding the mechanism of inheritance:

1. The factors responsible for inheritance are located in small, definite regions of

chromosomes. In other words, inheritance is due to small particles of chromosomes. These factors or chromosome particles are called **genes.**

2. Most higher plants have the diploid number of chromosomes, the vegetative cells containing two sets of homologous chromosomes.

3. Two genes thus interact, in the development of many characters in the diploid plant.

4. The gametes are haploid and consequently carry only one member of each pair of homologous chromosomes.

5. Members of a gene pair, *TT* and *tt*, while influencing a single character (height), determine different aspects of that character, such as tallness and dwarfness.

6. When different forms of a character are involved, such as tallness and dwarfness, one form is generally dominant, the other recessive.

7. When a plant, heterozygous for a given character, such as *Tt*, is self-pollinated, the resulting progeny will number three times as many dominant plants as recessive plants.

8. When a plant, heterozygous for two given characters, *TtRr*, is self-pollinated, the resulting progeny will be of four different types, in the following ratio: nine plants will show only the dominant characters (tall and round), three will show one dominant and one recessive (tall and wrinkled), three will have the second dominant and second recessive (dwarf and round), and one plant will have both recessives (dwarf and wrinkled).

9. The chromosomes carrying the genes segregate independently of each other; thus *T* may go with *R* or *r*.

10. The sum total of genes, particularly those under discussion, within a nucleus constitute the genotype, while the appearance of the plant due to these genes is called the phenotype.

Application of Genetics

The mechanism of inheritance is still being intensively studied. Meanwhile, knowledge of this mechanism is being utilized in many fields. Evolution, long of interest to many biologists, must be largely dependent upon the mechanism of inheritance, and so students of evolution employ genetic principles in their studies of the origin and development of plant and animal life. Evolution will be discussed in Chapter 26.

Of the innumerable new types of plants that have appeared in breeding plots, perhaps hybrid corn is the most widely known example. The principle underlying the production of hybrid corn was first stated by Shull in 1907. Corn is normally a cross-pollinated crop. Shull found that, if he self-pollinated corn plants for a number of generations (seven is a practical number), they became progressively smaller and less productive. Reference to Fig. 14.11 will show that the self-pollinated corn plants were becoming more and more homozygous. Upon reaching a certain size, further self-pollination resulted in little if any change. Shull now cross-pollinated two of his selfed lines and found that the resulting hybrid was larger and more productive than, not only its immediate parents, but also the original plants with which the experiment started. This observation was not at first fully appreciated by the midwestern corn producers. Hybrid corn developed slowly but has finally become the standard type raised for corn seed and has resulted in a great increase in corn production.

The procedure for development of the hybrid corn seed, in general, is as follows:

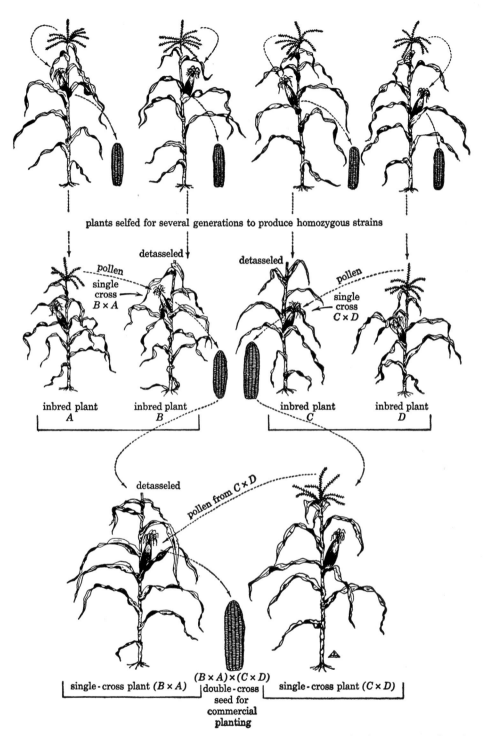

plants selfed for several generations to produce homozygous strains

detasseled

detasseled

pollen

single
cross
B × A

pollen

single
cross
C × D

inbred plant
A

inbred plant
B

inbred plant
C

inbred plant
D

detasseled

pollen from C × D

single - cross plant (B × A)

(B × A) × (C × D)
double - cross
seed for
commercial
planting

single - cross plant (C × D)

Fig. 14.11. Diagram showing the manner in which commercial hybrid corn is produced. (Redrawn from *Farmers' Bulletin* 1744, U. S. Dept. of Agriculture, Bureau of Plant Industry, Soils and Agricultural Engineering.)

Homozygous lines must be established. This step requires about 7 years of self-pollination, resulting in the development of many homozygous strains. Any two homozygous strains are then crossed to form F_1 hybrids, known to commercial corn breeders as *single cross hybrids.* Since there are many homozygous strains differing in some respects, it is possible to obtain a large number of different single cross hybrids, and, therefore, the selection of the best homozygous strains requires a thorough knowledge of the traits desired in the commercial strain. The seed produced in a field of such single cross hybrids, $A \times B$, Fig. 14.11 for instance, would give an F_2 generation with its resulting segregation of characters. This is impractical commercially and necessitates a further step. Two carefully selected single cross hybrids, $A \times B$ and $C \times D$, Fig. 14.11, are crossed, giving what is known as *double cross* seed. This is sold commercially and produces *double cross* hybrid plants of remarkable uniformity and yielding large amounts of grain. The steps in the production of double cross hybrid corn seed are shown in Fig. 14.11 and are outlined below.

Original corn plant inbred for 7 generations	Original corn plant inbred for 7 generations	Original corn plant inbred for 7 generations	Original corn plant inbred for 7 generations
Inbred strain *A* (detasseled)	Inbred strain *B* (furnishes pollen)	Inbred strain *C* (detasseled)	Inbred strain *D* (furnishes pollen)

single cross hybrid ($A \times B$) (detasseled)   single cross hybrid ($C \times D$) (furnishes pollen)

Double cross hybrid ($A \times B$) $\times$ ($C \times D$)

15

The Plant as a
Living Mechanism

The plant is a complex mechanism in which the activities of one part of its body influence those of other parts. In preceding chapters we discussed the structure and functions of individual cells, stems, roots, leaves, flowers, and seeds. In a study of cells and of separate tissues and organs we may lose sight of the *organism as a whole* and the interrelationships and interdependence of various structures and functions. The plant is more than a collection or colony of cells. These cells are "put together" and interrelated in such a way that they form a smooth-working living mechanism —an **organism.**

This chapter deals principally with growth, the factors that influence it, and how the growth activities of one part of the plant are correlated with those of another part. Necessarily and deliberately there is some repetition.

All plants, including seed plants, begin life as single cells. In all but the simplest plants (and with certain exceptions among higher plants) these cells are the zygotes. In fusion, the male gamete contributes its quota of chromosomes to an equal number supplied by the female gamete. Fertilization results in a doubling of chromosomes. But, when the male gamete unites with the female gamete, it does more than contribute chromosomal hereditary material; it also acts as a stimulus, setting into action a train of chemical and physical changes. The zygote divides to form two daughter cells, each daughter cell may divide to form two cells, etc., until a multicellular body (the embryo) has been formed. In common language, we say the plant has *grown* from the one-celled stage (the zygote) to a many-celled stage (the embryo). In this process which we call **growth,** there is increase in *number of cells,* in *size of cells,* and in their *complexity.* In other words, growth is more than mere enlargement; it involves **differentiation,** which means that there arise various kinds of cells, adapted to perform different functions. Even in the relatively simple embryo (Fig. 4.1) of a seed, we observe that all cells are not alike; we can already see a young plant with a **shoot** and a **root.** Thus, in growth there is a "becoming different," as well as a "becoming larger." Throughout all phases of growth the organism incorporates material taken from the environment.

STAGES IN GROWTH OF THE CELL

The individual cell goes through stages of growth (Fig. 5.6) from the earliest period, when it is freshly cut off as a daughter cell, to maturity. If the newly formed daughter cell is located in one of the primary meristems, it is characterized by its (1) small size, (2) thin, delicate walls, (3) dense cytoplasm, (4) relatively prominent nucleus, and (5) very small vacuoles. In young cells there is active synthesis of proteins, and, with other substances, their assimilation to form new protoplasm. The absorption of water, mineral salts, and foods from adjoining cells, the synthesis of proteins, and the formation of new protoplasm continue. These processes occur simultaneously and constitute the early phases of the cell's growth. Then follows **enlargement** of the cell, that is, an increase in volume. During this phase of growth, the cell absorbs large amounts of water, vacuoles increase in size, and the area of the cell wall becomes greater, but the increase in the amount of cellular protoplasm is slight as compared with increase in cell volume. As the cell enlarges changes may be initiated which result in a specialized cell. These changes are spoken of as **differentiation.**

At the tips of shoots and roots (Figs. 6.10, 7.4) cells in various stages of differentiation may be observed. Here, one sees cells in different phases of division, the mitotic figures being clearly evident, cell plates being laid down, and daughter cells being formed. Somewhat back of the region of active cell division are cells in the process of maturing.

It is not always possible to determine what kind of mature cell any particular newly formed daughter cell will become. We observe that some daughter cells become parenchyma cells (Figs. 6.16*F, G*);

others may take a course of differentiation which results in collenchyma cells (Fig. 6.16*D*); others may become vascular elements.

Differentiation of a cell involves (1) physical changes and (2) chemical changes, these resulting in a difference in physiological behavior. There may be changes in the shape of cells, increase in the thickness of their walls, and the development of structural features such as spiral and other types of thickenings in the walls of vessels. Also, chemical changes may occur in walls or in cell contents.

The original daughter cell wall is of cellulose-pectic composition. During maturation the wall may become impregnated with lignin (lignified), as in tracheids, vessels, stone cells, and fibers; or impregnated with suberin (suberized), as in cells of cork; or impregnated with cutin (cutinized), as in the outer walls of epidermal cells. Moreover, during cell maturation chemical changes may involve (*a*) the chemical nature of the cell sap, (*b*) the kinds of foods stored, (*c*) the kinds of other ergastic substances, and (*d*) the death of the protoplasm.

FACTORS INFLUENCING GROWTH

Let us consider the growth of a wheat plant as an example. Its growth behavior depends somewhat upon the *variety;* this statement means, in effect, that the inheritance of a plant determines in a measure its growth performance. Some wheat varieties grow rapidly and mature a crop in 100 to 110 days; other varieties, *under the same environmental conditions,* grow more slowly and come to maturity in not less than 145 to 155 days. Thus, **genetic factors** influence the plant's growth.

Growth is also determined by **environmental factors,** such as temperature, water, light, and available supply of mineral nutrients in the soil. Any change in these external conditions is reflected in growth. One who grows plants, be he home gardener, orchardist, a grower of vegetable crops, or a farmer on a large western ranch, makes an effort to control these external conditions and thus increase the quantity and character of growth. Successful crop production involves the skillful combining of genetic factors determining a plant's reaction to its environment and control and modification of the external environment in order to take full advantage of the genetic traits of a plant. It is this combination of heredity and environment that determines the world distribution of both agricultural and native plants. A simple and yet graphic experiment showing the close relation between a genetic factor in corn and the environment is illustrated in Plate IIIa. Light is generally necessary for chlorophyll synthesis and in addition, in germinating corn grains, a temperature of 55° F. Below this temperature the first leaves remain yellow for some time after being exposed to light. At the Bikini atom bomb test a mutant corn strain appeared which required a temperature of 62° F for even a retarded development of chlorophyll. Normal and mutant seedlings are shown in Plate IIIa; they are 12 days old and at the end of 3 weeks they will be indistinguishable. When germination proceeds at 77° F chlorophyll develops at a normal rate and the normal and mutant strains are not distinguishable.

Environmental factors that directly or indirectly influence growth may be classified as follows:

1. **Climatic factors,** those that act upon the plant through the atmosphere. The principal climatic factors are: temperature, light, carbon dioxide concentration, atmospheric humidity and precipitation, and wind.

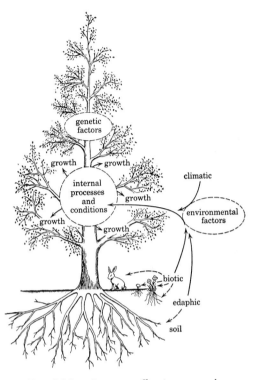

Fig. 15.1. Factors affecting growth.

2. **Edaphic factors,** those that operate through the soil. The principal edaphic factors are: available water in the soil, air in the soil, temperature of the soil, quantity and nature of the soil solutes.

3. **Biotic factors,** those arising from the presence of other plants and animals. Here are included: competition among different species, grazing by animals, soil bacteria, algae and protozoa, parasitic fungi, insects that injure plants, and insects that carry pollen.

Thus we learn that a plant's growth, development, and behavior are results of the numerous physiological processes and internal conditions of the various cells and tissues. These processes and conditions are controlled in turn by hereditary and environmental factors (Fig. 15.1).

Hereditary Factors. The particular set of genes which a plant possesses.

Environmental Factors. (Climatic, biotic, and edaphic.)

Internal
processes
and
conditions
↓
Growth,
development,
and
behavior

Boston variety of lettuce fails to form heads; rather, there develops an open rosette of leaves. At temperatures ranging from 60° to 70° F, however, the lettuce plants develop satisfactory heads. Also, it appears that either high temperatures or low temperatures may stimulate a premature formation of seed stalks, a phenomenon known as "bolting."

Effect of Temperature on Growth

Every process in the plant is influenced by temperature. Photosynthesis, assimilation, digestion, respiration, absorption of water, mineral salts, and gases, transpiration, formation of enzymes, permeability of membranes, rate of movement of materials within the plant, reproduction—in fact, all physical, chemical, and physiological processes in the plant are affected by temperature. These processes determine the character and rate of growth. Each one may be critical and limiting. Modification or disturbance of any one may affect growth in some part of the plant.

We customarily speak of the *optimum temperatures* that influence any particular process. By this term we mean the temperature limits (*maximum* and *minimum*) between which that particular process *can* take place in that particular kind of plant and the optimum temperature at which the process goes on *most actively*. The optimum temperatures for one process may differ considerably from those for another taking place in the plant at the same time. For example, the roots of many plants can absorb from the soil at temperatures much lower than those required for photosynthesis or for reproduction.

Temperature influences the structural development of plants. For example, at a temperature of 70° to 80° F the white

Effect of Light on Growth

In discussing the effect of light upon growth, we must consider (1) light intensity, (2) light quality, and (3) light duration. The term light includes all the energy (radiant energy) that reaches the plant from the sun or from artificial sources. Light may affect the plant and its various activities (hence its growth) in many ways including the following:

1. The synthesis of chlorophyll, and other processes associated with photosynthesis.

2. The temperature of the plant body aboveground. Part of the light energy that falls upon the leaves is changed to heat and raises their temperature. The important functions of the leaf—photosynthesis, transpiration, and synthesis of protein—are directly influenced by leaf temperature.

3. The opening and closing of stomata. The area of the stomatal aperture affects the exchange of oxygen, carbon dioxide, and water vapor between the leaf cells and the atmosphere outside of the leaf. Thus are the processes of respiration, photosynthesis, and transpiration directly influenced by stomatal opening and closing.

4. The direction of growth of certain plant organs (Fig. 15.2).

5. The form and anatomy of leaves (Fig. 15.3). Plants that grow in the sun (so-called sun plants) usually have (*a*) thick leaves, (*b*) a thick palisade parenchyma, (*c*) poorly developed spongy parenchyma,

(*d*) small intercellular spaces in the leaves, (*e*) a thick and heavily cutinized epidermis, (*f*) stomata confined to the lower side of the leaf or more abundant on the lower side, (*g*) frequently smooth, glossy leaf surfaces, and (*h*) often densely hairy leaves. Plants that grow in the shade (so-called shade plants) usually have (*a*) thin leaves, (*b*) a thin layer of palisade tissue or none at all, (*c*) well-developed spongy parenchyma, (*d*) large intercellular spaces in the leaves, (*e*) thin and slightly cutinized leaf epidermis, (*f*) stomata on both surfaces of the leaves, or the number on the two surfaces quite the same, (*g*) usually dull leaf surfaces, and (*h*) generally leaves devoid of hairs.

Light Intensity and Growth. Some plants normally grow in dense shade, that

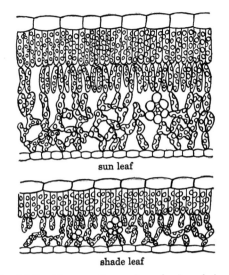

sun leaf

shade leaf

Fig. 15.3. Cross sections of sun leaf and shade leaf of same species.

Fig. 15.2. Influence of light on direction of growth of leaf petioles. *Aralia* growing on a shaded porch; all leaves face the light.

is, in light of *low intensity,* and other plants can endure the noon sun of a bright, cloudless summer day, in a light of *high intensity.* Moreover, as long as there is a supply of reserve food, plants will grow in total darkness. As compared with plants grown in the light, those in darkness are white or yellow in color, the internodes are long, the leaves are very much reduced in size, and their root systems are poorly developed. This condition is known as **etiolation.** Of course, such plants cease growth when the reserve food is exhausted. In general, absence of light increases, and presence of light decreases, the rate at which the stems elongate. This relationship may be observed in the growth of seedlings. Seeds buried in the soil germinate in darkness, and the stem grows upward very rapidly until it reaches the light; then the rate of stem elongation is reduced. The exposure of a seedling to light for only a few minutes per day is sufficient to prevent etiolation even though this is not enough light to cause a significant amount of photosynthesis to occur.

Thus we see that light may control growth in other ways than through photosynthesis.

In many plants, there is a rhythmic night-and-day growth rate of the shoot—greater at night than during the day, provided that the temperature at night does not fall too low. Plants grown in full light have shorter and sturdier stems and somewhat thicker leaves than those in the shade. One result of crowding plants is a reduction in the light intensity to which they are exposed. Such plants have longer and more spindling stems than those grown under less crowded conditions.

At the other extreme is the behavior of plants under continuous illumination. Many common plants may be grown from seed to seed under continuous exposure to light, either continuous artificial illumination or natural daylight supplemented with artificial lighting. Examples are cereals, flax, buckwheat, peas, and beans. Squash, red clover, tomatoes, and potatoes, how-ever, are among the plants that bloom but do not set seed when grown with continuous lighting.

Light Quality and Growth. In the chapter on the leaf, the effect of different wave lengths of light upon photosynthesis was discussed. The red and blue portions of the light spectrum are the most effective in photosynthesis.

By filtering sunlight with different kinds of colored glass it is possible to test the growth of plants when exposed to wave lengths that represent narrow bands of the different parts of the visible spectrum, and also to wave lengths not represented in the visible spectrum. The general conclusions of these experiments are as follows: Light of short wave lengths (blue light) tends to retard growth in length. Under the longer wave lengths (red light) plants show somewhat the characteristics of those grown in darkness. When exposed to infrared rays, plants have long internodes and a scarcity

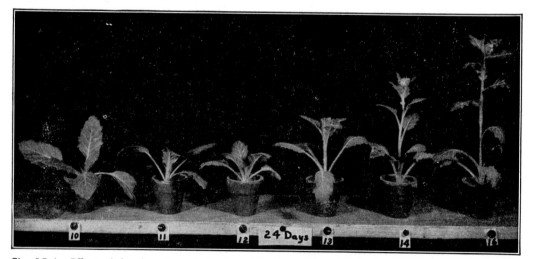

Fig. 15.4. Effect of day length on behavior of henbane (*Hyoscyamus*). Plants grown with 8-hour photoperiod until they were about a month old and then subjected to 24 photoperiods of 10, 11, 12, 13, 14, and 16 hours. Development of flower stalks occurs only when exposed to the longer photoperiods. (Photo by Bureau of Plant Industry, Soils and Agricultural Engineering, U. S. Dept. of Agriculture.)

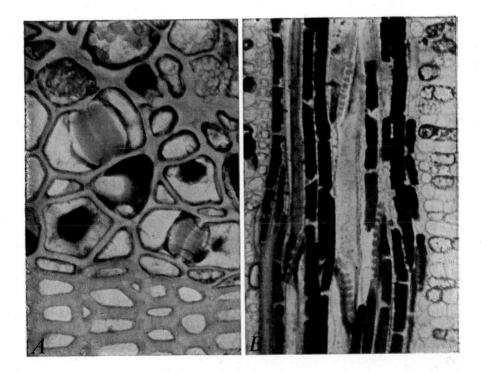

PLATE I

Phloem of grape. A, cross section, $\times 320$; B, longitudinal section, $\times 200$. The blue-stained callose is on the end walls of sieve tubes. (Courtesy of Esau and the University of California Press.)

PLATE IIIa →

A chlorophyll mutation causing etiolation in corn seedlings compared with normal green corn seedlings. The mutation arose in corn kernels subjected to radiation from an atomic bomb. (Courtesy of Phinney and University of California Press.)

PLATE II

Leaves of a Venus fly-trap closed on an insect (Black Star).

PLATE IIIb

Various effects of potassium deficiency on foliage and fruit of the orange. A, appearance of fruit and foliage in November on tree receiving ample potassium; B, appearance of fruit and leaves from tree slightly deficient in potash (November). (Courtesy of Chapman-Brown and Rayner and University of California Press.)

↓

PLATE IV *Amanita muscaria.* (Courtesy of J. Klute.)

of chlorophyll. However, such plants may produce large leaves in contrast to the scalelike leaves of dark grown plants.

Duration of Light and Growth. Although green plants are able to grow in total darkness if there is a supply of reserve food upon which to draw, a significant relationship exists between the reproductiveness of many plants and the relative length of light and dark periods to which they are exposed. This response to day length is called **photoperiodism.** A knowledge of the photoperiodic reactions of plants is of practical importance in agriculture. For example, it is possible for a floriculturist to delay the flowering of chrysanthemums and cause them to flower for the late fall market simply by extending the daylight period with several hours of artificial light. When flowering is desired the supplemental light is simply discontinued. More fascinating still is the fact that the same thing can be accomplished, and a considerable amount of electricity saved, simply by exposing the plants to a few minutes of light in the middle of the night. As long as these plants receive this small amount of light in the night they will not flower. If they are exposed to long periods of uninterrupted darkness, however, processes are initiated that lead to flowering.

Observations of plants growing under natural conditions and greenhouse experiments, have shown that some plants will flower only when the days are longer than a certain critical length that is characteristic for each species, or, more correctly, only when the nights are shorter than a certain critical length. Spinach, for instance, starts to flower when exposed for two weeks to days that are 13 to 14 hours or more long but will not flower if the days are less than 13 hours long. Plants that respond to day length in this way are called

Fig. 15.5. Effect of day length on behavior of *Chrysanthemum*. *A*, plant received light of natural short days of autumn and blossomed at the usual time. *B*, plant received an hour of light near the middle of each night for several weeks beginning just before flower buds would normally have been initiated; thus each long dark period was divided into two short ones. This interruption was sufficient to delay flowering. (Photo by Bureau of Plant Industry, Soils and Agricultural Engineering, U. S. Dept. of Agriculture.)

long-day plants and include beet, henbane (Fig. 15.4), spinach, and winter barley. Many long-day plants will not normally flower and reproduce by seeds in the tropics where even the days of midsummer are relatively short.

Other species of plants, such as *Chrysanthemum*, after a period of vegetative growth in the summer, normally bloom and set fruit in the autumn when the days are short and the nights long. These species that flower only when the daily period of illumination is shorter than a certain critical length are called **short-day plants**; examples are *Coleus, Aster, Dahlia, Cosmos,* and *Chrysanthemum* (Fig. 15.5). There are also species that bloom throughout the growing season, apparently indifferent to the relative length of day and night (examples: tomato, buckwheat, snapdragon).

Long-day plants can be made to bloom in the short days of midwinter if the length of daily exposure to light is increased by artificial lighting. For example, if a long-day plant, like lettuce, is grown in the greenhouse during the winter, and the normal length of exposure to daylight is increased by artificial illumination, the plants will come into bloom. Or, a short-day plant, like the *Chrysanthemum,* can be

brought into bloom earlier in the fall by placing it in a dark room for a part of each day.

Intensity of light is not the critical factor in determining the behavior of long-day and short-day plants; rather, it is the relative length of the daily alternating periods of light and dark which determines flowering behavior. This relationship is shown in Fig. 15.6. In some instances a difference of an hour or even less may determine whether a plant will remain vegetative or will become reproductive. Apparently, fixed length periods of light and darkness focus their influence on floral initiation; that is, the photoperiod (light period) determines whether the shoot tip shall remain in

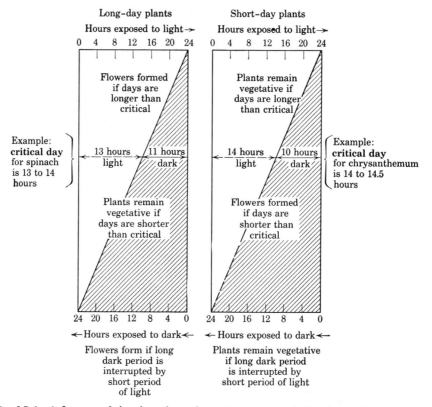

Fig. 15.6. Influence of day length on flowering in spinach (*Spinacia oleracea*) and *Chrysanthemum.*

a state of vegetative activity (Fig. 8.12) or begin the initiation of flower primordia (Fig. 12.29).

Carbon Dioxide Concentration of Atmosphere and Its Effect on Growth

Any factors influencing the rate of photosynthesis affect growth. One of these factors is the carbon dioxide content of the atmosphere, inasmuch as carbon dioxide is a raw material in photosynthesis.

Under natural conditions, the concentration of carbon dioxide in the atmosphere remains fairly constant (about 0.03 to 0.04 per cent). Experiments show that most plants manufacture more carbohydrates and grow faster, at least for short periods, if the percentage of carbon dioxide in the atmosphere is higher than normal. Although the carbon dioxide content of the atmosphere surrounding a plant may be increased, the amount of this gas that actually reaches the chloroplasts (where photosynthesis takes place) is by no means increased in the same proportion. There are structural and physiological conditions that limit the rate of diffusion of carbon dioxide from the outside atmosphere to the chloroplasts. Most plants maintained under continued high levels of CO_2 are usually affected adversely.

Effect of Atmospheric Humidity, Precipitation, and Wind Movements on Growth

The rate of water loss in the vapor form (transpiration) from a plant is influenced by the relative humidity of the atmosphere. The drier the air, the greater the water loss. If loss is so great that the plant cells lose their turgor, physiological processes, including growth, are greatly retarded.

It is obvious that the amount of precipitation determines the water content of the soil; this amount, in turn, influences that available to the plant.

The principal effect of wind is the increasing of transpiration. Thus, wind indirectly modifies the water content of the plant cells. It also affects the form of growth of trees, as witness the one-sided shape of exposed trees on seacoasts and mountain tops.

Effect of Available Water in the Soil on Growth

In Chapter 9 we discussed the relation between soils and absorption of water by roots. It was stressed that plants cannot absorb all the water from the volume of soil occupied by the roots; a certain percentage of water is left after the plant has permanently wilted. Plants that can resist, tolerate, or evade drought have various structural devices that tend to reduce the rate of transpiration, or they possess water-storage tissue, or they have deeply penetrating root systems and other habits of growth that enable them to survive with little available water. Resistance to drought is also a property of protoplasm itself.

The total water in the soil that is available to plants depends upon a number of factors, chief of which are: (1) precipitation, (2) humidity of the atmosphere, since it affects the evaporation rate from the soil surface, (3) height of the water table, (4) rate of water percolation downward in the soil, (5) soil structure as it affects the ability of the soil to raise water from the water table by capillarity, (6) soil texture, and (7) vegetative covering.

Available water in the soil affects every activity of the plant, including the amount and rate of growth.

Effect of Temperature of the Soil on Growth

The intake of water and solutes by roots decreases if the soil temperature sinks to a low level.

Chemical and biological activities in the soil are profoundly influenced by soil temperatures. These activities in turn have an influence on the physical condition and fertility of the soil. Thus, soil temperature is an important factor that affects directly and indirectly the growth behavior of plants.

Effect of Air in the Soil on Growth

The amount of air in the soil depends upon (1) the pore space and (2) the water content. Roots secure the necessary oxygen for respiration through root hairs and other epidermal cells. Inadequate soil aeration results in a reduction in the rate of absorption of mineral nutrients and water.

Most agricultural plants will not long survive with the root system submerged in a water-soaked soil. In nearly all agricultural soils, however, air content of the soil is not a limiting factor in plant growth.

Effect of the Quantity and Nature of Soil Solutes on Growth

In Chapter 9 we learned that plants, like animals, require specific nutrient materials. Although plants can manufacture their own foods, i.e., carbohydrates, fats, and proteins, they must be supplied with the proper raw materials. With the exceptions of carbon dioxide, water, and oxygen these raw materials are the mineral solutes found in the soil solution. A lack of any one of the essential nutrient mineral elements from the soil or its lack of availability to the plant, will result in a disruption of normal growth and a deficiency disease then develops (Plate IIIb). The nature of the disease will depend upon the element that is lacking, i.e., an absence of iron results in chlorosis between leaf veins, nitrogen deficiency is characterized by the yellowing of older leaves. In many instances if an element is made unavailable to a plant, there is then a translocation of ions or molecules containing this element from the older parts of the plant, where it may have been present, to the younger parts where it is used during growth. For instance, during nitrogen starvation, the proteins in old leaves are broken down by enzymes and the simpler organic nitrogen compounds that result move in the vascular tissue to the young regions. Here the nitrogen is again synthesized into proteins and growth continues at the expense of material from the older leaves that turn yellow and die. On the other hand assimilation fixes some elements rendering them unavailable for further movement through the plant. Calcium for example when it is combined with cell wall materials is not readily removed from the wall by the plant even during calcium starvation.

Not only do plants suffer from deficiency diseases but their growth may also be affected by the toxic action of soil minerals. Many elements, even those that are necessary in small amounts for plant growth, will in higher concentrations cause abnormal growth of the plant and even death.

Relation of Soils to Plant and Animal Nutrition

Nearly all chemical elements of the soil are found by analysis to enter into the composition of plants. Only a limited number of them, however, are thus far known to have an indispensable role in plants. A few, the micronutrient elements (iron, boron, zinc, manganese, copper, chlorine, and molybdenum) are required in such minute quantities that for many years their need defied detection. It is likely that further research will add to the list of elements essential to plant growth (page 178).

Animals derive mineral elements from the plants upon which they feed. If a certain element of the soil is scarce, the plants may also have a low percentage of that element. In other words, the mineral ingredients of the soil affect the mineral composition of the plants growing thereupon. And the quantities of mineral elements in the plants, in turn, influence the animals that feed upon them. Livestock develop marked symptoms of disease when grazing on forage growing on phosphorus-deficient soils. Even though the deficiency may not be so great as to cause disease of livestock, in many western states differences in the value of grazing lands are attributed to differences in the phosphorus content of the soil.

In Australia and New Zealand, a nutritional ailment of lambs has been traced to a deficiency of cobalt in the soil and, consequently, in the plants growing on the soil. As little as 12 parts of cobalt per 100 million parts of soil are sufficient to produce pastures in which lambs develop satisfactorily. The so-called "alkali disease" of livestock in certain western states is caused by unusual amounts of selenium in range vegetation on soils derived from shales high in selenium. Other illustrations could be cited. Suffice it to say that the quality of plant products as they affect both man and other animals is related to the soil and to the chemical elements available to plants.

Biotic Factors as They Affect Growth

We have just discussed those environmental factors influencing plant growth that have to do directly with atmospheric and soil conditions. But any individual plant, be it a tree in the forest or a corn plant in the field, is influenced by other plants and by animals. Living organisms (biotic factors) are just as much a part of the environment of a given individual plant as are temperature, light, mineral salts in the soil, and other climatic and edaphic (soil) factors. These biotic factors influence the rate of growth, the form of the plant body, and the chemical composition of the plant—in short, the growth behavior of the plant throughout its entire life. Let us enumerate some of these biotic influences.

1. Plants compete with each other for space, light, water, and mineral salts of the soil. There is competition aboveground and underground. Weeds, for example, are the "robber barons of agriculture"; they decrease crop yields by taking light, water, and mineral salts. Plants may be so crowded that no single individual makes normal growth.

2. Many plants depend upon insects to effect pollination. For example, fruit setting in an orchard may fail because bees are not present.

3. Grazing animals may completely alter the vegetative covering of an area. The outstanding cause of range depletion is excessive or improper grazing. The original vegetation on many of the range lands of the western states was dominated by perennial grasses. Chiefly because of overgrazing, they are now populated mostly by introduced and less valuable species.

4. The fertility of the soil is influenced by the activity of bacteria and fungi. Many of these organisms cause decomposition of organic matter, breaking it down into chemical constituents that are available to green plants. Soils also contain nitrogen-fixing bacteria.

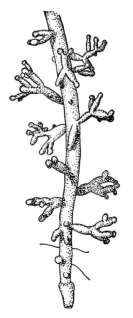

Fig. 15.7. Mycorrhiza on root of pine. (Redrawn from Priestley and Scott, *Introduction to Botany*, Longmans, Green & Co.)

5. Bacteria and fungi and also nematode worms and insects live parasitically on the roots of plants. Also, many different kinds of bacteria, fungi, and insects attack the aerial parts of plants and cause destructive diseases.

6. The growth of some plants, particularly forest trees, is influenced by an association of the roots with soil fungi. Certain roots may be covered with a mat of fungal hyphae, some of which may penetrate living root cells. The presence of the fungus may be beneficial in that it makes available to the host some of the nitrogen in organic compounds of the soil. Roots that have a fungal association as described are shorter and more extensively branched than are uninfected roots. Such roots are called **mycorrhizas** (Fig. 15.7). Mycorrhiza are beneficial also by virtue of their absorption and transfer of minerals from the soil to host tissue.

CORRELATION OF GROWTH

The growth of the cells, tissues, and organs of a plant is not haphazard but the various parts grow in relationship with one another. That is, the growth of the terminal bud influences the course of development of lateral buds, the activities of leaves influence the production of flowers, etc. How is the growth of thousands of cells so correlated that the form and structure of a normal plant results? We have seen how the food is produced by leaves and translocated into other parts of the plant; how minerals and water are absorbed by roots and move throughout the organism; and how external factors influence these activities. Substances in plants that are similar in behavior to the hormones of animals also play an important part in growth correlations.

We are familiar with the fact that animals have ductless glands which secrete certain chemical substances, hormones, that regulate physiological activities of the body. The thyroid in mammals is such a gland. It elaborates a hormone, thyroxine, which has a profound influence on growth and development. Decreased activity of the thyroid gives rise to cystic goiter, obesity, and other diseases. Thyroxine, a white crystalline substance, is now artificially synthesized and employed for treatment of these diseases.

Plant Hormones and the Control of Growth

Plants also produce natural **growth regulators, hormones,** that are active in small amounts and exercise specific effects upon cells or tissues other than those by which they are produced. Whereas in animals hormones are produced in special glands, in plants there are no special hormone glands; in plants these substances may be produced in rapidly growing embryonic tissues, wherever they occur, or in older cells of leaves. A plant hormone is defined as *an organic substance produced by the plant which acting in very small amounts regulates plant physiological processes.* Hormones usually move in the plant from the tissue where they are produced to a tissue where they act to produce special growth effects.

A number of synthetic organic compounds have been produced that exert the same effects on growth as do those naturally produced in plants. Therefore, it is proper to use the general term growth regulator to include both naturally produced and synthetic compounds.

Hormones and Enzyme Action

How do substances that occur in such low concentrations as the hormones regulate cell growth? We have seen that certain of the micronutrient elements are necessary for the action of specific enzymes. Likewise it has been found that at least some of the hormones exert their action through their influence on the functioning of enzymes. Many of the vitamins, among them thiamin, are known to be actually a necessary part of a specific enzyme system. If they are lacking, the enzyme will not function. The reaction that it controls will not take place and metabolism and growth will be influenced. This is true in both plants and animals. For example, thiamin is a part of an enzyme involved in the evolution of carbon dioxide during respiration; nicotinic acid is a component of enzymes that remove hydrogen during respiration; and pyridoxine is necessary for amino acid synthesis.

Thus the specific roles in cell metabolism of certain plant hormones are well established. On the other hand, however, others act in a manner not yet clearly understood. Among the latter are the hormones that regulate cell elongation. These, however, also probably function in the cell in association with certain enzymes but the exact enzyme systems involved are still not known. Let us now see how some of these regulators of plant growth have been studied.

The Discovery of Plant Hormones. One of the most active fields of plant physiological research today is the investigation into the nature and action of plant growth regulators. From this extensive research new knowledge is continually being gained that increases our ability to control plant growth. Less than forty years ago the existence of plant hormones was unknown. Today, growth regulators are sprayed from airplanes to kill weeds (a field of grain can be sprayed to kill mustard growing in it without injuring the grain), to thin fruit, and to delay fruit drop. In addition, they are used to induce the formation of roots on cuttings, to cause flowers to set fruit, to prevent sprouting, and to hasten fruit ripening.

Surprising as it may seem, much of our knowledge of the regulation of plant growth has come from studies of the growth of the coleoptile of oat (*Avena*) seedlings.

The coleoptile is a unique structure in grasses. In the embryo, it is seen as a sheath that surrounds the stem growing point and embryonic foliage leaves (page 284). When the seed germinates, the first structure to come aboveground is the coleoptile, a hollow, closed, and pointed organ. It protects the apical meristem and serves as a soil-penetrating organ. After a time, the closed end of the coleoptile is broken by the first foliage leaf. When the seedling is grown in the dark and the coleoptile has attained a length of 25 to 40 millimeters, and before the first foliage leaf protrudes, it is ready for use in various experiments of the type to be discussed.

It seems worth while to describe a number of early experiments with the grass coleoptile, chiefly that of *Avena,* because they are basic to an understanding of growth regulators; furthermore, they demonstrate scientific methods and techniques of investigation.

As early as 1880, Charles Darwin observed that grass coleoptiles curve toward the light, a phenomenon known as **phototropism** (Fig. 15.8A). If the tip of the coleoptile is covered with a small cap of tinfoil which does not permit illumination of the cells of the tip (Fig. 15.8B), there is no curvature, although the lower part of the coleoptile is illuminated from one side. When the upper part of the coleoptile is illuminated from one side and the lower part is covered with tinfoil to exclude light, curvature of the coleoptile occurs in the normal way (Fig. 15.8C). If 2.5 to 4 millimeters of the tip of the coleoptile is removed, there is no response to one-sided illumination; the coleoptile remains straight

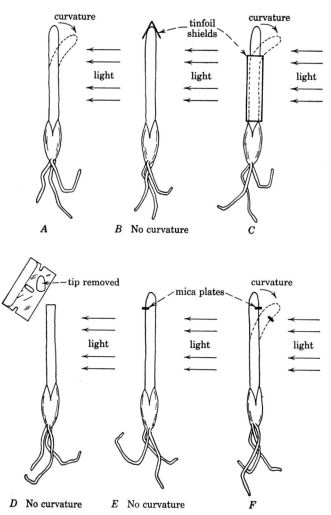

Fig. 15.8. Experiments with coleoptiles of oats (see explanation in text).

and cells in the lower part do not elongate (Fig. 15.8D).

From these simple but significant experiments, Darwin concluded "that when seedlings are freely exposed to a lateral light, *some influence is transmitted from the upper to the lower part,* causing the latter to bend."

Before describing experiments that demonstrate what the "influence" is that is transmitted and the manner of its transmission, let us consider the growth (elongation) of the cells of the coleoptile that result in the curvature. The actual bending of the coleoptile is the result of more rapid elongation (growth) of the cells on the shaded side than of those upon the illuminated side. In the experiments described above, it is apparent that the coleoptile tip, rather than the lower part, must be illuminated if it is to produce the substance that we assume must move downward to the cells in the lower part of the coleoptile and stimulate those on the shaded side to more rapid elongation than those on the illuminated side.

Boysen-Jensen (1910–1911) showed that, if a transverse incision was made on the shaded side of the coleoptile and a thin plate of mica inserted (Fig. 15.8E), its curvature did not occur, but that, when the incision was on the illuminated side, curvature did occur (Fig. 15.8F). This response led to the conclusion that the stimulus moves down the shaded side of the coleoptile, from the tip to the cells in the region of elongation, which are stimulated in their growth. Boysen-Jensen also found that the stimulus could be transmitted through a thin layer of gelatine. He cut off the tip of the coleoptile, placed a drop of gelatine over the stump, and then replaced the tip (Fig. 15.9A). With one-sided illumination there was curvature of the coleoptile.

These early experiments led to the definite discovery by Went (1928) of the hormonal nature of this growth stimulus. Went placed the tips of a number of coleoptiles on thin agar disks (Fig. 15.9B), where they remained for approximately two hours. Then the disks were placed on one side of the decapitated coleoptile. Curvature of the coleoptile resulted, the direction of curvature depending upon which side the block was placed. This experiment demonstrated that a definite substance would diffuse out of the decapitated coleoptile tips into the agar and would in

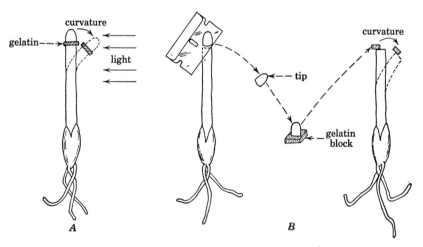

Fig. 15.9. Experiments with coleoptiles of oats (see explanation in text).

turn migrate from the agar to the cells in the stump. Moreover, it was found that the amount of curvature was proportional, within certain limits, to the concentration of the growth regulator in the agar blocks.

Other experiments show that the growth regulator moves in greater amounts from the coleoptile tip to the shaded side of the coleoptile than to the illuminated side. When a coleoptile tip is placed on two agar blocks (separated by a thin metal plate) and the tip lighted from one side, there is an unequal distribution of the growth substance; it tends to move toward the shaded side. Thus, more rapid growth is induced on the shaded side of the coleoptile, resulting in curvature of the organ.

Auxin. Plant growth regulators of the type found in oat coleoptiles and that promote cell elongation are called **auxins.** Their effectiveness in promoting growth is frequently tested by using the oat coleoptile in a manner similar to that used by Went and briefly described above. Because the generic name for oat is *Avena*, this curvature test is known as the **Avena test.**

Auxins are widely distributed in the plant kingdom, in both the higher plants and the lower plants. In higher plants they may occur in foliage leaves, in the hypocotyl, stems, flower stalks, roots, fruits, seeds, and even the pollen.

Although plants do not possess glands that secrete hormones, auxin is synthesized only in a few localized centers in the individual plant and is transported throughout the plant body from these centers. Thus, auxin helps to coordinate the various growth activities of the entire plant. In a normal green plant the apical buds and young expanding leaves are active centers of auxin synthesis and export. Older leaves in some plants may synthesize auxin but generally little auxin is exported from them.

A common growth regulator of the auxin type that has been identified in plants is 3-indoleacetic acid. This substance and several others of similar nature and action are now made synthetically.

The Use of Growth Regulators in the Control of Growth. *Control of Sprouting.* We have discussed the specific hormone of the auxin type, particularly as regards its influence upon cell elongation and curvature in the coleoptile of oat seedlings. Another hormonal influence on growth is inhibition of the development of lateral buds. For example, if the terminal bud is cut off, the lateral buds grow; but, if indoleacetic acid is applied to the surface of the decapitated stem, the lateral buds fail to grow. Bud development may be delayed or inhibited by application of certain auxins. For example, potato tubers exposed to the vapors of a synthetic growth regulator, do not sprout in storage.

Rooting of Cuttings. Cuttings of certain species normally root slowly or produce a very small number of roots. It is now possible in some of these species to secure vigorous root production (Fig. 15.10) by treating the cuttings with various synthetic substances, such as indoleacetic acid, indolebutyric acid, betanaphthoxyacetic acid, and numerous substituted phenoxy and benzoic acids. These growth regulators in proper concentration initiate cell divisions and stimulate the production of root primordia in the cuttings. The bases of the cuttings are immersed in the growth regulator solution for a period of from 12 to 24 hours, the strength of the solution ranging from 1 part of the substance in 5000 to 20,000 parts of water. The length of treatment and strength of solution that give optimum rooting vary with the species.

Root formation in cuttings of *Hibiscus* was found to depend upon a combination of indoleacetic acid and sugars and nitrogenous substances. The sugars and nitrogenous substances are contributed by the leaves, which explains the fact that rooting is very slight, even when cuttings are treated with a growth regulator, unless leaves are present.

Of significance is the fact that certain growth regulators affect the course of differentiation. For example, short segments of the tap root of dandelion normally develop buds from the upper cut surface, and callus and roots from the lower cut surface. If indolebutyric acid, for example, is applied to these segments, roots differentiate from both cut surfaces; or, if the growth regulator in tissues is decreased by proper treatments, leaves can be caused to differentiate from both ends of the segments.

Control of Fruit Development. The development of fruits, particularly tomatoes, without pollination has been induced by application of certain growth regulators. A high percentage of seedless fruit results when the flowers are treated before pollination; but flowers treated after pollination set fruit, most of which have seed. Substances employed for this purpose include indoleacetic acid, betanaphthoxyacetic acid, and 4-chlorophenoxyacetic acid. They are synthetic compounds readily available. Flower production in the pineapple has been induced by the application of growth substances, particularly naphthaleneacetic acid.

The Control of Abscission. Certain substances are effective in retarding the preharvest drop of fruit such as apples, pears, and citrus. After treatment with these chemicals, the fruits cling to the trees for a number of days longer than normally and may attain more satisfactory color and maturity. Growth regulators effective for this purpose are naphthaleneacetic acid and 2,4-dichlorophenoxyacetic acid ("2,4-D"). The growth regulator apparently retards the processes that result in the formation of the abscission layer at the base of the petiole (Fig. 8.11).

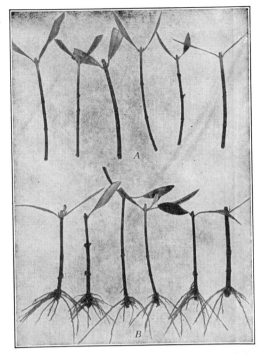

Fig. 15.10. Effect of growth substance (indolebutyric acid) on Mission olive cuttings after 10 weeks in sand. A, no treatment; B, cuttings soaked 24 hours in 50 parts per million of the growth substance. (Photo courtesy of Hartmann.)

Growth Regulators as Herbicides. Certain synthetic growth regulators, although stimulative in extremely small quantities, seriously disturb physiological processes in plants when added in larger amounts. Some of these compounds have turned out to be very potent weed-killers. Although not all growth regulators can be used to kill weeds, the so-called "phenoxy" compounds are particularly effective. Because these compounds are selective and kill broadleaved plants and leave the grasses relatively unharmed, they are particularly useful for destroying many kinds of weeds growing in combination with various grasses or crops of grain. Thus it is possible to spray a lawn with 2,4-D (2,4-di-

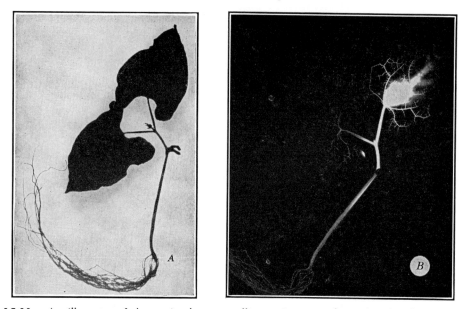

Fig. 15.11. A, silhouette of the entire bean seedling. B, autoradiogram of a bean seedling showing the path of movement of 2,4-D containing radioactive carbon. The application of 2,4-D to the leaf at the upper right is indicated by the white spot. (Courtesy of Crafts.)

chlorophenoxyacetic acid), one of the "phenoxy" compounds, and without injuring the blue grass kill dandelion growing in it.

The fact that growth regulators are translocated throughout the plant in the phloem makes these herbicides particularly effective in killing deep-rooted perennial plants. Studies of the factors affecting their movement in plants have been greatly facilitated through the use of radioactive isotopes. Figure 15.11 shows the movement of 2,4-D containing radioactive carbon through a plant.

Flowering Hormone. In Chapter 12, it was pointed out that the apical meristem of a stem which will differentiate foliage leaves is similar, at the very early stages of development, to that which will differentiate floral leaves. It appears that a growth regulator manufactured in leaves moves to the apical meristem and controls the course of differentiation; that is, it determines whether the shoot tip will become a vegetative shoot or a floral shoot; however, the exact nature of this hormone has not been determined.

Vitamins as Plant Hormones

Extensive research in the field of animal nutrition has shown that animals, including man, may suffer from certain so-called vitamin deficiencies. The diet may contain water, mineral salts, carbohydrates, fats, and proteins in sufficient quantities to supply their energy requirements, but "something" may be lacking which is necessary for normal development and good health. If this something, which we call a **vitamin,** is added, even in the minutest quantities, the individual recovers from the deficiency symptoms.

The classic example of a deficiency disease in human beings is beriberi. Years ago this disease was discovered chiefly among Orientals who lived on a diet consisting mostly of polished rice. If the rice was not polished, or if the polished rice diet was supplemented with certain other foods, the disease did not appear. It was found that the external coats of the rice grain possessed a constituent whose absense from the human diet caused beriberi. This substance was finally isolated in the pure condition; it is known as vitamin B_1.

Today, a number of different vitamins have been discovered, each with specific physiological roles. Not only do vitamins function in animal metabolism but many of these same chemicals have been found to regulate physiological processes in plants as well. One of the chief difficulties in studying the functions of vitamins in plants is that, in contrast to animals that are unable to synthesize vitamins, green plants in general produce their own supply. Thus it is difficult for a plant physiologist to produce a vitamin deficiency in a plant. If the plant manufactures the vitamin the physiologists cannot easily deprive it of the vitamin. Thus far it has been found that only a few green plants are unable to synthesize the amounts of vitamins essential for their own normal growth. An example of such a species is Japanese camellia (*Camellia japonica*), the seedlings of which fail to develop in sand cultures unless vitamin B_1 is added. However, when the seedlings are grown in fertile soil containing decomposed animal and plant materials, the addition of vitamin B_1 is not required. The plant absorbs certain quantities directly from these materials in addition to synthesizing them.

Certain organs in plants, however, are unable to produce all of the vitamins that they need. The culture of these organs isolated from the plant has led to a better understanding of the role that vitamins have in plant growth. As an example let us look at the influence of vitamins on root growth.

Being devoid of chlorophyll, roots are unable to synthesize sugar and hence are dependent upon the green organs of the plant. We may ask: Do the leaves produce substances, other than sugar, essential for the normal growth of roots? If growing root tips are cut off and placed in a medium containing water, essential mineral salts, and sugar, the isolated roots will not continue to make normal growth. They will grow for a prolonged period of time, however, if an extract of yeast cells is added to this medium. The growth substances in yeast extract are shown to be **thiamin, nicotinic acid,** and **pyridoxine,** all part of the vitamin B complex. The living cells of the roots of some species of plants cannot synthesize thiamin, nicotinic acid, or pyridoxine. These substances are manufactured in the leaves under the influence of light and move from them to the roots. Roots of other kinds of plants can produce pyridoxine but not nicotinic acid or thiamin.

Thiamin is widely distributed in the plant kingdom. It has been found in many kinds of bacteria, in yeasts and other fungi, in both fresh water and marine algae, and in mosses, liverworts, ferns, and the higher plants. Some bacteria, yeasts, and other fungi are able to synthesize thiamin, whereas others are not. In wheat grain there is almost as much thiamin in the bran as in the entire grain. It is now common practice to enrich white flour with thiamin.

Young plant tissues of higher plants, principally the leaves, are particularly active in synthesizing thiamin. From these tissues it moves to other parts of the plant. That thiamin is produced in leaves and translocated to roots may be shown by removing a girdle of bark from the stem of a plant. It will be found that thiamin accumulates above the girdle. If the girdle is made on the petiole between the leaf and stem, thiamin accumulates in the leaf.

As stated, thiamin is not produced in roots (at least in most plants which have been studied) but it is essential for root growth. Thus, thiamin may be classed as a root-growth hormone; it plays a role in the normal formation of roots in many seed plants.

Carefully controlled experiments lead us to believe that most ordinary plants growing with their roots in a soil containing the required mineral nutrients, including the micronutrients, and with their leaves in light, synthesize sufficient quantities of thiamin in the leaves to meet all requirements of the plant. Seeds usually are relatively rich in thiamin. Thus the seedling probably has an adequate supply of the vitamin to support normal growth until such time as newly formed leaves are synthesizing the substance. Cuttings, however, may be deficient in thiamin. A few leaves on stem cuttings promote root growth not only because they contribute carbohydrates to the roots but also because they may contribute hormones as well.

Vitamin C, ascorbic acid, has also been shown to be essential for the growth of at least some plants. It is synthesized by most plants and may be present in rather large amounts in green flowering plants and also in certain lower plants. Animals, except the primates and guinea pig, can also synthesize it.

The accumulation of this vitamin is independent of chlorophyll. Generally, the highest concentration of ascorbic acid is in the tissues of greatest cellular activity, such as in buds, young ovary, leaf mesophyll, and germinating seeds. Dormant seeds contain little or no ascorbic acid. It is formed, however, during germination, indicating that its precursor is in the dormant seed. The source of ascorbic acid in pea seedlings is the cotyledons. If the cotyledons of germinating peas are removed, seedling growth is checked; but, if ascorbic acid is made available, seedling growth is greatly accelerated, even though the cotyledons are removed.

Light probably has some influence on the accumulation of ascorbic acid. For example, the "sunny" side of an apple has more of this vitamin than the "shady" side.

Ascorbic acid is quite unstable. For example, potatoes in storage decrease rapidly in this vitamin; and, in 2 days of storage at room temperature, spinach may experience a loss of as much as 80 per cent in ascorbic acid. The ascorbic acid content of a plant is little influenced by the application of commercial or natural fertilizers.

The Vitamin Content of Plants

In view of the great importance of vitamins as factors necessary for the health and well being of animals and of plants extensive studies have been made to determine: (1) the vitamin content of different plants and various parts of plants, at different stages of their development; (2) the influence of environmental factors, including fertilizers, on their vitamin content; and (3) the effects of methods of harvesting, storage, processing (milling, preservation, freezing, canning, dehydration, and cooking) on vitamin content. Moreover, some attempts are being made to increase the vitamins of food plants by breeding methods.

Different parts of the same plant, or organ, may have quite dissimilar amounts of certain vitamins. For example, the wheat grain is richer in thiamin than any other parts of the plant. And in the grain itself the germ and the bran layers contain most of the B_1. The micrograms of thiamin in 100 grams of material are as follows: bran, 1400; germ, 2600; white straight flour, 120; white patent flour, 60; and whole flour, 690. In other words, in the milling of wheat as much as 82 per cent of thiamin of the grain goes into feeds, about 18 per cent into straight flour, and only about 6.7 per cent into patent flour. It has become the practice of bakers to add readily soluble crystalline thiamin and other vitamins to the flour in order to restore its vitamin value. Patent flour, compared with whole wheat, contains approximately one-sixth as much nicotinic acid and about one-half as much pantothenic acid and pyridoxine.

Vitamin content varies with stage of maturity of the plant. For example, as the tissues of cabbage mature, the concentration of ascorbic acid declines; but, as the tomato fruit matures, the concentration of ascorbic acid increases. Small, immature onions are higher in ascorbic acid content than more mature ones; peppers, on the other hand, increase in ascorbic acid as they mature. Most fruits increase in ascorbic acid up to prime maturity.

The manner of food preparation may have a marked effect on vitamin retention. Nutritionists tell us that the housewife "can peel away, soak away, drain away, and cook away 50 per cent or more of the original vitamin content of the food material." It is of interest to note that quick-freezing does not lower appreciably the vitamin content of most products.

In many kinds of edible seeds a number of the vitamins increase in concentration during germination. For example, in comparing dormant barley grains with germinating ones, the riboflavin increases from 0.9 to 7.2 micrograms per gram of dry matter; nicotinic acid, from 67.5 to 115.0; biotin, from 0.31 to 0.91; pantothenic acid, from 5.4 to 10.0; folic acid, from 14.5 to 50.0; and thiamin, from 6.8 to 9.0. Similar differences occur between the dormant and germinating seeds of other plants, such as oats, wheat, corn, and peas. There would thus seem to be a sound nutritional basis for the common inclusion of sprouted seeds in the diets of oriental peoples.

16

The Groups of Plants

Chapter 3 contains a brief discussion of systematic botany or taxonomy, that branch of botany dealing with the naming and classification of plants. In the grouping of the vast assemblage of the many different kinds of plants in the world, an effort is made to show evolutionary relationships, that is, to effect a **natural classification.** Various groupings have been proposed by those specializing in the classification of plants. As our knowledge of the structure, life history, and distribution of plants increased, systems of classification were made that better express the true relationships of plants than did preceding systems. Naturally, there are differences of opinion among systematic botanists as to the grouping of plants.

The plant kingdom may be divided into fifteen **phyla** shown on page 36. The phyla to be discussed in the following pages are listed in Table 16.1 on page 330. (Phyla II, IV, and VI are omitted.) The fifteen phyla are frequently grouped for convenience into assemblages of plants having certain similarities. These groupings do not, however, have important taxonomic significance. The first ten phyla are frequently called **thallophytes,** and they in turn may be divided into (1) the **fission**

plants (Phylum I), including the bacteria and the blue-green algae, (2) the **Algae,** exclusive of the blue-greens (Phyla II through VIII), and (3) the **fungi** (Phyla IX and X). The **mosses** and **liverworts** are placed in a single phylum (XI—the Bryophyta). The last four phyla comprise the **tracheophytes** or the **vascular plants.**

It will be noticed that the names of the phyla end in the suffix *phyta.* This comes from the Greek word *phyton,* meaning plant. The names of the algal phyla contain *phyco,* which is from the Greek word *phycos,* meaning seaweed. The initial syllables refer to an outstanding characteristic of each phylum. Thus, the name Chlorophycophyta means literally *green algal plants.* The names of the fungal phyla contain *myco;* this comes from the Greek word *mykos,* which means fungus.

THE THALLOPHYTES (PHYLA I TO X)

These plants have probably inhabited the earth for a longer period of time than any other plants, perhaps 1000 million years. During this long period of time, their structures and habits have been modified to such an extent that many true relationships within the group have been obscured. As a group, however, they do have certain characteristics in common. They all lack true roots, stems, and leaves. Three types of plant bodies are common: (1) single cells (Fig. 16.1A, D), (2) filaments of cells (Fig. 16.1B, E), and (3) masses of intertwining filaments (Fig. 16.1C, F). In some species, parenchyma tissue is present. Some thallophytes are surprisingly complex, possessing elaborate reproductive structures, and cells that probably function as conducting elements. Many thallophytes are aquatic plants; some have motile sex cells and require free water for fertilization.

Most algae are able to manufacture their own food; they are **autotrophic** plants. The fungi, on the other hand, are unable to synthesize carbohydrates from carbon dioxide and water and must obtain their food ready-made from dead or living organic matter; they are **heterotrophic** plants. This vital difference in the physiology of these two large groups of plants also accounts for some other differences between them. The algae are green, red, or brown, owing to the presence of pigments in plastids. Many fungi are colorless or are colored by pigments not associated with plastids.

The fission plants or Schizophyta are mostly single-celled forms, or chains or plates of associated single cells. The phylum name Schizophyta (from the Greek word *schizo*, meaning to split) recalls the type of reproduction characteristic of practically all members of the phylum. This is simple cell division, a process known as **fission**. The Schizophyta are usually sepa-

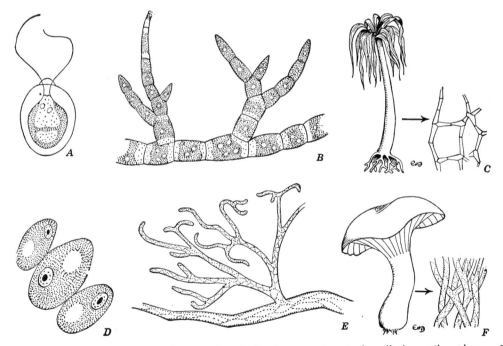

Fig. 16.1. Types of plant bodies in the thallophytes. *A*, single-celled motile alga. *B*, branched, filamentous green alga. *C*, complex brown alga composed of an intricate arrangement of branching filaments; some tissues may be parenchyma-like, and specialized cells are present (sea palm). *D*, single-celled fungus (yeast). *E*, filamentous fungus (water mold). *F*, fruiting body of a fungus, composed of branching filaments (a mushroom).

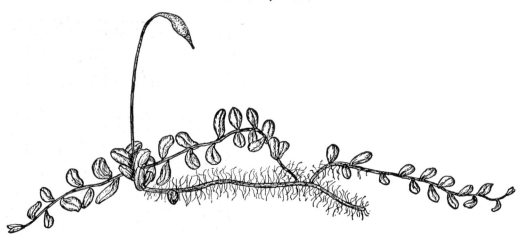

Fig. 16.2. A moss plant. The prostrate leafy portion is green and bears sperms and eggs. The upright leafless stem is green only when young; it bears spores. Numerous rhizoids occur on lower side of the stem.

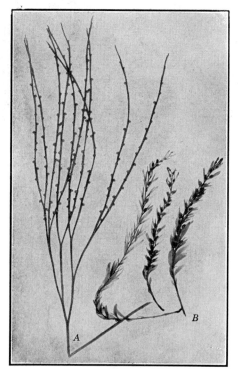

Fig. 16.3. The living members of the phylum Psilophyta. A, Psilotum; B, Tmesipteris. $\times \frac{1}{2}$. (Photo courtesy of Eames, Vascular Plants—Lower Groups, McGraw-Hill Book Co.)

rated into the bacteria, or Schizomycetes (the fission fungi), and the blue-green algae, the Schizophyceae. Some Schizophyta are autotrophic; others, heterotrophic.

THE BRYOPHYTES (PHYLUM XI)

The bryophytes comprise the liverworts and mosses They include an assemblage of plants quite unlike the thallophytes or the tracheophytes. Although they are a very ancient group of plants, they made their appearance on the earth many millions of years after the thallophytes. The first bryophytes probably arose from certain specialized algae, but there is no evidence that they gave rise to any of the higher plants (Fig. 16.8).

The bryophytes are essentially small land plants of moist habitats (Fig. 16.2). The prominent leafy plant produces eggs and motile sperm cells. This plant is able to absorb water and nutrients through filaments of cells, the **rhizoids** (Fig. 16.2), which grow into the moist substratum and function as roots. When a stalk is present, it is stiff and tough. It may possess an elementary sort of conducting system but no xylem and phloem tissues. The leaves attached to such a stalk are small and composed, generally, of a midrib of several cell layers, and an expanded blade, which usually is one layer of cells. Spores, formed as the result of meiotic cell divisions (page 353), are produced in special spore cases. In the mosses proper and in some liverworts, the spore cases occur at the summit of short stalks growing from the green leafy plants.

There are three classes in the Bryophyta:

Class 1   Hepaticae—the liverworts
Class 2   Anthocerotae—Anthoceros
Class 3   Musci—the mosses

Fig. 16.5. *Equisetum,* or horsetail; representative of the phylum Sphenophyta. $\times \frac{1}{2}$.

Fig. 16.4. *Selaginella,* a common hothouse plant, member of the phylum Lycophyta. $\times \frac{1}{3}$.

THE TRACHEOPHYTES (PHYLA XII TO XV)

The tracheophytes (Figs. 16.3 to 16.8) are land plants. All are characterized by a well-developed vascular system (Chapter 6). The plant body consists of roots, stems, and leaves (Figs. 16.4 and 16.6). In all of them, spores resulting from meiosis are produced by the green dominant plant. Spores are cells capable of reproducing new plants directly; however, the plants developed from these spores are very different from the green plants that produced them. The plants growing from the spores are

Fig. 16.6. Young fern (*Polypodium*) plant. Note roots, underground stem, and leaves; representative of phylum Pterophyta. × ½.

from the algae many hundreds of millions of years ago. There are but two genera, belonging to a single family, living today that represent this phylum. Numerous fossils have been found in the oldest rocks, and they indicate that the phylum was represented by some of the first land plants.

The Lycophyta and the Sphenophyta probably arose from the Psilophyta (Fig. 16.8). At one time, members of these two phyla formed great forests of large trees that covered extensive areas of the earth's surface. Coal, for the most part, is the remains of plants belonging to these phyla.

Fig. 16.7. A juniper from the class Gymnospermae of the phylum Pterophyta.

small, in many species they are dependent upon the spore-producing plants, and in all species they normally form eggs and sperms.

The spore-producing plants of the tracheophytes may be small, minute plants or large trees. Many tracheophyte phyla are very ancient; others are of recent geologic origin.

The four phyla of vascular plants are as follows:

Phylum XII   Psilophyta
Phylum XIII   Lycophyta
Phylum XIV   Sphenophyta
Phylum XV   Pterophyta

Of these four phyla, the first three represent very ancient groups of plants. The Psilophyta (Fig. 16.3) may have arisen

They are represented today by the **club-mosses** (Lycophyta) (Fig. 16.4) and the **horsetails** (Sphenophyta) (Fig. 16.5). Both phyla are today composed of small assemblages of rather inconspicuous plants, merely relics of large ancient forests.

The Pterophyta, of which the fern (Fig. 16.6) and the juniper (Fig. 16.7) are examples, may have arisen from the Psilophyta (Fig. 16.8). Plants of this tracheophyte phylum form the present dominant vegetation of the earth. There are three

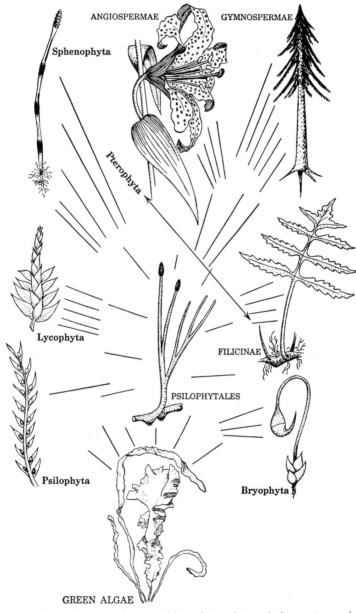

Fig. 16.8. A chart showing the possible relationships of the various plant phyla.

important classes within the Pterophyta (Fig. 16.8):

Class I   Filicinae—the ferns
Class II   Gymnospermae—the gymnosperms
Class III Angiospermae—flowering plants

Although the system of classification described in this chapter is favored by many present-day botanists, it is not the only classification employed and may well be superseded in the future by some better system. The system followed in this book is compared with another common system of classification in Table 16.1. The essential differences between these two systems of classification are two: (1) One system, that used here, supposes a closer relationship between the bacteria and blue-green algae than does the other, and (2) the system used in this text does not assume

that the Lycophyta, Sphenophyta and Pterophyta have as close an association as does the second system.

We shall now examine these various groups of plants from several viewpoints. In some instances we shall consider the structure and activities of such plants as bacteria, fungi, and yeasts that facilitate certain industrial or medical manufacturing processes. We shall study life cycles of fungi looking for critical stages that will make it possible to control the ravages of certain plant diseases. We shall note briefly a few little-known plants certain ones of which may be of great importance; for instance, we are learning from a few simple algae how plants make sugar. In other instances we shall compare plant structures in a general way and consider the problem of how plants arose—the problem of evolution.

Table 16.1. A Comparison of Two Systems of Plant Classification

System Used in This Text		A Second System
Schizophyta	fission plants	
Schizomycetes	bacteria	Schizomycophyta
Schizophyceae	blue-green algae	Cyanophyta
Chlorophycophyta	green algae	Chlorophyta
Chrysophycophyta	golden brown algae	Chrysophyta
Phaeophycophyta	brown algae	Phaeophyta
Rhodophycophyta	red algae	Rhodophyta
Myxomycophyta	slime molds	Myxomycophyta
Eumycophyta	true fungi	Eumycophyta
Phycomycetes	algal fungi	Phycomycetes
Ascomycetes	sac fungi	Ascomycetes
Basidiomycetes	club fungi	Basidiomycetes
Fungi Imperfecti	imperfect fungi	
Bryophyta		Bryophyta
Hepaticae	liverworts	Hepaticae
Anthocerotae	anthoceros	Anthocerotae
Musci	mosses	Musci
	vascular plants	Tracheophyta
Psilophyta		Psilopsida
Lycophyta	club mosses	Lycopsida
Sphenophyta	horsetails	Sphenopsida
Pterophyta		Pteropsida
Filicinae	ferns	Filicinae
Gymnospermae	conifers and allies	Gymnospermae
Angiospermae	flowering plants	Angiospermae
Dicotyledoneae		Dicotyledoneae
Monocotyledoneae		Monocotyledoneae

17

The Fission Plants

CLASSIFICATION

The problem of classifying plants is frequently a knotty one. Some of the difficulties may be pointed out in connection with this phylum. Bacteria and blue-green algae have many characteristics in common. Most are single-celled organisms; some grow into filaments and others form colonies of more or less definite form. They practically all secrete a gelatinous matrix. Of considerable importance is the striking similarity of the nuclear apparatus in the two groups; compare Fig. 17.7 with Fig. 17.16. It is generally thought that the bacteria are heterotrophic and the blue-green algae autotrophic and for this reason they are placed in separate phyla. But this distinction does not hold for there are autotrophic bacteria, some of which actually contain chlorophyll and certain species of the Oscillatoriaceae actually live as parasites in the digestive tract of animals. Table 17.1 points out the varied ways in which these organisms derive their food.

It must be emphasized that the bacteria are not classified as true fungi. They are fission plants and have no closer relation to the fungi than, for instance, the green algae do to the red algae. Most students of the blue-green algae group them with the bacteria in a single phylum. In this text we shall call this phylum the Schizophyta. Other arrangements will be found in other texts, the most popular being that of placing the blue-green algae in a phylum or division of its own and considering it to be one of the algal phyla (Table 16.1). The reasons for not doing this have been stated.

General Characteristics

This phylum of worldwide distribution comprises a large number of species, mostly single-celled or simple filamentous forms. Although it has generally been thought that no member possessed a sexual life cycle, some recent genetical studies of bacteria suggest the possible occurrence of fusion of cells and meiosis in several strains of the common colon bacillus. Multiplication of individuals in all members of the phylum results from the simple division of single cells, a process known as **fission**. This process has recently been studied in some detail by means of the electron microscope at a magnification of about 20,000 diameters. Many members of the Schizophyta form spores, but the spores are more a means of carrying the species over periods

331

unfavorable to growth than a means of multiplication.

Many individuals or cells forming individuals of this phylum are small, from 1 to 5 microns in diameter. Nuclei or nuclear materials are considered present, although nuclear organization is still not understood. The cell walls of many forms contain cellulose; in others, a compound known as **chitin** is present. Most species secrete a gelatinous **slime layer** enveloping the cell.

Energy and nitrogen sources within the phylum are varied. They are summarized in Table 17.1. Although this table is not complete, it does show not only that different representatives of the Schizophyta derive energy and nitrogen from varied sources, but also that physiologically, as well as structurally, bacteria and blue-green algae have much in common. Representatives may be found in both groups which fix nitrogen, or which utilize the energy of sunlight, or which obtain nitrogen from inorganic sources. Some members of the Schizophyta use sulfur and iron in their metabolism.

While the bacteria are not to be classi-fied as fungi, certain types of bacteria have characteristics that resemble those of fungi. Some bacteria recall slime molds while others are filamentous. The blue-green algae, in their turn, have certain characteristics in common with the higher algae. For instance, they contain the pigments **phycoerythrin** and **phycocyanin,** which are also found in the higher algae.

The phylum is divided into two classes: the Schizomycetes, or the bacteria, and the Schizophyceae, or blue-green algae.

CLASS SCHIZOMYCETES— THE BACTERIA

The study of bacteria forms the science of **bacteriology.** It is an important member of the science family. Well-trained bacteriologists occupy important positions in all medical schools, in agricultural colleges, and in most other institutions that carry on biological instruction and research.

Most bacteria are one-celled plants and among the smallest known living organisms. They are often referred to as "microbes" or "germs." They play an important role in

Table 17.1. Nutritional and Energy Requirements of the Schizophyta

Bacteria or Blue-green Algae	Source of Nitrogen	Source of Energy	Photosynthetic Pigments Present	Heterotrophic or Autotrophic
1. Many bacteria, possibly a few blue-green algae	Living organisms (parasitic)	Organic compounds	None	Heterotrophic
2. Many bacteria	Nonliving organic matter (saprophytic)	Organic compounds	None	Heterotrophic
3. Some bacteria	Free nitrogen of atmosphere	Organic compounds	None	Heterotrophic
Some blue-green algae	Free nitrogen of atmosphere	Radiant energy	Chlorophyll	Autotrophic
4. Soil bacteria	Ammonia and nitrates	Inorganic salts	None	Autotrophic
Soil bacteria	Ammonia and nitrates	Organic compounds	None	Heterotrophic
5. Purple bacteria	Organic or inorganic nitrogen	Radiant energy	A purple pigment, and chlorophyll	Autotrophic
6. Blue-green algae	Inorganic salts	Radiant energy	Chlorophyll	Autotrophic

the decomposition of organic matter, they are indispensable in maintaining soil fertility, they affect the quality of the water and milk we drink and of the food we eat, and they cause diseases of animals and plants. We are likely to gain the impression that all bacteria are harmful, because we associate them with such dread human diseases as typhoid fever, tuberculosis, and many other types of infections. But many kinds of bacteria are beneficial, in fact, indispensable in the life of the world.

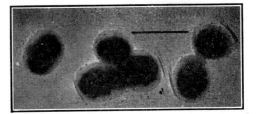

Fig. 17.1. *Pneumococcus,* enlarged 15,000 diameters. (Electron microscope photograph courtesy of Hillier.)

Forms of Bacteria

Bacteria are of three general shapes: **spherical, rod-shaped,** and **spiral.** Spherical bacteria are called **cocci** (**coccus,** singular) (Figs. 17.1, 17.2, 17.3), rod-shaped ones are called **bacilli** (**bacillus,** singular) (Fig. 17.4), and spiral forms are known as **spirilla** (**spirillum,** singular). There is some intergrading between these forms. It is sometimes difficult, for instance, to distinguish between a very short rod and a coccus that has elongated in preparation for cell division. Furthermore, shape depends to a certain extent upon the age and the environment. Figures 17.1, 17.2, 17.3, and 17.4 show electron microscope photographs of various types of bacteria. Each type has been magnified 15,000 times. Rod-shaped and spiral forms are usually found as single individuals, although they may, under certain growing conditions, form long chains. Many cocci exist normally in groups.

Bacteria of the coccus form, in chains resembling strings of pearls, are called **streptococci** (Fig. 17.2). Several species of the genus *Streptococcus* are very important. Some of the diseases they cause are scarlet fever, erysipelas, mastitis of cows, and sinus infections. *Streptococcus lactis* is an agent in souring milk. Coccus individuals are sometimes grouped into

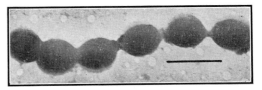

Fig. 17.2. *Streptococcus,* enlarged 15,000 diameters. (Electron microscope photograph courtesy of Hillier.)

Fig. 17.3. *Staphylococcus aureus,* enlarged 15,000 diameters. (Electron microscope photograph courtesy of Hillier.)

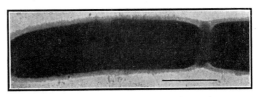

Fig. 17.4. *Bacillus anthrax,* enlarged 15,000 diameters. (Electron microscope photograph courtesy of Hillier.)

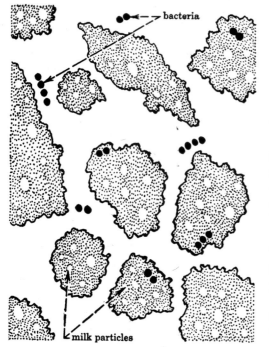

Fig. 17.5. Spatial relationship of bacteria and milk particles in a cubic centimeter of milk containing approximately 10,000,000 bacteria. (Redrawn from Lohnis and Fred, *Textbook of Agricultural Bacteriology*, McGraw-Hill Book Co.)

clusters; these are called *staphylococci* (Fig. 17.3). One species of *Staphylococcus* is the usual cause of boils and abscesses. Packets or cubes of 8, 64, or more cells have been given the name *Sarcina*.

Size of Bacteria

Bacteria are among the smallest living organisms. Some of them are close to the limit of visibility with the most powerful light microscopes. Several million bacteria may be present in a cubic centimeter of soil, or milk, and not be crowded in the least bit. If milk containing 10 million bacteria for each cubic centimeter is examined under a lens magnifying 440 times, the relation be-

tween bacteria and milk particles would approximate that shown in Fig. 17.5.

Bacteria and other microscopic objects are measured in units called **microns**. A micron is 1/1000 of a millimeter, or about 1/25,000 of an inch. Most bacteria average from 1 to 2 microns in diameter. If the cube *A* in Fig. 17.6 is 10 millimeters along one edge, there are 100 square millimeters in each face and 1000 cubic millimeters in the cube. Ten thousand cocci, each 1 micron in diameter, could be placed along one edge of this cube. There would be room for 100 million of them in one face, 1000 billion would fit nicely into the cube. Thus, 1 million bacteria per cubic centimeter of soil, milk, or blood is really a small proportion.

Strange as it may seem, the very smallness of bacteria is a factor of major importance in their life. All the nourishment, all

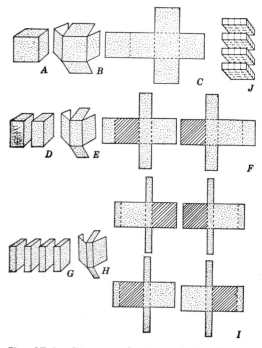

Fig. 17.6. Diagram showing relationship between volume and surface.

gases and inorganic salts that a bacterium requires must be taken in through its cell wall. All its waste products, all toxins or poisons, certain enzymes and other special substances that are in one way or another associated with bacterial activity must pass outward through the surface of the bacterial cell. Therefore, the more surface a bacterium possesses in relation to its volume, the more readily will these substances diffuse.

Just what is the relation between surface and volume? A cube, 1 inch on edge, contains 6 faces, each covering an area of 1 square inch; it contains 1 cubic inch of substance (Fig. 17.6A). If the faces of this cube were laid out side by side they would cover an area of 6 square inches (Fig. 17.6B, C). Now, suppose that we cut through the cube in the planes shown and form 2 smaller blocks (Fig. 17.6D). Two new faces will result, each 1 square inch in area. If all the surfaces represented by the original 6 faces and the 2 new ones are laid out side by side, we will have an area of 8 square inches (Fig. 17.6E, F). Thus, by cutting the original cube into 2 smaller blocks, the surface area has been added to without any increase in the original volume. Additional sections (Fig. 17.6G, H, I) increase the area exposed without increasing volume. About 25,000 bacteria could be placed along 1 edge of the original cube. If we suppose that we could cut this cube into small cubes of about the size of a bacterium (Fig. 17.6J), how much surface would be exposed? We would have to make 25,000 cuts in each of three directions, 75,000 cuts all told. Two faces would be exposed at each cut, and so we would have 150,000 new faces, each with a surface of 1 square inch, or about 350 square yards. That is roughly the area of the lane used for the 100 yard dash. With this great increase in surface, it is obvious that in a given time much more

water could penetrate this surface than the 6 square inches of the original cube! The small size of bacteria simply means that they have an enormous surface for their volume. It is because of this relationship that they can be so very active in comparison with the cells in a mass of parenchyma tissue, such as that forming a fruit. In this latter case gaseous interchange, and movement of nutrients, water, and waste products are restricted by the complexity of surrounding tissues.

Distribution of Bacteria

These minute organisms are ever present about us. They occur in the air, water, and soil. They exist on the surfaces of all animal and plant bodies and on the surfaces of almost everything we touch. They are present in milk and in all foods that have not been sterilized. Even foods that have undergone the usual process of sterilization will sometimes contain the spores of bacteria. In 1939 viable spores of certain heat-resistant bacteria were found in canned roasted veal that had traveled with the explorer Parry to the Arctic Circle in 1824. Bacteria occur naturally in the digestive tract of animals. Nitrogen-fixing bacteria are closely associated with the living cells in the roots of legumes.

After a rain or snow, the dust is washed from the air and carried to the ground, and then the air may be practically free of bacteria. Generally, the number of bacteria in the air decreases with altitude. The air at altitudes at which the jets fly is bacteria-free.

Water from deep, cold wells or springs is usually devoid of bacteria. Whereas the surface few inches of most soils teem with bacteria, the number decreases as the depth increases.

Although bacteria are almost universally distributed, it is possible, by taking great precautions, to keep rooms free of these organisms. Such precautions are observed in hospital operating rooms and in certain types of biological and bacteriological laboratories. Surfaces are washed with disinfecting fluid, sterilized gowns are worn, and only instruments that have been placed in boiling water are used. This condition of freedom from bacteria is known as **asepsis**. **Sterilization** is the destruction of all living forms, including bacteria, that may be within or upon a particular object.

Nutrition and Energy

Bacteria, like all other living organisms, need food for growth and multiplication. Food is any organic substance that supplies energy and basic organic materials for use in metabolism. Most bacteria utilize nonliving organic matter as a source of food. In other words, most bacteria are **saprophytes**. They may use relatively simple organic compounds, such as alcohol, sugars, and fats, or very complex organic compounds, such as proteins. For example, the bacteria in acetic acid formation utilize ethyl alcohol as a source of food and secure from its oxidation energy for their own purposes. These bacteria are common in cider, beer, and wine. The reaction may be represented as follows:

Alcohol + oxygen →

    acetic acid + water + energy

Many bacteria depend on sugars as a source of food. The lactic acid bacteria use simple sugars in milk, and the souring of milk is caused by these bacteria. Many species of bacteria rely on proteins as foods. In the process of decomposition proteins are broken down to simple products, many of which have offensive odors. Ammonia is one of the simplest products formed from proteins by bacteria.

In addition to the saprophytic bacteria, there are those that obtain their food from other living organisms. Such bacteria are **parasites**. Among them are the disease-causing bacteria of plants and animals. Sometimes the distinction between parasite and saprophyte is not clear-cut. For example, certain types of bacteria thrive as saprophytes in the soil. When they become embedded in wounded flesh, however, they may become parasites. Such are the bacteria causing tetanus and gaseous gangrene in man, and blackleg in cattle.

Some bacteria are able to obtain energy from simple inorganic salts, such as sodium nitrite, ammonia, and hydrogen sulfide. They bring about the oxidation of these simple substances and utilize the energy so released to synthesize organic materials from which enzymes, protoplasm, cell walls, and other cellular materials are formed. This synthesis is carried out in a manner comparable with that by which green plants manufacture foods.

We may classify bacteria on the basis of their method of obtaining energy, as follows: (1) most bacteria secure energy from the oxidation or breakdown of either non-living or living organic matter; (2) a few obtain energy by the oxidation of inorganic materials and use this energy to synthesize their own foods; (3) one group of bacteria can utilize the energy of sunlight for the manufacture of food.

Structure of Bacteria

Most bacteria are single-celled plants. All the activities of the living organism (respiration, assimilation, absorption, etc.) are carried on in this single cell. Although bacteria are regarded as simple plants structurally, the reactions carried on in them are extremely complex.

Bacteria possess a cell wall, but unlike that of typical plants it generally contains no cellulose although it may contain other carbohydrates. The protoplast is surrounded by a plasma membrane which, as in other cells, is differentially permeable. That such a membrane is present is borne out by the fact that the bacterial cell may be plasmolyzed. For example, when foods are preserved in sugar, sugar syrup, dry salt, or brine, the bacteria are unable to grow because of the withdrawal of most of the water in them by osmosis. Most bacterial cells are surrounded by a gelatinous sheath known as a **slime layer.** When thick and firm so as to have a discrete structure, it is known as a **capsule** (Figs. 17.1, 17.2, 17.3, 17.4).

The presence of a nucleus has been demonstrated in only a few instances. Nucleic acids, substances characteristic of nuclei of plants and animals, occur in all bacteria examined for their presence. Nuclei and mitotic-like figures may be seen in some forms with a light microscope (Fig. 17.7) and in some photographs made with an electron microscope (Fig. 17.8). As electrons have very little power to penetrate even such small objects as bacteria, the absence of a nucleus from bacteria examined by the electron microscope is not proof of

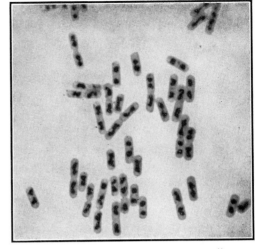

Fig. 17.7. Mitotic-like figures in *Bacillus anthrax.* (Photomicrograph courtesy of Rabinow.)

its nonexistence. Hereditary characters in bacteria are passed on from one generation to another, much as they are in higher plants; this fact must mean that some comparable sort of nuclear mechanism is present. Perhaps the nuclear material is scattered throughout the cytoplasm rather than organized into a well-formed body. Recent genetical evidence indicates that at least one chromosome equivalent is present in a

Fig. 17.8. Nuclearlike bodies in *Bacillus mycoides.* (Electron photomicrograph courtesy of Knyasi.)

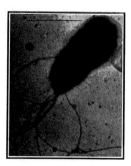

Fig. 17.9. *Bacillus Fischeri*, enlarged 15,000 diameters. Note flagella. (Electron photomicrograph courtesy of Johnson.)

strain of *Escherichia coli* and that occasionally fusion may occur.

Some sorts of bacteria are able to move with a speed roughly comparable to that of a good college swimmer. These motile forms have one to several long tenuous filaments of cytoplasm, called **flagella** (singular, **flagellum**), attached to the surface of the body (Figs. 17.9 and 17.10). Locomotion is probably obtained by a whiplike movement of these flagella.

Reproduction of Bacteria

Most bacteria divide by simple fission of the cell, in which process the cell is "pinched" in two much as a sausage might be cut by the tightening of a slip knot. Photographs taken with the electron microscope show the process (Fig. 17.11). The slime layer surrounding bacteria is distinctly demonstrated (Fig. 17.11a). Near the middle of the central cell (Fig. 17.11b) a band of some denser material may be noted. Adjacent to this band a notch in the cell is apparent. A deeper notch occurs in Fig. 17.11c. As the process nears completion, the two daughter cells pull apart, stretching the cell wall and plasma membrane (Fig. 17.11d). This thin, stretched

portion finally breaks and the ends of the two daughter cells round up.

The nucleus apparently divides previously to the division of the cell (Fig. 17.7), although it appears from this figure that chromatin merely pinches in two. There is some evidence that a single chromosome equivalent is present and that it divides longitudinally.

Under optimum conditions, a bacterium may divide and the daughters grow to full size, ready for another division, in 30 minutes. If such conditions were to prevail for 1½ days, 200 trucks of 5-ton capacity would be required to haul away the progeny of a single cell. Obviously, these conditions have never prevailed for so long a period. Nevertheless, the reproductive capacity of bacteria is enormous. Bacterial growth is everywhere held in check. Probably the most important means are: (1) lack of food; (2) the production of substances, unfavorable to growth, by the bacteria themselves, by other bacteria, by fungi, by higher plants, or by the host in which the bacteria may be living; and (3) competition for oxygen. The rate of increase of a bacterial population is, in general, very similar to that of other organisms, including

Fig. 17.10. *Caryophanon latum*, enlarged 8000 diameters. (Electron photomicrograph courtesy of Rabinow.)

Fig. 17.11. Stages in division of a bacterial cell. (Electron photomicrograph courtesy of Knyasi.)

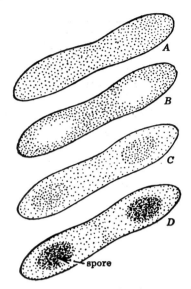

Fig. 17.12. Stages in the development of bacterial spores. (Redrawn from Knyasi.)

yeasts, fruit flies, and man. There is a short initial period during which increase in numbers is very slow, then the bacteria increase very rapidly and the population reaches a peak at which it remains constant for a time, and after the peak the number of bacteria decreases rather slowly.

When conditions for growth become unfavorable, some bacteria are able to form **spores** (Fig. 17.12) or special bodies that enable them to live over these periods. In spore formation the protoplast condenses into one or two masses of dense protoplasm with a very low water content. Fortunately, few disease-producing bacteria form spores.

Respiration of Bacteria

Bacteria, like all living organisms, require energy to carry on living processes. Organic substances are broken down through the action of enzyme systems into progressively simpler organic substances. Oxygen unites with certain of the simplest of these compounds, forming carbon dioxide and water. Energy may be released when certain substances are degraded into simpler substances. This destruction of complex food substances with the subsequent release of energy through the action of intracellular enzymes is called **respiration.**

Bacteria that generally use atmospheric oxygen in respiration are called **aerobes.** Many bacteria, however, are able to respire without atmospheric oxygen and without the subsequent oxidation of food materials to carbon dioxide and water (page 216); they are able to obtain sufficient energy from glycolysis, the oxidation of food to organic acids. They do not absolutely require the greater amount of energy that is released when oxygen combines with alcohol, pyruvic acid, or some other simple organic compound to form carbon dioxide and water. Indeed, a few species of bacteria cannot grow in the presence of oxygen. Bacteria that grow in the absence of oxygen are called **anaerobes.** If small amounts of oxygen hinder their growth, they are known as **obligate anaerobes.**

Influence of Environmental Factors on Bacteria

The ability of bacteria to adapt to changing environments varies greatly from species to species. Some bacteria can grow only in certain very specific and constant surroundings. Others are able to adjust themselves to a wide variety of conditions. We have already noted that some bacteria require oxygen, some do not grow in its presence, and some may grow either with or without it. Factors besides food supply and oxygen that influence the rate of bacterial growth are water, temperature, and sunlight.

Water. All bacteria require water to grow. They will not grow in foods containing much less than 15 or 20 per cent water. Strong salt and sugar solutions inhibit their growth; hence, salt and sugar may be used as preservatives. Most disease bacteria are unable to live if they become dried out in the air. When quick-frozen and dried in a vacuum bacteria may remain viable for years.

Temperature. Bacteria may grow at temperatures ranging from about 0° F to around 160° F, but individual species usually have a narrow range. Spores of certain bacteria in a moist atmosphere may resist temperatures of 240° F for some minutes, or withstand boiling water (212° F) for hours. Most disease-producing bacteria do not form spores and are easily killed at 140° F after about 10 minutes' exposure. Disease-producing bacteria in milk may be killed by heating the milk to 160° F and holding it at that temperature for 15 seconds. This process is known as **pasteurization.** On the other hand, many vegetables must be heated to high temperatures for 20 to 40 minutes to kill the spores of soil bacteria that might cause spoilage.

Sunlight. Bacteria are rapidly killed by direct exposure to sunlight, ultraviolet rays being particularly effective.

Classification of Bacteria

Because of their small size and similar structure, bacteria are very difficult to classify. For instance, two species of bacteria are known which are almost indistinguishable from each other. Both grow in association with the roots of plants. One, *Rhizobium leguminosarum*, does not harm the host but instead makes nitrogen of the air available to it. The other species, *Agrobacterium tumefaciens*, rapidly kills the host plant. Thus the two species, although very similar both morphologically and physiologically, differ in one very important physiological process that results, in one instance, in a beneficial relationship and, in the other, in a very harmful relationship (Figs. 17.13, 17.14).

In order to name bacteria correctly, one must have complete data as to their size, shape, motility, and spore formation. In addition, many physiological characters must be studied. For example, it may be necessary to know how it grows in milk, on agar, and on potato, what sugars it is able to ferment, what pigments it produces, and a number of other physiological reactions.

The Schizomycetes are separated into seven orders on the basis of obvious morphological and physiological differences. Some have characters that suggest molds or algae or one-celled animals. The largest order—the Eubacteriales, or true bacteria—have characteristics described in the previous pages. It is the only order that will be discussed here.

Order Eubacteriales. The Eubacteriales is divided into two suborders: (1) spore-forming bacteria, with a single large family, the Bacillaceae; (2) non-spore-forming bacteria, with eleven families.

The Spore-forming Eubacteriales. The family Bacillaceae contains several species of great economic importance. Most of them are normal inhabitants of the soil or of animal wastes. Many of them will grow well in the absence of oxygen, and some are able to secrete powerful poisons or toxins. *Clostridium botulinum* is common in garden and farm soils. It not infrequently occurs on vegetables, such as corn and beans. If *Clostridium botulinum* is not killed in the process of canning, it grows and multiplies in the canned product, producing one of the most powerful poisons known. Food poisoning from **botulinus toxin**, however, has become quite rare. Commercial canning processes are adequate to kill all spores, and home canners have been so well educated that home-canned food is as little likely to contain viable

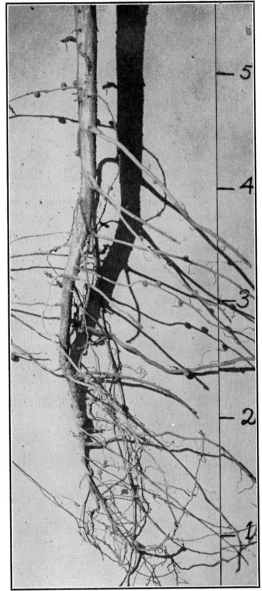

Fig. 17.13. Nodules produced by *Rhizobium leguminosarum* on the roots of a legume. (Photo courtesy of Francis Smith.)

Clostridium botulinum as is commercially canned food.

Clostridium tetani, like *C. botulinum,* is also a normal inhabitant of well-manured soils. When introduced into deep wounds it may produce a very potent toxin. Tetanus infections were common during wartime. The organism is almost invariably present in dirty wounds, where it multiplies. The toxin secreted by it causes lockjaw. Fortunately, both soldiers and horses may be injected with a substance that gives them almost complete protection against the toxin of *C. tetani*.

Non-spore-forming Eubacteriales. Although this suborder contains eleven distinct families, it is divided into three natural groups on the basis of food requirements.

1. One family (Nitrobacteriaceae) includes those bacteria that make their own food. These bacteria, like green plants, are autotrophic, although they do not possess chlorophyll.

2. Four families are heterotrophic but obtain the nitrogen they require from inorganic salts, such as sodium nitrate, or from atmospheric nitrogen.

3. The remaining six families are also heterotrophic but require organic substances as a source of energy and nitrogen. They may utilize dead plant or animal wastes; i.e., they are saprophytes. Or they may require living cells for their source of nitrogen, in which event they are parasites.

The Nitrogen Cycle

As has been mentioned in Chapter 5, carbon, oxygen, hydrogen, and nitrogen are four of the more important chemical elements essential for the building of protoplasm. Oxygen and nitrogen occur free in the atmosphere, oxygen and hydrogen in water, and carbon and oxygen in the gas carbon dioxide. As far as plants are concerned, oxygen, hydrogen, and carbon are available in unlimited quantities. In spite of the great amount of nitrogen present in the atmosphere, it is frequently a limiting

factor in plant growth. The green plant is unable to utilize nitrogen gas as such. Nitrogen must be combined with other elements, in such compounds as nitrates or ammonium salts, before it becomes available to green plants. These salts are not present in agricultural soils in large quantities. Even in native forest and grassland soils, salts containing nitrogen soon would be depleted were it not that various types of bacteria tend to maintain the nitrogen level of the soil. Plants, in association with man and other animals, compose a cycle in which nitrogen is continually being changed from one form to another. This is the **nitrogen cycle.** Similar cycles are also known for carbon, iron, sulfur, and other elements.

Let us consider the nitrogen cycle in some detail. The following processes are involved: (1) the incorporation of nitrogen into the complex organic compounds of the plant or animal cell; (2) the release to the soil of complex nitrogenous compounds by the animal or plant body, either as wastes or by death; (3) decay; (4) nitrification; (5) denitrification; and (6) nitrogen fixation.

Absorption and Assimilation. Although atmospheric nitrogen is unavailable for the growth of green plants, nitrogen in the form of nitrates and ammonium salts is readily absorbed by most plants from the soil solution. Nitrogen in these salts can then be incorporated into complex organic compounds.

Green plants incorporate nitrate nitrogen into complex organic compounds. The inorganic nitrogen thus becomes a part of complex plant proteins. The plant may die after a season or two, or it may lose only its leaves, or it may be eaten by an animal. The animal, in its turn, will use some of the protein nitrogen it obtains from the plant in elaborating its own protoplasm.

The excreta will contain some nitrogen. Eventually the animal will die. Thus organic nitrogenous materials produced by the plant or animal are returned to the soil.

Decay or Decomposition. The complex nitrogenous compounds in animal wastes and in dead plants and animals, almost without exception, are rapidly decomposed by various bacteria and fungi. By decomposition or by decay is meant the breaking down of proteins (and other compounds) into a number of simple compounds. The process is very complicated, occurring in many steps. Different bacteria and fungi may be associated with the various stages. The important nitrogenous end-product of the decay of the organic nitrogenous compounds derived from living organisms is **ammonia.**

Nitrification. This is a very special type of oxidation; energy is released in the process just as energy is released by a burning match. In nitrification, ammonium salts and nitrites are oxidized. The oxidation is speeded by bacteria of the genera *Nitrosomonas* and *Nitrobacter* that utilize the energy released to elaborate food substances. Nitrification involves two distinct steps: (1) ammonium salts or ammonia are changed to nitrites and (2) nitrites are changed to nitrates.

Ammonia + oxygen → nitrite + energy

$$NH_3 \quad + \quad O_2 \quad \rightarrow NO_2^- \qquad (1)$$

Nitrite + oxygen → nitrate + energy

$$NO_2^- \quad + \quad O_2 \quad \rightarrow NO_3^- \qquad (2)$$

Notice that in each step the amount of oxygen combined with nitrogen is increased. The nitrate thus formed is absorbed by roots of green plants and eventually enters into the composition of living protoplasm.

The nitrogen cycle, in its simplest form, can be represented as follows:

Nitrates in soil → absorption by green plants → change to protein →

death or waste products → decay → NH_3 →

$$NO_2^- \rightarrow \begin{cases} NO_3^- \\ \text{nitrates} \\ \text{in soil} \end{cases}$$

This statement does not, however, complete the nitrogen cycle. Nitrogen, at certain stages of the cycle, may become unavailable to plants. On the other hand, unavailable nitrogen may, at other stages, be made available. The loss of nitrogen from this simplified cycle is called **denitrification,** and the addition of nitrogen to the cycle is **nitrogen fixation.**

Denitrification. Many species of bacteria are able to change nitrates to nitrites, nitrites to ammonia, and ammonia to free nitrogen gas.

$$NO_3^- \rightarrow NO_2^- \rightarrow NH_3 \rightarrow N_2$$

It will be noticed that this process is, in general, the reverse of the combined processes of nitrogen fixation and nitrification. Denitrification requires energy. Denitrifying bacteria need a relatively large supply of sugars to supply this energy. From the soil fertility standpoint, denitrification is unfavorable in that it depletes nitrogen in the soil. The process is most active in soils that are poorly aerated or that contain an excessive amount of unrotted manure.

Nitrogen Fixation. The change of free nitrogen to nitrogen compounds is called **nitrogen fixation.** Certain types of bacteria and blue-green algae are able to use free gaseous nitrogen in the building of the proteins and other organic nitrogen compounds of their bodies. Thus they "fix" nitrogen. Nitrogen-fixing bacteria cannot live on nitrogen alone; they require oxygen, water, carbohydrates, mineral salts, and vitamins, just as do other living plants and animals. Their metabolism differs from that of other living things chiefly in their ability to utilize atmospheric nitrogen. With this nitrogen from the air, together with water, oxygen, mineral salts, and carbohydrates, they are able to synthesize proteins.

There are two groups of nitrogen-fixing bacteria: (1) **symbiotic bacteria,** those that invade the roots of legumes (peas, clovers, beans, vetches, Lespedeza, etc.) and also the roots of a few nonleguminous plants, and (2) **nonsymbiotic bacteria,** those that live free in the soil. The most common species of the former group is *Rhizobium leguminosarum.* The association between bacteria and legume roots leads to the development of many small nodules on the roots (Fig. 17.13). The term symbiotic, which describes this association, means that the bacteria supply nitrogen compounds to the legume roots and that the roots furnish the bacteria with carbohydrates. With an assured food supply the bacteria are able to change large amounts of gaseous nitrogen to organic nitrogen compounds that either are of direct use to the legume or, after slight changes, can be utilized by it. It has been estimated that in a single season the nodules on the roots of legumes in an acre of soil may add between 100 and 200 pounds of nitrogen to that acre. Considerable amounts of nitrogen are added each year to soils as the result of the activity of the free-living, nonsymbiotic, nitrogen-fixing bacteria, chiefly species of *Azotobacter* and *Clostridium.*

In recent years chemical companies in the United States have fixed annually approximately a million tons of nitrogen fertilizers and explosives. The commercial process was developed in Germany prior to World War I and since it insured a plentiful supply of fertilizers to German farmers as well as TNT to the German Army it made the invasion of France feasible. Since then the production of fertilizer nitrogen by the direct combination of atmospheric nitrogen with hydrogen or carbon monoxide has expanded rapidly. It is estimated that, in order for food production in the United States to keep pace with our increasing population, a yearly increment of 100,000 tons of synthetic nitrogen fertilizer is needed for farm lands. The modern chemical factory has become an important factor in the nitrogen cycle.

Bacteria and Plant Diseases

Not many species of bacteria cause severe diseases in plants, although practically all cultivated plants may suffer from one or more bacterial diseases. The classification of bacteria that cause diseases of plants is at present unsatisfactory. Some 135 species are grouped together in the genus *Phytomonas* and a number in the genus *Erwinia;* all are plant parasites. *Erwinia* is closely related to bacteria that cause typhoid and dysentery in man.

Crop destruction due to bacterial diseases amounts annually to many millions of dollars. It has been estimated, for instance, that in the 6 years from 1901 to 1906, inclusive, $10 million worth of pear orchards were destroyed in California by pear blight caused by the species *Erwinia amylovora.*

In discussing diseases, we must distinguish between the **causal agent,** the **host,** and the **diseases** themselves. For example, certain bacteria are agents that cause disease. The plants they infect are called host plants or simply hosts. The association between bacteria and the host results in an abnormal condition in the host which is a disease. Just as bacteria and host plants are named, so too does the disease have a distinguishing name.

Agrobacterium tumefaciens is a bacterial species of worldwide distribution. Apples, pears, peaches, grapes, raspberries, and many other kinds of plants in over 40 families may serve as host plants. The disease produced is called **crown gall** (Fig. 17.14). Table 17.2 gives a list of several bacteria, host plants, and diseases.

Bacteria gain entrance to the host plant through (1) stomata, (2) lenticels, and (3) wounds. Once inside they spread from the point of infection to other parts of the plant.

Injury to the plant tissue may be due to bacteria-secreted substances that kill the cells or that stimulate the living cells to produce harmful compounds, for example certain gums (Fig. 17.15), or large growths such as galls. In some diseases injury may be due to pressure caused by the increase in numbers of bacteria: cells may burst, or vessels and intercellular spaces may be obstructed.

An example of destruction caused by fire

Table 17.2. Relation between Bacteria, Host Plant, and Disease

Bacteria	Host Plants	Disease
Erwinia amylovora	Apple, pear, and other members of Rose family	Fire blight
Erwinia carotorora	Carrots, turnips, cabbage, lettuce, Irish potatoes, tomatoes, etc.	Soft rot
Phytomonas phaseoli	Bean	Bacterial blight
Phytomonas malvacearum	Cotton	Angular leaf spot

blight in pears has already been given. *Erwinia amylovora* is a native of the United States and very widely distributed. Fire blight was first described in 1794 on wild apples growing along the Hudson River in New York State. The bacteria grow rapidly in young succulent parts of many fruit

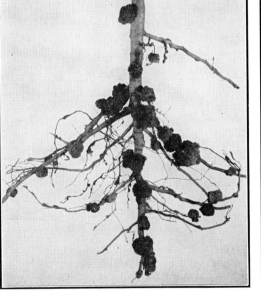

Fig. 17.14. Crown gall on almond. (Photo courtesy of Ark.)

Fig. 17.15. Bacterial gummosis of plum tree. (Photo courtesy Plant Pathology Division, Univ. of Calif.)

trees, and young leaves, blossoms, fruits, twigs, and bark may be infected. The bacteria are carried from one tree to another by pollinating insects, such as bees, by rain, and by man. Control is difficult, although it may be accomplished to some extent by pruning away all diseased parts as rapidly as they appear. A dilute spray of Bordeaux mixture (copper sulfate and lime) at blossomtime sometimes helps. One of the most promising control measures is the development, by plant breeders, of trees that are resistant to *Erwinia amylovora*.

Summary of Bacteria

1. Most bacteria are small one-celled plants ranging in size from 1/50,000 inch to 1/5000 inch in length.

2. The small size of bacteria is an important factor in their physiological activities. It results in a ratio of surface to volume which is enormous; the surface possessed by the bacteria that could be packed into a cube 1 inch on edge is about 300 square yards in contrast to the 6 square inches of surface possessed by a solid cube of similar size. All food, poisons, wastes, and raw materials must diffuse in and out of the bacterial cell. Because of the large surface area the total exchange of substances is rapid.

3. Bacteria possess a slime layer, cell wall, and protoplasm. Nuclei have been observed in many bacterial cells, and nucleic acids have been found in all forms examined. The protoplast is comprised of cytoplasm, vacuoles, and ergastic substances.

4. Bacteria multiply by fission.

5. Evidences of a sexual fusion have recently been found.

6. Some bacteria produce spores that enable them to survive extremely unfavorable conditions.

7. Most bacteria are heterotrophic; a few are autotrophic.

8. Bacteria obtain energy from oxidation of inorganic salts, from the breakdown of organic substances in the absence of oxygen (anaerobic), from organic substances in the presence of oxygen (aerobic), and from light.

9. Bacteria obtain their nitrogen from living organisms, from dead organic matter, from ammonium salts, from nitrites and nitrates, and from free nitrogen of the air.

10. Bacteria are very important agents in maintaining soil fertility. They play an important part in the removal of organic wastes from the earth and in returning nitrogen to the soil.

11. Bacteria are important agents in causing plant and animal diseases.

CLASS SCHIZOPHYCEAE— BLUE-GREEN ALGAE

General Characteristics and Distribution

All the algae belonging to this class, whether unicellular or filamentous, are usually composed of small cells. Even upon examination under the most powerful microscope the cells are difficult to describe accurately. Frequently in both unicellular and filamentous species the cells remain associated, surrounded by a gelatinous matrix, to form colonies of definite shapes. Many of these colonies are spherical; some are fan-shaped.

The Schizophyceae are widely distributed in and on soil, on rocks, trees, and leaves, in fresh and salt water, in hot springs, and on snow. They may be associated with fungi and even with higher plants.

Some members of the Schizophyceae play an important part in maintaining the fertility of the soil, and a few are able to fix atmospheric nitrogen. Evidence indicates that, when some species are growing in locations inhabited by nitrogen-fixing bacteria, the rate of nitrogen fixation is increased.

Other species of Schizophyceae grow readily on freshly eroded soil. They tend to protect the soil against further erosion and to increase its fertility so that other plants may gain a foothold.

Structure of Blue-green Algae

The protoplasts of the Schizophyceae do not contain true chromoplasts, nuclei, or vacuoles. The living protoplast is divided into two regions: (1) an outer region, the **chromoplasm,** which is colored and contains pigments some of which are found in the plastids in higher plants, and (2) a colorless central region known as the **central body** (Fig. 17.16A, C, D).

The pigments of the chromoplasm comprise chlorophyll *a*, four different carotenoids several kinds of phycocyanin, and phycoerythrin. Phycocyanin is blue, phycoerythrin is red, and both are water-soluble, whereas the chlorophyll and carotenoids are fat-soluble. Phycocyanin and chlorophyll are responsible for the general blue-green color of most blue-green algae. The range of colors is due to varying amounts of the different pigments in the chromoplasm. Still other pigments may occur in the gelatinous sheaths surrounding the cells.

Glycogen is thought by some investigators to be the first visible product of photosynthesis in Schizophyceae; by others, the first product is thought to be a compound composed of glycogen and a protein.

Although the central body has been extensively studied, there is, as yet, no agreement as to its structure or its function. Perhaps the majority of students of blue-green algae believe that it is nuclear in nature; it stains, in killed cells, with nuclear dyes and assumes shapes that suggest, but

by no means confirm, the occurrence of mitosis (Fig. 17.16B, E, F). Positive cytological tests for nucleic acids within the cell have been obtained, and various components of a nucleic acid have been isolated from one species of blue-green algae. A nucleolus and a nuclear membrane, however, have not been identified. Some investigators claim that reserve food materials are located in the central body and that it, therefore, cannot be compared with the nuclei of other plants.

The cell wall is composed of cellulose, pectin, and hemicellulose, substances found in the walls of higher plants. The gelatinous sheath surrounding most blue-green algae is composed of pectin or of pectinlike compounds.

Reproduction of Blue-green Algae

The single-celled forms reproduce vegetatively by cell division (Fig. 17.16A, B, C). Filamentous species theoretically could grow to unlimited lengths. Actually, the filaments break before they reach a great length. They may break because of some simple mechanical stress caused by animals or water currents, because of cell deaths that weaken the filament, or because of a weakness that develops between certain cells of many species (Fig. 17.16F). The fragments of filaments so formed are called **hormogonia.**

No motile spores or gametes have ever been observed among the Schizophyceae. Most of the filamentous species have certain cells that develop into characteristic nonmotile thick-walled spores. These spores tide the alga over unfavorable periods. All the filamentous Schizophyceae, except the Oscillatoriaceae, regularly produce a special type of cell known as a **heterocyst** (Fig. 17.16D). Heterocysts develop from ordinary vegetative cells and

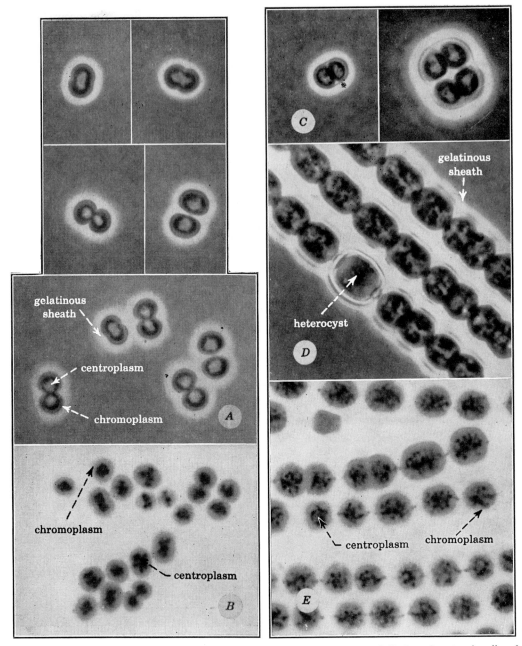

Fig. 17.16. Blue-green algae. A, living cells of *Synechococcus*; B, killed and stained cells of *Synechococcus*; C, living cells of *Chroococcus*; D, living cells of *Nostoc*; E, killed and stained cells of *Nostoc*; F, killed and stained cells of *Micrococcus*; G, killed and stained cells of *Oscillatoria*. ×800. (A to F courtesy of Cassel; G courtesy of Norris.)

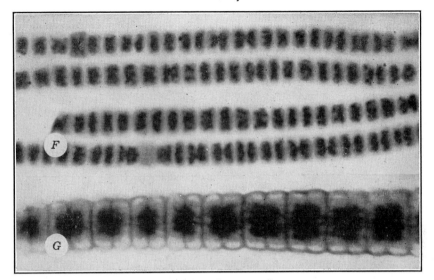

Fig. 17.16 (continued).

are sporelike in nature. They are probably reproductive structures which have become functionless, except for a few forms under exceptional conditions; they may germinate. In many species these heterocysts are associated with the breaking of the filaments or with the development of the characteristic nonmotile spores.

Oscillatoria is perhaps the most widely spread and easily obtainable blue-green alga. It forms a dark green mat on moist soil that is protected from direct sunlight. *Oscillatoria* is a filamentous form comprised of many discoid cells (Fig. 17.16G). When mounted in a drop of water on a slide, the filaments show a slow oscillating movement that has suggested the name *Oscillatoria*.

Another common blue-green alga is *Nostoc*. This is also filamentous but with distinctly spherical cells, giving the plant the appearance of a string of beads (Fig. 17.16D, E). The filaments are held together in colonies by a gelatinous matrix. The colonies are usually spherical and may become as large as a plum. They occur both on land and in water.

SUMMARY

1. The Schizophyta comprise a group of plants small in size, either single-celled or forming simple filaments or colonies. Practically all members of the group secrete a gelatinous slime layer about themselves. Chitin and cellulose may be present in cell walls.

2. All members of the group divide by fission and have obscure nuclear details. Sexual fusion if it occurs at all is rare.

3. Types of metabolism are varied: There are autotrophs, heterotrophs, parasites, saprophytes; some bacteria carry on photosynthesis, while a few blue-green algae are parasites. Some cannot respire without atmospheric oxygen, others cannot live in its presence, many are able to sur-

vive under either condition. Some bacteria obtain energy from one inorganic salt and carbon for organic synthesis from another inorganic compound.

4. Various kinds of pigments occur.

5. Maintenance of soil fertility, ridding the earth of waste organic products, and being the causal agents of disease are among the important activities of members of this phylum.

Classification

Phylum	**Schizophyta**
Class	Schizomycetes
Order	Eubacteriales
Genera and species	*Streptococcus*
	Staphylococcus
	Sarcina
	Escherichia coli
	Rhizobium leguminosarum
	Azotobacter
	Clostridium botulinum
	Clostridium tetani
	Nitrobacter
	Nitrosomonas
Class	Schizophyceae
Genera	*Oscillatoria*
	Synechococcus
	Chroococcus
	Nostoc

18

The Algae

CHLOROPHYCOPHYTA

CHRYSOPHYCOPHYTA

PHAEOPHYCOPHYTA

RHODOPHYCOPHYTA

DISTRIBUTION AND GENERAL CHARACTERISTICS

Algae are common in most semipermanent pools, in ponds, lakes, and streams, along ocean shore lines, and in the surface waters of oceans. Since water absorbs light which is necessary for photosynthesis, they do not grow at depths greater than several hundred feet.

Aquatic algae may be either free-floating or attached to rocks, logs, or other submerged objects. The small free-floating algae are referred to as **phytoplankton.** The term **plankton** is a collective name for all free-floating aquatic animals and plants. Some aquatic algae grow attached to or within larger plants, either algae or flowering plants. Frequently the association is specific, certain species always being found growing together.

The number of individual algal plants present in the phytoplankton of both salt and fresh water is enormous. It has been estimated, for instance, that the population of single-celled algae growing in the waters of Lake Waubesa, near Madison, Wis., would give an annual yield of 2592 pounds per acre of dry organic matter, or 25,920 pounds per acre of wet organic matter.

The plankton of these lakes is a major source of food for fishes. The annual production of fish from such a lake as Lake Waubesa compares favorably with the beef production of pasture land. For example, in 1939, Lake Waubesa yielded 550 pounds of fish per acre, whereas it requires excellent pasture to produce 200 to 300 pounds of beef per acre per year.

Most algae are **autotrophic plants;** that is, they contain chlorophyll (page 325), which is capable of absorbing the energy of sunlight, thus making the synthesis of carbohydrates possible. There are a few heterotrophic algae, most of which are saprophytic, although there are a few parasites.

The smallest algae are about the size of the larger bacteria; the largest (kelps) compare favorably with some of the larger vines. In these larger forms considerable cellular differentiation may occur. They possess, however, no special supporting or water-conducting tissues.

THE CLASSIFICATION OF ALGAE

Separation into phyla is based largely upon the pigments found in the plastids, upon food reserves, and upon the types of reproduction. We shall consider four of the seven phyla of algae (page 36).

Phylum III. Chlorophycophyta (green algal plants): Plastids grass green, containing chlorophyll *a* and *b* and some of the carotenoids found in the higher plants. Both unicellular and multicellular forms.

Phylum V. Chrysophycophyta (golden algal plants): Plastids yellow, yellow green, or golden brown, containing chlorophylls *a* and *c*, and various carotenoids. Many species are unicellular, the cell wall being impregnated with silica, characteristic of the diatoms. Others are filamentous or colonial similar to the green algae.

Phylum VII. Phaeophycophyta (brown algal plants): Plastids brown, containing the chlorophylls *a* and *c*, carotenoids, and a pigment called fucoxanthin. Multicellular.

Phylum VIII. Rhodophycophyta (red algal plants): Plastids red, containing the chlorophylls *a* and *d*; a red water-soluble pigment, phycoerythrin; and a blue water-soluble pigment, phycocyanin. Multicellular except in members of two genera. No flagellated cells are present.

REPRODUCTION OF ALGAE

We have seen in our discussion of the flower (page 251) that a sexual life cycle combines two complementary phenomena:

(1) In the formation of both pollen grains and the embryo sac, the chromosome number is halved. For example, the nuclei in the vegetative cells of lily, including the spore mother cells, contain 24 chromosomes. The nuclei of pollen grains and of the embryo sac, as a result of meiosis, contain but 12 chromosomes. (2) In fertilization, the egg and sperm, each with 12 chromosomes, unite to form a zygote that again has 24 chromosomes. A zygote is the protoplast resulting from the union of two gametes.

A complete typical sexual life cycle as it occurs in any plant is exemplified diagrammatically in Fig. 18.1. In all plants that reproduce sexually, including algae, a similar situation exists. The chromosome numbers are halved during meiosis and doubled during fertilization.

The importance of this process to plant life in general and to agriculture in particular was discussed in some detail in Chapter 14. Normally, sexual reproduction gives two principal results: (1) it perpetuates the species—individual follows individual—and (2) it brings about a variation in the individual members of the species.

Sexual Reproduction

The great majority of algae, and fungi as well, may reproduce sexually. In general, the sexual life cycles of all these

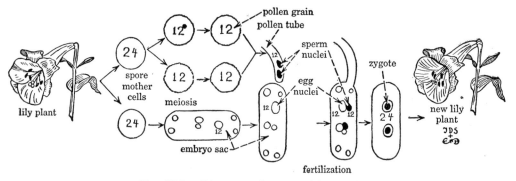

Fig. 18.1. Diagram of a sexual life cycle.

plants are basically similar. Only details differ. Before undertaking a description of the reproductive structures of the thallophyte phyla some definitions of terms will prove helpful.

The thallophytes do not form pollen, as do the flowering plants (Chapter 12). Spores, however, are formed as a result of meiosis. It is sometimes convenient to refer to these spores as **meiospores**. A **spore** may be defined as a cell, which, regardless of its method of formation, is able to give rise ultimately to a new plant without any preceding fusion. Meiospores are thus haploid cells, arising as a result of meiosis, which are capable of originating new haploid plants.

In sexual reproduction the two cells that fuse are known as **gametes**. The resulting protoplast is called a **zygote**.

$$\text{Gamete} + \text{gamete} \rightarrow \textbf{zygote}$$

If the gametes are *identical in appearance* they are known as **isogametes**. The union of isogametes is called **conjugation**. The zygote may germinate directly or develop into a **resistant spore** frequently called a **zygospore**. This type of sexual reproduction is called **isogamy** (Fig. 18.2*F*).

Usually the gametes differ from each other to a greater or lesser degree. Sexual reproduction involving *dissimilar gametes* is known as **heterogamy**. In a special, though common, type of heterogamy one gamete is large and nonmotile, whereas the other is small and motile. The larger gamete is called an **egg,** the smaller one a **sperm.** The union of a sperm and egg is known as **fertilization.** In some thallophytes the zygote may develop into a resistant spore, an **oospore;** in others, the zygote may develop directly into a new plant or into an embryo. This special type of heterogamy, involving egg and sperm, is called **oogamy** (Fig. 18.2*G*).

A. Conjugation (isogamy)

$$\text{Isogamete} + \text{isogamete} \rightarrow \textbf{zygote} \underset{\searrow}{\overset{\nearrow}{}} \begin{array}{l}\textbf{new plant} \text{ or} \\ \\ \textbf{zygospore}\end{array}$$

B. Fertilization (heterogamy)

$$\text{Egg} + \text{sperm} \rightarrow \textbf{zygote} \rightarrow \begin{array}{l}\textbf{new plant} \text{ or} \\ \textbf{embryo} \text{ or} \\ \textbf{oospore}\end{array}$$

Gametes are formed in structures called **gametangia** (Fig. 18.2*F*) (singular, **gametangium**). The male gametangium is called an **antheridium,** the egg-producing gametangium an **oogonium** (plural, **antheridia** and **oogonia**) (Fig. 18.2*G*).

Asexual Reproduction

Many thallophytes are able to reproduce **vegetatively,** or **asexually** (*a* = without; thus, asexually means *without sex*). Neither cell fusions nor changes in chromosome number are involved in asexual reproduction.

In general, there are three methods of asexual reproduction:

1. The thallus, or plant body, may simply break apart, each piece growing into a new plant. This method is called **fragmentation.**

2. Asexual spores of various types may be formed. These spores differ from meiospores in that they involve no change in chromosome numbers. The spores contain the same number of chromosomes in each nucleus as do the nuclei of the plant that produces them (Fig. 18.2*B, C, D*); consequently, no variation results. There are a large number of different kinds of asexual spores. In the algae many of these spores are motile and are called **zoospores** (Fig. 18.2*B*); others are **nonmotile spores.**

3. In single-celled thallophytes, reproduction frequently results from the division of the one-celled plant (Fig. 18.2*A*).

Both sexual and asexual reproduction are devices for propagating a species of plant.

They differ in that the individuals formed as a result of asexual reproduction are *identical* with each other and with the parent plant, whereas the individuals resulting from a sexual life history are likely to *differ* from each other and from the parent plants. For instance, cuttings or buds of a Hale peach tree will produce more Hale peach trees. It is, in fact, impossible to obtain Hale peach trees in any other way. If seeds of Hale peach trees are planted (seeds, it must be remembered, are structures in a sexual life cycle), the resulting peach trees will vary greatly.

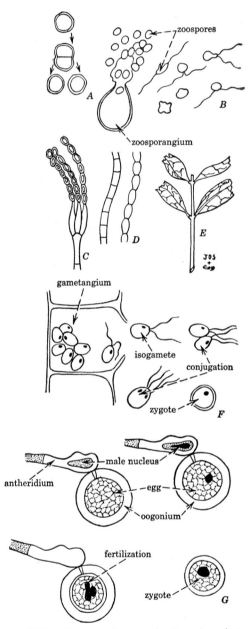

Fig. 18.2. Types of reproduction found in various plant phyla. A, cell division; B, zoospores; C, conidiospores; D, chlamydospores; E, cuttings; F, isogamy; G, heterogamy.

PHYLUM III. CHLORO-PHYCOPHYTA

DISTRIBUTION AND GENERAL CHARACTERISTICS

The Chlorophycophyta (green algal plants) are largely fresh-water forms. They are very abundant and widespread, growing well in most permanent or semi-permanent pools, in shallow running water, and on moist shaded soil. They are mostly of a grass-green color. The pigments in their chloroplasts, chlorophyll *a* and *b*, and the various carotenoids, are found also in the chloroplasts of the higher plants and in the same ratios. The chloroplasts of the green algae exhibit a great variety of shapes. They may be netlike, ellipsoidal, platelike, lobed, star-shaped, or spiral. Genera and even families may be distinguished by the shape of the chloroplast. In some plants the form of the chloroplast has suggested the generic name. For instance, certain green algae containing spiral chloroplasts belong to the genus *Spirogyra* (Fig. 18.7).

Starch is the reserve food of most species of Chlorophycophyta, although a few store oil.

In many species, proteinaceous bodies. the **pyrenoids**, may be observed embedded in the chloroplasts (Fig. 18.7). There is evidence that these structures are intimately associated with the elaboration of starch.

Vacuoles are present in the cells of most species. They are frequently crossed by delicate strands of cytoplasm. The cell wall is composed of cellulose. The nuclei are similar to those found in higher plants, and, usually, each cell contains a single nucleus. In some groups the cells are multinucleate.

Single-celled Chlorophycophyta are common. In some species the single cells are associated in colonies. Many species are characterized by filaments consisting of single cells joined end to end. In one order, the thallus comprises a filament several cells in diameter, and in a few genera a simple blade, one to a few cells in thickness, forms the thallus.

There are several thousand species of green algae. We shall describe representatives of the following six genera: *Pleurococcus, Chlorella, Chlamydomonas, Spirogyra, Ulothrix,* and *Cladophora.* With the possible exception of *Chlorella,* all may be easily collected within short distances of many botanical laboratories. Their characteristics are so distinctive that they may be readily recognized. Furthermore, they illustrate the form and activities of much larger groups.

Pleurococcus

This form is widely distributed, occurring abundantly in many moist, shady locations. It is a terrestrial genus, growing on tree trunks, on rocks, and on fence posts. Its preference for shade and moisture frequently results in a greater growth on the north side of these objects than on the south side.

Pleurococcus is usually regarded as a unicellular plant. Colonies of 2 to 8 cells, however, are not uncommon. Under certain conditions colonies of 50 or more cells

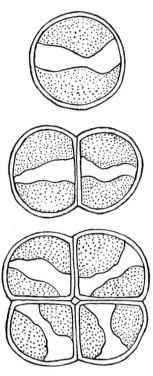

Fig. 18.3.   *Pleurococcus.*

may occur, and in these colonies irregular filaments may be observed. Solitary cells of *Pleurococcus* are spherical or ellipsoidal. They have a fairly thick wall with no outer gelatinous sheath. When in colonies, the mutual faces of adjacent cells are flat. Each cell possesses a single nucleus and but one chloroplast, which may have a lobed margin. The only method of reproduction is simple cell division (Fig. 18.3).

It is believed that *Pleurococcus* is not truly primitive but has been derived from a more complex form.

Chlorella

This is another single-celled genus. It has been employed extensively in studies on photosynthesis and respiration. Much of our present knowledge of the elaboration of carbohydrates has been obtained from

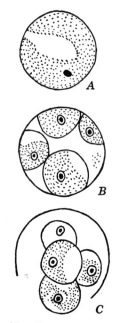

Fig. 18.4. *Chlorella.* A, vegetative; B, four new cells; C, release of four new cells.

merous species varying structurally in details from one another. They may occur in such large numbers in shallow pools and still water that they color the water. They are also abundant in soils. *Chlamydomonas* grows well under laboratory conditions and experiments with it have yielded information on the chemistry of fertilization. It has been found, for instance, that light coupled with what appears to be a nitrogen-carbohydrate relationship is an important factor in stimulating gamete formation. The similarity of this to the stimulation of flowering in higher plants makes it seem possible that new knowledge concerning sexual reproduction in these algae may provide information of significance that will be useful in work on the higher plants.

The details of structure of the *Chlamydomonas* cell vary somewhat from species to species. Vegetative individuals of most species are pear-shaped and have a cup-shaped chloroplast which, again depending upon the species, may have one or two pyrenoids, or may even lack the pyrenoid. There are two flagella at the narrow anterior end. Each individual is provided with a red **eye-spot** which may be located in

this alga. It may well be that from *Chlorella* we shall learn the secret of combining water and carbon dioxide to form sugar.

Chlorella contains a single U-shaped chloroplast that lies adjacent to the cell wall. If the cell under observation is oriented correctly, the shape of the chloroplast and its location within the cell may be distinctly seen.

Reproduction. The protoplast of each *Chlorella* cell gives rise to 2, 4, 8, or 16 spores, which are released by the disintegration of the wall of the mother cell. They may remain attached to each other for some time. Each of these spores enlarges directly into a mature cell, which in its turn gives rise to additional spores (Fig. 18.4). Thus, *Chlorella* reproduces asexually.

Chlamydomonas

Chlamydomonas is a very common single-celled motile alga. There are nu-

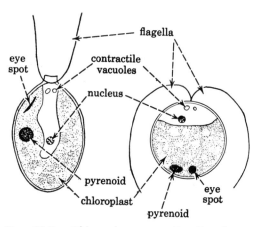

Fig. 18.5. *Chlamydomonas.* Details of two different species. (Redrawn after Moewus.)

various positions within the cell. Carotenoid pigments are responsible for the red color of the eye-spot which appears to function as a light sensitive organ. There are two vacuoles located at the anterior end of the cell just below the flagella. Because of their pulsating motion they are thought to be **contractile vacuoles** and to function in excretion. These details are shown in Fig. 18.5.

Reproduction. After a period of motility, it is normal for *Chlamydomonas* individuals to divide, generally becoming nonmotile as they do so. In most cases the protoplast divides twice forming four new cells within the old cell wall. A third division may sometimes occur giving rise to eight daughter cells. At this stage the old cell wall splits open or breaks down, releasing the new daughter cells that have now developed cellulose walls and flagella of their own. This phase of mitotic division or

asexual reproduction may go on indefinitely (Fig. 18.6), providing nutritional requirements are satisfied. Certain specific changes in these requirements, that appear to involve nitrogen balance, stimulate the daughter cells to act as gametes. This must involve at least two changes in their metabolism; (1) a block forms that halts their development into mature individuals, and (2) the formation of some stimulus that results in the fusion of two individuals. Depending upon the species, the gametes may be identical in appearance to the vegetative cells or they may be somewhat smaller because of a third, fourth, or even fifth division before the daughter cells are released from the parent envelope. The gametes of most species are alike morphologically and are therefore isogametes, sexual reproduction being isogamous. Varying degrees of heterogamy do occur in the group. In most species the zygotes are nonmotile and de-

green

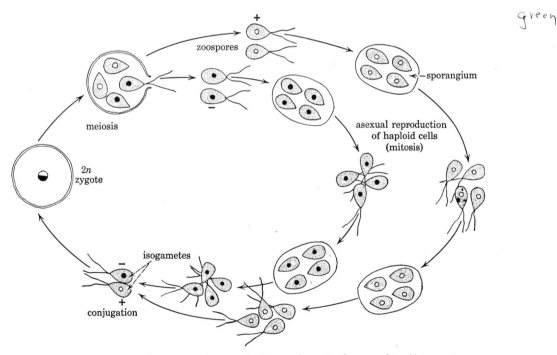

Fig. 18.6. *Chlamydomonas*. Stages in life cycle. (Redrawn after Moewus.)

velop into resistant spores able to survive unfavorable growth conditions. With the return of conditions favorable to growth the spore germinates, usually into four, sometimes into eight, motile daughter cells. The best available evidence indicates that the resistant spore is the only diploid cell in this life cycle and that meiosis occurs in its germination.

These details are shown in Fig. 18.6. Note that while only one cycle is shown it involves periods of asexual reproduction as well as the sexual stages of conjugation and meiosis. The life cycles of the great

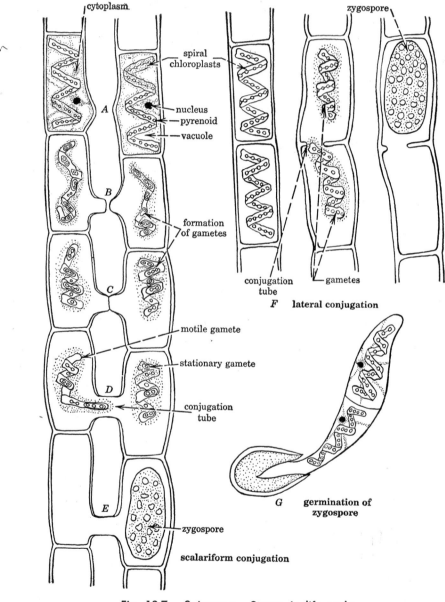

Fig. 18.7.   *Spirogyra.*   Stages in life cycle.

majority of plants are similar in that they may be comprised of asexual and sexual phases. The asexual phase generally serves, as in this case, to propagate the species when conditions are favorable for growth, while the sexual phase is usually associated with conditions unfavorable for growth. The two phases of reproduction may be drawn separately rather than in one continuous cycle, and they are of varying degrees of predominance and importance in different plants throughout the plant kingdom.

The great similarity of the gametes, to both mature and young motile individuals has suggested that sex may have originated in some algal genus similar to *Chlamydomonas*. The origin of sex, however, involves the dual and sudden appearance of both the fusion of gametes and meiosis and there is little information on the nuclear phenomena in this genus.

Spirogyra

This alga is usually found free-floating in fresh-water pools. It is a filamentous form, its filaments, and those of related genera, being slippery to the touch because of a mucilaginous sheath. The chloroplasts form distinct spirals within the cells, which may be compared to glass cylinders with lengths of green tape wound spirally within them. Each cell may contain one or more chloroplasts and also pyrenoids, which are distributed regularly along the chloroplasts. The nucleus is frequently suspended in the central vacuole of the cell by strands of cytoplasm (Fig. 18.7).

Asexual Reproduction. The filaments of *Spirogyra* increase in length by ordinary cell division. Asexual reproduction occurs by the fragmentation of the filaments, a process that may be induced in two different ways: (1) simple external mechan-

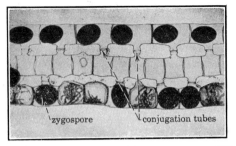

Fig. 18.8. *Spirogyra.* Zygospores. ×300. (Photo courtesy of Triarch Products.)

ical stresses are caused by water currents or aquatic animals, or (2) adjacent cells may disjoin because a gelatinous material is secreted between them.

Sexual Reproduction. This process occurs at definite periods during the growing season. The onset of sexual reproduction is indicated by the appearance of small protuberances on cells of adjacent filaments (Fig. 18.7A). The protuberances, or bumps, enlarge and push the filaments apart (Fig. 18.7B, C). At the point of contact the cell walls dissolve and a tubular connection, the **conjugation tube,** is formed between the two filaments (Fig. 18.7C, D).

While the conjugation tube is forming, the protoplasts condense. The entire protoplasmic contents of a cell constitute one gamete. In many species the gametes of only one of the two conjugating filaments are motile. The gametes do not possess flagella or cilia, but they have an amoeboid motion. The motile gametes leave the cells of the parent filament and move through the conjugating tubes into the cells of the adjacent filament (Fig. 18.7D, E).

The zygotes (Fig. 18.8) formed by the conjugation of these amoeboid gametes develop heavy walls and become resting zygospores. Meiosis takes place during their germination. Usually 3 of the 4 nuclei resulting from meiosis degenerate and but one plant is produced by a zygospore (Fig. 18.7G). Conjugation of protoplasts of adjacent cells of the same filament is characteristic of a few species (Fig. 18.7F).

Ulothrix

Another widely distributed aquatic filamentous green alga is *Ulothrix*. The cells forming the filaments are cylindrical, their length and diameter being approximately equal. The chloroplasts are parietal, forming curved plates extending from ½ to ¾ of the way around the cell. There is a single chloroplast in each cell. The basal cell of the filament is adapted as a **holdfast**

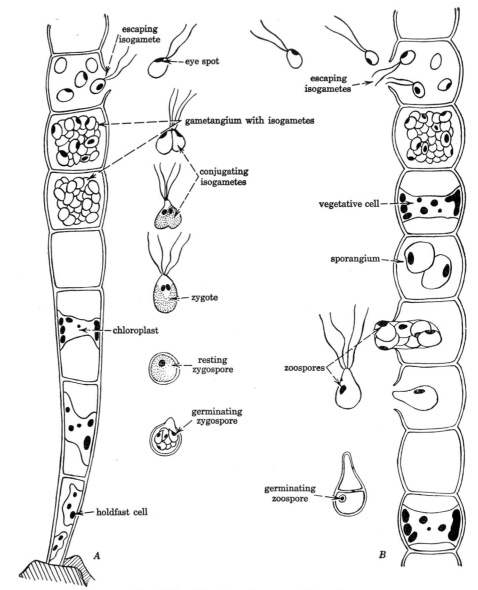

Fig. 18.9. *Ulothrix*. Stages in life cycle.

cell, by which the plant attaches itself to some solid object (Fig. 18.9).

Reproduction. Both motile asexual spores (zoospores) and motile isogametes are borne by *Ulothrix*. They are formed in cells that are not morphologically differentiated from each other or from the normal vegetative cells of the filament. Each sporangium produces from 2 to 32 two- or four-flagellated zoospores. They are pear-shaped and have a colored eye-spot, which is light sensitive. After swimming about for some time they settle down, and under favorable conditions each grows into a new filament (Fig. 18.9*B*). These cells are reminiscent of *Chlamydomonas*.

From 8 to 64 biflagellated isogametes are produced in each gametangium. Isogametes from *different filaments* (Fig. 18.9*A*,

B) fuse to form a zygote that soon rounds off to form a thick-walled zygospore. After a rest period it germinates, forming from 4 to 16 zoospores. These zoospores grow directly into new filaments. Meiosis occurs during the germination of the zygospore.

Cladophora

Species of *Cladophora* consist of branching, septate filaments. The cells of the filaments are multinucleate and contain numerous small, or one reticulate, chloroplast (stippled in Fig. 18.10*A*). *Cladophora* is an unusual genus in its very wide distribution in both fresh and salt waters. Its filaments are attached to the substratum by fairly long rhizoidal branches. Many species are perennial; the green filaments die

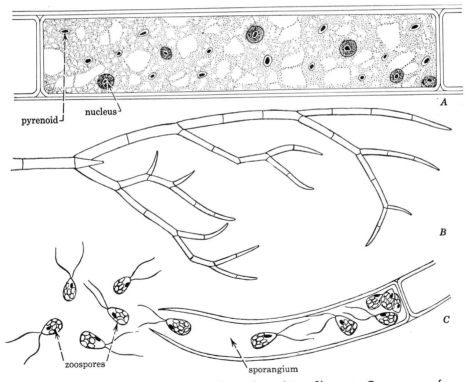

Fig. 18.10. *Cladophora.* A, detail of cell; B, branching filament; C, zoospore formation. (A after Czempycek.)

at the end of the growing season, but the prostrate rhizoidal system remains alive. Its cells are filled with reserve materials, and upon the return of favorable growing conditions certain rhizoidal cells give rise to new erect green filaments.

Alternation of Generations. A definite **alternation of generations** occurs in some species of *Cladophora*. This means that plants with a 2n number of chromosomes alternate with plants having an n number of chromosomes. It will be recalled that meiosis occurs in the 2n plant, resulting in meiospores, and that the n plant produces gametes. It is thus seen that alternation of generations means that a spore-producing generation alternates with a gamete-producing generation.

The 2n plant is frequently referred to as the **diploid plant,** or the diploid generation, or diploid phase; the n plant as the **haploid plant** or generation or phase.

In *Cladophora* the two generations (n and 2n) are indistinguishable morphologically. Both possess filaments composed of multinucleate cells that contain similar types of chloroplasts and dense cytoplasm.

Zoospores (meiospores) are produced in

within their cells contain the haploid number of chromosomes. This haploid filament produces isogametes. The gametangia are vigorously growing cells near the tips of branches. The haploid isogametes fuse to form a zygote. A new diploid filament develops from this zygote.

Life cycles may be abbreviated or diagrammed in a number of ways. It may be done by simple drawings as in Fig. 18.6 for *Chlamydomonas*, or simply in words, as is done for *Cladophora* below. In this diagram the **diploid** or 2n stage of the cycle is shown by **bold face** type and the two chromosome sets are designated by (2n). The haploid phase is designated by (n), one set of chromosomes, and the names of various structures are shown in light face type. Meiosis will occur with the change from the **diploid** (2n) to the haploid (n) condition; fertilization will always be indicated by the union of gametes (n) to form the zygote (2n). No effort will be made to indicate the monoecious or dioecious condition, except for some of the higher forms that have definite male and female gamete-producing plants. The life cycle described above for *Cladophora* may be represented as follows:

$$\textbf{Plant (2n)} \rightarrow \text{zoospores } (n) \rightarrow \text{plant } (n) \quad \begin{array}{c} \nearrow \text{gamete } (n) \searrow \\ \\ \searrow \text{gamete } (n) \nearrow \end{array} \quad \text{zygote (2n)} \rightarrow \textbf{plant (2n)}$$

vigorously growing cells near the tips of branches of the diploid plants (Fig. 18.10). Meiosis occurs in their formation; the zoospores contain but half as many chromosomes in each nucleus as did the cells of the filament that bore them. Hence, the original filament is diploid, the zoospores haploid. Upon germination the zoospores give rise to filaments similar in appearance to the diploid filaments except that the nuclei

In one species of *Cladophora* reduction division does not occur in the development of the zoospores. The zoospores develop at intervals during the year and are diploid like the plant that produces them. They are true asexual spores. In this species, meiosis occurs in the development of isogametes, which are consequently haploid. The zygote formed upon conjugation is diploid so that the haploid generation is represented only by the isogametes. This life cycle may be diagrammed as shown:

Thus two types of life cycles occur in different species of the genus *Cladophora*.

gamete (n)

Plant ($2n$) → zoospores ($2n$) → plant ($2n$)   zygote ($2n$) → plant ($2n$)

gamete (n)

SUMMARY OF METHODS OF REPRODUCTION IN GREEN ALGAE

Asexual Reproduction

1. *Pleurococcus.* Plant–plant–plant.
2. *Chlorella.* Spore formation: plant–spores–plant–spores.
3. *Chlamydomonas* and *Ulothrix.* Plant (n)–zoospores (n)–plant (n)
4. **Cladophora. Plant ($2n$)–zoospores ($2n$)–plant ($2n$)**
5. *Spirogyra.* By fragmentation of the filament: plant–plant–plant.

Sexual Reproduction

1. *Spirogyra.* Motile amoeboid isogametes; formation of a conjugation tube.

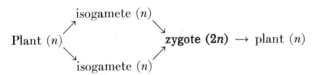

isogamete (n)

Plant (n)   zygote ($2n$) → plant (n)

isogamete (n)

2. *Chlamydomonas* and *Ulothrix.* Motile, free-swimming isogametes.

isogamete (n)

Plant (n)   zygote ($2n$) → plant (n)

isogamete (n)

3. *Cladophora.* (*a*) Free-swimming isogametes. Meiosis precedes gamete formation.

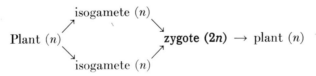

isogamete (n)

Plant ($2n$)   zygote ($2n$) → plant ($2n$)

isogamete (n)

(*b*) Alternation of a diploid spore-bearing plant with a haploid gamete-bearing plant.

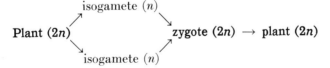

isogamete (n)

Plant ($2n$) → zoospores (n) → plant (n)   zygote ($2n$) → plant ($2n$)

isogamete (n)

PHYLUM V. CHRYSOPHY-COPHYTA

The plants of this phylum are characterized by a golden to golden brown or yellow-ish green appearance. This is caused by a preponderance of certain carotenes and xanthophylls in their plastids. Apparently all species contain chlorophyll *a* but chlorophyll *b* is absent. Other types of chlorophylls are, however, present in some of them. The great majority of forms are unicellular or united in colonies of varying shapes. Some are motile. A few genera are filamentous. Starch is never stored as a food reserve; oils occur frequently, perhaps generally. Many contain a whitish insoluble material, of unknown nature, thought to be a food reserve. Nuclei are very small but apparently fairly typical. Fresh water forms predominate and some genera have a close resemblance to certain green algae.

As a group they present problems in classification and the present arrangement may not be permanent. We shall consider, (1) the genus, *Vaucheria* of the class Xanthophyceae and, (2) the class Bacillarieae, the diatoms.

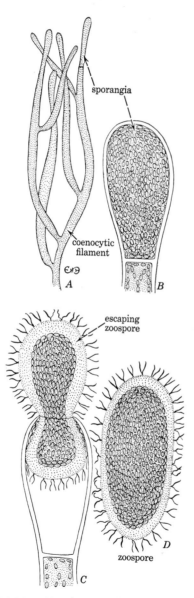

Fig. 18.11. *Vaucheria.* A, coenocytic filament; B, C, D, zoospore formation. (Redrawn from Smith, *Cryptogamic Botany*, Vol. 1, McGraw-Hill Book Co.)

Vaucheria

Vaucheria, and others of the order to which it belongs, are **coenocytic:** that is, the plant body is without crosswalls and multinucleate (Figs. 18.11A, 18.13). All species of *Vaucheria* are filamentous and may show considerable specialization. The filaments of *Vaucheria* and of other related species branch either sparingly or profusely. Many small chloroplasts are embedded in the cytoplasm that surrounds a central vacuole. Oil, rather than starch, is normally found as the reserve food material.

Species of *Vaucheria* are widespread and abundant. Most of them grow in fresh water, but some are terrestrial, forming extensive green felt mats on moist soil.

Asexual Reproduction. This type of reproduction may occur in any one of three different ways, depending upon the habitat: (1) Zoospores develop in all aquatic species. A sporangium is formed by the formation of a cross wall near the end of a side branch. The protoplast in this cell becomes a large multinucleate zoospore bearing numerous cilia (Fig. 18.11). (2) In species growing on moist soil, asexual nonciliate spores may be formed in a manner similar to that described above. (3) The coenocytic protoplasts of other terrestrial species may divide into numerous segments, around which heavy walls are secreted, forming asexual resting spores.

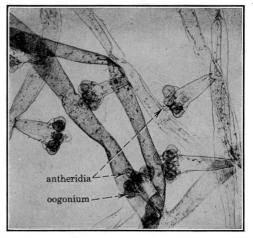

Fig. 18.13. *Vaucheria.* Gametangia. ✕100. (Courtesy of Triarch Products.)

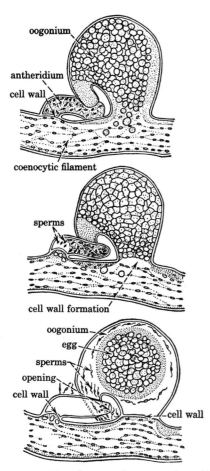

Fig. 18.12. *Vaucheria.* Gametangia. (After Couch.)

Sexual Reproduction. All species of *Vaucheria* reproduce sexually by heterogametes. The gametangia are developed on short side branches or as direct outgrowths of the main filament (Figs. 18.12, 18.13). The antheridium may be a hook-shaped structure located at the end of a slender branch and separated by a cross wall from the coenocytic filament (Figs. 18.12, 18.13). Many sperms are formed within each antheridium. The oogonium is an oval body with its base resting on the main filament (Fig. 18.12) or on a short side branch (Fig. 18.13). At first it contains many nuclei. As it matures all nuclei but one migrate into the vegetative filament. A cross wall at its base finally separates the mature oogonium from the coenocytic filament. A single egg, containing but one nucleus, develops in each oogonium.

The sperms are ejected from the antheridia and enter the oogonia through a pore (Fig. 18.12). Fertilization results from the fusion of a nucleus of a single sperm with the egg nucleus. The zygote develops into a resistant oospore. After a period of rest of several months, the oospore germinates directly into a new filament. Present evidence indicates that a reduction division occurs in the germination of the oospore.

Class Bacillarieae

General Characteristics and Distribution. The Bacillarieae are commonly known as the **diatoms.** The diatom cell possesses a nucleus, cytoplasm, vacuoles,

and chromoplasts. The chromoplasts, with few exceptions, are a deep golden brown. Chlorophyll *a* and *c*, fucoxanthin, and carotenoids are present. The cell wall is composed mainly of pectin impregnated with silica. The silica impregnation is very regular and forms markings characteristic of the species. In fresh-water forms, these markings may be very delicate and beau-

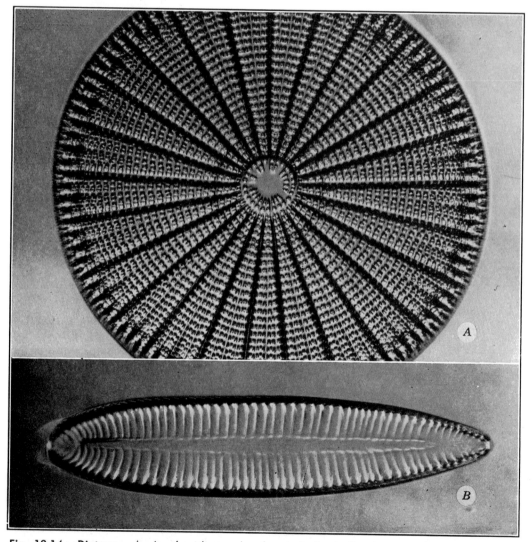

Fig. 18.14. Diatoms. A, *Arachnoidiscus ehrenbergi*; B, *Surirella elegans*. (Courtesy of General Biological Supply House.)

tiful (Fig. 18.14). The wall is formed of two halves that fit together like the two halves of a box or a glass petri dish (Fig. 18.16).

Diatoms are present in large numbers in almost all types of water: salt, brackish, and fresh. In spite of their almost universal distribution as a group, individual species are limited to rather narrow environmental conditions. Free-floating diatoms of the open oceans are of great importance to the deep-sea animal life since, in the last analysis, such life is dependent upon diatoms and other small algal forms for food.

An accumulation on the ocean floor of the siliceous cell walls of diatoms has resulted in enormous deposits of fossils,

which, now on land, are referred to as *diatomaceous earth*. In the Lompoc Valley of California, these deposits form a layer about 3000 feet thick. Some 244,000 tons of diatomaceous earth were mined in 1935 (Fig. 18.15). Diatomaceous earth has served as a carrier for liquid nitroglycerin in dynamite and for an abrasive in toothpaste. It is employed extensively in the filtration of liquids, notably in the sugar refineries. An excellent insulating material, especially at high temperatures, it is used in boilers and blast furnaces. Small amounts of it in cement greatly increase the strength of concrete.

Reproduction. Reproduction of diatoms takes place chiefly by cell division. In this process the halves of the walls separate

Fig. 18.15. Diatom quarry, Lompoc, Calif. (Photo courtesy of Johns-Manville Corp.)

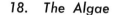

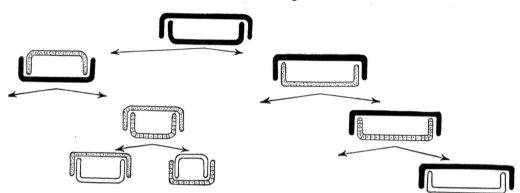

Fig. 18.16. Changes in size of diatom cell resulting from division of cell. (Redrawn from Smith, *Freshwater Algae of the United States*, McGraw-Hill Book Co.)

much as one lifts the top from a box or petri dish. Each daughter cell thus receives one-half of the old cell wall; one side of each daughter protoplast is without a wall. In repairing this lack the new wall grows so that it fits within the old wall. In other words, the new wall is always the "bottom" of the box (Fig. 18.16). The daughter cell receiving the "upper" half of the old wall is the same size as the parent cell, whereas the daughter cell receiving the "lower" half of the old wall is smaller than the parent cell. A continuation of this process would eventually lead to a diminution in the size of some cells (Fig. 18.16). This actually does happen in some species. Decrease in cell size, however, never goes beyond a certain minimum. The small cells either die or

form spores that give rise to large cells. In other species the smaller cell wall is apparently able to increase to the size of the larger so that all individuals maintain a constant size.

In many genera the spores that result in the rejuvenescence of the small cells are associated with sexual reproduction. Details of the process differ among the species but in most instances definite isogametes are produced which unite to form zygotes. Sexual reproduction also occurs in species that maintain a constant cell size (Fig. 18.17).

PHYLUM VII. PHAEO-PHYCOPHYTA

General Characteristics and Distribution

The Phaeophycophyta (brown algal plants) have long been known as the brown algae because of their dark greenish-brown coloration. This color is produced by a special carotenoid pigment, fucoxanthin, which is present in the chloroplasts. Chlorophyll *a* and *c* and the carotenoids characteristic of the higher plants are also present in the chloroplasts, but the green color is masked by the more abundant fucoxanthin.

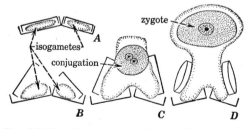

Fig. 18.17. Conjugation of two diatom cells. (Redrawn from Smith, *Freshwater Algae of the United States*, McGraw-Hill Book Co.)

The brown algae, with rare exceptions, grow in salt water, and most of them are found along the shores of the temperate and polar oceans. They are the common seaweeds of rocky coasts and grow from close to the high-water mark outwards to a depth of about 300 feet. Most species are attached to rocks (Fig. 18.22), but a few are firmly fastened to other algae. *Sargassum natans* is a free-floating species growing very abundantly over a large area of the Atlantic Ocean known as the Sargasso Sea.

Structure

The brown algae vary in size from microscopic plants with a few cells to very large plants 150 feet in length. Some are filamentous and in many instances profusely branched (Fig. 18.18); others have large, flat, leaflike structures that wave in the surf (Fig. 18.20); and several species are of

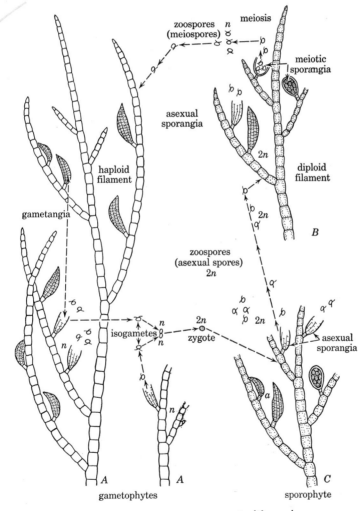

Fig. 18.18.   *Ectocarpus;* stages in life cycle.

miniature tree form, one being known as the sea palm.

Most brown algae possess a **holdfast,** an organ of attachment (Figs. 18.19, 18.20). It may be compared to a root in that it serves to anchor the plant firmly to its substratum. It does not, however, absorb nutrients, nor does it have the structure of a root. Some of the larger forms have a **stipe,** or stemlike region, and a **blade,** or flattened,

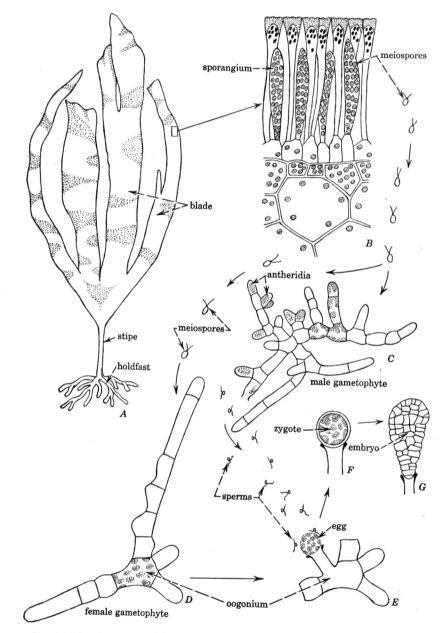

Fig. 18.19. Diagram of life cycle of a kelp. (Redrawn from Papenfuss.)

leaflike portion. Many brown algae are furnished with **bladders** that serve to keep them afloat.

The thalli of some Phaeophycophyta may exhibit considerable cellular differentiation. The outer and inner regions are usually distinct and some of the larger species contain sieve tubes. The cell walls are composed of cellulose and a gelatinous substance known as **algin.**

Some brown algae are annuals, and others are perennials. There is no relation between size and length of life. One of the larger kelps is an annual and grows about 60 feet in length in a season. On the other hand, one small species requires 15 years to attain a length of 8 feet.

The brown algae are of some economic importance. Algin is used as a stabilizer in ice cream, in marshmallows, and in other foods. One species is cultivated for food by the Japanese. They are also employed to some extent as fertilizers, and formerly they were the main source of iodine.

Fig. 18.20. Sporophyte of *Ecklonia maxima,* a large kelp. (Photo courtesy of Papenfuss.)

Reproduction

Several species of brown algae reproduce asexually by fragmentation of the thallus and by spores. The most notable example of fragmentation is *Sargassum natans.* It apparently has no other means of reproduction and is probably the most prolific of the brown algae.

Sexual reproduction occurs in most species that have been investigated, one exception being the above-mentioned *Sargassum natans.*

There are three general types of life histories:

1. An alternation of morphologically similar haploid and diploid generations—*Ectocarpus.*

2. An alternation of morphologically dissimilar haploid and diploid generations—Laminariales.

3. The almost complete suppression of the haploid generation, as in *Fucus.* In this genus the only haploid cells are the gametes.

Ectocarpus

This is a small filamentous brown alga, growing attached to other algae. The diploid plant may reproduce asexually by means of zoospores. The asexual sporangia that bear these diploid asexual zoospores are multicellular structures occurring on short lateral filaments (Fig. 18.18B, C). Strangely enough, these asexual sporangia are indistinguishable in appearance from the gametangia that are borne on the haploid plants (Fig. 18.18A). Asexual zoospores are produced by all cells of this asexual sporangium.

A second type of sporangium (meiotic sporangium) is found on the diploid plants. It is an enlarged spherical cell and is borne on a short side branch. The zoospores (meiospores) that are formed within it are haploid; reduction divisions occur in their formation (Fig. 18.18*B*).

The diploid plant of *Ectocarpus* thus produces two types of zoospores: (1) true asexual diploid zoospores that develop into other diploid plants and (2) haploid zoospores (meiospores) that develop into haploid plants.

The haploid plants are identical in appearance to the diploid plants even though their cells contain one-half as many chromosomes. The gametangia (similar in appearance to the asexual sporangia) are multicellular organs occurring on the ends of short branches. Isogametes are produced in every cell of the gametangium. The gametes conjugate to form a diploid zygote that grows into a diploid plant.

As we have learned, the alternation of a diploid generation with a haploid generation is called **alternation of generations.** The diploid generation always contains two sets of chromosomes that carry the factors responsible for the development of the individual plants. The haploid generation always produces gametes; it is the gamete-producing plant—the **gametophyte** (gamete + *phyton*, plant). The diploid generation as a result of meiosis produces spores; it is a spore-producing plant—the **sporophyte** (spore + *phyton*, plant).

The life history of *Ectocarpus* may be diagrammed as shown.

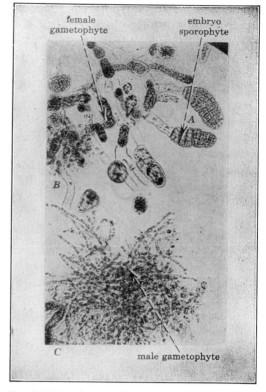

Fig. 18.21. Gametophytes and embryo sporophyte of *Ecklonia maxima*. (Photo courtesy of Papenfuss.)

Laminariales

The Laminariales, more commonly known as **kelps,** are the large seaweeds usually growing submerged on rocky coasts in cold waters of temperate and polar regions almost up to the permanent ice. There are about 20 species along the Atlantic Coast and over 40 along the Pacific Coast.

Asexual: **plant (2n)** → **zoospores (2n)** → **plant (2n)**

Sexual: **plant (2n)** → **zoospores (n)** → **plant (n)** → isogamete (n) → zygote (2n) → **plant (2n)**

isogamete (n)

The kelps are characterized by an alternation of generations in which the diploid and haploid plants are different in appearance: the sporophyte is large (Figs. 18.19*A*, 18.20), whereas the gametophyte may consist of only a few cells (Figs. 18.19*C, D,* 18.21). The most striking example of this difference in size is the giant kelp, *Macrocystis pyrifera.* The sporophyte may be 150 feet or more in length, and the gametophyte may consist of only a very few cells.

Reproduction. No asexual reproduction occurs among the kelps (except for vegetative reproduction from rhizomes). The large sporophytes are diploid. The production of zoospores is always accompanied by meiosis (Fig. 18.19*B*). Zoospores develop into either male or female gametophytes (Fig. 18.19*B, C, D*) that are very small. The sperms and eggs are extruded into the sea water, although the eggs may remain attached to the parent plant. After fertilization the zygote (Fig. 18.19*F*) develops into a flat mass of undifferentiated meristematic tissue called an **embryo** (Figs. 18.19*G*, 18.21*A*). The typical sporophyte or diploid plant is gradually evolved from this embryo. The life history is as diagrammed.

tached to the rocks by a well-developed **holdfast.** There is a short **stipe** between the holdfast and the thallus.

Reproduction. *Fucus* forms no asexual spores of any sort and only occasionally does fragmentation of the thallus occur. Sexual reproduction is oogamous.

The ends of the thallus are usually swollen and notched. Examination will reveal on some of the swollen portions the presence of small raised areas (Fig. 18.23*A*). A section through these areas shows small cavities that open through conical pores to the sea water. The cavities are called **conceptacles** (Figs. 18.23*B*, 18.24), and gametangia are formed within (Fig. 18.23*C*). The common Atlantic Coast species of *Fucus* are **dioecious;** that is, only one type of gametangia occurs on a plant—the plants are either male or female. Both sorts of gametangia occur in the conceptacles of the common Pacific Coast species; it is **monoecious.**

The oogonia are large spherical cells, separated from the wall of the conceptacle by a single stalk cell (Fig. 18.23*D*). Eight egg cells are formed in each oogonium. The antheridia are formed in great numbers at the tips of profusely branched fila-

male plant (*n*) → gametes (*n*)

Plant (2*n*) → zoospores (*n*)

zygote (2*n*) →

female plant (*n*) → gametes (*n*)

embryo (2*n*) → plant (2*n*)

Fucus

On rocky coasts some species of *Fucus* is quite likely to be the first seaweed exposed by the outgoing tide. These intertidal species of *Fucus* (Fig. 18.22) are from a foot to 3 feet in length. The thallus is flattened, narrow, and with regular Y-shaped branching occurring at intervals (Fig. 18.23*A*). The thalli are securely at-

ments (Fig. 18.23*E*). Many sperms are formed in each antheridium. The chromosome number is halved during the formation of both eggs and sperms.

A large number of sterile hairs, the **paraphyses,** surround the gametangia. Some extend out through the opening in the top of the conceptacle (Figs. 18.23*C*, 18.24).

The gametes are forced from the conceptacle when the plants are reflooded with the incoming tide, and fertilization occurs in the ocean water. The resulting diploid zygote develops into a many-celled pear-shaped **embryo** from which the characteristic vegetative thallus gradually grows.

The life history is as diagrammed.

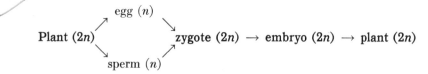

$$\text{Plant } (2n) \nearrow \text{egg } (n) \searrow \text{zygote } (2n) \rightarrow \text{embryo } (2n) \rightarrow \text{plant } (2n)$$
$$\searrow \text{sperm } (n) \nearrow$$

PHYLUM VIII. RHODO-PHYCOPHYTA

General Characteristics and Distribution

The chromoplasts of most Rhodophyco-phyta (red algal plants) contain two water-soluble pigments—a red one, **phycoerythrin,** and a blue one, **phycocyanin.** The latter is absent in a few forms. Phycoerythrin is present in sufficient quantity to mask the other pigments, thus giving a beautiful red coloration to most algae in this phylum. The chlorophylls present, *a* and *d*, are in low concentration. A number of carotenoid pigments are also present. The location of starch in the Rhodophyco-phyta is unique in the plant kingdom; the starch grains lie free in the cytoplasm. Numerous red algae form large amounts of

Fig. 18.22. *Fucus,* a common intertidal rockweed. $\times \frac{1}{3}$.

calcium salts, eventually becoming encased in an armor of calcareous material.

The cells are frequently uninucleate, although the larger cells of some species are multinucleate (containing from 3000 to 4000 nuclei). In more advanced forms the cell wall has pits and the protoplasts of adjacent cells are connected by protoplasmic strands.

Several species of red algae occur in fresh water but most live in marine waters of the temperate zones. They may be found at depths as great as 600 feet.

Certain red algae yield a product called **agar,** which is used extensively in all bacteriology, public health, hospital, and similar laboratories in a medium for the growth of bacteria. Melted agar has the peculiar property of solidifying when it has cooled down to approximately 90° F, but upon reheating it does not melt until above 212° F. This means that various nutrients can be mixed with it when it is a liquid, that bacteria can be placed in it even before it solidifies, and yet that it can be incubated at fairly warm temperatures. Agar has proved to be an ideal solid base for use in culture media by the bacteriologists and has made possible much of our present-day knowledge of bacteria. It has many other applications in modern food industries, being an ingredient of malted milk, marshmallows, jellied candies, and similar products. The preparation of agar has been

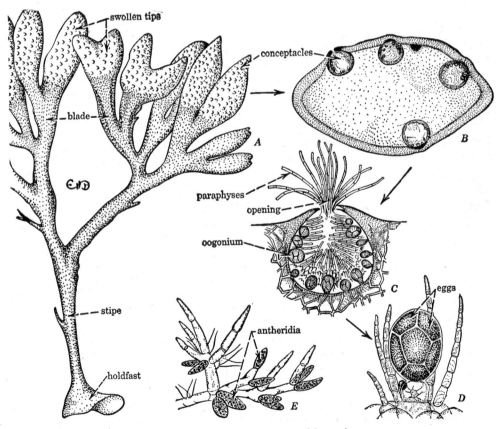

Fig. 18.23. *Fucus;* stages in life cycle.

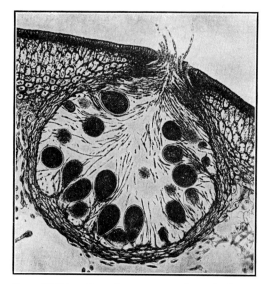

Fig. 18.24. Female conceptacle of *Fucus*. (Photo courtesy of Triarch Products.)

free-floating sperms coming in contact with it become attached and are held in place. That portion of the wall of the receptive neck that is in contact with sperms dissolves, leaving a free passage between the sperms and neck. The male nucleus of any sperm is now free to pass through this opening and down the neck of the carpogonium to the egg in the inflated base.

The fertilized egg cell does not develop into a new, free, individual plant. Instead, a few filaments grow upward from the zygote, forming a small structure called a

performed chiefly by the Japanese. The algae are harvested, and the agar is extracted by boiling. The extract is allowed to dry and is then shredded or powdered.

Reproduction

No motile cells, either gametes or spores, of any sort are produced by the Rhodophycophyta. Reproduction is more complicated and shows greater variation than in the other phyla of algae. The following account will serve to give the essential details.

The antheridia are single cells borne in groups on male plants (Fig. 18.25A). Each antheridium produces a single nonmotile sperm. The sperms are discharged and float passively in the water currents surrounding the female plants.

The female gametangium is a specialized flask-shaped cell called a **carpogonium**. The inflated base contains the egg. The elongated neck, extending upwards from the base, serves as a receptive organ. Any

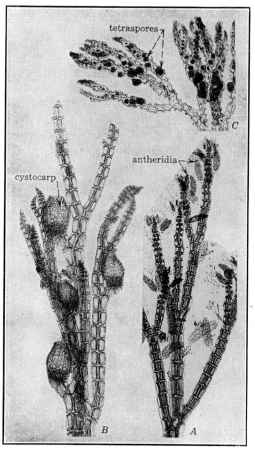

Fig. 18.25. *Polysiphonia*; stages in life cycle. A, male gametophyte; B, female gametophyte; C, tetrasporic plant. (Photo courtesy of Triarch Products.)

cystocarp (Fig. 18.25B). This cystocarp is regarded by some to be a plant growing parasitically on the parent plant that bore the egg cells. In some forms the cystocarp may be surrounded by an envelope of tissue formed directly from the vegetative gametophytic plant. The development of this envelope of gametophytic tissue is stimulated by fertilization.

The cystocarp soon develops spores, called **carpospores.** They are shed and may give rise, depending upon the species, tached to the receptive necks of the carpogonia on the female gametophytes. After fertilization, the zygote develops filaments that form a small cystocarp. An envelope of gametophytic tissue grows up around this cystocarp. Carpospores are eventually produced. They grow into a plant that will produce tetraspores, but which is, morphologically, similar to the gamete-producing plant. Upon germination the tetraspores form gametophytes, thus completing the life cycle.

Gametophyte (n) → carpogonium (n) → egg (n)

$\searrow$ zygote $(2n)$ → cystocarp $(2n)$ → $\nearrow$

Gametophyte (n) → antheridium (n) → sperm (n)

carpospores $(2n)$ → **sporophyte plant $(2n)$** → tetraspores (n) → gametophyte plant (n)

to either one of two sorts of plants: (1) gametophyte plants similar to the parent plant, or (2) plants similar morphologically to the parent gametophyte plant, but containing the diploid number of chromosomes and producing special meiospores called **tetraspores** (Fig. 18.25C). Upon germination the tetraspores develop into gametophytic plants.

Polysiphonia

Polysiphonia is a red alga growing very abundantly along the Atlantic and Pacific coasts. It is a highly branched, small, delicate plant. Its life history involves the three types of plants listed above. The male gametophyte produces nonmotile sperms, some of which, after being discharged into the sea water, become at-

Classification

Phylum	Chlorophycophyta
Genera	*Pleurococcus*
	Chlorella
	Chlamydomonas
	Ulothrix
	Spirogyra
	Cladophora
Phylum	Chrysophycophyta
Class	Xanthophyceae
Genus	*Vaucheria*
Class	Bacillarieae
Phylum	Phaeophycophyta
Genera and species	*Sargassum natans*
	Ectocarpus
	Macrocystis pyrifera
	Ecklonia maxima
	Fucus
Phylum	Rhodophycophyta
Genus	*Polysiphonia*

19

The Fungi

It is well·known that the ravages of human diseases have changed or modified the history of peoples. Likewise, epidemics of diseases that lay waste important food plants may influence greatly the course of events. From 1843 to 1847 a fungus, known scientifically as *Phytophthora infestans,* spread rapidly through the potato fields of Ireland. This fungus causes a severe disease of potatoes known as **late blight.** It not only kills the foliage but also infects the tubers, causing them to rot rapidly. Moreover, when stored, one diseased tuber is a source of infection for all others in the storage bin.

In the middle of the nineteenth century, Irish peasants were depending chiefly upon the potato as a source of food. Consequently, from 1843 to 1847, when weather conditions were just right for the rapid development of *Phytophthora infestans,* and when the potato disease that it caused attained epidemic proportions, the Irish experienced a disastrous food famine. During these years, over a million Irishmen moved across the ocean to New York City. They and their descendants have left an imprint upon American life. The potato famine in Ireland, produced by a fungus, not only was responsible for the death of a quarter of a million people and the mass movement of

Irish peoples to the United States, chiefly in 1846 and 1847, but also changed somewhat the trade policy of the British Empire, causing England to embark upon a policy of free trade. The Duke of Wellington is reported to have made the statement, regarding England's change to a free-trade policy, that "a rotten potato did it."

Some 80,000 different species of fungi have been recognized. They play an indispensable role in the life of the world. They help to maintain soil fertility; they decompose organic matter of both plants and animals that would soon make the surface of the earth uninhabitable were it not disposed of; they cause diseases of plants and animals, including man; and they are of great importance in various industries, such as in cheese making, manufacture of alcohol, and retting of flax.

The fungi as a group lack chlorophyll. Accordingly, they cannot make their own food from simple inorganic substances. They are dependent or **heterotrophic plants;** i.e., they must secure their food ready-made from some other living plant or animal or from the products or dead remains of one. We have learned that plants possessing chlorophyll can manufacture their foods from inorganic materials. Green plants are independent or **auto-**

trophic plants. The foods of green plants are carbohydrates, fats, and proteins. Likewise the foods of fungi and other nongreen plants are carbohydrates, fats, and proteins.

An organism securing its food from the *living tissues* of another plant or animal is called a **parasite.** An organism deriving its food from *dead tissues* or the *nonliving products* of another plant or animal is termed a **saprophyte.**

Common examples of parasitic fungi are those that cause mildew of roses, late blight of potatoes, and rust of cereals. Among the saprophytic fungi may be cited those that form mold on bread and cheese and those that cause rotting of wood. A parasite may or may not be "disease-producing," i.e., **pathogenic.** The fungus *Phytophthora infestans* is pathogenic; it produces a disease of the potato. On the other hand, certain bacteria subsist (are parasitic) on the roots of alfalfa, beans, and other members of the legume family but do not cause a disease. The organism upon which the parasite lives is the **host.** For example, the potato plant is the host of the parasitic fungus *Phytophthora infestans,* and man is host to the fungi that are responsible for athlete's foot.

Some parasites, like those that cause rusts of cereals, are obliged to secure their nourishment from living tissues. They are known as **obligate parasites.** And certain saprophytes, like some mushrooms, thrive only on nonliving organic materials. They are known as **obligate saprophytes.** On the other hand, some fungi have the faculty of growing as either a parasite or a saprophyte and are referred to as **facultative species.**

CLASSIFICATION OF FUNGI

In the names of the larger groups of fungi the termination *mycetes* appears. It comes from the Greek word *mycetes,* meaning

fungus. Thus, the name Phycomycetes may be broken down into *phyco* (in Greek, *phycos,* meaning seaweed and referring to algae) + *mycetes* (fungus). The Phycomycetes literally are the "algal fungi."

There are two fungal phyla. One, the Myxomycophyta or the **slime molds,** is a small phylum of interest mainly because the vegetative plant body consists of a naked mass of protoplasm. The prefix *myxo* is a Greek combining form from *myxa,* meaning slime. Thus Myxomycophyta means literally the slime fungus plants. The other phylum, the Eumycophyta or the **true fungi,** is a large one containing thousands of species of diverse forms. Here, the prefix *eu* is also from the Greek and means true. Eumycophyta are divided into four classes, as follows:

Class 1. The Phycomycetes (algal fungi). Common bread mold and the fungus that causes late blight of potatoes are examples.

Class 2. The Ascomycetes (sac fungi). Representatives in this group include a common mold that grows on jellies. Many sac fungi cause severe diseases of certain orchard trees, and one produces a destructive disease of elms.

Class 3. The Basidiomycetes (club fungi). Well-known members of this group are mushrooms and the fungi that cause rusts and smuts of the cereals.

Class 4. The Fungi Imperfecti (imperfect fungi). The fungi causing athlete's foot are members of this class. Also, many diseases of crop plants result from the attacks of representatives of this group.

Because of the very large numbers of fungi and their great importance in medicine, industry, and agriculture, several branches of science are concerned with them. For instance, one group of workers has studied the structure and activities of the true fungi. These scientists are not greatly concerned with the economic importance of fungi; rather are they interested in the life histories, in modes of reproduction, and food requirements. They are called **mycologists,** and their science is **mycology.** **Pathology** deals with the diseases of man, other animals, and plants. A **plant pathologist** is one who specializes in a study of plant diseases. He studies the life histories of the organisms that cause disease, the environmental factors that influence the growth of the organisms, and methods of combating the diseases. He is also interested in plant diseases due to other causes. The annual reduction in yield of orchard, garden, and field crops due to diseases in the United States amounts to many millions of dollars. On the other hand, the development of control methods by plant pathologists has reduced these losses by millions of dollars.

PHYLUM MYXOMY-COPHYTA

General Characteristics and Distribution

The slime fungi or slime molds, of which there are some 300 species, are of scientific interest because they seem to combine the characteristics of both plants and animals. The vegetative body consists of a slimy mass of naked protoplasm in which are many nuclei without separating walls. The vegetative body is called a **plasmodium** (plural, **plasmodia**) (Fig. 19.1). This plasmodium has no definite shape; it creeps slowly by amoeboid movement, usually over shaded rotting tree trunks, across leaves, or in crevices, engulfing solid particles of food as it goes. Most slime fungi are saprophytes. The absence of cell walls, the amoeboid movement, and the ability to take solid food particles into the protoplasm are characteristics that are usually associated with animals. When slime fungi reproduce, however, they form spores with cellulose walls; thus they have reproductive characteristics that are definitely those of plants.

Reproduction

Previous to the reproductive stage, the plasmodium moves to a drier substratum. After a time, the plasmodium ceases moving and forms one or more spore-producing

Fig. 19.1. Development of a sporangium by a slime mold plasmodium. ×8. (Redrawn from Bonner.)

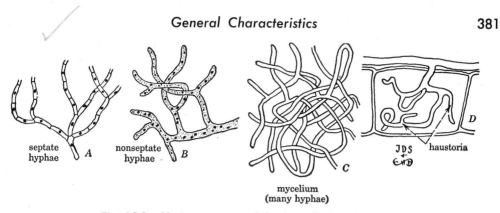

septate hyphae *A*   nonseptate hyphae *B*   *C*   *D* haustoria

mycelium
(many hyphae)

Fig. 19.2. Various aspects of the fungal plant body.

structures (sporangia) (Fig. 19.1). There is great variation in the form and color of the sporangia among the different species. Some have a very delicate structure and brilliant coloring. The spores formed within the sporangia are uninucleate and are surrounded by a cellulose wall. They are discharged from the sporangia and spread by wind. In the presence of water they germinate; the wall is ruptured, and the contents escape in the form of a flagellated or an amoeboid naked mass of protoplasm that may later multiply by fission. In some species of slime fungi, pairs of these bodies may fuse to form zygotes. Nuclear fusion occurs in the zygote. Each zygote may grow into a plasmodium, or zygotes may coalesce to form a plasmodium.

PHYLUM EUMYCOPHYTA

General Characteristics

With the exception of the simplest of the Eumycophyta, the vegetative thallus, or plant body of the members of this phylum, is composed of a mass of threads or filaments called **hyphae** (**hypha,** singular) (Fig. 19.2*A, B*). Three of the four different classes of this phylum have distinctive types of hyphae. The vegetative body may be feathery and delicate, as in common bread mold (Fig. 19.18) and other molds

(Fig. 19.3), or it may be quite hard and leathery, as in species that cause wood rot. The mass of hyphae forming the vegetative body is called the **mycelium** (Fig. 19.2*C*).

The cell walls of the hyphae may contain cellulose, as do the cell walls of higher plants, or they may contain **chitin,** a substance found mainly in the hard, horny parts of insects and crustaceans. The nuclei divide normally by mitosis. Cell division does not always follow immediately

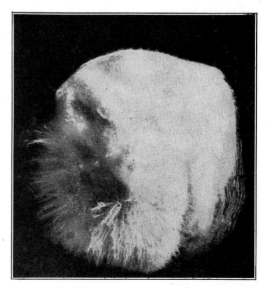

Fig. 19.3. Fusarium rot on peach. ✕ ¾. (Photo courtesy of Plant Pathology Division, Univ. of Calif.)

after nuclear division. In certain instances a half dozen or more nuclear divisions will occur before walls form between the daughter nuclei. In the Phycomycetes, the vegetative hyphae usually have no cross walls (**septa,** singular **septum**). They are multinucleate, there being complete continuity of the cytoplasm throughout the whole vegetative thallus. Hyphae of this sort are said to be **coenocytic,** and since no cross walls or septa are formed in such filaments (Fig. 19.2*B*) they are also called **nonseptate.** When cross walls are present the filaments are said to be **septate** (Fig. 19.2*A*).

Function of the Mycelium

The vegetative mycelium carries on the general activities of plant cells, such as absorption, digestion, respiration, and secretion, but not photosynthesis. Since it is incapable of synthesizing its own foods it must obtain nourishment either from nonliving organic matter or from living plants or animals. The food must be rendered soluble so that it may diffuse through the walls of the hyphae and reach the protoplast. Some fungi obtain food from even the hardest of woods and from solids of many other sorts. These solid substances are liquefied or otherwise rendered diffusible by enzymes that are secreted by the hyphae. For example, certain enzymes are secreted by fungi that break down the complex carbohydrates of wood to simple soluble sugars. Many fungi actually carry on very active digestion of solid materials. Some fungi have specialized hyphae known as **haustoria** that can penetrate living cells and obtain nourishment therefrom (Fig. 19.2*D*).

Since the principal function of the mycelium is to obtain nutritive materials, it is usually found in close association with a source of food. It may be growing inside a living tree, in a dead stump, on or in a leaf, in aging cheese, in a manure pile, or in many other kinds of organic substances. The mycelium of most fungi is not adapted to withstand much drying; hence it seldom grows openly exposed to the atmosphere, unless the relative humidity is high.

Reproduction

The sporangia, spores, gametangia, and gametes of the fungi show a great range of structure and recall in some respects the reproductive structures found in algae. Simple cell division and fragmentation occur in some fungi. Both motile and nonmotile spores are produced in various types of sporangia. Isogamy is characteristic of several genera. Heterogamy, involving gametangia resembling those of *Vaucheria,* occurs in several families. In two classes of fungi, the Ascomycetes and Basidiomycetes, the sexual cycle is complicated by the failure of the two haploid nuclei to fuse after the gametes unite. This characteristic results in two distinct types of hyphae: (1) those in which the cells are haploid with one haploid nucleus in each cell and (2) those in which the cells contain two haploid nuclei in each cell. In the latter type the two haploid nuclei fuse just previous to meiosis (Fig. 20.2).

Although the vegetative mycelium of most fungi is the actively destructive portion, the reproductive structures are of more importance from the control standpoint and as a basis of classification. Usually, fungi multiply and are disseminated by special reproductive structures; it is therefore important to prevent the dissemination of spores, or to stop their germination, or to kill the young hyphae after germination. It is seldom possible to rid the infected plant of a vigorous mycelium although recent experiments with the new antibiotics are yielding results which indicate that this may be possible.

Sexual Reproduction. As in the algae sexual reproduction involves two fundamental steps: (1) the union of gametes, during which the chromosome number per nucleus is doubled; and (2) meiosis, during which the chromosome number is halved.

Asexual Reproduction. As usual, asexual reproduction does not involve changes in the number of chromosomes. Asexual spores are frequently formed by one of the following methods:

1. Spores may be borne in specialized cells called **sporangia** (spore cases). The sporangia (sporangium, singular) may occur either on typical filaments, on special upright hyphae, or on highly branched hyphae. Aerial sporangia are formed by bread mold (Fig. 19.19). In other species the sporangia are submerged or germinate in thin films of water. The spores produced by such sporangia are motile and are called **zoospores.** Special sporangium-bearing or spore-bearing hyphae are called **sporangiophores** (Figs. 19.10, 19.19).

2. In other cases most of the cells of a septate filament separate from each other. Before separating, heavy walls are secreted around them. Reproductive bodies formed in this manner are known as **chlamydospores.** They are formed in enormous numbers by the various types of fungi (Fig. 18.2D).

3. End cells of a hypha may round up and be cut off from the remaining portion of the hypha. These rounded cells are light in weight, a condition that favors rapid dissemination of the fungus. Such cells are called **conidia.** If they germinate to form hyphae or new fungous plants these conidia may be called **conidiospores.** In many other species the conidia will produce zoospores, in which event they are also sporangia and may be called **conidiosporangia.** The hyphae that bear conidia are called **conidiophores** (Figs. 19.10, 20.1).

CLASS PHYCOMYCETES

Many Phycomycetes are severe plant pathogens. Some, however, may infect fish or insects or cause diseases in man. Many members of this class, like bread mold, are normally saprophytes or weak parasites. Some are minute forms of one to several cells, and a few of these smaller sorts are reported to attack small aquatic animals. Most representatives of the Phycomycetes develop a more or less extensive mycelium of indefinite form (Figs. 19.3, 19.18).

The hyphae of actively growing Phycomycetes are generally **coenocytic** and **nonseptate.** Septa may form occasionally, however, in old hyphae of some species, and normally the reproductive cells are cut off from the vegetative hyphae by cross walls.

The Phycomycetes are divided into several orders. The phycomycete specialists do not agree completely as to the best manner of classifying the plants in this class, and therefore, the number of recognized orders depends upon the authority one is consulting. We shall consider several forms of Phycomycetes distributed in the following orders: Chytridiales, Saprolegniales, Peronosporales, and Mucorales. Note that the names of the orders end in *-ales.*

Chytridiales. The Chytridiales are commonly known as the **chytrids.** They infect algae, flowering plants, and other fungi and may also live saprophytically. They are minute forms, all of them being microscopic. Two types of thalli are characteristic of the order:

1. A single cell (either naked, or with a wall) provided with numerous branched hairlike outgrowths (**rhizoids**) that penetrate the host cell or substrate and thus secure nourishment (Fig. 19.4A).

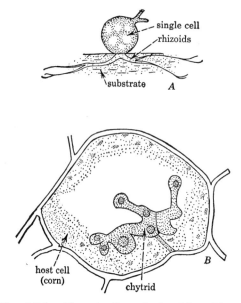

Fig. 19.4. Plant bodies of chytrids. (A redrawn from Karling; B redrawn from Tisdale.)

2. Small hyphae, usually with irregularly placed swellings (Fig. 19.4B).

The disease, brown spot of corn, is caused by a chytrid (*Physoderma zeae-maydis*) characterized by the second type of thallus. The sporangia formed by this fungus (Fig. 19.5A) may remain alive in the soil for sev-

eral years. When moisture and temperature are suitable, the sporangium swells, a small "door" swings open (Fig. 19.5B), and a mass of zoospores is extruded (Fig. 19.5C). The zoospores swim around in the soil solution for a time, eventually lose their flagella, and become somewhat plastic, moving slowly about, after the fashion of amoebae. In contact with the corn plant, these amoeboid cells come to rest on the stem or sheath. Then they send out thin hyphae, which penetrate the epidermal cells (Fig. 19.5D). Inside the epidermal cells they swell into relatively large, round cells (Fig. 19.4B), which in turn send out more hyphae. When the corn cells finally die the spherical fungal cells turn into sporangia that may remain alive in the soil for a number of years.

Infrequently, two chytrid cells unite and sexual reproduction occurs; the resulting zygote becomes a resistant spore.

Saprolegniales. Fungi of this order live in fresh or salt water and are generally saprophytic. Even the species that attack the gills of fish grow on tissues that have been weakened or suffered injury. Because of the aquatic habitat of many members of this order they are frequently called **water**

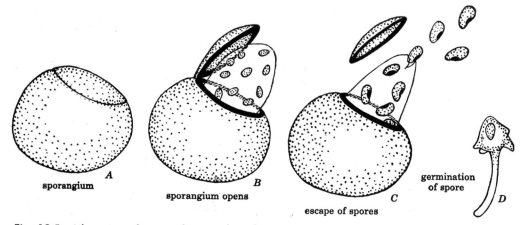

Fig. 19.5. Liberation of spores from a chytrid sporangium. ×250. (Redrawn from Tisdale.)

molds. They may be easily cultivated by placing small pieces of meat, egg albumin, hemp seeds, or dead flies in a dish of pond water (Fig. 19.6). After the mycelium has ramified through the dead fly or other substratum, hyphae grow outward into the water. A small ball of white hyphae, from one-half to an inch in diameter, may thus be formed. Reproductive cells are produced by these hyphae.

Asexual Reproduction. With ample food supply the mycelium increases in size with but little tendency to produce reproductive cells. If, however, a well-developed mycelium is transferred to distilled water, in which a food supply is lacking, sporangia will usually appear. Sporangia are formed at the ends of hyphae by a cross wall cutting off the tip of a hypha from the rest of the mycelium as in *Saprolegnia* (Fig. 19.7A). The sporangium is a multinucleate structure. After a time the protoplasmic contents of the sporangium divide into a large number of spores, each with one nucleus (Fig. 19.7B, C). Upon maturity the spores are discharged from the sporangium. In *Saprolegnia* each zoospore has two flagella attached to its anterior end which enable it to swim actively (Fig. 19.7D). After a time, the zoospores settle down, lose their flagella, develop a cellulose wall, and pass through a resting period. Upon resuming activity they escape from the wall; the two newly developed flagella are now attached laterally, and the zoospores, thus equipped, swim about for a period. If they come to rest on suitable substance, each sends out a tubular outgrowth that penetrates and infects this substance.

In a few species of water molds one or even both zoospore stages are suppressed. When zoospores emerge from the sporangia they may germinate directly into a new

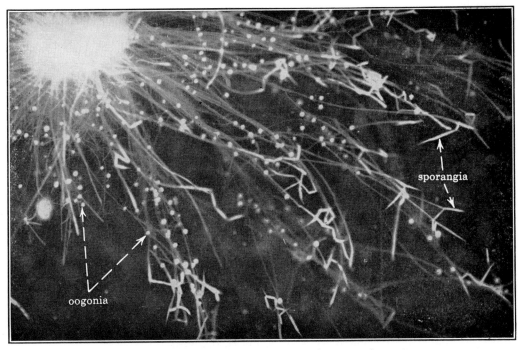

Fig. 19.6. Water mold growing on a hemp seed. ✕3.

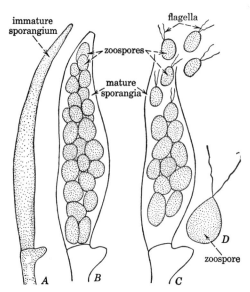

Fig. 19.7. Zoosporangia of *Saprolegnia*. (Redrawn from Coker, in *The Saprolegniaceae*, Univ. of N. C. Press.)

mycelium.   In certain other species, the spores never leave the sporangia but germinate while still enclosed within it, and the germ tubes pierce the old sporangial wall.   In still other species, spores are not even formed; the sporangia germinate directly into a coenocytic mycelium.

Sexual Reproduction.   The **oogonia** are spherical cells, formed at the tips of short side branches (Figs. 19.8*A*, 19.9*A*).   When mature, they are three to four times the diameter of ordinary hyphae.   The cytoplasm in the swollen tip becomes denser than that in regular hyphae.   From one to twenty eggs may be formed from the protoplasmic contents in each oogonium, depending upon the species.   The eggs are spherical, dense bodies of protoplasm, each containing one nucleus.

The **antheridia** are also formed at the tips of branches, in some species near the oogonia (Figs. 19.8*A*, 19.9*B*).   Each is separated from the main filament by a cross

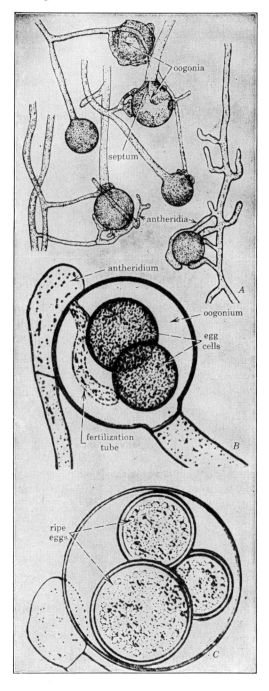

Fig. 19.8.   Gametangia in *Saprolegnia*. (Redrawn from Coker, *The Saprolegniaceae*, Univ. of N. C. Press.)

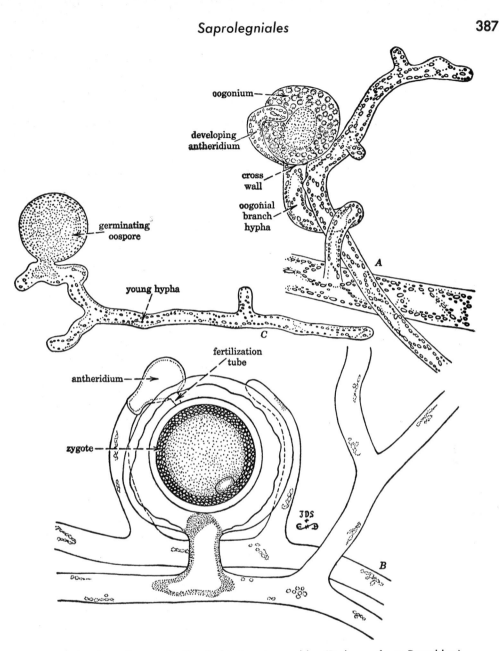

Fig. 19.9. Sexual reproduction in beet water mold. (Redrawn from Dreschler.)

wall. The antheridia are usually curved and not much greater in diameter than the hyphae from which they arise. The contents of a mature antheridium consist of several nonmotile male gametes. The antheridium comes in contact with an oogonium (Figs. 19.8A, 19.9B). In some instances, one oogonium may have several antheridia attached to it. A short slender hypha, the **fertilization tube,** grows from

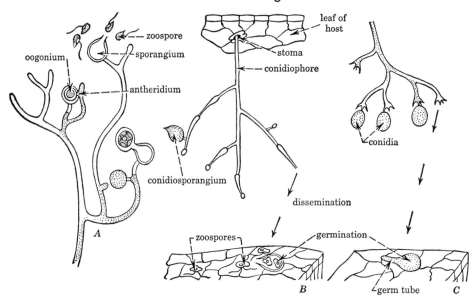

Fig. 19.10.   Asexual reproduction in the Peronosporales.   A, *Pythium*; B, *Phytophthora*; C, *Bremia*.

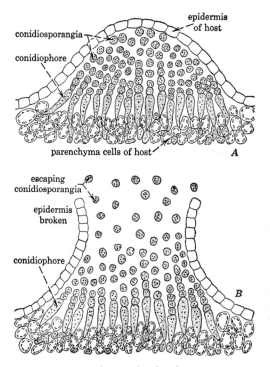

Fig. 19.11. Pustules on shepherd's purse caused by conidiosporangia of *Albugo*.

the side of an antheridium adjacent to an oogonium (Figs. 19.8B, 19.9B), penetrates the oogonial wall, and comes in contact with one or more eggs. If the oogonium contains several eggs, the fertilization tube usually branches, sending a branch to each egg. Nuclei (male gametes) from the antheridium migrate into the tube and any branches present. One nucleus and, possibly, some cytoplasm pass into each egg, and fertilization ensues. The fertilized egg or zygote develops a heavy wall, becoming an oospore (Fig. 19.9B), and usually will not germinate for several months, even under favorable conditions; hence, it is well adapted to survive unfavorable conditions. Upon germination, the oospore sends out new hyphae (Fig. 19.9C), which, if they find a source of food, rapidly grow into a typical mycelium. If food is scarce, the formation of zoospores follows soon after germination. Not uncommonly, eggs may develop into new hyphae without fertilization.

Peronosporales. Nearly all the Peronosporales are parasites. In general, heavy-walled oospores carry them over unfavorable periods (Fig. 19.17), and various sorts of asexual spores (Figs. 19.10, 19.11) bring about rapid multiplication under suitable conditions. Because many of them form a downy growth on the surface of the host or substrate they are sometimes called **downy mildews.**

Asexual Reproduction. The asexual reproductive structures of the different genera are adapted to various habitats and show more variation than do the sexual reproductive bodies.

A few Peronosporales, e.g., *Pythium*, may live in water or on moist soil as saprophytes; they may infect aquatic plants and are frequently responsible for the "damping off" of the seedlings of many farm and hot-house plants. In keeping with their moist habitat, these fungi are propagated by zoospores that strongly resemble those of the water molds. Sporangia are formed at the tips of the hyphae (Fig. 19.10A). When proper conditions prevail, the sporangia open and the zoospores emerge. The zoospores are small and are able to swim in the water films surrounding particles of moist soil. Eventually they germinate and develop a new mycelium. Seedlings may be infected at or just below the soil surface and are quickly killed.

Other Peronosporales (*Phytophthora, Plasmopara, Albugo*) require a moist habitat and grow best in rainy or humid weather, but they are strictly terrestrial. Many of them are parasites on flowering plants. The mycelium of downy mildews grows within a leaf or stem of a plant (Fig. 19.12) between the cells. Haustoria penetrate the cells.

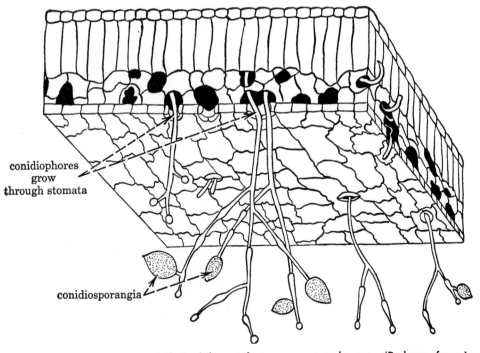

conidiophores grow through stomata

conidiosporangia

Fig. 19.12. Conidiosporangia of *Phytophthora infestans* on potato leaves. (Redrawn from Jones, Giddings, and Lutman.)

Fig. 19.13. Downy mildew on lettuce leaf. (Photo courtesy of Plant Pathology Division, Univ. of Calif.)

move about in the film of water on the leaf surface. They soon send out small hyphae called **germ tubes** that penetrate the host tissues and bring about new infections (Fig. 19.10*B*, *C*). *Phytophthora infestans* reproduces asexually in this manner. One fact that the potato growers of England and Ireland learned from the great potato famine of 1846 was that the disease was most severe in the dampest areas and almost nonexistent in dry areas.

Downy mildew of grape is produced by a fungus having asexual reproduction similar to that of *Phytophthora*.

Downy mildews are very common fungous infections on many cultivated and wild plants (Fig. 19.13). They are frequently found on grapes, beans, grasses, melons,

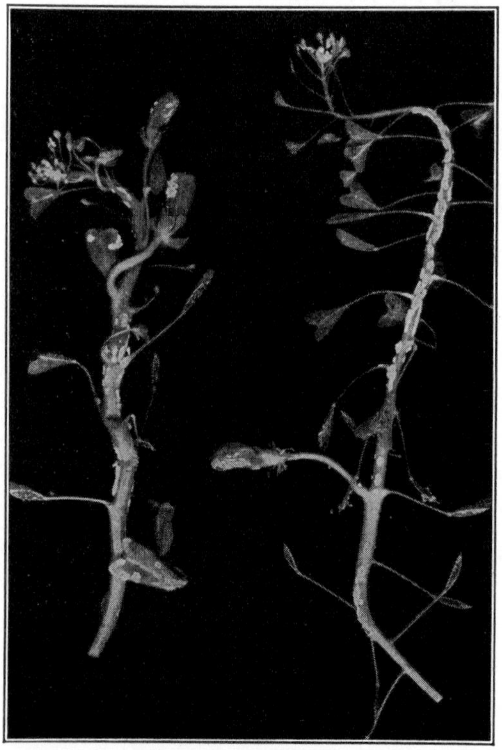

Aerial sporangia are formed in one of two ways: (1) on long sporangiophores that extend out through the epidermis of the infected plant (Figs. 19.10*B*, 19.12) (*Phytophthora*, *Plasmopara*, and others) or (2) in compact pustules beneath the epidermis of infected plants (*Albugo*) (Fig. 19.11). In both structures the sporangia are disjoined from the special hyphae producing them and are disseminated by air currents. Upon germination they usually produce zoospores. Sporangia of this sort may also be called **conidiosporangia** (since they are pinched off), and the branched hyphae that bear them are known as either **sporangiophores** or **conidiophores**.

Some conidiosporangia eventually come to rest on the leaves of susceptible plants. When moisture on the leaf surface is sufficient, zoospores escape from them. The zoospores are very small and are able to

Fig. 19.14. *Albugo* on shepherd's purse. (From Holman and Robbins, *A Textbook of General Botany*, John Wiley & Sons, Inc.)

alfalfa, peas, sugar beets, and other plants. They are easily identified by the conidiophores that may, in severe cases, nearly cover the leaf. Brought into the laboratory, the sporangia can sometimes be induced to germinate by floating them on cold water.

A small group of the Peronosporales, known as the "white rusts," develop sporangia beneath the epidermis of such crop plants as mustards and spinach. There is but one genus (*Albugo*) in this group. The conidiophores do not grow out of the stomata as in the downy mildews. Instead, they collect in pustules under the epidermis of the stem or leaf. Conidiosporangia are cut off in chains from the tips of the conidiophores. They accumulate in large numbers and finally rupture the epidermis, forming creamy-white pustules (Figs. 19.11, 19.14).

In some of the Peronosporales (*Peronospora*) the conidia, formed at the tips of hyphae, are dispersed by air currents but never give rise to zoospores. Instead they germinate directly by sending out one to several germ tubes, which infect the host plant (Fig. 19.10C). A downy mildew causing a severe disease of sugar beets behaves in this manner.

Summarizing, the types of asexual reproduction in Peronosporales may be char-

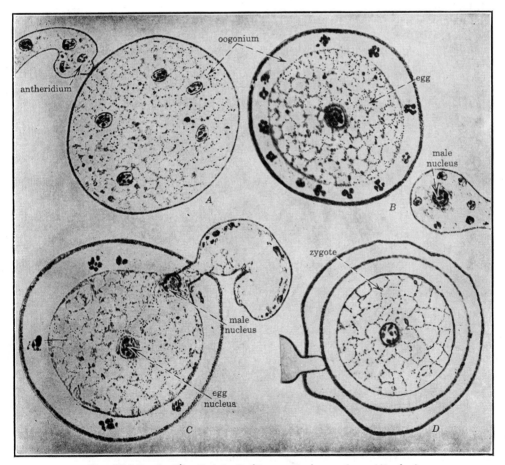

Fig. 19.15. Fertilization in *Pythium*. (Redrawn from Miyake.)

acterized as follows: (1) Sporangia germinate while still attached to the parent hyphae, giving rise to zoospores (*Pythium*). (2) Conidiosporangia are dispersed by wind to other hosts, where the zoospores are liberated (*Phytophthora*). (3) Conidia are identical in appearance, manner of formation, and method of dispersal to that just described (No. 2 above) but, upon germination, they give rise to germ tubes (*Peronospora*).

Sexual Reproduction. Sexual reproduction in the Peronosporales is similar to that observed in the Saprolegniales. In many forms it immediately precedes death of the host plant. Gametangia (oogonia and antheridia) are formed on short side branches, the ends of which have been cut off by cross walls (Figs. 19.15, 19.16). Some end cells swell to form spherical oogonia, each one of which contains one egg. Close by, the antheridia are formed from end cells

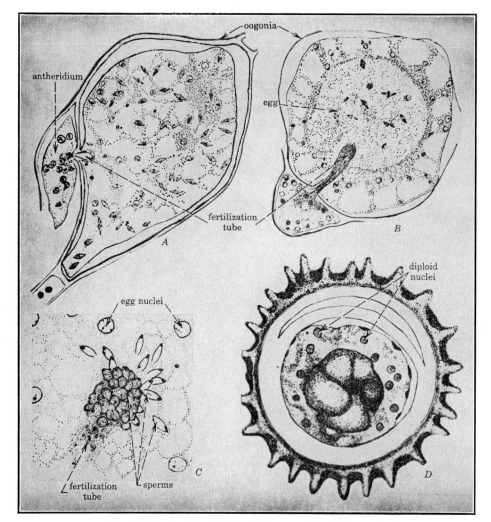

Fig. 19.16.   Fertilization in *Albugo.*   (From Stevens.)

of other side branches. One antheridium presses closely to the wall of an oogonium. A fertilization tube forms and penetrates the oogonial wall until it contacts the egg. Fertilization results by the fusing of one sperm nucleus with an egg nucleus. The resulting fertilized egg becomes an oospore by developing a thick cell wall that protects the protoplasm against adverse conditions (Fig. 19.17). When conditions are favorable for growth, the oospore germinates, forming, either immediately or after the development of a short hypha, a large number of zoospores, each of which may develop into a hypha.

Mucorales. The Mucorales are mostly saprophytes or weak parasites, a few being parasitic on other fungi. The mycelium may be rather extensive, but it is of no definite shape. The hyphae are normally nonseptate and coenocytic, although septa may form in old hyphae. Constrictions or enlargements may also form in some hyphae.

The mycelium at first grows chiefly within the substrate, which may be composed of various kinds of organic matter. Eventually, aerial hyphae develop so that the surface of the substrate may become covered with a mass of hyphae (Fig. 19.18).

Common bread mold, *Rhizopus nigricans,* is a member of the Mucorales which is of worldwide distribution. It grows well on a large variety of organic substances. Although it is mainly a saprophyte, it does attack and does considerable damage to sweet potatoes, berries, and fruit while in transit or in storage. It grows very luxuriantly on sweet potatoes and bread, and these foods may be utilized as media for the growth of laboratory cultures.

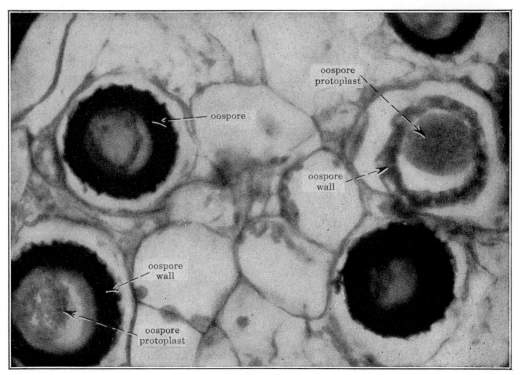

Fig. 19.17.   Oospores of *Albugo.*   ×150.

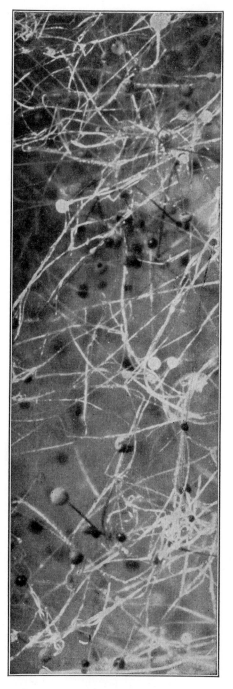

Asexual Reproduction. After the mycelium has become well established upon and in a substrate, certain aerial hyphae, usually of larger diameter than those in the substrate, grow just above its surface for a short distance and then come in contact again with the substrate. They are known as **stolons**. At the point of contact with the substrate new hyphae form. Hyphae are of three types: (1) stolons; (2) short, branched hyphae, called **rhizoids**, that penetrate the substrate and serve to anchor the mycelium and to absorb nutrients; and (3) hyphae that grow upright and produce sporangia at their tips and therefore are **sporangiophores** (Fig. 19.19).

The development of a sporangium is as follows: The tip of the sporangiophore swells, and a bulging wall cuts off an apical cell, which becomes the sporangium. The dome-shaped wall separating the sporangium from the parent hypha is called the **columella**. Numerous spores are formed from the protoplasm within the sporangium, and when the spores are ripe the outer wall of the sporangium falls away and the spores

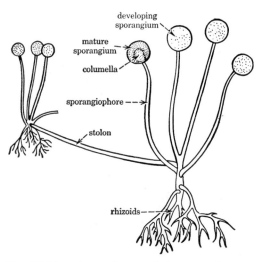

Fig. 19.18. Hyphae, mature sporangia (*black*), and immature sporangia (white) of *Rhizopus nigricans.* ×4.

Fig. 19.19.   Asexual reproduction in *Rhizopus nigricans.*

are dispersed by air currents and insects. On a suitable substrate, the spores germinate and develop new hyphae. Immature sporangia are white, mature ones black (Fig. 19.18).

Sexual Reproduction. The characteristic type of sexual reproduction in the order Mucorales is conjugation. The first step is the chance contact of the tips of short club-shaped hyphal branches (Fig. 19.20). Once in contact, the ends of these two short hyphae swell and elongate slightly. A cross wall forms back from the tip of each hypha, separating a terminal cell from the parent hypha. The two tip cells thus formed are gametangia, and the multinucleate protoplast enclosed in each is a **coenogamete**. The two coenogametes are similar in form and behavior and hence are **isogametes**. The walls of the gametangia that are in contact dissolve, permitting the two isogametes to fuse. The zygote resulting from this union develops into a **zygospore**, which has a thick wall and is quite resistant to unfavorable conditions.

There is some variation in the way different species of the Mucorales develop isogametes and zygospores. Let us assume that in a given community no bread mold has ever been found. By chance one bread mold spore is brought in and grows, producing many millions of spores that spread the fungus throughout the community. We now have a strain of bread mold growing in this community that has arisen from a single spore. The probabilities are that isogametes will never form, because many Mucorales, although morphologically similar, are physiologically differentiated into **sexual strains**. Their similar appearance and behavior make it impossible to designate them as male and female. Instead they are called, for convenience, **plus (+)** and **minus (−) strains**. The bread mold

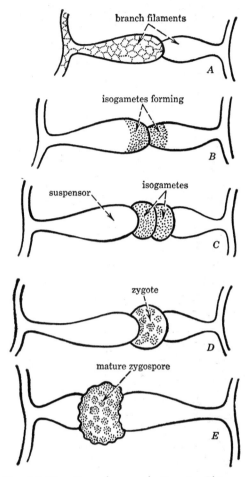

Fig. 19.20. Sexual reproduction in *Rhizopus nigricans.*

introduced, under these conditions, into this community would be either plus or minus. A plus strain does not conjugate with a plus strain, nor a minus strain with a minus strain, and hence no sexual reproduction will occur. Asexual reproduction, however, will be normal. If the opposite strain were now introduced and established, isogametes and zygospores would form. Species of fungi that are differentiated into plus and minus strains are said to be **heterothallic**.

The zygospores of some Mucorales germinate only with difficulty. This is true of common bread mold, *Rhizopus nigricans.* In these plants little is known about segregation of the plus and minus characters. In other species the zygospores do germinate readily and the segregation of the two sexual strains has been observed.

Significant Features of the Phycomycetes

A. Vegetative mycelium.
  Chytridiales: A single bulbous cell with hairlike outgrowths (the rhizoids); small hypha with bulbous swellings.
  Saprolegniales, Peronosporales, Mucorales: A coenocytic mycelium; saprophytes, parasites and intermediate types; parasites mainly plant pathogens.
B. Reproduction.
  Asexual.
    Chytridiales: Zoospores.
    Saprolegniales: Zoospores form in elongated sporangia.
    Peronosporales: Zoospores from attached sporangia and conidiosporangia; germination of conidia by germ tubes.
    Mucorales: Aerial sporangia; spores dispersed by air currents.

Sexual.
  Chytridiales: Isogamy and heterogamy.
  Saprolegniales: Heterogamy, one to several eggs in each oogonium.
  Peronosporales: Heterogamy, one egg in each oogonium.
  Mucorales: Isogamy with coenogametes; heterothallic.

Classification

Phylum	Myxomycophyta
Phylum	Eumycophyta
Class	Phycomycetes
Order	Chytridiales
Genus and species	*Physoderma zeae-maydis*
Order	Saprolegniales
Genus	*Saprolegnia*
Order	Peronosporales
Genera	*Pythium*
	Phytophthora
	Plasmopara
	Albugo
	Bremia
	Peronospora
Order	Mucorales
Genus and species	*Rhizopus nigricans*

PHYLUM EUMYCOPHYTA

CLASS ASCOMYCETES (SAC FUNGI)

General Characteristics

In most localities it is quite impossible to derive a profitable crop from an orchard without an intelligent spray program. This may be due to the rather wide distribution of many sac fungi that are parasitic upon fruit trees. The object of the spray program is to control these fungi, as well as insects.

The fine flavors of some cheeses are due to Ascomycetes, and some of the edible mushrooms are members of this class. Ascomycetes include several severe, though uncommon, human pathogens, and certain other representatives are known to the medical profession mainly for the beneficial drugs derived from them. Ergot, a drug widely used to control bleeding, is derived from an Ascomycete that infects grasses. Yeasts, also members of this class, are a source of many vitamins and of great importance in the production of alcohol and in bread making.

The hyphae of the sac fungi are septate and for the greater portion of their life the cells are mononucleate. The septa are perforated by a central opening enabling the protoplasm to flow from cell to cell. It is this mycelium which is the active vegetative portion of the plant ramifying through the host or substrate, causing disease or decay.

Asexual Reproduction

Various types of asexual spores are chiefly responsible for the dissemination of Ascomycetes during their period of active growth. In mild climates asexual spores may survive the unfavorable seasons, but they are usually killed by cold or by very hot and dry weather.

In many Ascomycetes the spores are formed from the end cells of specialized hyphae. In the process, the end cells round up, are cut off, and are subsequently carried away by wind (Fig. 20.1). The spores so formed are called **conidiospores** or, frequently, simply **conidia,** and the specialized hyphae **conidiophores** (see page 354). Frequently the conidiospores remain attached to each other for some time, forming long chains. In many species the conidiophores are associated in a definite and characteristic manner.

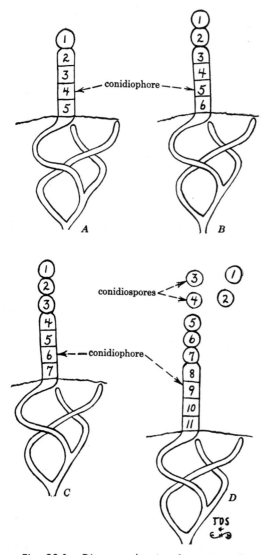

Fig. 20.1. Diagram showing formation of conidiospores.

Sexual Reproduction

Meiosis in most Ascomycetes results in eight meiospores enclosed within a terminal cell (Fig. 20.2). The appearance of these spores suggests beans or marbles within a cellophane sac, thus the common name **sac fungi.** The Greek word for sac is *ascus* (plural, *asci*), from which is derived the class name, Ascomycetes. The meiospores are generally called **ascospores.** The **asci** are always the terminal cells of special hyphae. They are usually located in a reproductive structure, the **ascocarp** (Fig. 20.3), and have developed by a specialized modification of fertilization from the female gametangium, the oogonium, or, as it is known in this group, the **ascogonium** (Fig. 20.2). The male gametangium is called an **antheridium,** as in preceding groups.

The ascocarp, composed of both vegetative and ascus-bearing hyphae, is characteristic of the species. It may be microscopic or as much as 6 inches in diameter. There are three general types of ascocarps:

1. **Perithecium**—Hollow, flask-shaped body with narrow opening (Fig. 20.4A).

2. **Cleistothecium**—Hollow, completely closed sphere (Fig. 20.4B).

3. **Apothecium**—Open cup-shaped body (Fig. 20.4C).

The end cells (asci) of the ascus-bearing hyphae, in many forms, line the inner surface of the ascocarp. This surface layer is the **hymenium** or fertile layer. Sterile cells, called **paraphyses,** also arise in the hymenium (Fig. 20.5) and are more numerous and generally longer than asci.

In most Ascomycetes the ascocarps are the direct result of cellular fusion. The description that follows is a generalized account of cellular fusion as it occurs in many Ascomycetes. The gametangia develop from the haploid mycelium growing within the host or substrate. The female gametangium, or oogonium, is a single cell (Fig. 20.2). Antheridia are elongated cells borne on short side branches of adjacent filaments. Both gametangia may have special accessory cells. After an antheridium establishes contact with an oogonium, the male nuclei pass into it. Male and female nuclei pair, but do not fuse as is normally the case. This process now stimulates the growth of hyphae from the oogonium and

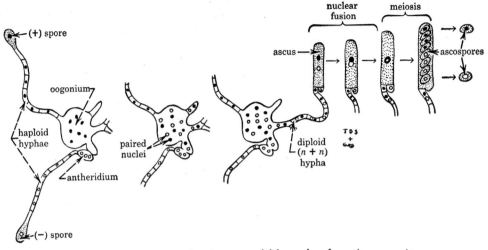

Fig. 20.2. Diagram showing sexual life cycle of an Ascomycete.

from the surrounding haploid mycelium. The cells forming from the oogonium are binucleate, each having one male and one female nucleus. This is not a true diploid condition; it may be designated by **n + n** rather than 2n and the paired nuclei are frequently referred to as a **dikaryon**. Since it is from these hyphae that the asci will eventually develop they may be spoken of as **ascogenous hyphae**. The coordinated growth of the haploid and ascogenous hyphae results in the formation of the **ascocarp**. The terminal cells (Fig. 20.5) of the very much branched ascogenous hyphae together with the ends of some haploid hyphae form the **hymenial layer**. The hymenial layer is more or less surrounded on the outside and protected by the vegetative haploid hyphae which form a layer called the **peridium**. It is in the young ascus that the nuclei of the dikaryon finally fuse to form a true diploid cell. Meiosis occurs immediately after the nuclear fusion and is followed, in most species, by a mitotic division to give rise to eight ascospores.

The sexual phase of most Ascomycetes is thus complicated by the failure of the male

and female nuclei to fuse immediately after the union of protoplasts from the antheridium and oogonium. This gives rise to a prolonged stage between the union of the sex protoplasts and the fusion of the sperm and egg nuclei. Fertilization in the Ascomycetes may then be said to involve two steps: (1) the union of the two sex protoplasts, or **plasmogamy**, and (2) the union of the two nuclei or **karyogamy**. These stages are shown diagrammatically in Figs. 20.2 and 20.5.

The reproductive bodies of the Ascomycetes vary in structure and development. For instance, the simplest type of structure and development occurs in the yeasts, which

Fig. 20.3. Ascocarps of *Peziza*. ×1.

are single-celled fungi. In some yeasts two cells unite. Meiosis occurs immediately after conjugation, and ascospores develop (Fig. 20.8).

At the other extreme are filamentous forms in which the oogonium develops a beak and no antheridia are formed. Instead, bodies called **spermatia** are produced at some distance from the oogonium. The spermatia come in contact with the beak of

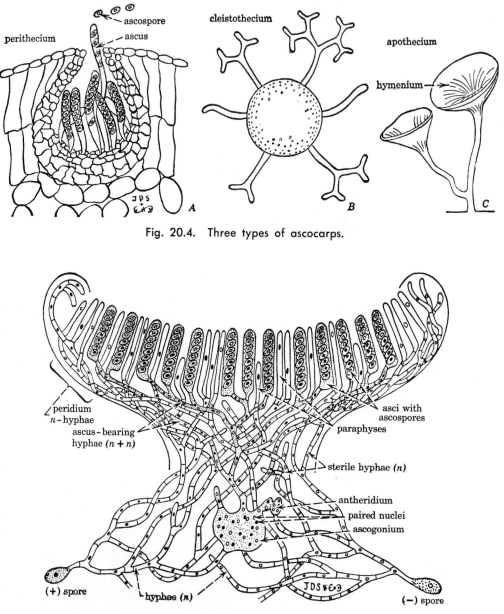

Fig. 20.4.   Three types of ascocarps.

Fig. 20.5.   Diagram of a cross section of an apothecium.   (Redrawn from Sharp, *Fundamentals of Cytology,* McGraw-Hill Book Co.)

Table 20.1.   Classification of Ascomycete Genera Discussed Below

Subclass	Order	Genus	Common Name
Protoascomycetes	Endomycetales	*Saccharomyces*	Yeasts
Euascomycetes	Exoascales	*Taphrina*	Leaf-curl fungi
	Aspergillales	*Penicillium*	Blue mold
	Erysiphales	*Erysiphe*	Powdery mildews
	Pezizales	{ *Peziza*	Cup fungi
		{ *Sclerotinia*	Brown rot fungus
	Hypocreales	*Claviceps*	Ergot

the oogonium. A nucleus from the spermatium passes into the beak and migrates downward to the female nucleus in the inflated base of the oogonium, thus effecting fertilization.

In the Ascomycetes so far described, the development of the ascocarp has been preceded by cellular fusion. In some forms an ascocarp may develop without cellular fusion.

Classification of the Ascomycetes

The fact that about 25,000 species of Ascomycetes exist, many of them severe pathogens, presents a formidable problem to the taxonomist. To group all of these species into a system that will show their relationships and be convenient to use is no mean task. They are commonly grouped into four subclasses and fifteen orders. We shall consider briefly seven genera grouped as shown in Table 20.1. They will give a picture of the range in structure and habit of the Ascomycetes.

Saccharomyces (Yeasts)

Yeast cells may be spherical, ellipsoid, more or less rectangular, or, in vigorously growing cultures, sometimes hyphalike. Their rate of growth seems to influence their shape to some extent. Under ordinary microscopic magnification living cells appear lacking in much structural detail,

although a membrane, enclosing a protoplast with cytoplasm, vacuoles, and granules, probably of reserve food, generally may be seen. A nucleus is present but difficult to observe unless the slides are specially prepared (Fig. 20.6B).

Reproduction. Yeasts are normally single-celled Ascomycetes. In old cultures the cells may remain attached, forming short, branched chains. Some yeasts divide by fission, as do bacteria. In the majority of yeasts, however, new cells grow out from the mother cell, much as a small bubble would form if a piece of thin rubber were made to expand through a small opening in some heavier material. The small "bubbles" formed from the mother yeast cell are called **buds**. They enlarge and finally separate from the parent cell. This process of vegetative reproduction is termed **budding** (Fig. 20.6A).

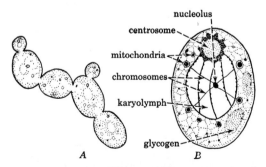

Fig. 20.6. Yeast plants (*Saccharomycetes*). A budding; B, a yeast cell, diagrammatic. (Redrawn from Alexopoulos, *Introductory Mycology*, John Wiley & Sons, Inc.)

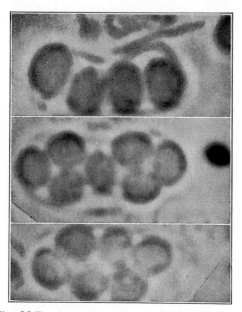

Fig. 20.7. Ascospores of yeast (*Schizosaccharomyces octosporus*). ×500. (Photo courtesy of Castor.)

Most yeasts form asci, each containing from one to eight ascospores (Fig. 20.7), the number being constant for a given species. As in other Ascomycetes, the production of asci usually is associated with a sexual cycle. In the formation of ascospores, the nucleus of a diploid cell divides into several nuclei, and each, with some associated cytopasm, becomes delimited as a spore. The spores lie within the parent cell, which is essentially an **ascus** (Fig. 20.7). During the formation of ascospores, a reduction division occurs. Thus, in yeast, the parent cell is diploid, and the ascospores are haploid. In some yeasts the nuclei of adjoining vegetative cells fuse, the resulting zygote dividing to produce ascospores, which multiply by vegetative division. In certain other yeasts a fusion of haploid ascospores takes place.

The life cycle of *Saccharomyces cerevisiae*, the common yeast of commerce is of considerable interest because it may reproduce asexually by budding in both haploid and diploid phases. Its life history is shown in Fig. 20.8 and is of such a nature as to make this species particularly suited for studies of fundamental biological significance. The life cycle may be written simply:

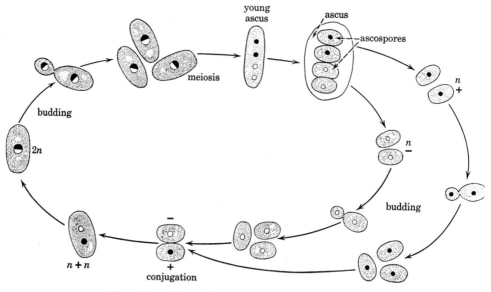

Fig. 20.8. Life cycle of *Saccharomyces cerevisial*.

Plant (2*n*) → plant (2*n*) → ascospores (*n*)

plant (*n*) → plant (*n*)

plant (*n*) → plant (*n*)

plant (2*n*)

| Asexual reproduction | Meiosis | Asexual reproduction | Conjugation |

Economic Importance of the Yeasts. The main sources of energy for many yeasts are sugars, which are oxidized in respiratory processes within the yeast cell. Oxygen is not required for the first steps of the oxidation. The sugar, nevertheless, is broken down to a simple organic acid (see page 214), and energy is released in the process. If the oxygen supply is ample this acid is oxidized, with the release of relatively large amounts of energy, to carbon dioxide and water. If the oxygen supply is deficient the organic acid will be changed to carbon dioxide and alcohol. Thus, yeasts growing in a sugar solution well supplied with oxygen will produce carbon dioxide and water, and the yeast plants will multiply rapidly. On the other hand, yeasts growing in a sugar solution poorly supplied with oxygen will form carbon dioxide and alcohol and will multiply slowly. The oxidation of sugars to carbon dioxide and alcohol by yeasts without the presence of oxygen is known as **alcoholic fermentation.** This process is utilized in the production of industrial alcohol, in wine making, in brewing, and in bread making.

Yeasts have played a very important part in vitamin research. Several vitamins are synthesized by yeast plants, which are an important commercial source of these highly valued substances.

Taphrina

All members of this genus are highly pathogenic to plants, especially fruit trees. They infect leaves, flowers, fruits, and young shoots. They induce unequal growth in leaf cells, causing diseases frequently referred to as **leaf curls.** The fungus causing peach leaf curl is best known. The mycelium of this fungus is intercellular in the palisade tissue of leaves. Here, it stimulates some cells to more rapid growth, which results in wrinkling of the leaf. Eventually the hyphae push their way between the epidermis and the cuticle, where the individual cells swell, round off and thicken their walls, and form a compact layer. These cells then elongate, rupturing the cuticle, and become asci, each one of which contains ascospores. Thus the asci are produced at the surface of the infected organ. The opening buds as they start to grow in the spring are infected by spores that have overwintered between the bud scales. Lime sulfur applied just before the buds open is a very effective control. Typical gametangia are not formed.

Penicillium

In the yeasts the ascospores are produced in typical vegetative cells; in *Taphrina* special asci are formed but they are not grouped in ascocarps. In *Penicillium* the asci are grouped in an ascocarp but distributed at random within it rather than being oriented in a hymenial layer. These ascocarps are of the cleistothecial type. The sexual stages of the great majority of forms associated with *Penicillium* have never been observed so the genus to which it belongs is classified as a member of the

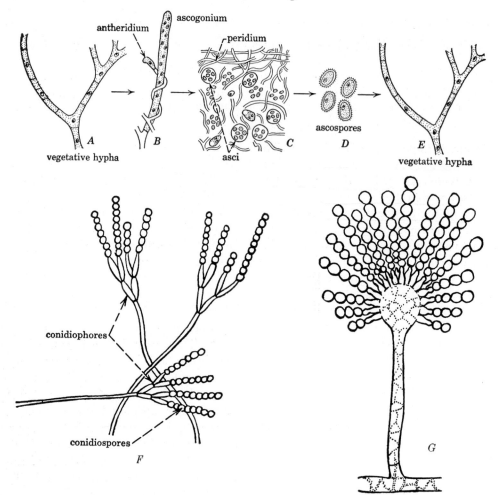

Fig. 20.9. A–E, sexual stages of *Penicillium vermiculatum* (Dangeard); F, conidia of *Penicillium;* G, conidia of *Aspergillus.* (A–E redrawn from Alexopoulos, *Introductory Mycology,* John Wiley & Sons, Inc.)

Fungi Imperfecti by some authorities (page 426).

The ascogonium of *Penicillium vermiculatum* is an elongated slender multinucleate cell and the antheridium simply a club-shaped swollen hypha. Details of fertilization and meiosis are obscure but eventually cleistothecia develop containing scattered asci. The sexual cycle is shown in Fig. 20.9A to E. Asexual reproduction is by means of conidia. It must be emphasized that the asexual stage is the usual and greatly predominant mode of reproduction, the sexual stage being rare indeed. The life cycle diagram thus gives much greater emphasis to the sexual stage than is actually the case.

Penicillium and a closely related genus, *Aspergillus*, comprise probably the most widely spread fungi. They are the com-

Fig. 20.10. *A, Penicillium* on apple; *B,* powdery mildew on grapes; *C, Penicillium* on
orange. (*A* and *B* courtesy of Plant Pathology
Division, Univ. of Calif.)

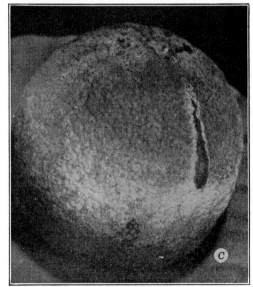

mon blue and green molds and occur on
citrus fruits, jellies, and preserves. Their
conidia are everywhere in the air and soil,
and in the biological laboratory they are
frequent contaminations in culture media.
Figure 20.10*A* shows a growth of *Penicillium*
on apple, and Fig. 20.10*C* shows it on an
orange. Enzymes that they secrete are
particularly active in digesting starch and
other carbohydrates. When purified, these
enzymes are important industrial preparations. *Aspergillus oryzae* is used in the
preparation of rice wine and soybean
sauces. Several species of *Aspergillus* are
important in cheese manufacture. A disease resembling tuberculosis is caused by
Aspergillus fumigatus, and a number of
other *Aspergillus* species cause diseases in
plants.

Asexual reproduction in *Penicillium* and
Aspergillus is effected by means of conidiospores. In *Penicillium* the spores are
formed on profusely branched conidiophores (Fig. 20.9*F*). In *Aspergillus* the
tip of the conidiophore swells and conidiospores form in long chains radiating from
this swollen tip (Fig. 20.9*G*).

Erysiphe

General Characteristics. The powdery appearance of the surface of leaves infected with many members of *Erysiphe* and related genera suggests the common name, **powdery mildews.** All the powdery mildews are obligate plant parasites (Fig. 20.10*B*). Their food requirements are closely integrated with the metabolism of the host plants and so frequently the host plant is not killed. This relationship insures the fungus a continued food supply. Many can live only on a special host, whereas others have a wide host range. They grow poorly or not at all in artificial culture media. These characters indicate a high degree of specialization and a longstanding relationship between parasite and host.

The mycelium is generally confined to the surface of the leaves, flowers, or fruits. Haustoria penetrate epidermal and parenchyma cells, from which they secure nourishment. At first the mycelium on the surface of the leaf appears like a delicate cobweb. Eventually it assumes a white powdery or dusty appearance owing to the development of numerous conidiospores.

Asexual Reproduction. This type of reproduction is effected by conidiospores and usually accounts for the rapid propagation of the fungus during the growing season. The conidiophores are short filaments that stand outward from the mycelium on the surface of the host (Fig. 20.11). The spores themselves may remain attached to each other and form long characteristic chains. Sulfur dusted on the host plants at this stage of the fungal life cycle is an effective control.

Sexual Reproduction. The ascogonium is always located at the end of a hypha and may be slightly swollen. The antheridia are small cells, also occurring at the tips of hyphae. An antheridium becomes closely appressed to an ascogonium; an opening appears in the wall separating the gametangia, and the male nucleus migrates through it into the ascogonium. Binucleate hyphae develop from the binucleate zygote, and simultaneously adjacent haploid vege-

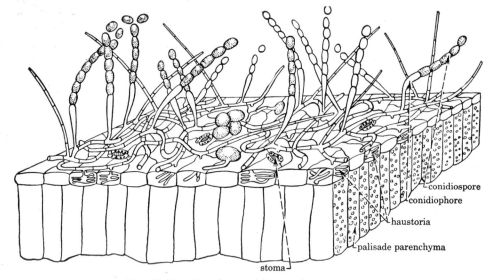

conidiospore
conidiophore
haustoria
palisade parenchyma
stoma

Fig. 20.11. Powdery mildew on leaf surface.

tative hyphae also develop. A small **cleistothecium** (an ascocarp without an opening) is formed and encloses one or several asci. Nuclear fusion and reduction division take place in the ascus, and ascospores develop. The ascospores usually are dis=

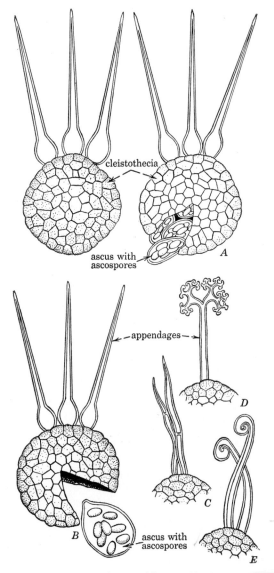

Fig. 20.12. Powdery mildews. Various types of cleistothecia. (Redrawn from Owens, *Principles of Plant Pathology*, John Wiley & Sons, Inc.)

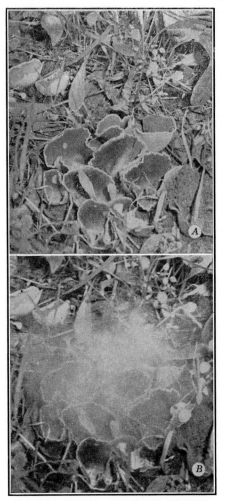

Fig. 20.13. *Peziza.* A, apothecia quiescent; B, cloud of ascospores discharged upon stimulation of apothecia. ×⅓.

charged by force from the cleistothecium.

The cleistothecia are readily seen as small black specks on the surface of infected leaves. **Appendages**, characteristic of the genera, extend outward from the cleistothecia (Fig. 20.12). Appendages may aid in the dispersal of the cleistothecia and in attaching them to a new host.

While the powdery mildews may not kill their host, they weaken it and greatly reduce the crop yield. Powdery mildews

Fig. 20.14. Stem of apricot infected with *Sclerotinia.* ×1. (Photo courtesy of Plant Pathology Division, Univ. of Calif.)

cause diseases of apple (Fig. 20.10*A*), grasses, grains, grape, cherry, and many other plants.

Sclerotinia

The ascocarps of the order to which *Sclerotinia* belongs are cup or disk-shaped (apothecia) (Fig. 20.17). They may be as much as 6 inches in diameter, depending upon the species, and are sometimes brilliantly colored. One genus, *Morchella* (the morels), is edible. A saprophyte,

Peziza (Fig. 20.13), is common and probably the best known. Brown rot of stone fruits, a very severe disease of peaches, cherries, plums, apricots, and nectarines, is caused by a disk fungus (*Sclerotinia*, Fig. 20.17), which infects mainly blossoms and fruits (Figs. 20.14, 20.15). Because of these infections the orchardist may experience lower yields or spoilage of the ripe fruit on the tree or during shipment.

Life History of Sclerotinia.

1. Ascospores formed during early spring infect blossoms (Fig. 20.16*A, B, C*).

2. A mycelium develops within the ovary (Fig. 20.16*D*), resulting in its complete destruction. At this stage conidiospores may appear.

3. Conidiospores produced in blossoms rapidly infect healthy fruits (Fig. 20.16*E*) under favorable weather conditions.

Fig. 20.15. Peaches rotting from infection of *Sclerotinia.* ×⅓. (Photo courtesy of Plant Pathology Division, Univ. of Calif.)

4. An extensive mycelium develops within the fruit, causing it to rot (Figs. 20.15, 20.16*F*, *G*).

5. The rotted fruit dries, becoming a mummy. It may drop to the ground or remain on the tree (Fig. 20.16*G*).

6. In early spring, gametangia form in the mummied fruits that have fallen to the ground.

7. Fertilization ensues.

8. Apothecia develop from ascogenous and vegetative hyphae (Figs. 20.16, 20.17*H*).

9. The resulting asci shoot ascospores several inches into the air (Fig. 20.13) and reinfection occurs.

10. Bordeaux mixture or lime sulfur applied as the buds swell together with a destruction of the mummies will control brown rot.

Claviceps

The genus *Claviceps* is parasitic on grasses, including grains. A dormant mycelium that replaces the mature grain is known as **ergot**. It possesses several alkaloids that have medicinal properties. Ergot constricts the blood vessels, particularly those that pass into the hands and feet, thus depriving the extremities of a normal blood supply. In humid summers in Central Europe, *Claviceps* may infect rye heavily. In centuries past, before the nature of the fungus was understood, ergot would be milled along with the grains of rye. The contaminated flour, which might contain as much as 10 per cent of powdered mycelium, would be baked into bread. A continued diet of bread from this flour resulted in much misery. Because of the contraction of the blood vessels and the limited supply of blood reaching feet or hands, gangrene set in. Hands, arms, and legs would die and finally drop off. The disease was known as "Holy Fire." Today ergot is a valued drug used to control hemorrhage, particularly during childbirth. Although it is no longer of concern in human diet, certain cattle diseases may be caused by ergot from various infected grasses.

Life History of Claviceps.

1. Ascospores are mature when the first flowers of rye, wheat, or other host grasses open. A given race of *Claviceps* infects certain species of cereals or grasses. The mature ascospores infect the young flowers (Fig. 20.18*A*).

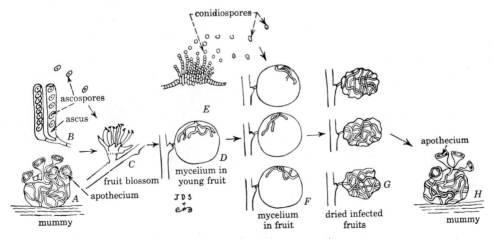

Fig. 20.16. Life cycle of brown rot fungus.

2. A mycelium develops throughout the ovary of the infected flower. Finally it completely replaces the ovary, assuming its general shape (Fig. 20.18*B*).

3. Conidia appear on the surface of this mycelium, together with a sticky, sweet secretion. Insects collect the secretion and, in doing so, disperse the conidia.

4. The compact mycelium replacing the ovary grows upward and becomes a hard and horny body. It is somewhat longer than the mature grain and is purple in

Fig. 20.17. Apothecia of *Sclerotinia*. (Photo courtesy of Plant Pathology Division, Univ. of Calif.)

color. This dormant, elongated mycelium is the **ergot.** It is composed of a compact mass of tough hyphae that, in a dormant condition, survives periods unfavorable to growth (Fig. 20.18*C*).

5. When conditions become suitable, the hyphae of the ergot produce ascogonia and antheridia. After fertilization the ascogenous hyphae, accompanied by adjacent vegetative hyphae, develop a short, upright stalk. The stalk supports a number of small flask-shaped perithecia (Fig. 20.18*D, E*).

6. Meiosis takes place; asci and ascospores are formed within the perithecia (Fig. 20.18*F*).

7. As the asci mature, they extend out of the perithecial opening. Pressure develops in the asci, shooting the ascospores into the air.

Significant Features of the Ascomycetes

General Characteristics.

1. The mycelium is septate. The cells of the main vegetative hyphae have a single haploid nucleus. The ascogenous hyphae have two haploid nuclei $(n + n)$ in each cell.

2. Many are severe plant pathogens, causing diseases of fruit and nut trees and of grains.

3. Some saprophytic forms, such as the yeast, are of considerable economic importance.

4. Yeasts are simple Ascomycetes, consisting of a single cell.

Reproduction.

1. *Asexual.*

   (*a*) Usually by means of conidiospores.
   (*b*) Budding in the yeasts.

2. *Sexual.*

   (*a*) Definite gametangia are not developed in the more primitive species, rather typical ascogonia and antheridia form in the more advanced types.
   (*b*) Fertilization generally involves:

     (1) The union of two protoplasts without the fusion of the nuclei (plasmogamy).
     (2) Stimulation to growth of ascogenous hyphae $(n + n)$ and of haploid vegetative hyphae.
     (3) Union of two haploid nuclei in ascus (karyogamy), $(n + n \rightarrow 2n)$.

   (*c*) An ascocarp develops as a result of the growth of ascogenous and haploid vegetative hyphae,

     (1) The inner layer (hymenium) of the ascocarp gives rise to asci.
     (2) The outer layer (peridium) of the ascocarp is composed of haploid vegetative filaments.

   (*d*) There are three types of ascocarps: (1) cleistothecia, (2) perithecia, and (3) apothecia.

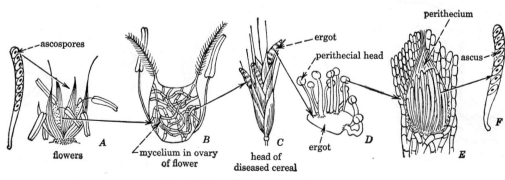

Fig. 20.18. Life cycle of *Claviceps.*

(e) Meiosis occurs in the formation of the ascospores in the ascus. Eight ascospores are generally produced in each ascus.

CLASS BASIDIOMYCETES

Representatives of the Basidiomycetes include mushrooms, toadstools, bracket fungi, puffballs, and the species causing such diseases as wheat rust and corn smut. Many of them are saprophytes, being particularly important in the decay of dead forest trees. Others are parasitic and cause considerable damage to forest and orchard trees, wheat, corn, onions, snapdragons, roses, and many other plants.

Reproduction and Classification

No specialized sex organs are formed by the Basidiomycetes; nearly all, however, reproduce sexually. Conjugation can occur (1) between ordinary hyphal cells, (2) between two special cells, or (3) between special spermlike bodies and receptive hyphae. Some species are **heterothallic;** i.e., only plus and minus strains conjugate. Other species are **homothallic,** conjugation taking place between any two cells of any two hyphae, or even between cells of the same hypha. In both types, previous to conjugation the cells of the vegetative mycelium contain a single nucleus; after conjugation the resulting cell contains two haploid nuclei $(n + n)$. The two nuclei in each cell do not fuse until just before meiosis. Fusion of the two nuclei and subsequent meiosis take place in special cells known as **basidia.** The meiospores formed by these basidia are called **basidiospores.** The basidia may be either (1) a single club-shaped cell (Fig. 20.19), (2) a single

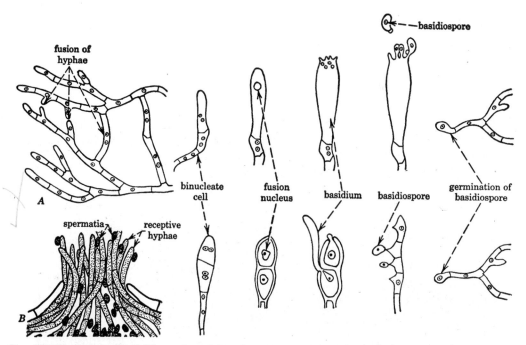

Fig. 20.19. Generalized life cycles of Basidiomycetes showing only fusion of protoplasts, fusion of nuclei, and meiosis (production of basidiospores). *A,* common mushroom; *B,* a fungus causing wheat rust.

short, filamentous cell, or (3) a short four-celled filament (Fig. 20.19). The club-shaped basidia occur on special spore-bearing structures, as in mushrooms, bracket fungi, and puffballs. This type of basidium characterizes the subclass Homobasidiomycetes. When the basidium is a single short, filamentous cell or a short four-celled filament, it results from the germination of special resistant spores (Figs. 20.27, 20.32). Basidiomycetes with this type of basidia constitute the subclass Heterobasidiomycetes. In both types the basidiospores are attached to the basidia by short stalks, the **sterigmata** (singular, **sterigma**).

A generalized life history of a Basidiomycete is shown diagrammatically in Fig. 20.19.

Subclass Homobasidiomycetes

General Characteristics and Distribution. The mushrooms, bracket fungi, and puffballs are Homobasidiomycetes. Only a few are parasitic, but these few do extensive damage to forest trees (Figs. 20.25, 20.26), to some orchard trees, and to a small number of garden crops. Several Homobasidiomycetes are always found growing in association with certain species of trees. It is believed that some of them may form a symbiotic relationship with tree roots, the fungus in a number of instances being able to make nitrogen more available to the roots. Certain Homobasidiomycetes obtain their carbohydrates from wood and may even cause extensive decay of timbers in mines and buildings. Specialized tissues and organs may be formed, some of the $n + n$ hyphae becoming specialized to transport food and water, and others becoming tough and woody.

Although both haploid and $n + n$ mycelia develop extensively, the $n + n$ phase is of special interest because it gives rise to the spore-bearing body, or **basidiocarp** (sporophore) (Fig. 20.20), in which the basidia are developed. The hyphae form a tangled mass in the substrate or host and emerge to form a basidiocarp—the mushroom, puffball, or bracket fungus. As the basidiocarp grows, the ends of certain hyphae generally become aligned in a layer that will bear spores when mature. This is

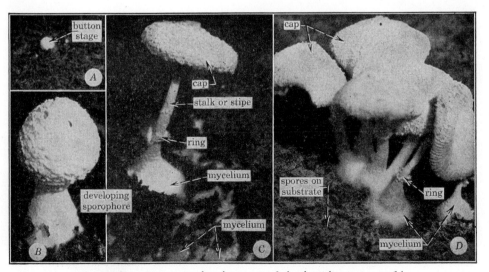

Fig. 20.20. Stages in development of the basidiocarp. $\times \frac{1}{2}$.

the **hymenium layer,** the cells of which gradually enlarge to become basidia.

There are five orders of Homobasidiomycetes. We shall consider mainly the Agaricales, of which common mushrooms (Plate 4) and bracket fungi are members. Many of them are edible, and a few are violently poisonous. The common edible mushroom of commerce, *Psalliota campestris,* is a species of the order (Fig. 20.21). The mycelium, or, as it is known to the mushroom growers, the **spawn,** grows extensively in the substrate. It is common in many pastures and is cultivated in well-rotted horse manure.

The Basidiocarp. The basidiocarp of a typical mushroom such as *Psalliota campestris* (Fig. 20.21) consists of a short upright stalk or **stipe,** attached at its base to a mass of mycelium and expanding on top into a broad cap or **pileus.** Many mushrooms have a ring of tissue around the stipe rather close to the pileus. This occurs because when young the pileus was attached to the stipe at this point. The underneath side of the pileus of *Psalliota* is formed by thin **gills** radiating outward from the stipe. These gills are lined with a hymenium or spore-bearing layer. If a young gill is sectioned, the majority of basidiospores will still be attached to the basidia. Four basidiospores are attached to each basidium by short stalks, the **sterigmata.** If the gill is very young, developing basidia on which basidiospores have not yet been formed may be observed (Fig. 20.22). Figure 20.23 shows a section through three gills. Note two stages of development of basidia and the loose tangle of hyphae forming the center of the gill. When a basidiospore is discharged it is shot horizontally from its position on the basidium straight into the space between two gills. A basidiospore is somewhat like a toy rubber balloon, having

Fig. 20.21. *Psalliota campestris,* the common edible mushroom. ×1.

a large volume for its weight. It is shot from the basidium with a force sufficient to carry it about midway between the two gills. It then falls straight downward. It has been estimated that some basidiocarps may discharge as many as a million spores a minute for several days.

If the cap of a mushroom is placed on a piece of paper and carefully protected from wind, the spores in falling straight downward will form a print, known as a **spore print**. Spore prints are important in the identification of mushrooms. They indicate the color of the spores and the pattern of the gills.

The spores of *Psalliota campestris* are brown, whereas those of other Agaricales may be white, black, red, yellow, or ocher. The spores of *Amanita muscaria*, the "Death Angel," are white. *Amanita muscaria* has other distinguishing features: When the basidiocarp is in the button stage it is completely surrounded by a thin tissue known as the **universal veil** (Fig. 20.24*A, B, C*). As the basidiocarp expands,

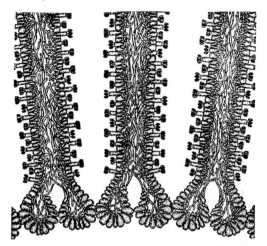

Fig. 20.23. Section showing three gills of a mushroom. (Redrawn from Buller, *Researches on Fungi,* Longmans, Green & Co.)

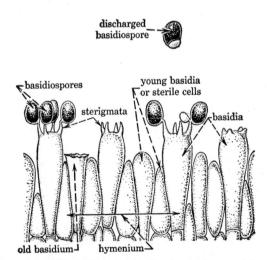

Fig. 20.22. Section of gill of a young mushroom. (Redrawn from Buller, *Researches on Fungi,* Longmans, Green & Co.)

this veil is torn (Fig. 20.24*D, E*). Part of it remains attached to the cap (Fig. 20.24*F, G*), where ruptured fragments of it may be seen in the mature mushroom; the remaining part stays underground, forming a cup-shaped structure out of which the stalk grows (Fig. 20.24*F, G*). The enlarged basal structure is referred to as the **volva** or "death cup." Plate IV (Chapter 15) shows *Amanita muscaria*. The fragments of white on the reddish yellow cap are remnants of the universal veil. The white gills and ring are not visible. The volva of *A. muscaria* tightly clasps the stipe; it may be seen here as the swollen, scaly base. Note how the basidiocarp has pushed up through a thick cover of pine needles.

Amanita phalloides is one of the most deadly poisonous of all mushrooms. It may be recognized by: (1) its white spores; (2) the volva or "death cup" (one must be sure to dig deeply); (3) the ring on the stipe below the cap; (4) the color of cap, which is reddish in the center and fades to yellow toward the edges; and (5) the torn

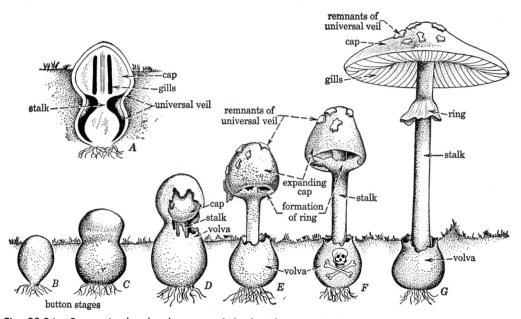

Fig. 20.24. Stages in the development of the basidiocarp of *Amanita*. (Redrawn from Gibson, *Our Edible Mushrooms and Toadstools*, Harper & Bros.)

remains of the universal veil on top of the cap. As a general precaution, one should avoid all white-spored mushrooms with a death cup and a ring on the stipe. Many

Fig. 20.25. A bracket of pore fungus. ×¼. (Photo courtesy of Hinshaw.)

species of Agaricales, however, are excellent eating.

Not all Agaricales have gills. In some the lower surface of the cap or bracket has many small pores that extend upward to form small tubules. The hymenium lines the tubules. Many bracket fungi found on the trunks of forest trees are pore fungi (Fig. 20.25).

Some bracket fungi cause serious damage to forest trees and lumber in mines and wooden buildings. During World War II much green lumber had to be used, and destruction by fungi of improperly cured lumber resulted in much loss. One of the best-known fungi in this group is *Fomes applanatus* (Fig. 20.26). It causes a disease of forest trees known as *white-mottled rot*, to which many hardwoods, such as poplar, birch, maple, basswood, oak, and elm are susceptible. True firs, Douglas fir, spruce, and hemlock may also suffer from this disease.

The basidiocarp of *Fomes applanatus* is a very elegant shelf-shaped bracket or conk. The conks are perennial and grow to a large size. They are gray on top, and the lower surface has millions of pores lined with a creamy-white hymenium. Bruising the hymenial layer produces a dark line, making conks a favorite medium for vacation "artists."

Most of the bracket fungi of the forest are facultative parasites. They live normally in the dead heartwood, to which they gain entrance by wounds. They are, however, able to invade the living cells of sapwood, which they may destroy.

Other types of basidiocarps also occur, such as those in puffballs, bird's-nest fungi, etc.

Subclass Heterobasidiomycetes

General Characteristics. The basidium of the Heterobasidiomycetes is a short, swollen filament developing directly from a specialized resistant spore (Figs. 20.27, 20.32). Most members of the subclass are parasites on vascular plants. Like the Homobasidiomycetes, they possess, as far as is known, both haploid and $n + n$ phases, and reduction division takes place in the development of the basidia or basidiospores. Asexual reproduction may occur

Fig. 20.26. Basidiocarps of *Fomes applanatus*. $\times \frac{1}{3}$. (Photo courtesy of Brownell.)

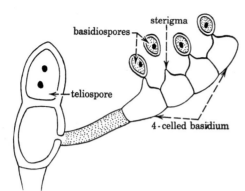

basidiospores

sterigma

teliospore

4-celled basidium

Fig. 20.27. Stages in the life cycle of *Puccinia graminis.* Teliospore with basidium and basidiospores.

in either the haploid or $n + n$ phase or in both. Conjugation may take place between two nonspecialized cells, as in the Homobasidiomycetes. In some forms, however, special cells conjugate or a spermlike cell may conjugate with a receptive hypha.

Some of the Heterobasidiomycetes may have two hosts; i.e., separate phases of their life history are passed on different plants. Such forms are **heteroecious.** If only one host is required to complete their life history, they are said to be **autoecious.**

Uredinales. The Uredinales, or rust fungi, are of worldwide distribution. They are known to infect a very large number of higher plants, and all are obligate parasites. Black or red spores develop in pustules (**sori**) on the leaves of many grasses, roses, mallows, etc., and they, particularly the red spores, suggested the name of **rust.**

There are many types of rust fungi and they show marked variation in their life history. In nearly all of them, however, basidiospores are produced on short four-celled basidia that usually develop from an overwintering spore, known as a **teliospore** (Fig. 20.27). Fusion of the two haploid nuclei and reduction division occur during the development of the basidia and basidio-

spores. The details of conjugation are obscure in many species.

Common wheat rust, caused by *Puccinia graminis,* is of great economic importance, and its life history is well known. It produces all the different types of spores common to the order. We shall follow its life history in detail.

❋ *Life History of Puccinia graminis.* In the early spring, the overwintering teliospores germinate on the soil or stems, in fact any place where there is moisture.

Teliospores of *Puccinia graminis* are two-celled spores. A short four-celled basidium develops from each cell; only one is shown in Fig. 20.27. A single haploid basidiospore is formed from each cell, so that four basidiospores eventually develop from each cell of the teliospore. Two of these four basidiospores are plus strain (+), two are minus strain (−).

The basidiospores are carried by air currents and can infect only the young leaves, fruit, or twigs of common barberry bushes. They germinate chiefly on barberry leaf surfaces and produce a germ tube, which penetrates the epidermis. Soon a mycelium develops in the tissues of the host. Then, after a time, pustules, called **spermagonia,** appear on the upper surface of leaf. In section a spermagonium is pear-shaped and has a small pore opening through the upper epidermis to the exterior of the leaf (Fig. 20.28*B* & *C*). Some hyphae extend upward through the pore; others, lining the interior of the spermagonium, cut off large numbers of spermlike cells, called **spermatia.** These are forced out of the spermagonia through the pores.

Puccinia graminis is heterothallic; both *plus and minus spermagonia and spermatia* appear on barberry leaves. These develop from plus or minus basidiospores, both kinds of which are haploid. Spermatia are transferred to adjacent spermagonia where they come in contact with the **receptive hy-**

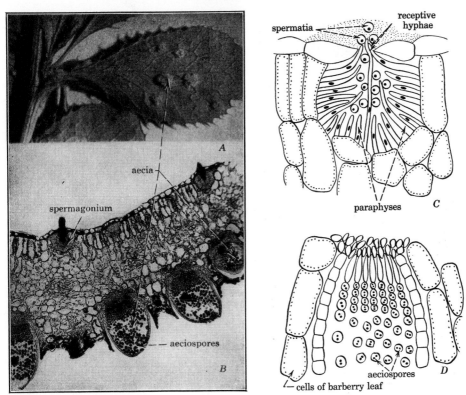

Fig. 20.28. Stages in life cycle of *Puccinia graminis*. A, aecia as they appear on lower surface of barberry leaf; B, section through barberry leaf showing spermagonia and aecia; C, spermagonium; D, aecium. (A, B, photo courtesy of Triarch Products.)

phae which are essentially female organs comparable to the female gametangia of other forms. When plus and minus strains intermingle, spermatia of one strain fuse with receptive hyphae of the opposite strain. Thus a plus ($+$) spermatium fuses with a cell of a minus ($-$) receptive hypha, and vice versa. An $n + n$ diploid mycelium results; its cells each contain two haploid nuclei.

Shortly after fusion, a mass of $n + n$ hyphae appears in the spongy parenchyma of the barberry leaf close to the lower epidermis. Here a second series of pustules called **aecia** are formed (Fig. 20.28B). The aecia face downward and the upper side toward the leaf mesophyll beomes

lined with $n + n$ hyphae. The growth of the aecia eventually brings about the rupture of the lower epidermis and binucleate **aeciospores,** cut off from the ends of the numerous hyphae lining the base of the aecium, are exposed to the atmosphere (Fig. 20.28B & D). The aeciospores thus released are disseminated by wind; they can infect only wheat plants. In surface view the aecia present the appearance of a group of small cups and are frequently called **cluster cups** (Fig. 20.28A).

The hyphae of germinating aeciospores gain entrance to wheat plants by growing through the stomata. A delicate mycelium develops and the hyphae form haustoria that draw nourishment from surrounding

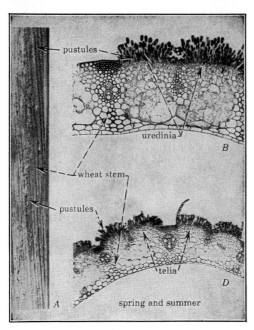

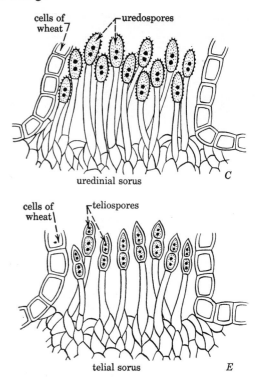

Fig. 20.29. Stages in life cycle of *Puccinia graminis* on wheat. *A,* sori on wheat stem; *B,* C, uredinia; *D, E,* telia. (Photos courtesy of *Triarch Products.*)

cells of the wheat plant but do not kill them. About ten days after infection, red binucleate spores, **uredospores,** are produced by the mycelium. The epidermis of the wheat plant is ruptured by the mass of spores, forming open sori, the **uredinia** (Fig. 20.29*A, B, C*). The uredospores thus produced are carried by wind currents to other wheat plants. The fungus is spread throughout a grain field during the growing season by the red uredospores. The progress of the disease throughout a wheat-growing area may be so rapid as to attain epidemic proportions.

As the wheat begins to mature, the production of red uredospores by the infecting mycelium gives way to the production by the same mycelium of heavy-walled two-celled overwintering spores—teliospores. The sori in which teliospores are formed are called **telia** (Fig. 20.29*D, E*).

Each cell of the teliospore is, at the outset, binucleate; the two haploid nuclei, one $(+)$ and one $(-)$ are still present and distinct (Figs. 20.29*E*, 20.30*A*). These two haploid nuclei now fuse (karyogamy), the true diploid condition resulting. As in the Ascomycetes and Homobasidiomycetes, meiosis follows directly upon nuclear fusion. In the rusts, a short hypha (basidium) grows from each cell of the teliospore, the four haploid nuclei resulting from meiosis migrate into it, and cell walls develop forming a short four-celled basidium. Basidiospores now form, one from each cell of the basidium (Fig. 20.30), and the cycle starts again.

Puccinia graminis is **heteroecious;** it requires two hosts to complete its life cycle. Certain other rusts are **autoecious,** needing but one host to complete their life cycle. Not all rusts develop all the spore types found in *Puccinia graminis,* nor do they all have an identical life history.

Wheat rust may be controlled in cold climates by eradicating all barberry bushes (the alternate host) near wheat fields. If uredospores are killed by winter weather, no barberry plants will be infected. In regions with warm winters the uredospores may overwinter and wheat rust may therefore be more difficult to control.

Varieties of wheat have been bred that are immune to *Puccinia graminis tritici.* In this breeding work, many strains, so-called **biological strains,** of the fungus have been found. Indeed, new rust strains seem to appear from time to time, and so it becomes necessary to continue the breeding of wheat varieties that will be relatively resistant to them.

Significant Steps in Life History of *Puccinia graminis.*

1. Two hosts, wheat and barberry, are necessary to complete the life history. In other words, *Puccinia graminis* is heteroecious.

2. Uredospores (one-celled, red) and teliospores (two-celled, black) are produced on the wheat plant. Uredospores can infect other wheat plants; they are killed by vigorous winters. Teliospores cannot infect any plant; they are overwintering spores, germinating in the spring on the soil or wherever else they find moisture.

3. A short four-celled basidium develops from each of the two cells of a teliospore. Meiosis takes place in this development. One basidiospore (haploid) forms from each of the four cells of the basidium. Basidiospores, either plus or minus, infect young tissues of the barberry.

4. Plus or minus spermagonia (both kinds, haploid) develop in the upper portion of the barberry leaf. The spermagonia produce spermatia and receptive hyphae.

5. Fertilization results from union of a spermatium with a receptive hypha of the opposite strain.

6. The resulting $n + n$ mycelium forms an aecium that discharges binucleate aeciospores from openings in the lower surface of the leaf.

7. Aeciospores infect young wheat plants, producing an $n + n$ mycelium.

Ustilaginales. All members of the Ustilaginales are plant parasites causing a group of diseases known generally as the **smuts.** Two families are generally recognized: Ustilaginaceae and Tilletiaceae. The life histories of the fungi causing cereal smuts vary, particularly in the manner of infection of the hosts: there may be **local infection, blossom infection,** or **seedling infection.** We shall discuss several genera under these headings.

Local Infection. Ustilago zeae, a member of the Ustilaginaceae, causes common corn smut (Fig. 20.31A & B). Infection by

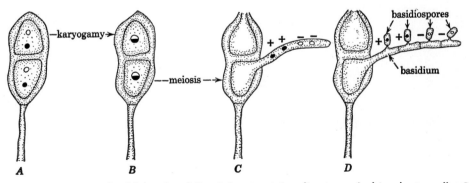

Fig. 20.30. Stages in the life cycle of *Puccinia graminis* teliospore; *A,* binucleate cells; *B,* 2n cells; *C,* step in formation of basidium and basidiospores; *D,* basidium with basidiospores.

Fig. 20.31. Smuts (*Ustilago*); *A*, ear of corn with smutted kernels; *B*, smut infection of corn leaf; *C*, smut of oats.

spores of *U. zeae* is said to be **local**, meaning that any meristematic tissue of the corn plant may be infected. The infections remain localized, producing pustules or large tumors. Perhaps the most noticeable tumors are those that occur in the corn ear. The kernels become much enlarged due to the development within them of an extensive mycelium which gives rise eventually to a mass of black heavy-walled overwintering spores. Since haploid nuclei fuse and meiosis occurs within them they are teliospores. These spores may lie dormant in the soil, on old corn stalks, or in manure.

A four-celled basidium develops when the teliospore germinates. Two plus and two minus basidiospores are formed, one from each of the four cells of the basidium (Fig. 20.32). The basidiospores may infect corn plants directly or they may produce **sporidia,** which may multiply by budding and which are able to bring about infection. At any rate, a small haploid mycelium, either plus or minus, develops soon after infection (Fig. 20.33). Plus and minus mycelia develop closely together, and conjugation occurs by the fusion of cells from small haploid mycelia of opposite strains. After conjugation the $n + n$ mycelium, depending upon its location in the corn plant, may form a small pustule or develop into a tumor as large as a baseball. Most of the hyphal cells in the pustule or tumor change into teliospores.

Blossom Infection. Spores of *Ustilago tritici* and *Ustilago avenae* can infect *only the pistil* of wheat and oat flowers. They are known as **blossom-infecting smuts,** and the disease they produce is called the loose smut of wheat or oats. Teliospores that mature in heads of diseased plants at the time healthy plants are in blossom are transferred to healthy blossoms by air currents (Fig. 20.34). The young pistil is directly invaded and a small mycelium eventually

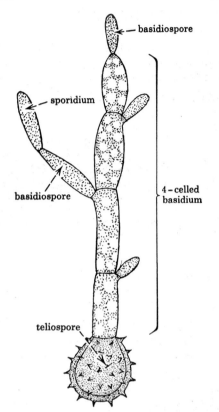

Fig. 20.32.   Teliospore of *Ustilago zeae* with basidium.

develops in the embryo. The infection has no injurious effect on the developing grain, which matures normally. The mycelium within the embryo remains small and dormant thus carrying the fungus over seasons unfavorable to growth. When the grain germinates the mycelium within resumes activity. It grows best in or near meristematic tissue and thus keeps pace with the development of the wheat or barley plant. The presence of the mycelium close to the meristematic tissue has an accelerating influence on the growth of the host, which matures rapidly, producing flower heads before uninfected plants. The mycelium invades the developing ovary, eventually replacing the host tissue completely.

The entire head of grain becomes a black, loose mass of teliospores (Fig. 20.31C), and when the spores blow away nothing is left but the axis of the spike. The teliospores are blown to healthy blossoms (Fig. 20.34), and the ovaries are attacked.

Seedling Infection. **Tilletia tritici,** belonging to the family Tilletiaceae, causes **bunt** or **stinking smut** of wheat. Only young seedlings can be infected. The smuts of this family are consequently referred to as the **seedling-infecting smuts.**

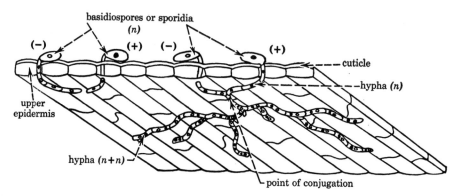

Fig. 20.33. Undersurface of upper epidermis of a corn leaf showing diagrammatically the formation of a *n + n* mycelium of *Ustilago zeae.*

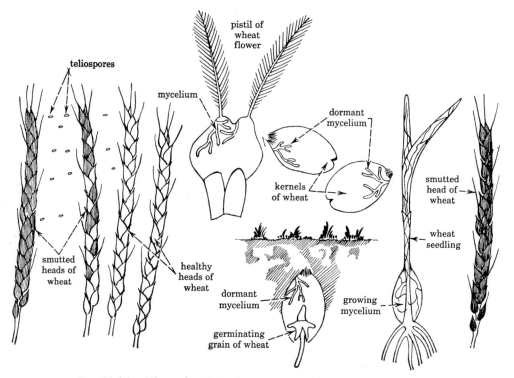

Fig. 20.34. Life cycle of *Ustilago tritici*, a blossom-infecting smut.

As in the blossom-infecting smuts, masses of smut spores (teliospores) replace the mature grain of wheat (Fig. 20.35). In contrast to loose smuts, however, the grain coats remain intact, and infected grains resemble normal ones. At harvest time the infected grains are broken and the teliospores are thoroughly mixed with the healthy grains, to which they firmly adhere. As the name stinking smut indicates, the teliospores have a very unpleasant odor. Grain mixed with them is unfit for flour or for animal feed. The presence of large numbers of smut spores as dust during threshing greatly increases the fire hazard; explosions and serious fires are not infrequent when heavily smutted grain is threshed.

The teliospores carry the fungus over the season unfavorable for growth. Adhering to the grain, they are sown with it. Meiosis occurs in the teliospore, and frequently several mitotic divisions follow, producing several haploid nuclei within. Upon germination of the teliospore a short haploid mycelium is formed that gives rise to numerous spores called **sporidia**. The sporidia conjugate by means of conjugation tubes, either while still attached to the haploid mycelium or after falling away. After conjugation a short $n + n$ mycelium is formed which produces conidia. Seedlings may be infected by these conidia, or a second short mycelium may form that produces another crop of conidia. At any rate, infection of seedling wheat plants is brought about by conidia. The young mycelium grows best in, or adjacent to, meristematic tissue. It keeps pace with the developing wheat plant. When the grain starts to head out, the mycelium enters the young ovaries of developing flowers. Hyphal filaments may eventually replace all normal cells of the grain, except the coats. Teliospores are formed by these hyphal cells, and the cycle is repeated (Fig. 20.35).

Comparison of Seedling- and Blossom-infecting Smuts. In both types, teliospores are formed in the inflorescence of cereals. In seedling infection the teliospores overwinter in the soil or *on the grain.* Upon germination they produce sporidia that conjugate and develop a small mycelium from which conidia are cut off. Conidia infect only seedling grain plants. In blossom-infecting smuts, teliospores lead to the infec-

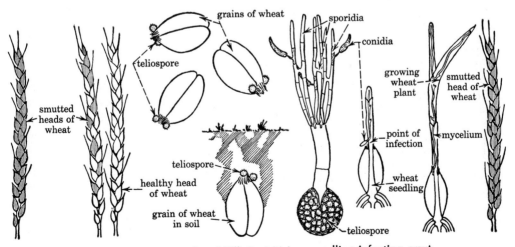

Fig. 20.35. Life cycle of *Tilletia tritici*, a seedling-infecting smut.

tion of the pistils of nearby flowers, and the rudimentary mycelium remains dormant *in the grain* over winter. In both types of infection the young seedling wheat plant has within its cells an actively growing smut mycelium that keeps pace with the development of the cereal. This mycelium invades young ovaries and fills the ovary with hyphal cells, which become teliospores.

Significant Features of the Basidiomycetes

A. Vegetative characteristics.

1. Hyphae septate; extensive haploid mycelium, one haploid nucleus in each cell; extensive $n + n$ mycelium, two haploid nuclei in each cell.

2. Homobasidiomycetes: mostly saprophytic forms, a few species parasitic on trees.

3. Heterobasidiomycetes: parasitic on plants; some, such as the rusts, heteroecious with complicated life cycles; in a few species true basidiospores not produced.

B. Reproductive characteristics.

1. Asexual: asexual spores not formed by the Homobasidiomycetes; various sorts formed by different species of Heterobasidiomycetes; uredospores and aeciospores by the rusts, sporidia by some smuts.

2. Sexual: no motile sex cells, or gametangia.

   (*a*) Homobasidiomycetes: (1) union of two haploid hyphal cells; (2) $n + n$ mycelium with two haploid nuclei in each cell developed from the union of the two haploid hyphal cells; (3) basidiocarp (mushroom, puffballs, bracket fungi) produced by the $n + n$ mycelium; (4) hymenium consisting of club-shaped basidia developed on the basidiocarp; (5) two haploid nuclei fuse in the basidia; (6) meiosis and four basidiospores formed.

   (*b*) Heterobasidiomycetes: (1) basidia develop from resistant teliospores; may be short filamentous cells or short four-celled filaments; meiosis occurs in formation of basidia; (2) fertilization with eventual fusion of two haploid nuclei varies considerably from species to species.

CLASS FUNGI IMPERFECTI

About 24,000 species of fungi, in some 1200 genera, are known only by their asexual stages. The class name, Fungi Imperfecti, arises from the custom of calling the sexual stages of fungi **perfect stages** and the asexual stages **imperfect stages**. Since only the imperfect stages of this large group of fungi are known, they are called the Fungi Imperfecti. Obviously, the classification is an artificial one.

In general, the structure of the hyphae, which are septate, and of spores suggests that many imperfect fungi may be Ascomycetes; others may be Basidiomycetes. The Fungi Imperfecti may be considered to be Ascomycetes or Basidiomycetes whose sexual stages have not been observed or no longer exist. The classification of these fungi is fraught with great difficulties largely because a natural classification is based upon sexual stages and the morphology of sexual and asexual stages is by no means coordinated. For instance two forms may have very similar conidial stages but very different sexual stages. The various categories of classification in this class are designated as **form-genera** or **form-families** to show that the members of the genera or family do not necessarily have a natural or family relationship. For instance some species have been named simply on the basis of the host upon which they were found, a procedure that resulted in naming hundreds of literally nonexistent "species."

Only a single form-group will be mentioned, the form-order Moniliales; it is the largest in the class having over 10,000 form-species. Most of the fungal pathogens of man belong here. Some of them have recently been demonstrated to be causal agents of various types of allergy. *Penicillium* and *Aspergillus* are genera frequently placed in this order because there are many species belonging to these genera whose sexual stages are unknown. This means that the *Penicillium* of Roquefort cheese and the forms from which penicillin is obtained are Fungi Imperfecti because the formation of asci has never been observed, even though tons of mycelium of these species have been grown.

Penicillium notatum has won deserved fame because **penicillin,** a drug derived from it, will inhibit the growth of bacteria without injuring human tissue. Substances such as penicillin, formed by one organism which inhibits the growth of other organisms, are called **antibiotics** (Fig. 20.36). Our knowledge of them dates back to 1870 but their significance was not fully appreciated until the discovery of penicillin.

In 1928, Fleming investigated extracts of *Penicillium* and after demonstrating its antibiotic properties gave it, in the year following, the name penicillin. It was not until after 1940 that a concentrated effort was made to produce penicillin on a commercial scale.

Many thousands of pounds of the mycelium of *Penicillium notatum* have been grown, and the species has been subjected to intensive study, yet no sexual stages have ever been observed. The absence of sexual reproduction presents the geneticists who are studying *Penicillium notatum* with a difficult problem. Nevertheless, they have succeeded in growing strains that produce many times more penicillin per pound than do the original strains. Figure 20.37 illustrates several steps in the commercial production of penicillin.

Several forms in the Moniliales are adapted to capture and to destroy microscopic animals. A few actually trap nematode worms by forming small rings each of which quickly constricts when stimulated by the contact of a nematode crawling

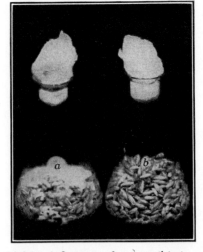

Fig. 20.36. Influence of an antibiotic. Both flasks were inoculated with the same amount of a fungus. Flask *a* received no antibiotic, whereas an antibiotic was added to flask *b*. (Photo courtesy of Division of Plant Pathology, Univ. of Calif.)

through it. A nematode-trapping form and several types of conidiophores are shown in Fig. 20.38.

THE LICHENS

General Characteristics and Distribution

The lichens are composite plants composed of algae and fungi. The algal components are generally single-celled forms belonging to either the Chlorophycophyta or the Schizophyceae. When free from the fungus, the algae may exist normally. The fungal component in all but three of some four hundred genera is an Ascomycete; the three exceptions have the characters of the Basidiomycetes. The fungal component of the lichen cannot live separated from the alga unless supplied with a special nutritive medium.

The association of a fungus and an alga in the lichen is generally believed to be

Fig. 20.37. Steps in the production of the drug penicillin. A, high-producing culture (strain Q176) of *Penicillium* obtained by treating an ordinary culture with ultraviolet light; B, spore culture of strain Q176 used to inoculate the large fermentation tanks; C, interior view of a large fermentation tank; D, the white sheet is mycelium, which is being pressed free of the liquid culture medium that contains the penicillin. (Photos courtesy of Cutter Laboratories, Berkeley, Calif.)

symbiotic; i.e., both the fungus and the alga derive benefit from the association. The alga furnishes food for the fungus, which supplies moisture and shelter for the alga.

A section through a lichen thallus reveals four distinct layers. The top and bottom layers consist of a compact mass of intertwining fungal filaments. The algal cells form a green layer beneath the top mass of fungal filaments, and a loose layer of hyphae lies directly below the algal cells (Fig. 20.39).

Lichens are widespread. They form luxuriant growths on the frozen, northern tundras, where they supply feed ("reindeer moss") for deer. In our own country they

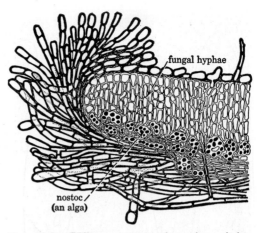

Fig. 20.39. Cross section through a lichen thallus. (Redrawn from Darbishire.)

frequently cover rocks, trees, and boards exposed to sun and wind (Fig. 20.40). They are slow but efficient "soil formers"; rocks are disintegrated slowly by their action. Sufficient soil may thus be formed to support the growth of mosses and some flowering plants.

Asexual Reproduction. Lichens may multiply simply by the distribution of small pieces of the vegetative thallus. Many lichens produce special disk-shaped bodies, composed of both a fungus and an alga, which serve as a means of vegetative reproduction. These bodies are called **soredia** (singular, **soredium**).

Both the algal and the fungal components may produce spores. The alga may grow independently, but if, upon germination of the fungal spores, the young hyphae do not find the required algal cells they soon die.

Sexual Reproduction. Sexual reproduction is characteristic of the type of fungus present in the lichen. Since the fungal component is, in the great majority of lichens, an Ascomycete, ascocarps with asci and ascospores are formed. Upon the ger-

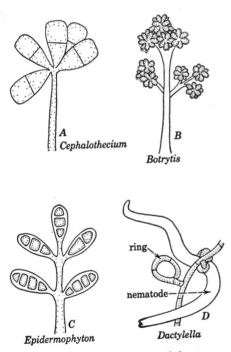

Fig. 20.38. Conidia; A, B, C, of form-genera of moniliales; D, nematode capturing rings of *Dactylella*. (A, B, C redrawn from Alexopoulos, *Introductory Mycology*, John Wiley & Sons, Inc.; D redrawn from Dreschler.)

Fig. 20.40.   Lichen hanging from oak tree branches.

mination of the ascospore the germ tube must find its proper algal associate in order to survive.

Classification

Phylum	Eumycophyta
Class	Ascomycetes
Subclass	Protoascomycetes
Order	Endomycetales
Genus and species	*Saccharomyces cervisiae*
Subclass	Euascomycetes
Order	Exoascales
	Taphrinales
Genus	*Taphrina*
Order	Aspergillales
Family	Aspergillaceae
Genera	*Aspergillus*
	Penicillium
Order	Erysiphales
Family	Erysiphaceae
Genus	*Erysiphe*
Order	Hypocreales
Family	Clavicipitaceae
Genus	*Claviceps*
Order	Pezizales
Family	Pezizaceae
Genus	*Peziza*
Family	Sclerotineaceae
Genus	*Sclerotinia*
Class	Basidiomycetes
Subclass	Homobasidiomycetes
Genera and species	*Psalliota campestris*
	Amanita muscaria
	Amanita phalloides
	Fomes applanatus
Subclass	Heterobasidiomycetes
Order	Uredinales
Genus, species, and strain	*Puccinia graminis tritici*
Order	Ustilaginales
Family	Ustilaginaceae
Genera and species	*Ustilago zeae*
	Ustilago tritici
	Ustilago avenae
Family	Tilletiaceae
Genus and species	*Tilletia tritici*
Class	Fungi Imperfecti
Form order	Moniliales
Form genera and species	*Penicillium notatum*
	Aspergillus
	Dactylaria brachophaga

21

The Viruses

Discovery and Characteristics. Toward the close of the last century, Iwanowski, a Russian plant scientist, carefully pressed some sap from a stunted and diseased tobacco plant. With a small amount of this sap he inoculated a healthy tobacco plant. The healthy plant soon developed signs of a disease similar to that of the plant from which the sap was taken. The experiment was repeated, but this time the sap from the diseased plant was forced through a filter with pores so small that bacteria could not pass through them. The healthy plants inoculated with this filtered sap soon contracted the disease of the original plant (Fig. 21.1). This was a new discovery: a disease could be transmitted from one plant to another by a filtered sap that was free of visible living bodies even when viewed by the most powerful light microscopes. The sap contained "something" that caused an infectious disease. Diseases transmissible from one plant to another by an agent too small to be distinguished even when enlarged some 3000 times are called **virus diseases.** Such diseases occur in both plants and animals. The name **virus** is given to the agent or substance that causes the disease. The nature of viruses is still an interesting scientific puzzle.

Smallpox, poliomyelitis, and measles are examples of virus diseases of man. Dog

Fig. 21.1. A, healthy tobacco plant; B, tobacco plant infected with curly top. (Photo courtesy of Esau.)

431

Fig. 21.2. The electron microscope. (Photo courtesy of Hillier.)

distemper is caused by a virus. The so-called mosaic diseases of plants, characterized by a mottling of the leaves, are also virus diseases. Even though the actual agent causing these virus diseases was long unknown, much has been learned of methods to combat the diseases. For instance, in 1796, an English country doctor named Jenner transferred material from the pustules of cows suffering from cowpox to a fresh scratch in the skin of man and found that this treatment would successfully prevent smallpox in man. It was general knowledge amongst country people that milkers never contracted smallpox. Jenner purposely rubbed dried material from cowpox pustules on scratches on the arm of his small son and later exposed him to virulent smallpox. The boy did not con-

tract the disease. Application of this principle, now known as **vaccination,** has reduced the incidence of the once-dreaded smallpox almost to zero.

Culture of Viruses. The study of viruses has been difficult because, except for the recent development of knowledge about the virus of poliomyelitis, it has only been possible to culture them in living cells. Rabbit skin, tobacco leaves, bacteria, or cultures of living tissues have been necessary as media for multiplication of viruses. Tobacco virus is, for instance, increased in quantity by growing it in tobacco leaves; cowpox virus may be grown on rabbit skin or obtained from cattle. The virus of infantile paralysis presented special problems in that only rhesus monkeys can serve as satisfactory experimental hosts. Using information obtained from preparing muscle tissue for a study of respiration (page 214) a procedure was developed for disintegrating monkey kidneys in a Waring Blendor and using the cell mass so prepared as a culture medium for the poliomyelitis virus. Such a tissue mass, while certainly not composed of living cells, has some properties associated with living cells. This technique made possible the commercial production of a vaccine for poliomyelitis. However, the methods of production and testing are so difficult that the vaccine was in short supply after its introduction and better methods of immunization will eventually be worked out.

The Electron Microscope. The Radio Corporation of America has recently improved a microscope that uses a beam of electrons, much as an ordinary microscope utilizes a beam of light (Figs. 21.2, 21.3). Magnifications of some 13,000 diameters may be obtained with this instrument; the very best compound microscopes, using ordinary light, magnify about 2000 times. Although extremely small particles may be studied with the electron microscope, the instrument has its limitations. The objects of study must be exceedingly thin and in vacuum. Virus particles are among the objects that have been studied and photographed with the electron microscope (Fig. 21.6). These particles seem to be variously shaped, although most of them are spherical or rod-shaped.

It has been known for some time that bacteria could be killed and disintegrated by certain filterable viruses called **bacteriophages.** The actual infection and destruction of a bacterium by virus particles have recently been observed with the electron microscope. Thus, *Escherichia coli*, small bacteria that normally inhabit the large intestine of man, may be destroyed by inoculating a pure culture of the bacteria with the proper virus. The electron microscope shows that, shortly after inoculation of the bacterial culture, some small virus particles become attached to the surface of a bacterium (Fig. 21.4A). Then later many virus particles are ejected from the disintegrating bacterium (Fig. 21.4B, C). This process requires less than 30 minutes. Theoretically, this small bacterium, which is close to the limit of visibility with an ordinary light microscope, could contain about 37,000 virus particles.

The Nature of a Virus. In 1935, W. M. Stanley isolated a protein from tobacco plants infected with tobacco mosaic virus. The protein was not present in the healthy plants but occurred only in diseased plants. Furthermore, when it was injected in small amounts into healthy plants, not only did it bring about the mosaic disease in the healthy plants, but also it increased greatly in quantity. A very minute amount injected into a plant increased over 1 million times in 4 days. The particles of this protein aggregate to form crystallike structures (Fig. 21.5).

Such viruses may be studied chemically and physically just as ordinary protein is

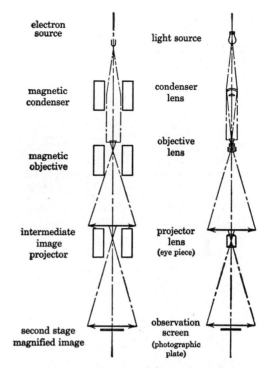

Fig. 21.3. Comparison of the path of electrons in the electron microscope with the path of light in an ordinary microscope. (Courtesy of Hillier.)

studied. Virus particles are very complex and may be broken apart chemically and their component parts examined. One portion of the virus particle responsible for tobacco mosaic is a **nucleic acid** (see page 54); other viruses that have been studied chemically also contain nucleic acid. It is significant that a nucleic acid is present as one component part of a virus and also is associated with nuclei and cell division in all the higher plants and animals.

The virus body causing chicken pox is a cubelike structure somewhat smaller than the smallest bacteria. As compared with the virus body of tobacco mosaic, it is very complex. The particle, when photographed by the electron microscope, is seen to have five dense areas so distributed as to suggest a five-spotted die (Fig. 21.6). Apparently a limiting surface structure surrounds each particle because the particles show certain osmotic phenomena.

The chicken pox virus has not yet been isolated as a crystalline structure and there is evidence that it may not be composed entirely of protein. Chemical analysis of

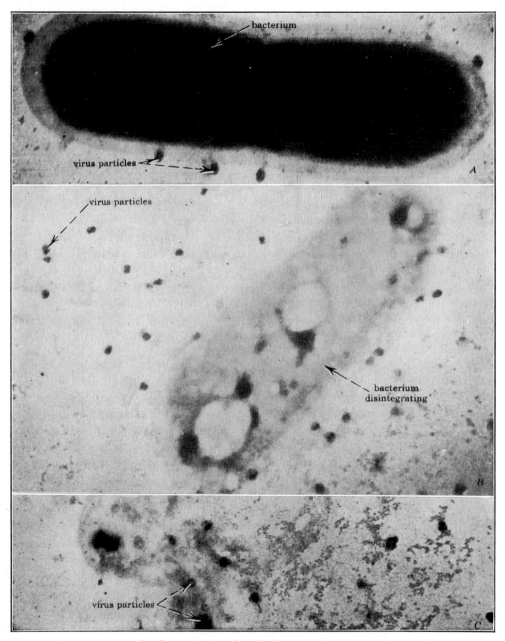

Fig. 21.4. Disintegration of a bacterium and multiplication of virus particles. (Electron photograph courtesy of Luria.)

carefully purified chicken pox virus shows it to contain hydrogen, carbon, nitrogen, sulfur, and phosphorus in approximately the same ratio as in the crystalline virus of tobacco. Both viruses contain nucleic acids. The chicken pox virus contains a fatty substance not present in the tobacco virus. In some respects the chicken pox virus more closely resembles bacteria than it does the crystalline virus of tobacco. It may contain certain enzymes necessary for respiration, although there is no evidence that it is able to carry on respiration. Other enzymes may be part of the virus particle. However, enzyme studies of viruses are complicated by two observations: (1) the viruses avidly absorb enzymes when placed in solutions containing enzymes, and (2) the types and concentration of enzymes always found associated with the virus are the same types and in the same concen-

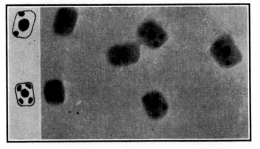

Fig. 21.6. Particles that cause chicken pox. (Electron photomicrograph courtesy of Smadel.)

trations as those found in the host cell. It is possible that the virus particle is so constructed that it contains certain essential protoplasmic systems and depends upon the host cells for other factors that it needs in order to grow and to reproduce itself.

No definite conclusions with respect to the "living" or "nonliving" nature of the elementary body of the chicken pox virus can as yet be drawn. It has a structure which resembles that of bacteria, and it appears to be too complex to be considered as a molecule. On the other hand, it lacks certain enzyme systems, including a normal respiratory system, which have always been associated with life. Thus, we may say, with out present limited knowledge, that viruses appear to be at the borderline between living cytoplasm and nonliving organic matter. Even within the virus group, certain viruses seem to closely approach living matter whereas others seem to be merely very complex organic molecules.

Classification of Viruses and Virus Diseases. Many angiosperms are susceptible to virus infection. It is also known that bacteria may be attacked by a viruslike agent. So far, no virus diseases of gymnosperms, mosses, ferns, or algae have been reported. Tobacco itself may suffer from 15 different viruses, and potatoes from 18. As early as 1935, virus diseases were known for 1100 species of angiosperms. Further-

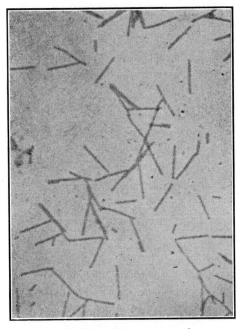

Fig. 21.5. Particles that cause tobacco mosaic. (Electron photomicrograph courtesy of Rawlins.)

more, a single virus may break down into distinct strains. Fifty-four strains have been described for the common tobacco mosaic. No satisfactory system for the classification of this large number of viruses has thus far been devised. Although many factors contribute to the difficulty of classifying viruses, the most important ones are: (1) Only a few viruses have been isolated in a pure form. (2) Viruses, except for that causing poliomyelitis, may be cultured only in living tissue. (3) Plant viruses are

Fig. 21.7. A, healthy sugar beet leaf; B, sugar beet leaf infected with mosaic virus; C, cells from healthy leaf; D, cells from diseased leaf. (Photo courtesy of Esau and Bennett.)

not specific; one virus usually infects several plants, and one plant may be infected with several viruses. (4) Although some viruses have been isolated as crystalline structures, there is still confusion as to whether viruses as a group should be considered as minute living organisms or nonliving complex proteins.

Symptoms of Virus Diseases of Plants. One of the most common symptoms of virus infection in plants is the occurrence of light-green or yellow areas on leaves (Fig. 21.7B). These areas range from small circles to large irregular patches. Uniform stripes or irregular bands of the normal green color may appear in the leaf. In some instances the entire diseased plant may be a much lighter green than the healthy one. Many variegated horticultural varieties of plants undoubtedly are infected with some mild-acting virus. The diseases characterized by mottling or variegation of leaves are referred to as "mosaics," and almost all are regarded as virus diseases. We have, for instance, tobacco mosaic, potato mosaic, and sugar cane mosaic.

The yellow or lighter areas of diseased leaves are usually thinner in cross section than are those of normal healthy leaves. The chloroplasts may be absent or very reduced in size (Fig. 21.7C, D) and in number, or they may be yellow in color. This reduction in the green pigment, and therefore in the color of the leaf, is called **chlorosis.** A chlorotic leaf is one that has light-green or yellow areas. Not all chlorotic leaves, however, harbor a mosaic virus; chlorosis may be due to a variety of conditions.

In addition to being chlorotic, the leaves of virus-infected plants may be irregular in shape with a rough or puckered surface, or rolled in along the edges, or reduced in width; or they may turn yellow and drop prematurely (Fig. 21.8).

Flowers of infected plants frequently are dwarfed, or mottled, or streaked. The streaking of flowers occasionally produces a highly prized horticultural variety; many hundreds of dollars have been paid for tulip bulbs infected with a virus that causes a streaking of the flowers (Fig. 21.9). Fruits

Fig. 21.8. Healthy plants compared with those infected with a virus. A, healthy bean; B, diseased bean; C, healthy grape; D, diseased grape. (Photo courtesy of Plant Pathology Division, Univ. of Calif.)

Fig. 21.9. Tulip flower infected with a virus disease. (Photo courtesy of McWhorter.)

Viruses seem to interfere in many plants with those tissues which are responsible for the production, as well as the translocation, of food (Fig. 21.10). This damage may result in a stunting of all organs of the plant (Fig. 21.1). To the plant grower it means a greatly reduced crop yield or even a loss of plants. For instance, peach yellows (a virus disease) causes an estimated loss of 450,000 trees annually in New Jersey, Pennsylvania, and Maryland. In a single area the spindle tuber virus disease of potatoes decreased the yield 88 per cent over a 4-year period.

Transmission of Viruses. Any organism that carries a disease-causing agent from one living thing to another is called a **vector.** Insects, particularly those that feed on plant juices, are the most important vectors of viruses of plants. Certain types of aphids, thrips, and leafhoppers account for the transmission of viruses from one plant to another. The aphids feed by injecting a long stylet into plant leaves or stems and sucking out plant juices. They obtain sap mostly from phloem tissues, from parenchyma cells of the cortex of stems, and from the mesophyll of leaves. The stylet may wind its way between cells of the cortex until it reaches the phloem, or it may pass directly through all cells in its path (Fig. 21.11). Thrips have large front mandibles with which they chisel their way into epidermal cells. They then suck out the cell contents.

may be small, distorted, and mottled. Tomatoes, peppers, melons, and beans infected with certain viruses show a distinct mottling; tomatoes and cucumbers may be distorted and much reduced in size. Stems may show discoloration of various sorts; frequently they are dwarfed and contain cankers or dead areas.

Viruses belonging to the mosaic group induce changes primarily in parenchyma tissue (see page 97). Vascular tissues, however, may be injured also, as the result of a primary injury to the parenchyma tissue of leaves and stems. Other viruses primarily harm the conducting tissue, particularly the phloem. The sieve tubes are injured and frequently killed, forming a mass of dead cells on the outer edge of the vascular bundle. This mass impairs the movements of food in the plant and results in injury to other plant tissues.

When insects feed on plants infected with virus diseases they ingest the virus along with the cell sap. The virus passes into the intestine of the aphid or thrip, is absorbed into the blood stream, and is carried to the salivary glands. The saliva secreted by the feeding insect now carries the virus, and any plant upon which the aphid or thrip feeds may become infected with the virus. There is some reason to believe that the virus may undergo development while

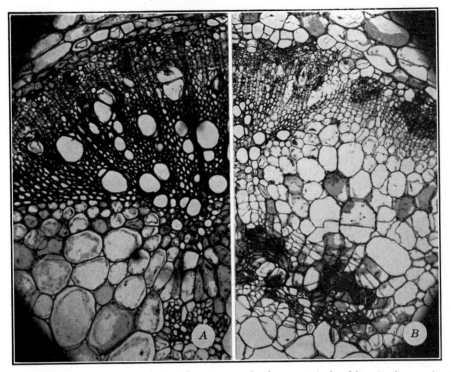

Fig. 21.10. Healthy and diseased vascular tissues of tobacco. A, healthy; B, diseased. (Photo courtesy of Esau.)

in the insect. With certain diseases, the insect cannot infect a healthy plant immediately after feeding upon a diseased plant; an **incubation period** (within the insect) of several days must intervene before the virus is capable of causing infection when secreted with the saliva.

Some viruses can be transmitted from one host plant to another only through specific insects. Often, however, the relation between insect, virus, and plant is not specific. One insect may carry several virus diseases, several different insects may carry the same virus, and several species of plants may be infected with the same virus. The virus that causes Pierce's disease of grapes, for instance, may be carried by 15 different species of insects and can also affect 37 other species of plants. Some viruses are so very infectious that they may be carried

from one plant to another by almost any sort of contact. Workers in the tobacco field may carry tobacco virus from one plant to another on their hands or clothing. The tobacco virus is not destroyed in the manufacture of smoking tobacco. Thus, should

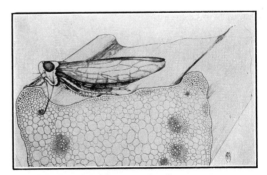

Fig. 21.11. Leaf hopper feeding on beet petiole. (Courtesy of Bennett.)

cigarettes made from virus-infected leaves be used by a field worker, he may easily carry the virus on his hands to healthy plants. Tobacco virus may also cause a disease of tomato plants.

A few of the more common virus diseases of plants are: aster yellows, which has been transmitted by leafhoppers to more than 120 species in 30 different families, includ-ing such crop plants as celery, lettuce, carrot, and parsley; beet curly top, trans-mitted by leafhopper to numerous species in at least three families; sugar cane mo-saic; mosaic of legumes; phony disease of peach; potato mosaic; tobacco mosaic; tomato spotted wilt; wheat mosaic, trans-mitted in some unknown manner through the soil.

22

The Bryophytes

CHARACTERISTICS

The phylum Bryophyta includes the mosses and liverworts. Although all bryophytes are morphologically distinct from the thallophytes, it is difficult to separate them from the algae in general on the basis of any single character. Perhaps the two greatest differences between the algae and bryophytes are the general structure of the plant bodies and the gametangia. It will be recalled (page 326) that the plant body of the thallophytes is generally composed either of single cells or filaments of cells, or of intertwining filaments resulting in a more or less complex body. Layers of parenchyma tissue occur in some forms. With the exception of one stage in the life history of the mosses, the bryophyte plant body is never filamentous. It is composed of blocks or sheets of cells forming a parenchymatous tissue (see page 456).

The gametangia of the thallophytes are unicellular or, if multicellular as in *Ectocarpus*, lack a protective jacket of sterile cells. The gametangia of the bryophytes, on the other hand, are multicellular and always have a protective jacket of sterile cells. Each and every cell of the multicellular structure of *Ectocarpus* produces gametes. However, the multicellular female gametangium characteristic of all members of the Bryophyta produces but a single gamete, the egg, which is surrounded by a layer of protecting cells. The male gametangia each produce numerous sperms, but the sperm-producing cells are always surrounded by a protective layer of parenchyma cells. These differences are shown in Table 22.1.

Water is required by most algae and bryophytes to effect fertilization.

A definite alternation of generations occurs in all members of the Bryophyta, and the sporophyte (diploid) generation is always more or less dependent on the gametophyte (haploid) generation. In all Bryophyta an **embryo sporophyte**, consisting of a spherical or elongated mass of tissue, is formed directly after the germination of the zygote (Figs. 22.3C, 22.7).

Asexual spores are not formed in Bryophyta. Members of this phylum reproduce asexually either by fragmentation of the gametophyte or by special bodies known as **gemmae** (Fig. 22.11).

The bryophytes occur on soil, on the trunks of trees, on rocks, and many are truly aquatic.

Table 22.1. Tabulation of Differences between Thallophytes and Bryophytes

Thallophytes	Bryophytes
Mostly aquatic	Mostly terrestrial
Only a few of the most advanced develop embryos	All develop simple embryos
A few of the most advanced have sieve tube-like elements	Some mosses have cells suggesting sieve tubes, otherwise food conducted in relatively undifferentiated cells
None have water-conducting elements	Simple water-conducting cells
In general no specialized water and nutrient absorbing tissue. Rhizoids and haustoria may occur in some fungi	Rhizoids anchor and absorb water and mineral nutrients
Mostly filamentous or a lacework of intertwining filaments, parenchyma in a few	Only one stage of mosses is filamentous, all others are formed of parenchyma cells
A definite alternation of generations in many forms	All have an alternation of generations
Both sporophytes and gametophytes independent	Gametophyte independent; sporophyte dependent
Sporophyte frequently large and complex	Sporophtye small and relatively simple
Gametangia either single cells or groups of sin ɡle cells not accompanied by a jacket of sterile vegetative cells	Gametangia always composed of the gamete-producing cells protected by a jacket of sterile vegetative cells

Alternation of Generations

As just mentioned, all Bryophyta have a distinct alternation of generations; a haploid plant, producing gametes, alternates with a diploid plant; meiosis occurs in the diploid plant, and haploid spores containing *n* chromosomes in each nucleus are formed. Thus a haploid gamete-producing plant—the **gametophyte**—regularly alternates with a diploid spore-producing plant—the **sporophyte.**

have originated when unknown factors delayed meiosis so that this process occurred, not immediately upon the germination of the zygote, as it does in many algae, but only after many mitotic cell divisions had intervened. These cell divisions intervening between fertilization and meiosis have resulted in the sporophyte plant. We shall see in our study of the last five phyla (pages 441–502) how the interval between fertilization and meiosis lengthens, resulting in larger and more complex sporophytes. Because of this intimate relationship between fertilization and meiosis, the spores formed by the sporophyte as a result of meiosis are one stage of the sexual cycle. They do not, as do the asexual zoospores of *Saprolegnia* or *Vaucheria* or the uredospores of wheat, reproduce an exact replica of the plant that produced them. Thus we should consider both the sporophyte and gametophyte as two phases in a complete sexual life history.

Classification

The Bryophyta are divided into three classes: the Hepaticae (liverworts), the Anthocerotae (*Anthoceros*), and the Musci (mosses). The Hepaticae are the most primitive bryophytes. The simplest liverworts consist of a flat, ribbonlike, green thallus which produces gametes and a meiospore-producing capsule or sporangium embedded within the gametophyte

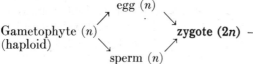

egg (*n*)

Gametophyte (*n*) (haploid) ↗ ↘ zygote (2*n*) → sporophyte (2*n*) → meiospores (*n*) →
                                 (diploid)

sperm (*n*)   gametophyte (*n*) (haploid)

Formerly, it was customary to call the gametophyte a sexual plant and the sporophyte an asexual plant. We have seen, however, that fertilization and meiosis are but two phases of a single sexual cycle. It is believed that the sporophyte plant may

thallus. The name liverwort is very old having been used in the 9th Century. It was probably applied to these plants because of their fancied resemblance to the liver and the belief that plants resembling human organs would cure diseases of the organs they resembled. At any rate a prescription for a liver complaint in the 1500's called for "liverworts soaked in wine."

Less primitive Hepaticae have simple stems and leaves and the sporophytes are borne above the green gametophyte. The mosses are probably the best known class of the Bryophyta. They have either an upright or prostrate leafy gametophyte and may form extensive mats on moist, shady soil. The sporophyte is raised above the leafy gametophyte. *Anthoceros* has the simplest gametophyte of the group but its sporophyte has a meristematic region which is a type of tissue more characteristic of higher forms than of the Bryophyta.

CLASS HEPATICAE

General Characteristics and Distribution

The Hepaticae are commonly known as the liverworts. There are some 8500 species of liverworts. The great majority of them grow in moist, shady localities. The gametophyte is the prominent plant, and the sporophyte is usually partially parasitic on the gametophyte. This latter generation, which is green, may grow either as a flat ribbon or as a leafy shoot. In either event the plant body is frequently called a **thallus**, even though its internal structure does not correspond to that of the thallophytes. Of the four orders in the Hepaticae, we shall consider briefly the characteristics of two genera, *Riccia* and *Marchantia*, both belonging to the order Marchantiales.

The gametophytes of the Marchantiales are small, green, ribbon-shaped plants (Figs. 22.1, 22.9, 22.10). They branch regularly by a simple forking at the growing tip, resulting in a number of Y-shaped branches. In some species a rosette may be formed. Air chambers that open by a pore and that are formed by, or con-

Fig. 22.1. Habit of A, *Riccia*, and B, *Ricciocarpus*. ×1. (Courtesy of Russell.)

tain, special cells adapted for photosynthesis, form the upper portion of the thallus (Figs. 22.2, 22.12A). Several types of storage cells generally make up the lower half.

Rhizoids, special elongated cells, performing the functions of roots (anchorage, and absorption of water and mineral nutrients) extend downward from the lowermost layer of cells. The thallus is thus differentiated into distinct upper and lower portions. Scales, frequently brown or red, are formed on the lower surface (Fig. 22.2).

Riccia

Riccia is a widely distributed genus, and, although it requires water for active growth, most species will withstand considerable drought. Several species are aquatic, growing either on mud or on the surface of small ponds.

Gametophyte.   The gametophyte is a small, green thallus, frequently forming a rosette (Fig. 22.1). The tissue on the lower side is composed of colorless cells that may contain starch.   The tissue on the upper side consists of vertical rows of chlorophyll-bearing cells between which are air chambers (Fig. 22.2). The gametangia are embedded in deep, lengthwise depressions or furrows, in the dorsal surface of the thallus.

Antheridia and archegonia are usually found on the same gametophyte.

Antheridia.   The antheridia of different representatives of the Bryophyta are similar in structure though they may vary somewhat in shape.   In *Riccia* they are pear-shaped and composed of two types of cells: (1) fertile and (2) sterile (Figs. 22.3A, 22.4).   Fertile cells give rise to sperms, which are relatively numerous, small, and dense with protoplasm.   The sterile cells form a protective jacket, one cell in thickness, around the fertile cells.   The antheridia of *Riccia,* and of other Bryophyta, are thus composed of a mass of fertile cells, all of which develop into sperms, and a protective jacket of sterile cells.   The antheridia are connected to the gametophyte by a short stalk.

Mature sperms consist mainly of an elongated nucleus with two long flagella.   They may be shot from the mature antheridium with considerable force, or they may be extruded slowly in a single gelatinous mass. In any event they do not leave the antheridium until enough moisture is present to allow them to swim about.

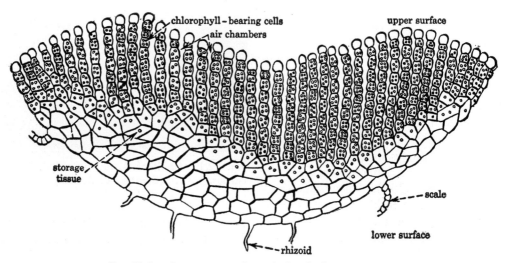

Fig. 22.2.   Cross section through the thallus of *Riccia*.

Archegonia. The archegonium of *Riccia* is a flask-shaped structure consisting of two parts: (1) an expanded basal portion, the **venter**, and (2) an elongated **neck** (Fig. 22.5). Four **cover cells** are located at the top of the neck. Each archegonium contains a single egg cell, which is located in the venter. A short stalk attaches the

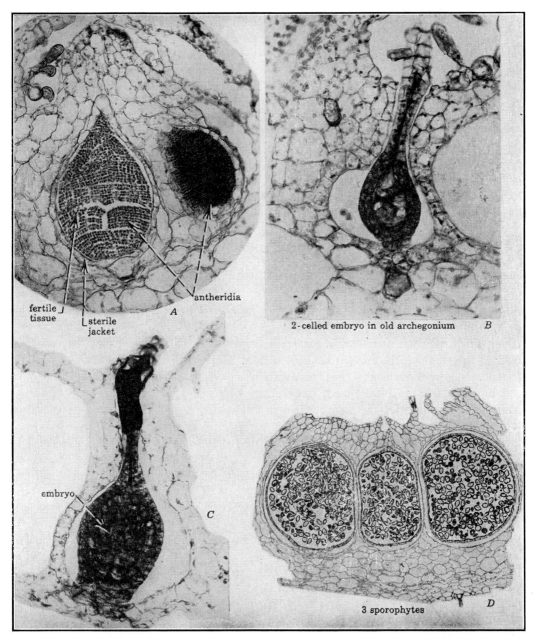

fertile tissue   sterile jacket   *A*   antheridia

2-celled embryo in old archegonium   *B*

embryo   *C*

3 sporophytes   *D*

Fig. 22.3. Photomicrographs of sections of thallus of *Riccia*. ×100. (Photo courtesy of Triarch Products.)

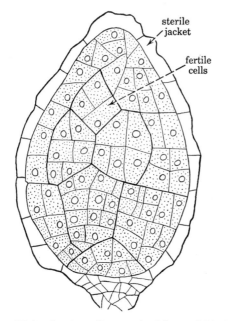

Fig. 22.4. Section of an antheridium of *Riccia*.

phyte. This mass of undifferentiated, parasitic cells comprising the young sporophyte is an **embryo.** It is located within the venter of the archegonium.

Further development of the embryo involves differentiation of an outer layer of cells to form a protective jacket of sterile tissue surrounding a mass of cells that are capable of forming spores. This fertile or spore-forming tissue is called **sporogenous tissue.** The sporogenous cells continue to divide by ordinary cell division until many have formed. All these cells are **spore mother cells,** and will undergo meiosis, producing spores with the haploid number of chromosomes (Fig. 22.8).

Meiosis consists of two cell divisions, during which the number of chromosomes is halved. Since two divisions are involved,

archegonium to the gametophyte. Archegonia of a similar structure are found in other Bryophyta.

Shortly before the egg cell is mature, the cover cells separate. At the same time the cells in the center of the neck dissolve, so that an open canal connects the venter with the moisture outside of the archegonium (Fig. 22.5). The free-swimming sperms move toward certain chemical substances formed by the archegonium, for they swim to it and then down the canal, opened by the dissolution of the neck canal cells. This response to chemical stimuli is known as a **chemotactic response.** Several sperms may enter the archegonium, but only one fertilizes the egg in the venter (Fig. 22.6).

The Sporophyte. As a result of the fusion of sperm and egg nuclei, the zygote contains the diploid, or $2n$, number of chromosomes. Mitosis now proceeds in a more or less orderly manner until a spherical mass of some 30 or more similar cells is formed (Figs. 22.3C, 22.7). These cells are partially dependent upon the gameto-

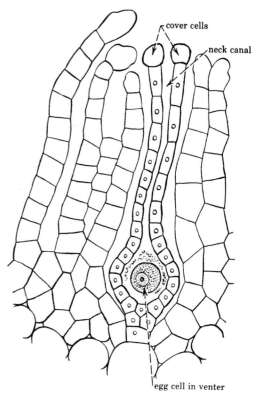

Fig. 22.5. Section of an archegonium of *Riccia*. (Redrawn from Smith, *Cryptogamic Botany,* Vol. 2, McGraw-Hill Book Co.)

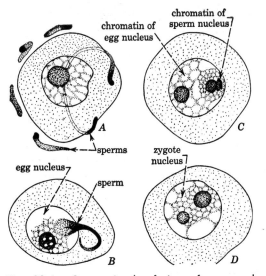

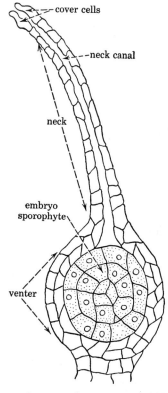

Fig. 22.6. Stages in the fusion of egg and sperm in a liverwort that is similar to *Riccia*. (Redrawn from Showalter.)

Fig. 22.7. Section of a young embryo sporophyte of *Riccia* embedded in center of archegonium. (Redrawn from Smith, *Cryptogamic Botany*, Vol. 2, McGraw-Hill Book Co.)

four spores are formed from each spore mother cell. Each group of four spores, formed from a single spore mother cell, is usually referred to as a **tetrad** or **quartet** of spores.

The mature sporophyte of *Riccia* (Figs. 22.3D, 22.8) is called a **sporangium** or **capsule**. It is composed of a jacket of sterile cells enclosing a mass of spores. The sporophyte wall breaks down when the spores are mature. These spores remain embedded in the gametophyte thallus and are not released until after the death and decay of the gametophyte. Furthermore, the sporophyte is dependent on the gametophyte for its nutrients. When the spores germinate each grows into a typical gametophyte plant.

The complete life history of *Riccia* may be diagrammed as shown.

Significant Steps in the Life History of *Riccia*

1. The gametophyte, a small, green, flat plant, absorbs water and mineral salts from the soil and carbon dioxide from the air. It contains chlorophyll and can synthesize food. All gametophytic nuclei are haploid (n chromosomes).

2. The gametangia (antheridia and archegonia) develop in a furrow on the upper surface of the gametophyte.

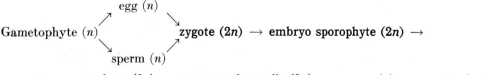

3. Each antheridium produces thousands of sperms.

4. A single egg is formed in the venter of each archegonium.

5. The gametes (eggs and sperms) contain n chromosomes.

6. When sufficient moisture is present, the mature sperms are extruded from the antheridium. The neck of the mature archegonium is opened and sperms swim down to the egg in the venter.

7. Each egg is fertilized by a single sperm.

8. The zygote, as a result of the union of two haploid gametic nuclei, contains $2n$ chromosomes.

9. An embryo sporophyte, consisting of a spherical mass of undifferentiated cells, partially parasitic upon the gametophyte, develops from the zygote. Each nucleus of the embryo sporophyte contains $2n$ chromosomes.

10. The cells of the embryo differentiate into a sporangium consisting of a jacket of sterile cells enclosing a mass of fertile cells.

11. Spore mother cells, each with $2n$ chromosomes, form in the sporangium.

12. The spore mother cells undergo meiosis. A quartet of spores forms from each spore mother cell. All the spore mother cells contain $2n$ chromosomes, the spores n chromosomes.

13. Upon the death and decay of the old

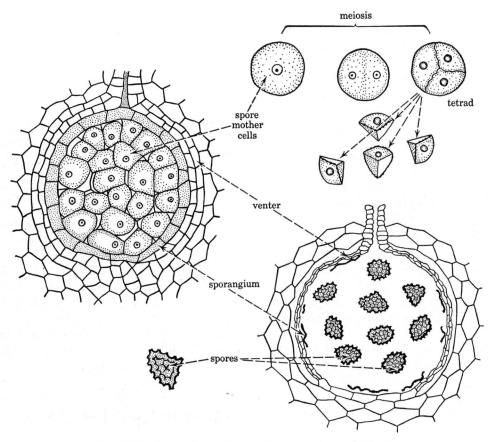

Fig. 22.8. Spore formation in the sporophyte of *Riccia*.

gametophyte, spores are liberated and new gametophytes are developed from them.

Marchantia

Marchantia may grow in large mats on moist rocks and soil in shady locations. It is widely distributed and fairly common on the banks of cool streams. It is somewhat better adapted to growing on land than *Riccia,* but considerable moisture is still required for active growth and for fertilization.

Gametophyte. The gametophyte of *Marchantia,* and of other members of the

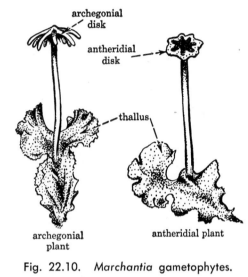

Fig. 22.10. *Marchantia* gametophytes.

Fig. 22.9. Male and female plants of *Marchantia.* ✕ ¾. (Courtesy of Russell.)

Fig. 22.11. Gemmae cups of *Marchantia.* ✕1.

family to which it belongs, differs from that of *Riccia* in that the gametangia are on special disks, raised some distance above the vegetative thallus (Figs. 22.9, 22.10). The thallus, although having the same gen-

eral appearance as that of *Riccia,* is coarser and larger. On its upper surface are polygonal areas, with a small but conspicuous pore in the center. These areas, with their air pores, mark the outlines of air chambers,

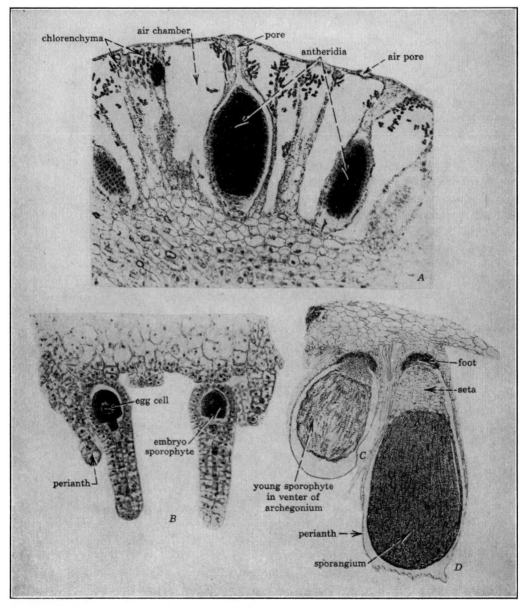

Fig. 22.12. Photomicrographs of reproductive disks of *Marchantia*. (Photo courtesy of Triarch Products.)

each filled with short filaments of cells containing chloroplasts. The thallus has a midrib (Fig. 22.10). As in *Riccia,* the lower surface of the thallus is composed of colorless cells, some of which are modified for storage. Rhizoids, which anchor the thallus and serve as organs for absorption, grow from the cells covering the lower surface. Several rows of scales are also attached to this lower surface.

Asexual Reproduction. Marchantia reproduces asexually in two ways: (1) older parts of the thallus die and the younger portions, no longer attached, develop into new individual plants; (2) small cups, known as **gemmae cups,** form on the upper surface, and small disks of green tissue, called **gemmae,** grow from the bottom of these cups (Fig. 22.11). The gemmae, when mature, are disjoined from the thallus and distributed over nearby areas. New gametophyte plants grow from the gemmae.

Sexual Reproduction. The gametangia are very similar in structure to those of *Riccia.* The antheridia are pear-shaped bodies composed of a jacket of sterile tissue surrounding the sperms (Fig. 22.12A). They are borne on disks raised above the thallus on slender stalks, called **antheridiophores** (Figs. 22.9, 22.10). The antheridiophores are modified portions of the thallus having furrows, rhizoids, and air chambers. The antheridia develop in cavities on the upper surface of the disk, the youngest antheridia being close to the outer margin of the disk. The mature sperms are extruded in a gelatinous mass.

The archegonia are flask-shaped and have the same structures as those of *Riccia* —the venter, the neck, and the cover cells (Fig. 22.12B).

The antheridia and archegonia of *Marchantia* are found on separate plants; that is, the gametophytes are either male or female. The archegonia are borne on spe-

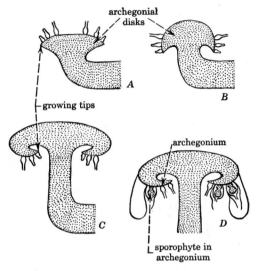

Fig. 22.13. Diagram showing development of archegonia of *Marchantia.* (Redrawn from Smith, *Cryptogamic Botany,* Vol. 2, McGraw-Hill Book Co.)

cialized branches called **archegoniophores.** The disk at the top of the archegoniophore is frequently an eight-lobed structure. In development, the lobes bend downward and then grow inward toward the stalk (Fig. 22.13). Thus the youngest portion of an older disk-bearing archegonia is on the underside and close to the stalk. The archegonia develop on the lower surface of the disk but in tissue similar to that found on the upper surface of the thallus. The striking fingerlike processes are developed between the lobes. The archegonia mature, and fertilization takes place when the disk of the archegoniophore is but slightly elevated above the thallus.

Sporophyte. The zygote develops, as in *Riccia,* into the embryo, which is a spherical mass of undifferentiated, colorless, dependent tissue (Fig. 22.12B). It is diploid, the nuclei of all its cells containing $2n$ chromosomes. Subsequent growth, however, is more complicated than in *Riccia.* Some cells of the embryo divide to form a mushroomlike growth that becomes embedded in the gametophyte tissue. This growth is called the **foot.** The cells in the central portion of the embryo form a stalk or **seta.** As the seta elongates, the lower cells develop into a **sporangium.** The lengthening of the seta suspends the sporangium below the disk. While this development is taking place, the stalk of the archegoniophore elongates, lifting the disk with its archegonia well above the thallus.

Fertilization stimulates the enlargement of the old achegonium, which keeps pace with the enlargement of the developing sporophyte. As a result, the sporophyte is continually enclosed within the archegonium, which, because of its increase in size and change in function and shape, is now known as the **calyptra** (Fig. 22.14A). In addition, the surrounding gametophyte tissue produces two other envelopes that protect the sporophyte.

The mature sporophyte is composed of three parts: the **foot,** the **seta,** and the **sporangium** (Fig. 22.12D). The foot is an absorbing organ. The seta serves to lower the sporangium away from the archegonial disk and thus to facilitate the distribution

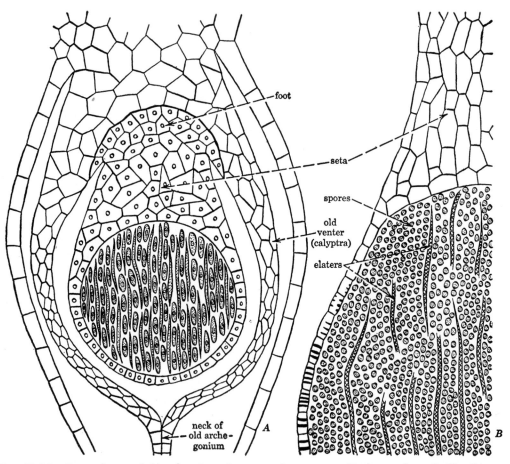

Fig. 22.14. Sporophytes of *Marchantia.* A, young; B, mature. (Redrawn from Smith, *Cryptogamic Botany,* Vol. 2, McGraw-Hill Book Co.)

of the spores. Before meiosis, the sporangium or capsule is composed of a jacket of sterile cells surrounding a mass of spore mother cells, among which are a number of sterile elongated cells (Fig. 22.14A). Four spores, each containing n chromosomes, develop from each spore mother cell. The elongated sterile cells are transformed into spiral elements, which change shape under the influence of varying moisture conditions. These cells are called **elaters** and they aid in the dispersal of the spores (Fig. 22.14B).

The dissemination of spores is aided by two structural features not found in *Riccia:* (1) the sporangium of the sporophyte hangs from the lower side of the raised archegonial disk, and (2) elaters help to empty the spore case. The spores develop immediately into new gametophytes.

The life history of *Marchantia* can be represented as shown.

differentiate into a foot, a seta, and a sporangium.

6. The foot is an absorbing organ. It is embedded in the gametophyte, from which it receives nourishment.

7. The sporangium consists of a jacket of sterile cells surrounding a mass of sporogenous tissue interspersed with elongated sterile cells.

8. The seta is a stalk that, in lengthening, lowers the sporangium below the surface of the archegonial disk.

9. Repeated mitotic cell divisions in the sporogenous tissue result in spore mother cells, each containing $2n$ chromosomes.

10. The spore mother cells divide by meiosis into quartets of spores, each containing n chromosomes.

11. The elongated sterile cells are transformed into spiral elaters.

12. The presence of the elaters and the

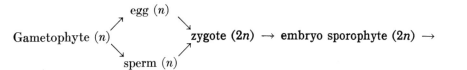

egg (n) — Gametophyte (n) — sperm (n) — zygote ($2n$) $\rightarrow$ embryo sporophyte ($2n$) $\rightarrow$

mature sporophyte ($2n$) $\rightarrow$ spore mother cells ($2n$) $\rightarrow$ spores (n) $\rightarrow$ gametophyte (n)

Significant Steps in the Life History of *Marchantia*

1. The gametophyte thallus absorbs water and mineral salts from the soil and carbon dioxide from the air. It is green and can synthesize foods. All nuclei of the gametophyte have n chromosomes.

2. The gametangia (antheridia and archegonia) are borne on upright branches called antheridiophores and archegoniophores.

3. The zygote is diploid, containing $2n$ chromosomes.

4. The embryo sporophyte, consisting of a spherical mass of undifferentiated cells, is formed from the zygote.

5. The cells of the embryo sporophyte

hanging position of the sporophyte aid in disseminating the spores.

13. The spores germinate immediately into new gametophyte plants.

CLASS ANTHOCEROTAE

The Anthocerotae have the simplest gametophytes of the Bryophyta. They are small, green thallus plants with little internal differentiation of vegetative tissues. They are slightly lobed with numerous rhizoids growing from the lower surface (Fig. 22.15). The antheridia are similar in structure to those encountered among the Hepaticae. They are located in roofed chambers in the upper portion of the thal-

Fig. 22.15.   *Anthoceros.*   ×1¼.   (Courtesy of Russell.)

The sporophyte (Figs. 22.15, 22.17) of the Anthocerotae is in striking contrast to those of the Hepaticae. The subepidermal cells contain chloroplasts, and typical stomata are found in the epidermis. A foot embedded in the thallus serves as an absorbing organ. The sporangium is an up-

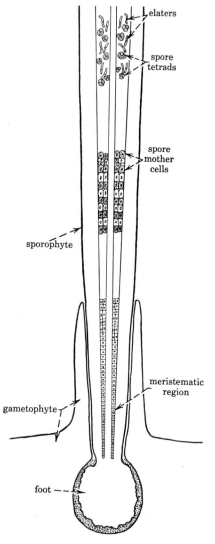

Fig.   22.17.   Longitudinal   median   section through sporophyte of *Anthoceros*. (Redrawn from Holman and Robbins, *A Textbook of General Botany*, John Wiley & Sons, Inc.)

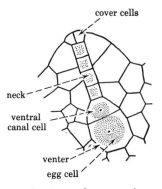

Fig.   22.16.   Section   of   an   archegonium   of *Anthoceros.*

lus. The archegonia are embedded within the thallus and in *direct contact* with the vegetative cells surrounding them (compare Figs. 22.3C and 22.16).

right elongated structure. The sporogenous tissue forms a cylinder parallel with the elongated axis of the sporangium. The spores mature not all at once but in progression from the top down. A meristematic region lies just above the foot and continually adds new cells to the base of the sporangium. Its presence means that spores may be produced over long periods.

Under exceptionally favorable growing conditions, the sporophyte may lengthen greatly. Some sporogenous tissue at the base of the sporangium may be replaced by a conspicuous conducting strand. The foot enlarges and, through decay of the gametophyte, comes into more or less direct contact with the soil. Such sporophytes are capable of maintaining themselves independently for some time.

CLASS MUSCI

General Characteristics and Structure

We have seen that the liverworts are small and inconspicuous plants; they are not generally noticed where they grow on some stream bank or moist roadside. Although the mosses are small plants, they are nevertheless conspicuous. They fre-

Fig. 22.19. *Mnium*, gametophyte with attached sporophytes.

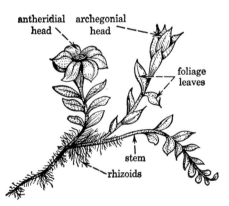

Fig. 22.18. *Mnium*, showing location of gametangia.

quently cover rather large areas of stream banks. They grow on rocks, on trees, and sometimes submerged in streams. Some are able to resist considerable drought, but, like the liverworts, all require moisture for active growth and reproduction.

The mosses as a class show great structural uniformity. The gametophytes of nearly all species have two growth stages:

(1) a creeping, filamentous stage (the **protonema**), from which is developed (2) the moss plant with an upright or horizontal stem bearing small spirally arranged green leaves (Figs. 22.18, 22.19). Rhizoids are found at the base of the stem, whereas gametangia occur at the tips of either the main or lateral branches (Fig. 22.18).

From the protonema, leafy shoots arise from buds (Fig. 22.20), and a protonema derived from a single spore may give rise to many moss shoots, each with numerous rhizoids at its base. The rhizoids, unlike those found in most of the liverworts, are composed of filaments of cells. They absorb water and solutes, anchor the leafy shoot to the soil, and may give rise to protonemata under favorable conditions.

The mature sporophyte, like that of some of the Hepaticae, is composed of a foot, seta, and sporangium. Unlike the Hepaticae sporophyte, it has a greater amount of sterile tissue and the capsule is considerably more complex (Fig. 22.25).

Although there are three orders of mosses their structural uniformity is such that a single life history is sufficient to illustrate the general features of development in this class.

Gametophyte. The germinating spores of mosses do not develop directly into a leafy gametophyte but first become a filamentous structure, consisting of cells placed end to end. This early stage of the gametophyte is called the **protonema** (Fig. 22.20). The protonema is not a permanent structure, although it may branch considerably under favorable conditions and cover a rather large area of soil, sometimes forming a green coating resembling algal

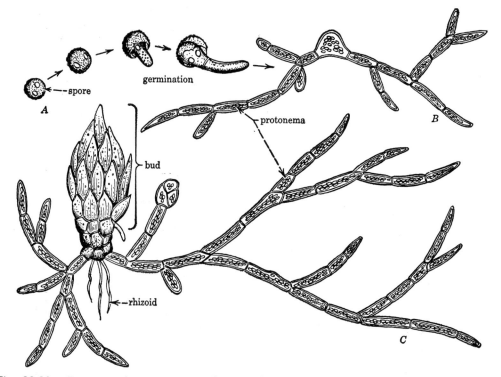

Fig. 22.20. *Funaria.* A, germination of spore; B, protonema; C, protonema with bud. (Redrawn from Schimper, *Recherches sur les Mousses.*)

growth. The cells composing the protonema contain numerous chloroplasts.

The mature stem of the leafy gametophyte is differentiated into a **central cylinder,** a **cortex,** and an **epidermis.** Recent
observations indicate that certain cells of
the central cylinder (Fig. 22.21A) may
function in the upward movement of water
and solutes. There are, however, no vessels
or tracheids such as occur in the vascular
plants. Some cells are strikingly similar to
sieve-tube members (Fig. 22.21*B*).

Sexual Reproduction. The gametophytes
of many mosses are **monoecious;** that is,
both antheridia and archegonia are produced by the same gametophyte. (Fig.
22.18). Some mosses are **dioecious;** in
other words, antheridia and archegonia are
produced on separate gametophytes. The
gametangia of *Funaria* are formed at the
summit of the leafy shoot. First antheridia
develop, and then the gametophyte may
branch and the archegonia form at the
tips of the branches. In *Mnium* and *Polytrichum* the shoots bearing antheridia are
easily recognized, for the leaves surrounding them are spread somewhat like the
petals of a flower. The group of antheridia
appears as an orange spot in the center of
the terminal cluster of leaves (Figs. 22.18,
22.22).

The antheridia of most true mosses (Fig.
22.23) are essentially similar to those of
liverworts. The cells forming the sterile
jacket of the antheridium contain chloroplasts that become orange-red when the
antheridium ripens. As in liverworts, the
sperms consist mainly of an elongated nucleus, and each has two long cilia. The
antheridia are surrounded by club-shaped,

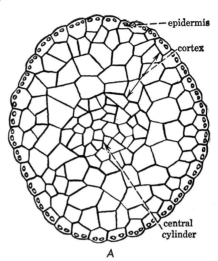

epidermis
cortex
central cylinder

A

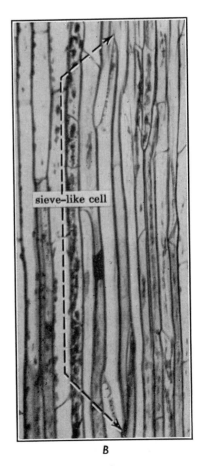

sieve-like cell

B

Fig. 22.21. Conducting tissue of mosses; A,
cross section of stem of gametophyte of *Funaria.* B, phloem-like tissue in stem of gametophyte of *Polytrichum.* (A redrawn after Smith,

Cryptogamic Botany, Vol. 2, McGraw-Hill Book
Co., B courtesy of Gifford.)

Fig. 22.22. Antheridial heads of *Polytrichum*. ×1.

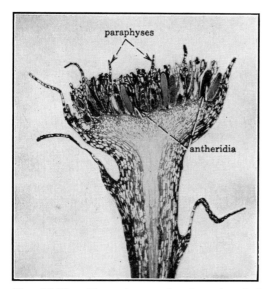

Fig. 22.23. Photomicrograph of antheridial head of *Mnium*. ×35. (Photo courtesy of Triarch Products.)

Mosses, like liverworts, are dependent upon the presence of water to effect fertilization, as well as the opening of the antheridia and the archegonia.

Sporophyte. Soon after fertilization the zygote begins to develop into a spindle-shaped embryo that differentiates into a sporophyte consisting of a foot, seta, and sporangium or capsule. The foot penetrates the base of the venter and grows into the apex of the leafy shoot. It absorbs water and nourishment from the gametophyte for the growth and development of the sporophyte. The seta elongates rapidly, raising the sporangium one-half inch or more above the top of the leafy gametophyte (Fig. 22.19). The old archegonium increases in size as the sporophyte enlarges. When the seta elongates, the top of the expanded archegonium is torn from its point of attach-

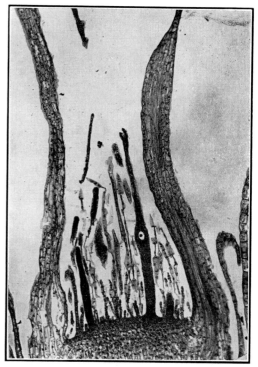

Fig. 22.24. Photomicrograph of archegonial head of *Mnium*. (Courtesy of Triarch Products.)

multicellular, sterile hairs with conspicuous chloroplasts. They are called **paraphyses.**

The archegonia differ from those of the Hepaticae in having a longer neck and a longer stalk between the venter and the tip of the gametophyte (Fig. 22.24).

ment to the gametophyte and elevated with the sporangium. The old archegonium, now known as the calyptra, remains for some time as a covering for the sporangium.

The sporangium of mosses is larger and more complex than that in the Hepaticae. It may measure from a sixteenth to an eighth of an inch in diameter and twice that in length. It is surrounded by an epidermal layer composed of cells similar to those in the epidermis of higher plants. Stomata occur in the epidermis covering the lower half of the sporangium. The sterile tissue forming the inner portion of the sporangium may conveniently be divided into three regions, each of which may be recognized by the type of cells comprising it. A fourth region is formed from the fertile sporogenous cells (Fig. 22.25). The sterile regions may be briefly characterized as follows: (1) the cells comprising the base of the sporangium contain chloroplasts and are fairly compact; (2) the cells forming the outer region of the upper half of the sporangium also contain chloroplasts, but these cells are rather loosely associated, large air chambers being regularly formed; (3) the cells forming a core in this upper portion are devoid of chloroplasts and are compact, forming a mass of thin-walled cells referred to as the **columella**. The fourth region, composed of sporogenous cells, forms a layer around the columella. As in the liverworts, the cells of the sporogenous tissue may increase in number by mitotic cell division. Spore mother cells, each containing the diploid number of chromosomes, develop from the sporogenous cells. Meiosis takes place in spore mother cells, and spores containing n chromosomes result. They are haploid, the first cells of the gametophyte generation.

The columella projects upward forming a small dome above the main mass of the sporangium. The four or five outer layers of cells of this dome differentiate into a

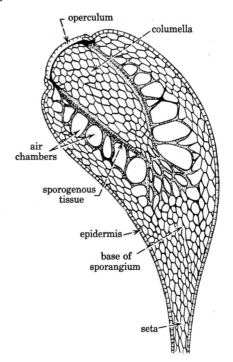

Fig. 22.25. Median longitudinal section through a mature sporangium of *Funaria*. (Redrawn from Schimper, *Recherches sur les Mousses.*)

dry, brittle cap called the **operculum** (Fig. 22.25). The cells immediately beneath the operculum form a double row of long, triangular teeth called the **peristome**. The broad bases of the teeth are attached to thick-walled deciduous cells forming the **annulus** around the upper end of the sporangium. When the sporangium matures and becomes dry, thin-walled cells holding the operculum in place break down, allowing the operculum to fall away and thus expose the teeth of the peristome. By this time most of the thin-walled cells within the columella have collapsed and the cavity thus formed is filled with a loose mass of spores.

The peristome teeth are rough and are very sensitive to the amount of moisture in the air. When they are wet or the atmospheric humidity is very high, they bend

into the cavity of the sporangium; when
dry, they straighten and lift out some of
the spores, which are then disseminated by
air movements. If a spore comes to rest
on moist soil and if illumination and temperature are favorable, it germinates and
grows into a protonema.

The life history of *Funaria* may be represented as shown.

of gametic nuclei, contains $2n$ chromosomes.

9. An embryo sporophyte, consisting of
a spindle-shaped mass of undifferentiated
cells, parasitic on the gametophyte, develops from the zygote.

10. The embryo develops into a sporophyte consisting of a foot, a seta, and a
sporangium. The sporangium of most

$$\text{Gametophyte } (n) \rightarrow \text{ leafy plant } (n) \nearrow^{\text{egg } (n)} \searrow_{\text{sperm } (n)} \nearrow \text{zygote } (2n) \rightarrow$$

(protonema)

embryo sporophyte $(2n)$ → mature sporophyte $(2n)$ → spore mother cells $(2n)$ →

spores (n) → gametophyte (n)
(protonema)

The Significant Steps in the Life History of a Moss

1. The gametophyte consists of: (*a*) a
filamentous, branched, algallike growth
called a protonema and (*b*) leafy shoots
that develop from buds on the protonema.
The shoots consist of a stalk bearing rhizoids at its lower end and leaves throughout its length. The gametophyte is green
and able to synthesize food. All gametophyte nuclei are haploid.

2. The antheridia and archegonia develop at the apex of the leafy gametophyte.

3. Each antheridium produces hundreds
of sperms.

4. A single egg is formed in the venter
of each archegonium.

5. The gametes (eggs and sperms) each
contain n chromosomes.

6. When sufficient moisture is present the
mature sperms are extruded from the antheridium. The neck of the mature archegonium is open and the sperms swim down
it to the egg in the venter of the archegonium.

7. The egg is fertilized by one sperm.

8. The zygote, as a result of the union

mosses is more complex than those found in
the Hepaticae and the Anthocerotae. In
addition to the sporogenous tissue, it contains several types of sterile tissues, among
which may be mentioned the operculum,
annulus, and peristome.

11. Spore mother cells, each containing
$2n$ chromosomes, form from the sporogenous cells.

12. The spore mother cells undergo meiosis. Four spores result from each mother
cell.

13. When spores germinate they form the
protonema.

CLASSIFICATION

Phylum	Bryophyta
Class	Hepaticae
Order	Marchantiales
Genera	*Riccia*
	Ricciocarpus
	Marchantia
Class	Anthocerotae
Genus	*Anthoceros*
Class	Musci
Genera	*Funaria*
	Mnium
	Polytrichum
	Sphagnum

23

The Vascular Plants

GENERAL CHARAC-TERISTICS

In contrast to the algae, fungi, liverworts, and mosses, the vascular plants, tracheophytes, possess a well-developed vascular system that serves for the conduction of water, mineral salts, and foods. Most of them are land plants, but some require free water for fertilization. The sporophyte is the dominant generation; except for the youngest stages in the formation of an embryo, it is independent of the gametophyte. The gametophytes are small, and in the conifers and flowering plants they are dependent upon the sporophyte. The plant body of the sporophyte is, in its simplest form, an axis, with meristematic tissue terminating the opposite ends which form shoots or roots.

CLASSIFICATION

There are four phyla of vascular plants: (1) Psilophyta, (2) Lycophyta, (3) Sphenophyta, and (4) Pterophyta. Of the four, the phylum Pterophyta is by far the largest, for it includes all the ferns, trees, shrubs, and herbs which dominate the present-day vegetation. Representatives of the phylum Pterophyta were not always dominant. Plant fossils found in coal mines, or otherwise preserved for many millions of years, indicate that there was a period in the earth's history when the plants looked very different from those with which we are familiar today. At one time the Pterophyta were lacking or but poorly represented in the earth's vegetation. Then, members of the Lycophyta and Sphenophyta were the dominant plants (Table 26.1). Today these phyla are represented by a few small forms. It is believed the four phyla mentioned above had a common origin; they are related rather as "brothers" than as direct descendants. This relationship is shown in Fig. 16.8.

That changes have occurred in the vegetation of the earth's surface is a well-established fact; beautifully preserved portions or imprints of plants are found buried in many types of sedimentary rocks, in coal deposits, and in peat bogs. Such plant remains are called **fossils** (Fig. 24.16). Sometimes fossils appear to be remains of plants almost identical with some living today. For instance, although the Coast redwoods of California are now confined to a very narrow fog belt along the coast of northern California and southern Oregon,

461

fossil redwoods show that they were once prevalent in the Northern Hemisphere (Fig. 23.1). Fossil vascular plants differ in greater or lesser degree from present-day forms. All of them, however, can be classified, and it is possible to draw conclusions regarding their relationship with existing plants. Some of these fossils will be discussed under the headings of their appropriate phyla.

PHYLUM XII.   PSILOPHYTA

This phylum is represented in the existing flora by a single family, the Psilotaceae, comprised of two genera, *Psilotum* and *Tmesipteris*. They are rare plants found mainly in the tropics, one form of *Psilotum*

growing as far north as Florida. Figure 23.2 shows the simple plant body of *Psilotum nudum*. Roots are not present and the leaves are small. The branching, upright stem is slightly flattened and contains chlorophyll. A fungus is always associated with the branched rhizome, which is clothed with many rhizoids. The vascular tissue is simple (Fig. 23.3), consisting of poorly developed phloem and of xylem in a radial arrangement. The xylem is composed of spiral and scalariform tracheids.

Fossil Psilophyta are quite well known. They are found in the older sedimentary rocks, indicating that the plants flourished well over 300 million years ago. In spite of their great age their structure may be beautifully preserved. The presumed habit

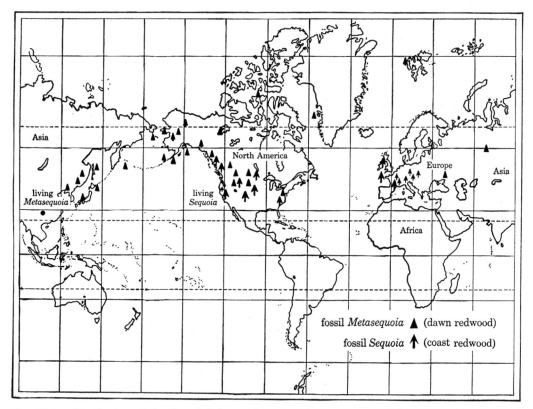

Fig. 23.1.   Distribution of fossil and living redwoods, *Metasequoia* and *Sequoia*. (Courtesy of Chaney.)

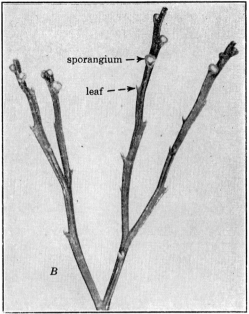

Fig. 23.2. *Psilotum nudum.* A, plant, notice sporangia on branches at left, $\times \frac{1}{6}$; B, end of branch showing scale leaves and sporangia at node-like swellings, $\times \frac{3}{4}$; C, plant growing from trunk of tree fern, $\times \frac{1}{3}$.

of one species, *Rhynia major*, and a cross section of its stem are shown in Figs 23.4, 23.5. Note the remarkable preservation of cellular structure. The plant consisted of a slender rhizome upon which were borne erect, cylindrical stems that branched sparingly. True leaves were absent. Sporangia developed at the tips of some branches, and typical quartets of spores suggesting normal meiosis have been found. Rhizoids growing from the rhizome absorbed moisture and nutrients and anchored the plant to the soil.

PHYLUM XIII. LYCOPHYTA

The Lycophyta are represented by two families (Lycopodiaceae and Selaginel-laceae) in our modern flora. The most widely distributed and best-known genera are *Lycopodium* and *Selaginella*. There are many fossil Lycophyta belonging to several orders, Lepidodendrales being one of the best known. Representatives of this order were forest trees, some of which bore seeds. The leaves of the living members of this phyla are generally small and usually arranged in a spiral. Recall that in flowering plants leaf gaps occur at the juncture of leaf and stem (Figs. 6.41 and 7.9). Pay particular attention to Fig. 7.9 noting the gaps formed by the departure of the leaves as compared with the solid core of xylem in the root. Leaf gaps are never formed at the junction of stem and leaf in the Lycophyta, so that a rotted stem of a

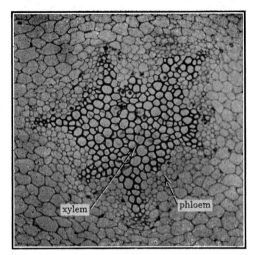

Fig. 23.3. Cross section of *Psilotum* stem. (Photo courtesy of Arrowsmith.)

member of this phylum would have a closer resemblance to the root portion of Fig. 7.9 than to the stem portion.

Lycopodium

Approximately 400 species are in this genus. Most are trailing plants, many forming short upright branches, that sometimes recall pine seedlings. They are frequently called "ground pine" or "clubmoss." Widely distributed, they are found in largest numbers in subtropical and tropical forests. They cannot grow in arid habitats. Several species grow in the eastern United States but none occur in the more arid states of the West (Fig. 23.6). Some eastern species are in danger of extinction because of their ready sale in florist shops, for Christmas decorations.

Mature Sporophyte. The main stem branches freely and is prostrate. Upright stems, approximately 8 inches in height, grow from the horizontal stem. Both types of stems are sheathed with small green leaves. Small, but well-developed, adventitious roots rise irregularly from the underside of the horizontal stem. As in many

higher plants, the primary root, which grows from the embryo, is not long-lived.

Lycopodium species possess a vascular system which, though similar to that found in the higher plants (pine, apple, lily), is

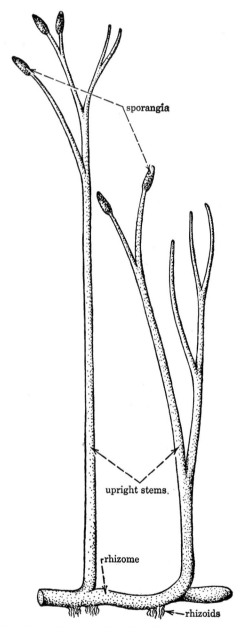

Fig. 23.4. Presumed habit of *Rhynia*, a plant that lived over 300 million years ago. (Redrawn from Kidston and Lang.)

much simpler (Fig. 23.7). A cross section of a *Lycopodium* stem shows that the strands of xylem and phloem alternate with each other. In this respect the stem of *Lycopodium* resembles roots, rather than stems, of flowering plants (pages 94 and 144). The xylem is composed of tracheids only, whereas the phloem contains sieve tubes and some parenchyma cells. *Lycopodium* stems also lack pith, as do the roots of most higher plants.

Lycopodium may reproduce either by asexual or by sexual means. In some species small masses of tissue, called bulbils, are formed which drop off the plant and grow directly into new plants.

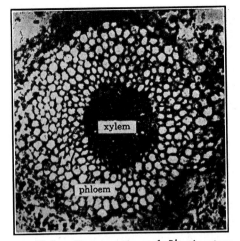

Fig. 23.5. Cross section of *Rhynia* stem. (From Kidston and Lang.)

Fig. 23.6. Three species of *Lycopodium*. ✕ ⅓. (Photo courtesy of Eames, *Morphology of the Vascular Plants—Lower Groups*, McGraw-Hill Book Co.)

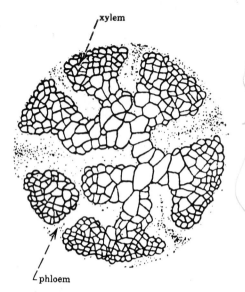

Fig. 23.7. Cross section of *Lycopodium* vascular cylinder. (Redrawn from Eames, *Morphology of the Vascular Plants—Lower Groups,* McGraw-Hill Book Co.)

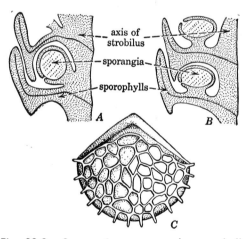

Fig. 23.8. Sporangia, spore, and sporophylls of *Lycopodium*. (*A* and *B* redrawn from Sykes, *C* redrawn from Pritzel.)

formation of four meiospores from each spore mother cell.

The sporangia, which are of just one type, grow either in or near the axils of the small leaves sheathing the stem. The leaves bearing the sporangia are called spore-bearing leaves or **sporophylls** (Fig. 23.8). In some species they closely resemble ordinary non-spore-bearing leaves in their structure and appearance (Fig. 23.6*A*). In other species they differ in size, shape, position, and color from the sterile leaves (Fig. 23.6*B, C*). Such modified sporophylls are grouped closely to-

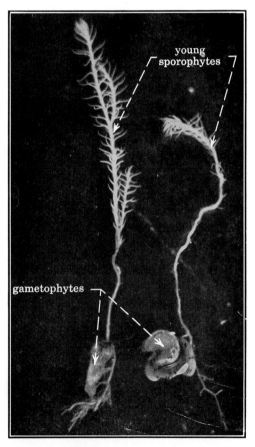

Fig. 23.9. Gametophyte of *Lycopodium* with attached young sporophyte. ×1. (Material courtesy Eames.)

Sexual reproduction involves both sporophyte and gametophyte generations. The sporophyte (diploid) is dominant and has been described above. Meiosis, which occurs in the young sporangia, results in the

gether at the ends of stems, forming a cone or **strobilus.**

Gametophyte. The spores do not germinate readily. The gametophytes in some species grow aboveground and are green, in other species the gametophytes are subterranean and lack chlorophyll. The gametophytes are always associated with a fungus. The underground types of gametophytes (Fig. 23.9) are difficult to find and, being difficult to grow in culture, are not well known. Those that have been studied are monoecious, and the gametangia resem-

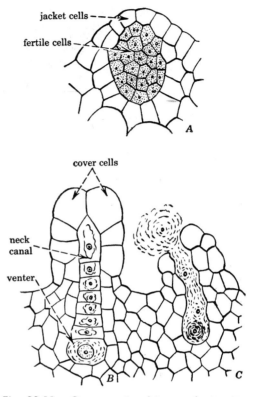

Fig. 23.11. Gametangia of *Lycopodium*. (Redrawn from Bruchmann.)

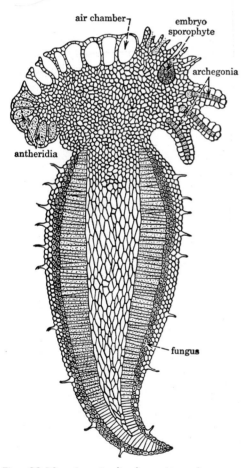

Fig. 23.10. Longitudinal section of gametophyte of *Lycopodium*. (Redrawn from Bruchmann.)

ble those of *Anthoceros.* The gametangia are borne on the upper portion of the gametophyte (Fig. 23.10); the cells of this portion are free of fungal filaments. The archegonia consist of a neck, projecting slightly from the gametophyte surface, and a venter with one enclosed egg. The antheridia are composed of a mass of fertile cells, buried shallowly in the gametophyte (Fig. 23.11) and surrounded by a jacket of sterile cells. The sperms have two cilia, and fertilization occurs when sufficient free water is present to allow the sperms to swim to the mature archegonia.

Embryo Sporophyte. The embryo sporophyte possesses (1) a well-developed foot, (2) the rudiments of a short primary root, (3) leaf primordia, and (4) a short shoot

Fig. 23.12.   Habit of *Selaginella*.   ×1.

apex. The embryo grows directly into the mature sporophyte plant.

Selaginella

Selaginella species resemble those of *Lycopodium* in their general appearance but are smaller in size. They number more than 500, and, although they are widely distributed, most of them are tropical; a few grow in the temperate zones. Some species are adapted to withstand periods of drought and hence may grow in relatively dry localities.

Mature Sporophyte. As in *Lycopodium*, the sporophyte of *Selaginella* generally consists of a branched, prostrate stem with short, upright branches, usually but a few inches high. In some species the stem is

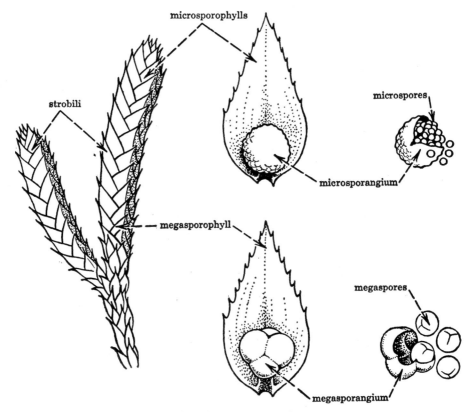

Fig. 23.13.   Exploded view of strobilus of *Selaginella*.

upright and as climbers may reach 50 feet in height. Both horizontal and upright stems are sheathed with small leaves in four longitudinal rows or ranks (Figs. 23.12, 23.15A). The vascular anatomy of *Selaginella* resembles that of *Lycopodium* except that well-formed vessels occur in some species.

As in *Lycopodium*, the spores are borne in sporangia, which grow in or néar the axils of sporophylls. Although the sporophylls do not differ greatly in appearance from the sterile leaves, they are always grouped to form cones, or strobili, at the ends of upright branches.

Two types of sporangia are formed: **megasporangia** (*mega*, Gr., large) and **microsporangia** (*micro*, Gr., small). As the names indicate, the megasporangia produce larger spores. A single strobilus usually contains both types of sporangia, in some species the microsporangia being borne above the megasporangia (Fig. 23.13).

Within a developing megasporangium, all but one of the spore mother cells degenerate. This remaining spore mother cell, nourished in part by the fluid resulting from the degeneration of the others and in part by the tapetal cells (the layer of cells surrounding the spore cavity) increases greatly in size. During meiosis, four large spores, called **megaspores**, are formed (Fig. 23.13). Each megaspore upon germination will give rise to a female gametophyte.

Only a few spore mother cells within the developing microsporangium degenerate. The 250 or so that remain undergo meiosis, each forming four small spores, the **microspores** (Figs. 23.13, 23.14). Upon germination, each microspore produces a male gametophyte.

The production by a given species of two distinct types of meiospores—megaspores and microspores—is called **heterospory**. Thus *Selaginella* is heterosporous; *Lyco-*

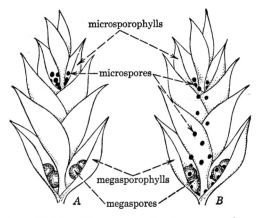

Fig. 23.14. Movement of microspores from microsporangia to base of megasporophylls in *Selaginella*.

podium, which produces but one spore type, is said to be **homosporous**.

Female Gametophyte. Repeated cell divisions within the megaspore result in the female gametophyte, which is contained within the megaspore until it nears maturity. Its increase in size eventually ruptures the megaspore wall, and a small cushion of colorless gametophytic tissue protrudes from the megaspore along the lines of rupture (Fig. 23.15). Archegonia develop on the protruding cushion. Although similar in structure to the archegonia of the liverworts, they are much more reduced in size. They are sunken within the gametophyte tissue; only two short cells of the neck protrude.

The megaspore (containing the female gametophyte) may be shed from the cone or strobilus at almost any stage in the development of the gametophyte. In some species it may be retained in the strobilus until well after fertilization. In any event, fertilization occurs only when sufficient water, either rain or dew, is present, allowing the sperms to swim to the archegonia.

Male Gametophyte. Upon germination, the microspore divides into two cells. One of them, the **prothallial cell**, is small and does not divide further; it represents the vegetative portion of the male gametophyte (Fig. 23.16). The other cell, by repeated divisions, develops into an antheridium composed of a jacket of sterile cells enclosing 128 or 256 biciliated sperms. This development occurs *within* the microspore wall. Microspores are shed from the microsporangium midway in the development of the male gametophyte and grow to maturity without direct connection with the parent sporophyte or the soil. The sperms

escape when the microspore wall ruptures. Usually the microspores sift down to the bases of the megasporophylls. In this position they are close to the developing female gametophytes, and fertilization is made possible (Fig. 23.14).

The sperms swim to the archegonia, which grow on that portion of the female gametophyte which protrudes from the megaspore. Fertilization ensues, and the resulting zygote initiates the diploid or sporophyte generation.

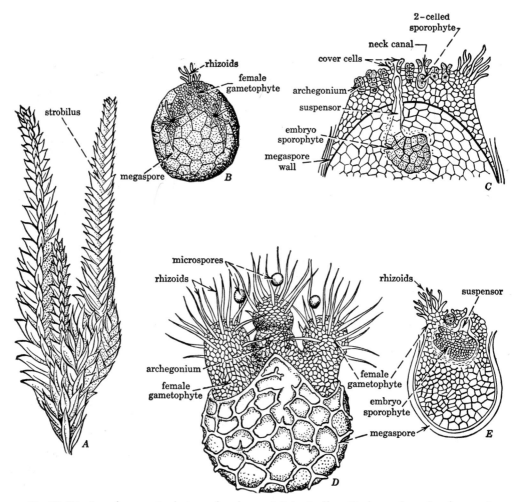

Fig. 23.15. Female gametophyte and embryo of *Selaginella*. (Redrawn from Bruchmann.)

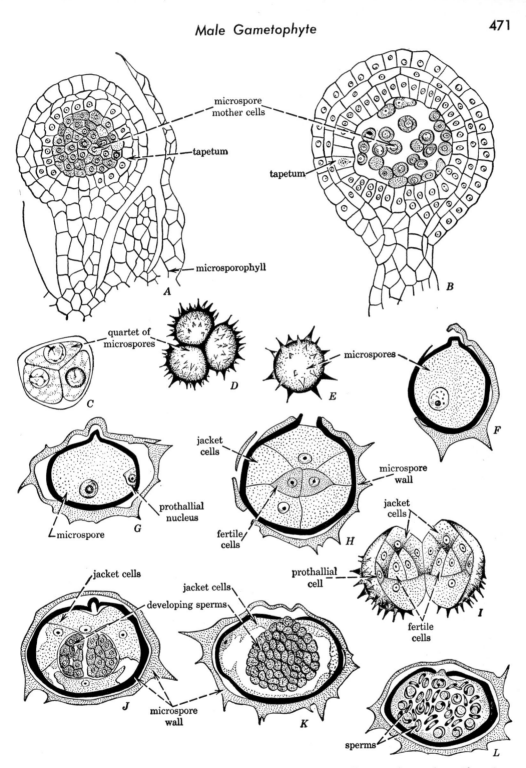

Fig. 23.16. Development of male gametophyte of *Selaginella*. (Redrawn from Slagg.)

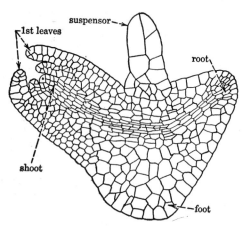

Fig. 23.17. Embryo of *Selaginella*. (Redrawn from Bruchmann.)

Embryo Sporophyte. Of the two cells formed by the first division of the zygote, only one develops into an embryo. The other cell grows into an elongated structure, the **suspensor**, which forces the developing embryo into the gametophyte where there is a food supply (Fig. 23.15E).

The embryo is a structure with (1) a foot, (2) a root, (3) two embryonic leaves, and (4) a shoot (Fig. 23.17). In certain species of *Selaginella* the embryo is held by the megaspore and retained within the strobilus. It does not pass into a dormant state, as do seeds, but continues to grow. Young sporophytes may be found extending from the strobilus of parent sporophytes. Should the developing embryo pass into a period of dormancy while being held by the mother sporophyte, a condition would arise that approaches the seed habit.

The life history of *Selaginella* is diagrammed below.

Lepidodendrales

The Lepidodendrales is an important fossil order of the phylum Lycophyta. Many representatives were heterosporous, and true seeds were formed by some species. No members of the order are in existence today. It was, however, a dominant order at the period when the great deposits of coal were being formed. If one can imagine a lush forest of *Selaginella*-like trees, 150 feet tall and 6 feet in diameter, a fair picture of this forest may be obtained. There were also smaller, shrubby and herbaceous Lepidodendrales. Since two spore types, and seeds, were formed by these ancient plants, we must believe that both heterospory and the seed habit are very old plant characters and not characters confined to present-day plants.

Significant Features of the Phylum Lycophyta

1. Spores are borne on or near sporophylls, grouped at the ends of upright branches to form cones or strobili.

2. Both homospory and heterospory occur.

3. The gametophytes of *Lycopodium* may be colorless and subterranean, and are associated with a fungus; in other species they are autotrophic.

4. The gametophytes of *Selaginella* develop within the spores.

5. The spores of some species of *Selaginella* are retained in the strobili until the gametophytes have matured and fertilization has occurred.

6. Members of the fossil order Lepido-

megaspore mother ⟶ megaspore (n) ⟶ female   ⟶ egg
cell ($2n$)   gametophyte (n)

Sporophyte ($2n$)   zygote ($2n$) ⟶

microspore mother ⟶ microspore (n) ⟶ male   ⟶ sperm
cell ($2n$)   gametophyte (n)   embryo ($2n$)

dendrales were heterosporous and produced seeds.

7. The vascular system in the stems of the Lycophyta resembles that found in the roots of Angiospermae.

PHYLUM XIV. SPHENO-PHYTA

Members of this phylum once grew very abundantly, as is evidenced by the fact that they are well represented in the fossil record. Today, the phylum is represented by a single family (Equisetaceae) with but one genus (*Equisetum*) of about 25 species (Fig. 23.18). Many species inhabit cool, moist places, but *Equisetum arvense* grows in dry habitats. Most species are characterized by the presence of silica in the walls of some of the outer cells. Because of this trait, they were used in colonial days to scour pots and pans and hence were called scouring rushes. The genus is commonly known as the horsetails.

Fig. 23.18. Habit of *Equisetum.* ✕⅓.

Equisetum

Mature Sporophyte. The sporophyte of *Equisetum* is the dominant phase of its life history. In one tropical species the sporophyte is vinelike and may reach 25 feet in length. Usually, however, 5 feet represents the maximum upright growth. All species are perennials and have a branched rhizome from which the upright stems arise. The stems, depending upon the species, may either branch profusely or sparingly. In either event, they are straight and marked by ridges and distinct nodes (Figs. 23.18, 23.19D). The tissue just above the nodes remains meristematic and structurally weak so that the stems may be easily pulled apart at these points. The bases of the nodes are sheathed by whorls of small simple leaves that are fused laterally (Figs. 23.18, 23.19D). When branching occurs, the branches arise at the nodes, immediately below the leaves, and, since there are frequently many leaves in a whorl, many branches may form at each node (Figs. 23.18, 23.19). The leaves are much reduced in size, nongreen, and, in many species, short-lived. The stems are green and, therefore, the organs of food manufacture. Roots occur only at the nodes of the rhizomes or bases of upright stems. The leaves of plants of this phylum are generally arranged in a whorl, and alternate with the branches at nodes. Leaf and branch gaps are present as in the flowering plants but their arrangement is different. The ribbed stem of the Sphenophyta is such a characteristic feature that fossil stems

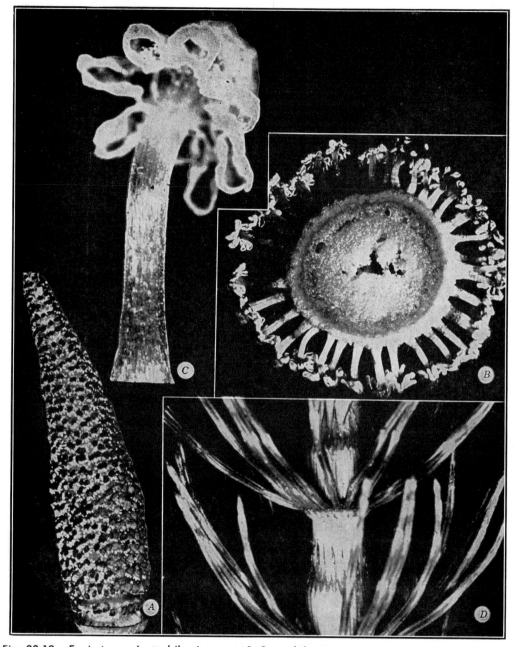

Fig. 23.19. *Equisetum.* A, strobilus intact, $\times$1; B, strobilus in cross section, $\times$3; C, sporangiophore, $\times$20; D, stem showing nodes, leaves, and branches, $\times$1. (Photos courtesy of Arrowsmith.)

showing ribs are regularly placed in this
phylum.

In all species of *Equisetum* the sporangium-bearing organs, the **sporangiophores**,
are specialized structures very different
from ordinary leaves (Figs. 23.19C, 23.20).
They are grouped together in **strobili** at the
summit of the main upright branches and
occasionally on lateral branches. In most

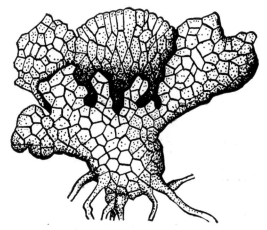

Fig. 23.21. Gametophyte of *Equisetum*. (Redrawn from Walker.)

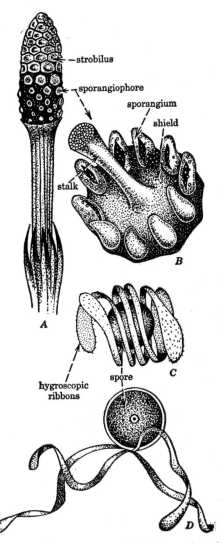

Fig. 23.20. *Equisetum*, exploded view of strobilus. (Redrawn from Wettstein.)

species the cones or strobili are borne on
the ordinary vegetative shoots; in a few
species they are formed only on special
fertile shoots (Fig. 23.18).

The sporangiophores are stalked shield-
shaped structures borne at right angles to
the main axis of the cone. The cone may
be compared to a pole to which open um-
brellas have been fastened, the handle of
the umbrella being at right angles to the
pole (Fig. 23.19B). The sporangia are attached to the underside of the shield, close
to its edge. They extend horizontally inward, toward the axis of the cone.

Meiosis is normal, four meiospores with
the haploid number of chromosomes being
formed from each spore mother cell. All
meiospores are alike. *Equisetum*, therefore, is homosporous. The spores have a
thick, double wall, and, when they are mature, the outer half of the wall unfolds to
form narrow hygroscopic ribbons that move
under the influence of moisture changes
and aid in the distribution of spores (Fig.
23.20). The spores are fragile and normally live but a few days.

Gametophytes. The gametophytes are
small, green bodies about the size of a pin-
head and consist of a cushionlike base with

many erect, delicate lobes (Fig. 23.21). They may be easily cultured.

The gametangia are similar to those of *Lycopodium*. Fertilization takes place only when there is free water. The sperms are spiral, multiciliate cells.

The zygote develops directly into an embryo. No suspensor is formed. The embryo is similar to those already described, except that the foot is small or lacking.

Significant Features of the Phylum Sphenophyta

1. The genus *Equisetum,* consisting of about 25 species in the family Equisetaceae, is the only living group of this once widely distributed phylum.

2. The stem of *Equisetum* has distinct nodes and internodes. Meristematic tissue occurs just above the nodes, which are sheathed by whorls of small, brownish, short-lived leaves. Photosynthesis is carried on by the green stems.

3. The strobili are composed of specialized structures, sporangiophores consisting of shield-shaped disks, supported by short stalks growing at right angles to the stem.

4. The autophytic gametophyte is a single thallus with many lobes.

5. Present-day species of *Equisetum* are homosporous; certain extinct species of Sphenophyta were heterosporous.

Table 23.1. Comparison of Psilophyta, Lycophyta, and Sphenophyta

Generation	*Psilotum*	*Lycopodium*	*Selaginella*	*Equisetum*
	A branching stem, scale leaves, or leaves, no roots.	Prostrated branching stem with upright branches, roots and leaves	Prostrate branching stem with upright branches, roots and leaves, also scales	Rhizome, upright, jointed stem, small leaves, stems carry on photosynthesis
Sporophyte	Autophytic Simple vascular system -	Autophytic Simple vascular system	Autophytic Simple vascular system but vessels are present	Autophytic Simple vascular system
	One type of sporangia	One type of sporangia	Megasporangia Microsporangia	One type of sporangia
	Homospory No sporophylls No cone	Homospory Sporophylls present A cone in some species	Heterospory Sporophylls all similar Cone	Homospory Sporangiophores Cone composed of sporangiophores
	No ovules	No ovules	No ovules Embryo develops within female gametophyte on sporophyll	No ovules
		Suspensor	Suspensor	No suspensor
Gametophyte	Irregular subterranean structure associated with fungus	Irregular to tapered subterranean structure associated with fungus	Male gametophyte, one prothallial cell and an antheridium within microspore	A single thallus resembling *Anthoceros* Autophytic
	Gametangia embedded in thallus	Gametangia embedded in thallus	Female gametophyte small amount of tissue within megaspore, cushion protrudes in which gametangia are embedded	Gametangia embedded in thallus, neck of archegonium protruding
	Motile sperm	Motile sperm	Motile sperm	Motile sperm

CLASSIFICATION

Phylum	Psilophyta
Family	Psilotaceae
Genera	*Tmesipteris*
	Psilotum nudum
Family	Rhyniaceae
Genus	*Rhynia*
Phylum	Lycophyta
Family	Lycopodiaceae
Genus	*Lycopodium*
Family	Selaginellaceae
Genus	*Selaginella*
Phylum	Sphenophyta
Family	Equisetaceae
Genus	*Equisetum*

24
The Vascular Plants

PHYLUM XV. PTEROPHYTA

The phylum Pterophyta is the largest of the four phyla of vascular plants. All the common plants of the modern flora (ferns, conifers, and flowering plants) are Pterophyta. The phylum is divided into three classes: (1) Filicinae or ferns (Fig. 24.1); (2) Gymnospermae, the conifers and related plants (Fig. 24.2), and (3) the Angiospermae or flowering plants (Fig. 24.3).

The plant body of most of the Filicinae or ferns consists of a rhizome, or horizontal stem, which bears roots and leaves (Fig. 24.1). Some tropical ferns grow into moderate-sized trees (Fig. 24.4). Ferns possess a definite alternation of generations, and, although both generations are independent, the sporophyte is dominant. With the exception of two families (water ferns), the ferns are homosporous. The sperms are motile, and free water is needed for fertilization. Ferns produce no seeds. They are widely distributed, being common over most of the earth. Many of them are cultivated as ornamental plants.

The best-known Gymnospermae are the conifers, such as the common pines, spruces, hemlocks, and others of our softwood evergreen forests. The gymnosperms include seven orders, three of which are represented only by fossil forms. They are widely distributed over most of the earth. All gymnosperms develop seeds.

The Angiospermae (flowering plants) form the dominant present-day flora. In keeping with their wide distribution, they show considerable variation in external morphology. Their reproduction involves a flower from which fruits and seeds develop.

CLASS FILICINAE

Most ferns are shade-loving plants and of relatively small size. A few small forms of the temperate zones grow under hot, dry conditions, however, and some tropical ferns attain the size of trees. The Filicinae comprise four orders, the largest of which, the Filicales, includes the **true ferns.** The Filicales are divided into eleven or more families, of which the largest and best known in the United States is the Polypodiaceae. Most of the following discussion will deal with representatives of this family. There are also several fossil orders. One of them, the Coenopteridales, will be briefly discussed because of its characteristic leaf structure.

The Mature Sporophyte

The sporophyte, which is the dominant generation of all ferns, possesses an underground stem or rhizome from which leaves and adventitious roots arise (Fig. 24.1). The leaves are the most prominent part of the fern plant and vary greatly in size and form. They differ from the leaves of the flowering plants in two important respects: (1) they have an apical meristem that usually continues active for some time, and (2) spores frequently are borne on their

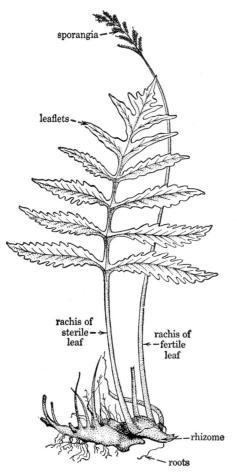

Fig. 24.1. The sensitive fern (*Onoclea sensibilis*), a representative of the Filicinae. (Redrawn from Diels in Engler and Prantl.)

Fig. 24.2. Sugar pine (*Pinus lambertiana*), a representative of the Gymnospermae.

lower surface (Fig. 24.5). Young fern leaves are rolled in tight spirals and consist chiefly of meristematic tissue (Fig. 24.6). As the leaf matures, it unwinds from the base upwards. The upright expanded por-

Fig. 24.3. *Amaryllis,* a representative of the Angiospermae. $\times \frac{1}{4}$.

phloem differs from that found in gymnosperms and angiosperms and is thought to indicate a primitive condition. A cross section of a fern rhizome illustrating the different arrangement of vascular tissue is shown in Fig. 24.7. Note that there are several distinct vascular bundles each one consisting of a central core of xylem surrounded by phloem. Other arrangements occur in other species. The xylem consists mainly of tracheids; vessels are known to occur in only two genera.

Vegetative Reproduction. This type of reproduction may occur in one of two ways: (1) by death and decay of the older portions of the rhizome and the subsequent

Fig. 24.4. A tree fern (*Cyathea*) growing in Golden Gate Park. $\times \frac{1}{50}$.

tion is mature, but the leaf continues to grow by cell division at its coiled tip. The uncoiled, fully expanded fern leaf lacks meristematic tissue, as the cells of all such tissue have differentiated into permanent cells. In certain species the apical meristem may remain active for years, resulting in leaves nearly 100 feet long.

Most fern leaves are compound, although simple types exist in all groups. The most common type of fern leaf has a stout or rigid petiole, which is prolonged to form the **rachis** from which leaflets arise.

The vascular system of ferns is well developed. The arrangement of xylem and

separation of the younger growing ends; and (2) by the formation of deciduous leaf-borne buds, which become detached and grow into new plants. Such buds occur in only a few genera.

Sexual Reproduction. In the sexual life cycle, independent sporophyte and gameto-phyte generations alternate with each other. The vegetative structure of the sporophyte has been described above. The spores are borne in sporangia, which ordinarily develop on the lower surface or margins of the leaves (Figs. 24.5, 24.8). Not all leaves are fertile, that is, spore-producing; and the

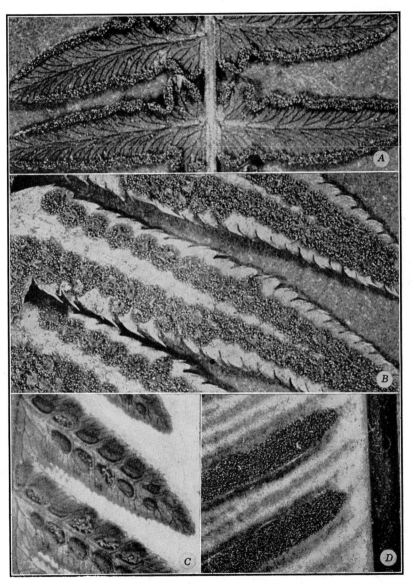

Fig. 24.5. Arrangement of sporangia on different species of fern leaves. ×2. (Photos courtesy of Arrowsmith.)

Fig. 24.6. Immature coiled fern leaves (Cyathea). $\times \frac{1}{5}$.

(3) grow only along the margins or edges of the leaf.

When the sporangia are grouped together in sori, a structure called the **indusium,** which is sometimes umbrellalike, may be present, thereby protecting the young and developing sporangia. Frequently, marginal sporangia are protected by the curled edge of the leaf, which forms a so-called **false indusium.**

The sporangium is a delicate watch-shaped case, consisting of a single layer of epidermal cells, only one row of which possesses heavy walls. This row, which nearly encircles the sporangium (in the Polypodiaceae), is the **annulus;** it functions in opening the dried mature sporangium and aids in the dispersal of the ripe spores (Fig. 24.8).

The young sporangium is filled with sporogenous cells, which eventually give rise to spore mother cells. Meiosis in the spore mother cells results, as always, in spores with a reduced number of chromosomes. Ferns, with the exception of two families, the Marsileaceae and the Salviniaceae, are homosporous. These two families, though widely distributed, are small, uncommon, and unfernlike in appearance.

fertile leaves may not always be similar to sterile (non-spore-producing) ones. The distribution of sporangia on the leaf surface varies considerably in the different genera and species (Fig. 24.5). They may: (1) cover much of the lower surface, (2) be grouped in **sori** (singular, **sorus**) and grow in a definite relationship with the veins, or

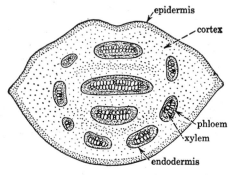

Fig. 24.7. Cross section of rhizome of *Pteridium.*

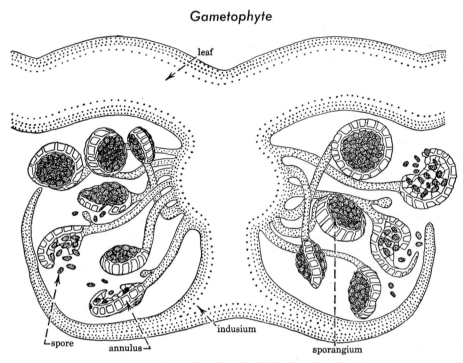

Fig. 24.8. Section through a fern leaf showing details of a sorus.

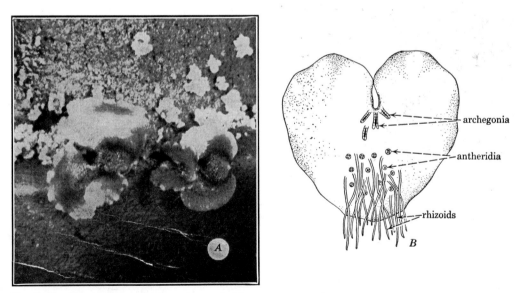

Fig. 24.9. Fern gametophytes. A, prothallia growing on flower pot, ×2; B, diagram. (A courtesy of Gifford.)

Gametophyte

The gametophytes, or **prothallia,** of the Polypodiaceae are small, flat, green, heart-shaped structures with rhizoids on their lower surface (Fig. 24.9). In most species they apparently mature rapidly and are not long-lived. Antheridia and archegonia are borne on the same prothallium. Antheridia are formed when the prothallium is very young and are scattered over its lower surface. The antheridia are small and have a jacket formed from only three or four sterile cells (Fig. 24.10). Antheridia project only slightly from the surface of the gameto-

phyte. Normally, 32 sperms develop within each antheridium.

The archegonia form later than the antheridia and are usually clustered close to the notch, also on the undersurface of the gametophyte (Figs. 24.9*B*, 24.11). They, too, are small but are typical, consisting of a short neck and a venter that encloses the egg cell. The neck cells protrude slightly from the lower surface of the gametophyte.

Fertilization occurs when moisture is present and the sperms are thus able to swim to the neck of the archegonium. The resulting zygote is diploid and rapidly develops into an embryo sporophyte compris-

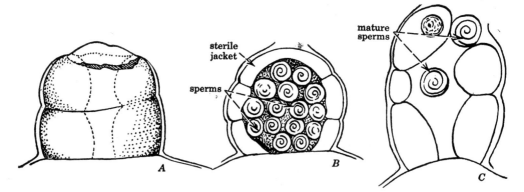

Fig. 24.10. Fern antheridia. (Redrawn from Hartmann.)

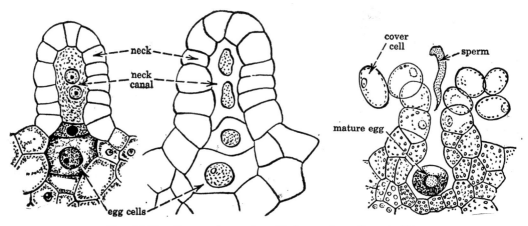

Fig. 24.11. Fern archegonia. (Redrawn from Campbell.)

ing a foot, root, stem, and leaf (Fig. 24.12). The embryo develops directly into a young sporophyte (Fig. 24.13).

Significant Features of the Order Filicales

1. The sporophyte plant, in most species, consists of a rhizome bearing adventitious roots and upright leaves.

2. A well-developed vascular system is present.

3. Usually the leaves are dissected into leaflets, arranged pinnately on a stout midrib or rachis. They are condensed branch systems and when young, have meristematic tissue at their tips.

4. Sporangia are borne on the undersurface of the leaves. They may be grouped into sori, which, in some species, are protected by an indusium.

5. All but two families of the Filicales are homosporous.

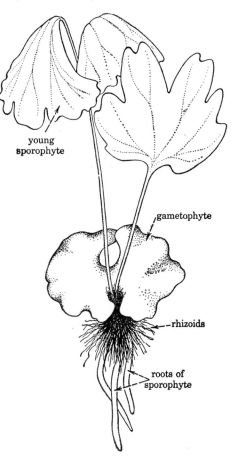

Fig. 24.13. Fern gametophyte with attached young sporophyte.

6. The gametophytes (prothallia) are independent of the sporophyte. They are small, green, heart-shaped, and short-lived plants. Both antheridia and archegonia are borne on the same gametophyte.

Order Coenopteridales (Fossil Ferns)

The fossil ferns as represented by some of the Coenopteridales, though different in external appearance from present-day ferns, possessed sporangia, spores, and a vascular system which resembled the corresponding structures of present-day ferns. They were small plants, either erect, creeping, or

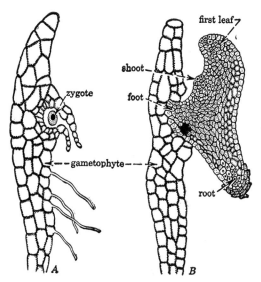

Fig. 24.12. Sections through fern gametophytes showing development of embryo sporophyte. (Redrawn from Holman and Robbins, *A Textbook of General Botany,* John Wiley & Sons, Inc.)

climbing. They are of interest because of their primitive leaves, which differed only slightly from the stem. As the shoot developed, it branched; one division continued to grow, whereas the other soon ceased growth. This short, determinate branch of the main axis was the leaf. Structurally it closely resembled the stem. This primitive type of fern leaf forms one basis for the belief that the leaves of flowering plants are in reality condensed branch systems.

CLASS GYMNOSPERMAE

General Characteristics and Classification

This class of plants is represented by such common trees as the pines, spruces, firs, and cedars. All possess well-developed cones (Fig. 24.18) in which seeds are borne; the seeds are not protected, as in flowering plants (Chapter 12) by an ovary wall. For example, the seed of the peach is surrounded by the matured ovary wall, which is in part fleshy and in part hard and stony. In the Gymnospermae, on the other hand, the seeds are borne on the surface of the scales that comprise the cone, and, though well protected by the scales, they are not surrounded by floral parts. Such seeds, lacking the protection of an ovary wall, are said to be "naked" (Fig. 24.14)—thus the name Gymnospermae, derived from the two Greek words *gymnos* (naked) and *sperma* (seed). It will be recalled that the fossil Lepidodendrales, belonging to the Lycophyta, bore seeds, thus indicating that the seed habit is not of geologically recent origin.

The external morphology of gymnosperms shows considerable variation, as may be seen from the following examples: (1) Fossil gymnosperms so resemble ferns that they are commonly called "seed ferns." (2) Some modern gymnosperms of Mexico and other tropical areas are palmlike in

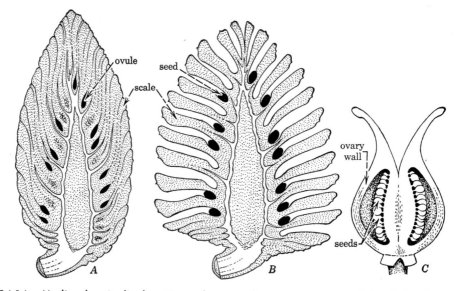

Fig. 24.14. Median longitudinal sections of cones of a gymnosperm and the fruit of an angiosperm, showing the uncovered seeds of the gymnosperm and the covered seeds of the angiosperm.

appearance. (3) Most North Temperate gymnosperms have needle or scale leaves and are mainly evergreen. (4) Some gymnosperms of the temperate regions, particularly of Australia, are broad-leaved. (5) Certain gymnosperms are shrubby and thrive under very arid conditions.

The vascular tissue of the class has been discussed at some length in the chapter on the stem. It should be recalled that vessels are absent from the xylem in all but a few species, that companion cells do not occur in the phloem where there are sieve cells rather than sieve-tubes. Pith is present in the stems but not in roots.

There are about 650 species of gymnosperms, divided into seven orders and many families and genera. We shall consider very briefly three orders: Pteridospermales (the seed ferns), Ginkgoales, and Coniferales (pines, spruce, hemlock, etc.). Coniferales will be discussed in more detail than the others.

Fig. 24.15. Probable appearance of a seed fern. (From Andrews.)

Order Pteridospermales

The Pteridospermales are extinct, but they are well known as fossil plants. They grew over much of the earth when coal deposits were being formed. Their fossils, consisting of beautifully preserved stems, roots, leaves, seeds, and even pollen grains are found encased in rock mined as waste material in coal mines (Fig. 24.16). They have a distinct fernlike appearance (Fig. 24.15) and for many years were regarded as ferns. When, however, seeds were found attached to the leaves it became necessary to revise their classification. Since the seeds were naked these plants were regarded as gymnosperms. The structure of the seeds (Fig. 24.16D) resembles that of such modern gymnosperms (see page 501) as the cycads and Ginkgo. Furthermore, pollen grains have been found associated with the fossil seeds in such a manner as to suggest strongly a life history similar in its essential steps to that of living gymnosperms. Because of these findings, the Pteridospermales are now considered to be the most primitive gymnosperms.

Order Ginkgoales

Only one living representative, the maiden-hair tree (*Ginkgo biloba*) remains of this very ancient order of plants. It has been reported as growing wild today in the forests of remote western China. It has, however, been grown for centuries on the grounds surrounding Chinese and Japanese temples and is now cultivated in many countries. It is a large tree with characteristic small, fan-shaped leaves (Fig. 24.17), which are divided into two lobes. The trees are dioecious.

Reproduction. With the exception of a few algae and some fungi all living plants so far studied have been characterized by motile sperms, and free water has been necessary for fertilization. Moreover, the gametophytes have been mostly independent of the sporophyte. It will be recalled that *Selaginella* has these characteristics except that the female gametophytes are occasionally retained by the sporophyte until well after fertilization. The sexual cycle in Ginkgo is somewhat comparable to that of *Selaginella;* however, the female

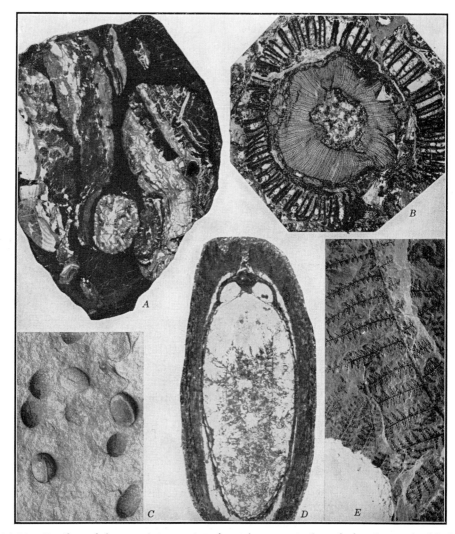

Fig. 24.16. Fossil seed ferns. *A,* a section through a mass of coal showing embedded plant material; *B,* cross section of fossilized stem of *Lyginopteris,* an ancient plant that grew in England; *C,* seeds of a large seed fern that grew in Illinois; *D,* median longitudinal section of the seed of a seed fern; *E,* impressions in rock of leaves of *Lyginopteris,* from Scotland. (Photos *A, B, D, E* courtesy of Andrews; *C* courtesy Chicago Natural History Museum.)

gametophytes are almost completely surrounded by sporophyte tissue, and, though motile sperms are formed, the fluid in which they swim is produced by the parent sporophyte.

The female gametophytes of Ginkgo are buried in the ovule (see page 499), where small reduced archegonia are formed. The archegonia have two neck cells and no neck-canal cells except the ventral canal cell. Entrance to the ovule is through a small opening, the micropyle, at one end of the ovule. Microspores develop in catkinlike strobili on male trees. When mature the microspores are shed and are carried by air currents to the mature ovules on female trees. The microspores are drawn into the micropyle and come to lie in contact with the nucellus. In this posi-

tion they develop into male gametophytes, forked structures that grow parasitically into the upper portion of the nucellus. When a male gametophyte nears an archegonium, two motile sperms are released into a cavity just above the archegonium. One sperm eventually passes into an archegonium and fuses with the egg nucleus in the venter. An embryo develops from the zygote. Integuments surround the embryo, which soon becomes dormant, thus forming, with the enveloping female gametophyte, a true seed.

The important feature of this life history is the development of a method to *insure fertilization without the necessity of free water*. Such a development has made possible the evolution of an extensive dry land flora.

Fig. 24.17. *Gingko biloba* growing on the campus of the University of California at Berkeley.

Fig. 24.18. Mature pine cones. A, *Pinus lambertiana;* B, *Pinus jeffreyi;* C, *Pinus ponderosa;* D, *Pinus murrayana.* $\times \frac{1}{2}$.

Order Coniferales

Classification. Without exception, the well-known and economically important gymnosperms of the temperate zones belong to the order Coniferales. There are nine families and numerous genera. They comprise the pines, hemlocks, firs, spruces, junipers, yews, redwoods, and many others.

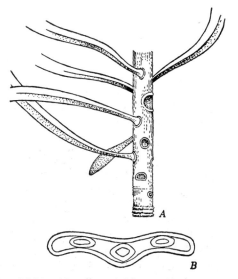

Fig. 24.20. Needles of *Abies*. (Redrawn from Bailey, *The Cultivated Conifers in North America*, The Macmillan Co.)

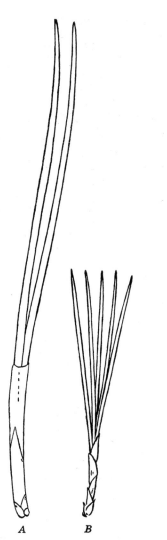

Fig. 24.19. Fascicles of pine needles. A, Norway pine; B, white pine. (Redrawn from Bailey, *The Cultivated Conifers in North America*, The Macmillan Co.)

Not all of them bear cones, yet the cone is such a conspicuous feature of a large number of them that the order has been named the Coniferales or the cone bearers. True cones are formed by the majority of them (Fig. 24.18); juniper berries are in reality cones with fleshy adhering scales (Fig. 24.26). In the yews, on the other hand, the seeds are surrounded at the base by a more or less pulpy, berrylike body and are not borne in cones (Fig. 24.28). In either event the seeds are naked, not being surrounded by an ovary wall.

The following brief descriptions of several common genera will serve as illustrations of the more important conifers.

Family Pinaceae. *Pinus* (Pines). The pines are large trees, or shrubs. The trees may be either pyramidal or flat-topped (Fig. 24.2). The leaves are needlelike, two or more growing together (except in *Pinus monophylla*) in a fascicle or group, which is sheathed at the base (Fig. 24.19). The cones vary greatly in size and shape and

Fig. 24.21. Cone of *Abies*. ✕ ½.

an important timber tree of the western states. It may grow to a height of 200 feet with a diameter of 12 feet. Its leaves are flat, like those of the true firs, but have white lines on either margin and a groove along the upper surface. The cones are from 2 to 4½ inches long, pendulous, and

are very characteristic of the species to which they belong (Fig. 24.18).

Abies (Firs). The firs are stately trees of a symmetrical pyramidal shape. The leaves are flat and linear; in cross section (Fig. 24.20) they are relatively broad, without marked angles. The cones are erect on the branches and shatter at maturity (Fig. 24.21).

Picea (Spruces). These trees closely resemble the firs, from which they can be distinguished by the position of the leaves on the branchlets (Fig. 24.22) and by the angular appearance of the leaves in cross section. The cones are pendent and do not shatter at maturity (Fig. 24.23).

Tsuga (Hemlocks). The trees of this genus are pyramidal with slender horizontal branches. The leaves are usually two-ranked, linear, flat, and with a short petiole. They resemble the leaves of firs but are much shorter. The cones are small (Fig. 24.24).

Pseudotsuga (Douglas Fir). Only two species are in this genus. One of them, the Douglas fir (*Pseudotsuga taxifolia*) is

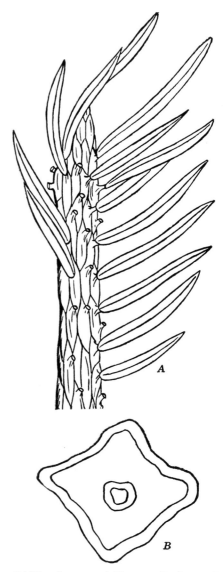

Fig. 24.22. Leaves of *Picea*. (Redrawn from Bailey, *The Cultivated Conifers in North America*, The Macmillan Co.)

easily recognized by the bracts that extend outward below each scale (Fig. 24.25).

Juniperus (Junipers). This genus is composed of both trees and shrubs. The trees are inclined to be somewhat irregular in shape and frequently have more than one trunk. The leaves are of two sorts: (1) in some species, spreading and needlelike, and (2) in other species, scalelike and closely pressed to the twigs. The cone of the junipers is usually called a "berry"; it is a fleshy structure enclosing several seeds. Morphologically, it is a modified cone, composed of fleshy adhering scales that completely enclose the seeds (Fig. 24.26).

Larix (Larches). The trees belonging to this genus grow in the cooler portions of the Northern Hemisphere. They differ from most other members of the Pinaceae in that they are deciduous. The American larch, or tamarack, is a tall tree frequently found in bogs. The needles are short, linear, and grouped in crowded clusters on short spurs. On the leading shoots, however, the needles are arranged spirally. The cones are small and persistent (Fig. 24.27).

Fig. 24.23. Branch of *Picea rubens* with cones. × ½. (Photo courtesy of Bailey, *The Cultivated Conifers in North America*, The Macmillan Co.)

Family Taxaceae. (Yews.) With two exceptions, ovulate cones are not borne by members of the yew family. The seed of this family so strongly resembles a drupe or a nut that it is usually referred to as a fruit. Figure 24.28 shows the seed of *Torreya taxifolia* or the stinking cedar of the southern states. The embryo is protected by an outer flesh called an **aril**, and an inner hard pit. Both these tissues may be

Fig. 24.24. Branch of *Tsuga* with cones. (Redrawn from Bailey, *The Cultivated Conifers in North America*, The Macmillan Co.)

Fig. 24.25. Branch of *Pseudotsuga* with cones.
×1.

The leaves of the yews, as illustrated by Fig. 24.29, are flat and linear, not unlike those of the firs.

derived from the integuments of the ovule; hence, the structure is morphologically a naked seed. The seed of the ground pine (*Taxus canadensis*), which forms a shrubby ground cover in the forests of the North Atlantic states, is similar (Fig. 24.29). The outer red aril almost encloses the seed and drops away when the seed is mature.

Yews are not common in the United States. Two examples have been mentioned; two other species occur on the Pacific Coast, *Taxus brevifolia* and *Torreya californica*. Possibly the best-known yew is the English yew, which, because of the excellent bows that were made from its wood, is closely linked with English history and folklore.

Fig. 24.26. *Juniperus*, tree and branches with cones.

Life History of a Conifer

All conifers produce two kinds of spores —microspores and megaspores—borne in cones that are morphologically distinct. The two types of cones are known, respectively, as **staminate** and **ovulate cones.**

Staminate Cone. Staminate cones average a half inch, or less, in length by a quarter inch in diameter. They are borne in groups, usually on the lower branches of the trees (Fig. 24.30). Each cone is composed of a large number of small scales (microsporophylls) arranged spirally on the axis of the cone. Two microsporangia develop on the undersurface of each scale (Fig. 24.31).

The stages of microspore development are quite similar to those of *Selaginella* and to the spores of mosses and ferns. Sporogenous cells give rise to spore mother cells, which are surrounded by a nutritive cell layer, the **tapetum.** Each spore mother

Fig. 24.28. Branch of *Torreya* with seeds. ×½. (Photo courtesy of Bailey, *The Cultivated Conifers in North America,* The Macmillan Co.)

cell undergoes meiosis and four microspores result. As usual, the microspore contains the haploid number of chromosomes. The nucleus within the newly formed microspore divides several times by mitosis, forming a **pollen grain** that contains two viable haploid nuclei and vestiges of several vegetative cells (Fig. 24.31). The pollen grain is finally shed from the microsporangium. Enormous numbers of pollen grains are formed. They are light in weight and bear two wings, which facilitate dispersal by wind.

Ovulate Cone. The ovulate cone is the well-known cone of the pines, firs, and other genera of the conifers. As we have seen, cones are characteristic of the species to which they belong. Each is composed of an axis, upon which are borne, in a spiral fashion, a large number of woody scales. Two **megasporangia**, in **ovules,** develop on the upper surface of each scale (Fig. 24.32). Upon maturity they become seeds; the ovulate cone is, therefore, a seed-bearing cone. It is always larger than the staminate cone of the same species. The seed-bearing cones are borne singly or in pairs and, in numerous species, high up on the tree. In length they range from an inch or less to 20 inches.

Fig. 24.27. Branch of *Larix* with cones.

Fig. 24.29. Branch of *Taxus* with seeds; note berry-like aril surrounding seed at *A*, and mature seed without aril at *B*. ×1.

The scales bearing the ovules are called **ovuliferous scales.** The ovules first appear as small protuberances on the upper surface of this scale, close to the axis of the cone (Fig. 24.32). A protective layer of cells, the **integument,** early develops on the outer surface of the ovule. At the end of the ovule, nearest the axis of the cone,

Fig. 24.30. Staminate cones of *Pinus halepensis.* ×1¼.

there is a small opening, the **micropyle,** through which pollen grains may enter.

One megaspore mother cell lies in the center of each ovule of pine; several are contained in the ovules of the redwoods and cypresses. Like the microspore mother cells, the megaspore mother cells are surrounded by a nutritive tissue, the nucellus (Fig. 24.32*D*).

Female Gametophyte. The megaspore mother cells soon divide by meiosis. Four megaspores, usually arranged in a single row of four cells (Fig. 24.33), result from the meiotic division of each spore mother cell. The nucleus within each megaspore has the haploid numbers of chromosomes. Generally, only one of the four megaspores develops into a female gametophyte. The germination of the megaspore and growth of the female gametophyte progress very slowly. Several months are required in most conifers, whereas in pine an interval of 13 months occurs between the origin of the megaspore and the formation of the mature female gametophyte.

The development of the female gametophyte takes place entirely within the ovule. There are approximately eleven mitotic divisions within the megaspore before cell walls begin to appear between the newly formed nuclei. Walls gradually form, however, resulting in a small mass of gameto-phytic tissue, completely enclosed by the diploid cells of the ovule. The sporophytic tissue of the ovule adjacent to the female gametophyte is the **nucellus**. While the cell walls are being laid down in the developing female gametophyte, two or more archegonia differentiate at its micropylar end. Reference to Fig. 24.34 shows that the ovule at this stage consists of the integuments, nucellus, and the female gametophyte, which contains several archegonia, each with its enclosed egg. Directly beneath the micropyle is a space, the **micropylar chamber**. Note the nucellar tissue lying between the micropylar chamber and the archegonia.

Pollination. It will be recalled that pollination in typical flowers is the transfer of pollen from the anther to the stigma; in conifers, it is the transfer of pollen from the staminate cone to the ovulate cone. Conifer pollen is wind-blown. Since, in many species, the ovulate cones are borne on the higher branches of the tree and the staminate cones are concentrated on the lower branches, and since the pollen does not blow vertically upward, cross pollination is usual. Pollination occurs in most conifers when the ovulate cone is young (Fig. 24.32A)—at about the time of meiosis. At this age the scales of the young cones turn slightly away from the axis so that the pollen grains sift down to the axis of the cone. Here, they come in contact with a sticky substance secreted by the ovule. As this material dries it draws some pollen grains through the micropyle into the micropylar chamber. The pollen grain develops slowly into a male gametophyte (pollen tube) (Figs. 24.34, 24.35). Thus the male and female gametophytes of the conifers develop to maturity in close proximity within the ovule. They are both dependent upon nucellar tissue (sporophyte) for nourishment and protection.

Male Gametophyte. A layer of nucellar tissue separates the female gametophyte from the micropylar chamber. The pollen grain lodged in the micropylar chamber

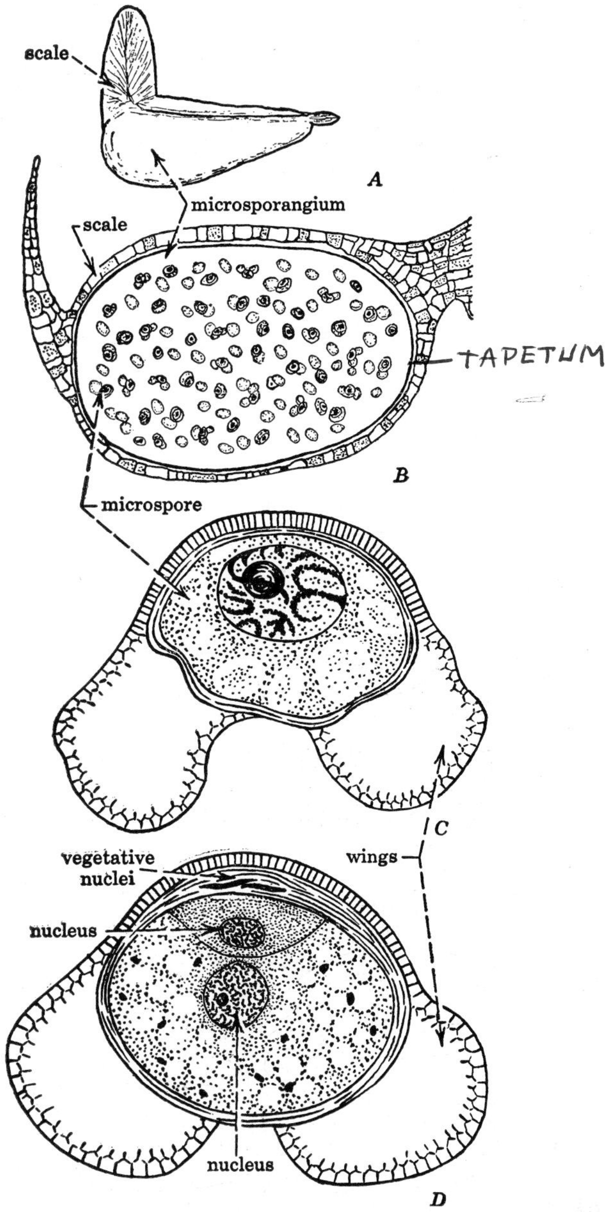

Fig. 24.31. Microsporangia and microspores of *Pinus*. (C and D redrawn from Coulter and Chamberlain, *Morphology of the Gymnosperms*, Univ. of Chicago Press.)

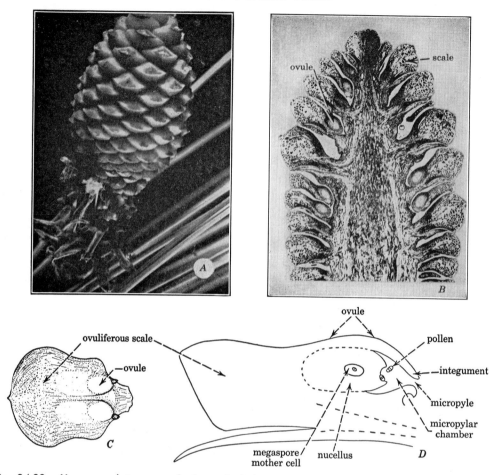

Fig. 24.32. Young ovulate cone of pine. A, habit, ×2; B, median longitudinal section, ×6;
C, sketch showing location of ovules on scale; D, diagram of median longitudinal section of ovule
and scale. (B, photo courtesy of Triarch Products.)

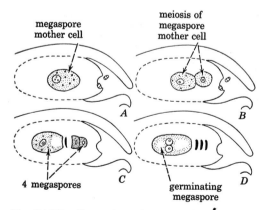

Fig. 24.33. Formation of megaspores in ovule
of pine.

sends out a tube, the **pollen tube,** which
grows into the nucellar tissue. The tube
may branch slightly, and it apparently
secretes enzymes that digest the nucellar
tissue (Fig. 24.34). Several nuclear divisions occur in the tube but no cell walls
are formed. Two of the last-formed nuclei
are **sperm nuclei.** This branched pollen
tube, containing two sperm nuclei and several vegetative nuclei, is the **male gametophyte** (Fig. 24.35).

Fertilization. The development of the
male and female gametophytes is so coordinated that the egg is formed and ready

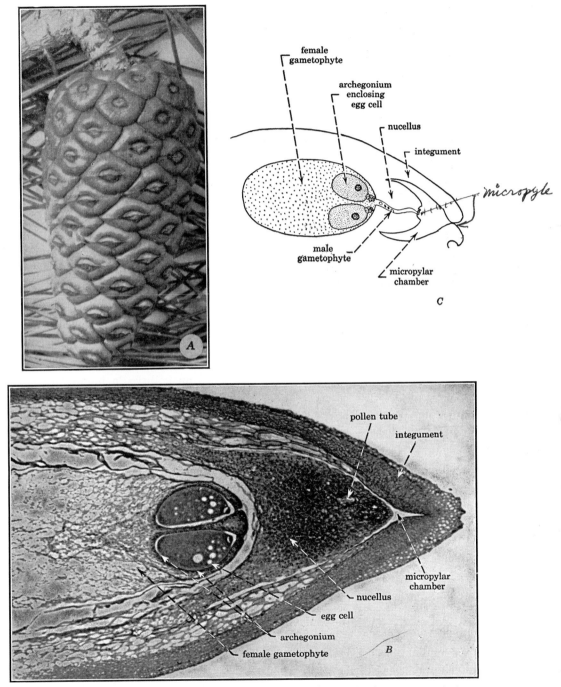

Fig. 24.34.   Ovulate cone of pine about 13 months old, ready for fertilization.   A, habit, ×1; B, ×30; C, longitudinal sections.   (B, slide courtesy of Triarch Products.)

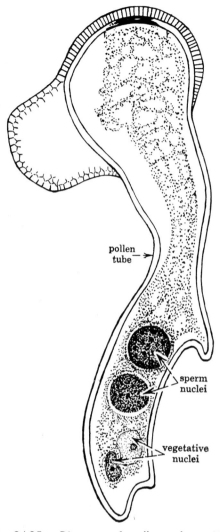

pollen
tube

sperm
nuclei

vegetative
nuclei

Fig. 24.35. Diagram of pollen tube. (Redrawn from Coulter and Chamberlain, *Morphology of the Gymnosperms,* Univ. of Chicago Press.)

for fertilization when the pollen tube containing two sperm nuclei has reached the archegonium. The sperm nuclei, together with other protoplasmic contents of the pollen tube, are discharged directly into the egg cell. Sperm nuclei do not possess cilia and hence are not actively motile. One sperm nucleus comes in contact with the egg nucleus and unites with it. The non-functioning sperm nucleus and the other

protoplasmic material discharged into the egg cells soon undergo disorganization.

Embryo. The formation of the embryo is preceded by the development of a relatively elaborate **proembryo.** This structure, in pines, consists of four tiers of four cells each (Fig. 24.36). The four cells farthest from the micropylar end of the proembryo may each develop into an embryo. The intermediate cells are the suspensor cells; they elongate greatly and push the embryo cells deep into the female gametophyte (Fig. 24.36). While this development is taking place the female gametophyte continues to grow. It enlarges and becomes packed with food to be used not only for the growth of the embryo but also as a reserve in the seed.

It will be recalled that the female gametophytes usually contain two or more archegonia apiece. Since the egg in each archegonium may be fertilized and since each of the four embryo-forming cells may give rise to an embryo, a number of embryos

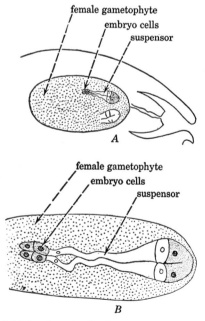

female gametophyte
embryo cells
suspensor

A

female gametophyte
embryo cells
suspensor

B

Fig. 24.36. Longitudinal sections of ovule of pine showing development of proembryo. *A,* ovule; *B,* proembryo enlarged.

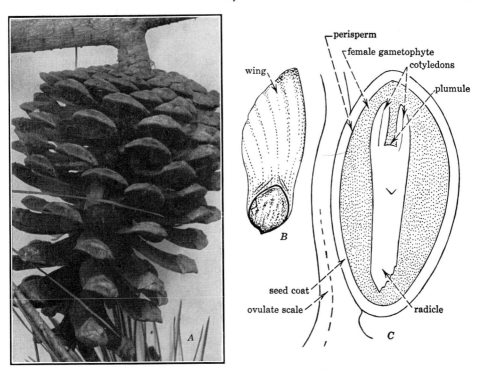

Fig. 24.37. Mature pine cone ×1 (A) and seed (B, C).

may develop in every seed. Normally, however, only one embryo survives, but seeds with two well-formed embryos are not rare.

The mature embryo consists of several **cotyledons** or seed leaves, the **shoot tip,** the **hypocotyl,** and a **radicle** or rudimentary root. It is embedded, as previously mentioned, in the enlarged female gametophyte. Both embryo and female gametophyte are surrounded by (1) the dried nucellus, or **perisperm** and (2) a hard protective **seed coat,** formed from the integuments of the ovule. The whole structure is the **seed** (Fig. 24.37). In many pines the seeds are winged. The development of the seed is summarized in Table 24.1.

Normally, in pines, the seed matures some twelve months after fertilization, and since fertilization is effected about thirteen months after pollination two years intervene between the initiation of the ovule and the formation of the seed.

Gymnosperm seeds may remain dormant for many years, and some may remain embedded in the old mature cones for 6 years or more. Heat causes the cones of some species to open and release the seeds. This behavior has considerable survival value since large numbers of seeds are released after fires, and injured trees are thus replaced by young ones. In many species, however, the seeds are shed soon after they are mature.

Table 24.1. Comparison of Ovule and Seed of Pine

Time of Pollination	Time of Fertilization	Mature Seed
Ovule	Ovule	Seed
Megaspore mother cell	Female gametophyte archegonium egg cell	
		Embryo by way of proembryo
Pollen grain	Pollen tube sperm nucleus	
Integument	Integument	Seed coat
Tapetum	Megasporangium or nucellus	Perisperm
Megasporangium		
Micropyle	Micropyle	Micropyle

SIGNIFICANT FEATURES OF THE GYMNOSPERMAE

1. All forms in this group bear seeds which are not surrounded or protected by an ovary wall: a true fruit is never formed.

2. All are trees or shrubs of varying form; many have needle or scale leaves, and most of these forms are evergreen. Some have broad leaves and in others the leaves are palmlike.

3. With few exceptions vessels are lacking in the xylem, and companion cells are absent from the phloem.

4. The best known gymnosperms of the Northern Hemisphere bear cones of one sort or another. In the yews the seed is surrounded by a fleshy aril.

5. Sexual reproduction involves:

a. The production of microspores, through meiosis in staminate cones and their transformation by several nuclear divisions in the microspore into pollen grains.

b. Pollination by wind.

c. The development of an ovule on the upper surface of the scales of the ovulate cone.

d. The production of megaspores through meiosis within the ovule.

e. The development of a female gametophyte within the ovule from one megaspore. Several reduced archegonia form within the female gametophyte.

f. The penetration of a pollen tube or male gametophyte through the nucellus and discharge of the sperm cells into the egg cells. A few gymnosperms have motile sperm cells.

g. A proembryo forms from the zygote, one end of which gives rise to the embryo.

h. The female gametophyte enlarges and stores food.

i. The seed consists of a hard seed coat, the perisperm, the food storing female gametophyte, and the embryo.

Classification

Phylum	Pterophyta
A. Class	Filicinae
1. Order	Filicales
Family	Polypodiaceae
B. Class	Gymnospermae
1. Order	Pteridospermales
2. Order	Ginkgoales
Genus and species	*Ginkgo biloba*
3. Order	Coniferales
a. Family	Pinaceae
Genus and species	*Pinus monophylla*
Genus	*Abies*
Genus	*Picea*
Genus	*Tsuga*
Genus and species	*Pseudotsuga taxifolia*
Genus	*Juniperus*
Genus	*Larix*
b. Family	Taxaceae
Genus and species	*Torreya taxifolia*
species	*canadensis*
Genus and species	*Taxus brevifolia*
species	*californica*

A generalized life history of a pine

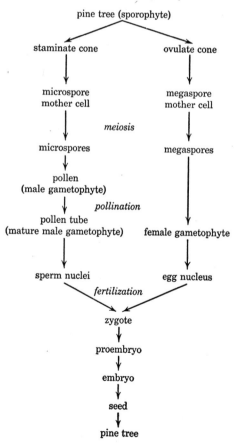

25
Angiospermae

The Angiospermae, or flowering plants, are the dominant plants of the world today. They include most all the crop plants of orchard, garden, and field. Hardwood forests, shrublands, grasslands, and deserts are composed chiefly of flowering plants. In fact, except for the coniferous forests and the waters of the world, the conspicuous and dominating vegetation wherever we go is mainly flowering plants. They have plant bodies showing great variation, from the simple stemless, free floating duckweed (*Lemna*, Fig. 2.3) through a whole series of herbaceous types, to shrubs of varying sizes and finally to trees such as the oaks and beeches. Structurally they are adapted to a land habitat and certain forms, as exemplified by the cacti (Figs. 2.14, 2.15 and 6.48), are able to live and grow in very dry deserts. We have already studied the structure and physiology of the angiosperm plant body in considerable detail.

THE FLOWER, FRUIT, AND REPRODUCTION

The outstanding and unique structure of the Angiospermae is the *flower* (Figs. 12.1, 12.3, 12.24, 12.26, 25.1) and the *fruit* (Figs. 13.1, 13.5, 13.21) that develops from the ovary of the flower (Figs. 12.5, 13.1, 13.2) with its enclosed *seeds* (Figs. 12.3, 13.5, 13.10). The flower is a shoot bearing floral leaves. In a complete flower (Figs. 12.1, 25.1) the floral leaves are sepals, petals, stamens, and carpels. Some flowers have only the essential reproductive structures (Fig. 12.13), stamens and carpels. Other flowers are unisexual (Fig. 12.14), that is, having either stamens or carpels, not both. Other variations in flower structure are described on pages 219–246.

Free water is not needed for fertilization in the angiosperms; motile, ciliated sperms are not produced by any members of this class. Sexual reproduction is made possible by the production of pollen (Figs. 12.4, 25.1C), by pollination, and by the growth of a pollen tube (Fig. 25.1D), phenomena which make possible the eventual union of egg and sperm (Fig. 25.2A, B, C).

All flowering plants bear seeds (Figs. 12.3, 13.5, 13.23). In this respect they resemble the gymnosperms. In the angiosperms the seeds are borne within a closed structure, the ovary, which eventually becomes the fruit (Fig. 13.1). In the gymnosperms, on the other hand, the seeds are not

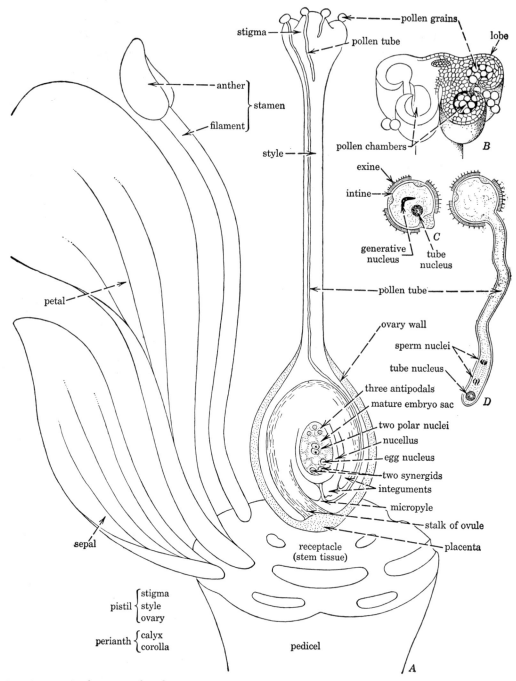

Fig. 25.1. *A,* diagram of a flower; *B,* cross section of an anther; *C,* mature pollen grain; *D,* germinating pollen grain. (*C* and *D,* redrawn from Bonnier and Sablon, *Cours de Botanique,* Librairie Générale de l'Enseignement.)

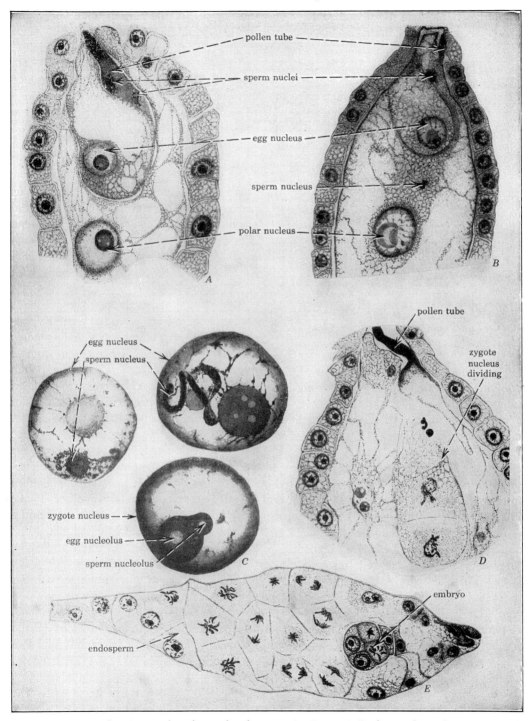

Fig. 25.2. Fertilization and embryo development in *Crepis*. (Redrawn from Gerassimova.)

Table 25.1. Comparative Terminology of Floral Parts

Stamen	Microsporophyll
Pollen sac	Microsporangium
Microspore	Microspore
Pollen grain	Germinated microspore or young male gametophyte
Pollen tube	Mature male gametophyte
Carpel	Megasporophyll
Nucellus	Megasporangium
Megaspore	Megaspore
Embryo sac	Female gametophyte
Ovule	Ovule

surrounded completely by any structure, but are borne on the upper surface of a scale (Fig. 24.14).

Flower Structure Compared with Reproductive Structures of More Primitive Forms

Since the flower is the structure of the Angiospermae adapted for sexual reproduction its parts should, in some degree, be comparable to the reproductive structures of more primitive forms. Let us examine the flower with this in mind. The petals and sepals, the showy and protective whorls of floral leaves, are not directly represented in any of the lower forms. Meiosis occurs in the anthers of stamens and microspores are produced in pollen sacs (Figs. 12.4, 25.1*B*). The stamen then is a microsporophyll and a pollen sac is a microsporangium. The pollen grain itself containing, as it does, two nuclei or cells (Fig. 25.1*C*) would be the first stage in the development of the male gametophyte. The pollen tube would constitute the mature male gametophyte. Meiosis takes place within the ovule. The tissue immediately surrounding the developing megaspore is the nucellus which is borne within the ovule (Figs. 12.11, 25.1*A*). It will be recalled that the ovules, in many instances, are attached to

the margins of the carpels which are floral leaves (Fig. 12.8). Thus the carpel, since it bears megaspores, is a megasporophyll and the nucellus is the megasporangium. Generally one of the megaspores gives rise to an embryo sac or female gametophyte (Fig. 25.1*A*). These two sets of terms are summarized in Table 25.1.

Life Cycle

With these comparisons in mind let us proceed with an outline of the essential steps in the life cycle of an angiosperm. The dominant vegetative plant is the sporophyte and, as already amply emphasized, the flower is the organ concerned with sexual reproduction.

The Male Gametophyte. The anther is the particular part of the stamen responsible for the production of microspores which are produced by meiosis from a microspore mother cell within the pollen sac (Fig. 12.4). Each microspore contains one haploid nucleus, which soon divides into generative and tube nuclei (Fig. 25.1*C*). While this mitosis is taking place a heavy sculptured wall forms about the microspore and a mature pollen grain results. The pollen is now shed and conveyed in one fashion or another (page 251) to a stigma where it germinates and a pollen tube penetrates the stigma (Fig. 25.1*A* and *D*), grows through the style, down to the ovule within the ovary. The tube nucleus, depending upon the species of plant, may degenerate early or may persist until the pollen tube is well developed. In any event, the generative nucleus usually divides within the pollen tube into two sperm nuclei (Fig. 25.1*D*). Each sperm nucleus with its associated cytoplasm is a sperm cell. The pollen tube with the sperm cells and the tube nucleus, if present, constitutes the mature male gametophyte.

The Female Gametophyte. An enlarged cell within nucellar tissue of a young ovule undergoes meiosis and forms four megaspores arranged in a row (page 230). While this process is occurring, integuments form about the nucellar tissue, resulting in the formation of a typical ovule (Fig. 12.11). The three megaspores closest to the micropyle generally disintegrate. The remaining megaspore undergoes three successive mitotic divisions. Typical migration of the eight nuclei so constituted results in the formation of a seven-celled embryo sac or female gametophyte with the following cells: one egg cell, two synergid cells, one endosperm mother cell with two polar nuclei, and three antipodal cells (Fig. 25.1A).

Fertilization and Seed Development. With the penetration of the pollen tube to the mature embryo sac the stage is set for fertilization. In all previous forms we have studied this involves only the fusion of an egg cell with a sperm. In the angiosperms fertilization involves, not only the union of the egg cell with the sperm cell, but in addition, the union of a second sperm cell with the endosperm mother cell to form the primary endosperm cell (Fig. 25.2). Since there are two nuclei in the endosperm mother cell the nucleus of the primary endosperm cell will have three sets of chromosomes (page 232). The union of the two sperms, one with the egg, the second with the endosperm mother cell is **double fertilization.**

The zygote generally develops a small proembryo, from one end of which the typical embryo of the seed develops. The fate of the primary endosperm cell depends upon the species. Probably in all forms it develops into an endosperm which plays some role in nourishing the developing embryo (Fig. 25.2E). In a few genera, notably the grains (page 278, Fig. 13.25), the endosperm enlarges and persists in the seed

Table 25.2

A generalized life history of an angiosperm

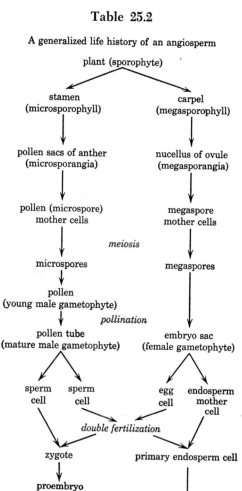

to form the main source of nourishment for the young seedling. There are three general types of seeds depending upon the various combinations of cotyledon number and the location of stored food (Figs. 13.23, 13.24, and 13.25). A seed always includes a dormant embryo and a food supply to enable the young seedling to establish itself. The food is most generally stored in the cotyledons of the embryo or in the endosperm.

With the germination of a seed and the development of the seedling into a flowering plant the life cycle of an angiosperm is completed. The essential steps are shown in Table 25.2.

Comparative Reproductive Structures

Certain comparative details between the structures and life histories of members of the Pterophyta are given in Table 25.3. The seed of pine and the corn grain are compared in Table 25.4. Details concern-

Table 25.3. Comparison of the Pterophyta

	Filicinae	Gymnospermae	Angiospermae
Sporophyte	Rhizome, roots, and leaves	Roots, stems, and leaves	Roots, stems, and leaves
	Herbs	Trees and shrubs, no herbs	Trees, shrubs, and herbs
	Stem: several strands of vascular tissue with xylem of each surrounded by phloem,	Stem: one core of xylem surrounded by phloem, vessels in one shrubby genus only	Stem: one core of xylem surrounded by phloem, or several vascular strands with phloem exterior
	Vessels occur in two genera	Sieve cells	
	Sieve elements but no companion cells in phloem	Pith present in stems not in roots	Pith in stems not in roots of dicots, in some monocot roots
	Stem resembles root of angiosperms		
	No cambium	Cambium develops in all species	Cambium in perennial forms; absent generally in annuals
	Leaves bear spores in sporangia	Staminate and ovulate cones, generally, with staminate and ovulate scales	Flowers, stamens, and carpels
	No cones		
	Some meristem at tip of leaves		
	Homospory	Heterospory	Heterospory
		Microspores in microsporangia	Microspores in anther
		Megaspores in megasporangia or a nucellus	Megaspores in nucellus
	No ovule	Ovules present, exposed on scales	Ovules present, enclosed within carpel
	Embryo attached to gametophyte	Embryo develops within a seed	Embryo develops within a seed
Gametophyte	Heart-shaped, small, green, completely independent thallus	Pollen tube; male gametophyte	Pollen tube; male gametophyte
		Female gametophyte within ovule	Female gametophyte; embryo sac within ovule
	Antheridium of approximately 6–10 cells	Antheridium practically absent	Sperm cells formed by pollen tube
		Sperm cells formed by pollen tube	
	Motile sperms	Motile sperms in several primitive genera, but free water not needed for fertilization	Nonmotile sperms only
		Nonmotile sperms in all other forms	
	Archegonia partially embedded in gametophyte	A very greatly reduced archegonium completely embedded in female gametophyte	Archegonium only suggested by synergid cells of the embryo sac

ing the Psilophyta, Lycophyta and Spheno-phyta are given in Table 23.1.

In all Pterophyta the sporophyte is the dominant generation, but only in the Fili-cinae are both gametophyte and sporophyte generations independent. In the Gymnospermae and the Angiospermae there occurs a further reduction in the size and complexity of the gametophyte to a condition of complete dependency on the parent sporophyte. This is accompanied by an overall increase in the general complexity of the sporophyte. It can be stated that, as a guiding principle, the more advanced forms in this phylum are more highly adapted to grow and to flourish in a dry land habitat than are the more primitive forms. The most obvious developments designed to accomplish this adaptation are those which remove any dependence of the plants on free moisture for fertilization, as well as adaptations, both vegetative and reproductive, which enable the plant to grow and to reproduce on dry land.

Protection of the Female Gametophyte. The gynoecium of the angiosperm flower is essentially a modified leaf or leaves, enclosing an ovule, in which the female gametophyte is to be found. The ovary, as we know, eventually develops into a fruit. This envelopment of the ovules and subsequently the seed by the ovary wall is a new development which sets the angiosperms apart from all other groups of plants. Recall that in ferns the egg cells have little protection from their immediate environment. The gametophyte thallus in ferns is a delicate structure, and the venter of the archegonium opens directly, by way of the ventral canal, to external moisture (Fig. 24.11). Without in any way considering phylogenetic relationships, recall next the female gametophyte of *Selaginella* (Fig. 23.15). It may be afforded some protection

Table 25.4. Comparison of Pine Seed and Corn Grain

Pine Seed	Corn Grain
Seed coats	Seed coats fused with pericarp
Numerous cotyledons	One cotyledon
Food stored in female gametophyte	Food stored in endosperm
Radicle	Radicle protected by coleorhiza
Plumule protected by cotyledons	First leaves protected by coleoptile

by the parent sporophyte but the motile sperms must reach the egg under their own power and the archegonium opens to the external environment by a very short neck canal. In pine the female gametophyte has gained the protection of the integuments of the ovule and the scales of the ovulate cone, as well as being retained within the megasporangium. Pollen must still, however, be deposited very close to the female gametophyte in order to effect fertilization. The situation in pine no longer requires free water for movement of sperms and except for a few primitive gymnosperms motile sperms are absent from this class.

The female gametophyte (embryo sac) of the angiosperms, within the ovary wall, has gained, in the ovary wall, an added protective barrier. However, this has necessitated further adaptations to enable the sperms to pass this added protection: (1) the development of the receptive stigma and (2) the growth of the pollen tube through the style (Fig. 25.1).

Size of Gametophytes. Reduction in the size of the gametophytes has thus proceeded to a point in which the male gametophyte, the pollen tube, consists of one vegetative nucleus and two sperm cells (Fig. 25.1*D*). The female gametophyte is a seven-celled structure one of which is an egg cell. A second cell, the endosperm mother cell, is an innovation in that it too is receptive to a sperm cell. The remaining five cells are vegetative cells (Fig. 25.1A). It should be pointed out that the embryo sacs of some angiosperms have more cells, while a few have less. Should the gametophyte stages be completely eliminated, gametes, instead of meiospores, would result from meiosis. This actually occurs in animals and in at least one plant genus, the seaweed *Fucus* (page 373). The haploid phase in these forms is reduced to the sperm and egg cells.

Nourishment for the Developing Embryo. Double fertilization is still another difference between the life cycle of the angiosperms and more primitive forms. In these latter forms nourishment for the young developing sporophyte is generally provided by the female gametophyte (Figs. 23.15, 24.37C) or in the case of many ferns by the simple monoecious gametophyte (Fig. 24.13). In the angiosperms food for the developing seedling is stored either in the endosperm (Figs. 13.24, 13.25) or in the cotyledons of the embryo itself (Fig. 13.23).

The Fruit. Fertilization in the angiosperms as in all other forms stimulates the zygote and certain surrounding tissue to further development. In the angiosperms the ovary wall is stimulated to produce a fruit and the fruit is a development originating with, and characteristic of, the angiosperms. The protection of the seed from its surroundings, by the ovary wall, is accompanied by various devices for releasing the seed from its enclosure or otherwise bringing it under conditions favorable for germination. Among these adaptations may be mentioned the different sorts of dehiscence (Figs. 13.10, 13.11), various kinds of fleshy fruits (Figs. 13.7, 13.21), and the reduction of the ovary wall so that it becomes indistinguishable from the seed coats (Fig. 13.14).

Evolution in the Angiosperms

If, as assumed, the angiosperms represent the culmination of an extensive evolutionary development it would appear likely that, within the class itself, evolution has been, and probably still is, active. In other words, families of angiosperms must be related and it should be possible to arrange the families in an order that would give some indication of their relationship. Some families will be more primitive than others; and from the more primitive types the more advanced and specialized forms have presumably arisen. What is the primitive floral type? What have been the trends in the evolution of the flower? What system of classifying flowering plants will be most truly natural?

Besseyan System. Many systems of classifying plants have been proposed; two are in general use in America today. One of these was proposed by Engler and forms the basis for the arrangement of plants in many books on classification. A second system that has found much favor with American botanists was proposed by Bessey; it is described here. This system regards the order Ranales as being the most primitive. In this order the Magnoliaceae is one of the more primitive families with the Ranunculaceae somewhat more advanced. The tulip-tree (Fig. 12.1), magnolias (Figs. 12.2, 13.10B), and buttercups (Fig. 25.3) are representatives of these two families and while both have flowers with many characteristics in common, the fact that magnolias are trees or shrubs and most Ranunculaceae are herbaceous forms, and geologically trees appeared before herbs (Table 26.1), indicates that the Magnoliaceae is the more primitive family. In both magnolias (Fig. 12.1) and buttercups (Fig. 25.3) the flower parts are arranged as follows:

1. The floral axis is elongated.
2. All, or at least some, of the flower parts are spirally arranged.
3. Stamens and carpels are numerous and separate.
4. Sepals and petals are numerous and separate.
5. The flowers are perfect and complete.
6. The floral symmetry is regular.
7. The perianth segments and stamens are attached to the receptacle *below* the points of attachment of the carpels (i.e., the flowers are hypogynous).

These, then, are a group of characteristics indicative of primitive flowers; changes in any of them indicate more advanced forms. The principal tendencies then in the evolution of the flower, according to the Besseyan system, are changes in these characteristics and they may be enumerated as follows:

1. From an elongated to a shortened floral axis.
2. From a spiral to a whorled condition of floral parts.
3. From numerous and separate stamens and carpels to few and coalesced stamens and carpels.
4. From numerous and separate sepals and petals to few and coalesced sepals and petals.
5. From complete and perfect flowers to incomplete and imperfect flowers.
6. From regular to irregular flowers.
7. From hypogyny to epigyny.

According to the Besseyan view, there were at least three main lines of advance from the primitive Ranalian type of flower as exemplified by magnolias and buttercups. These lines culminated in (1) the mints (Labiatae), (2) the asters (Compositae), and (3) the orchids (Orchidaceae). In comparing plants with evolution in mind, it must be emphasized that, not only do certain characteristics have more weight than others, but groups of characteristics must be given thoughtful consideration. For example, epigyny is thought to be an advanced condition.

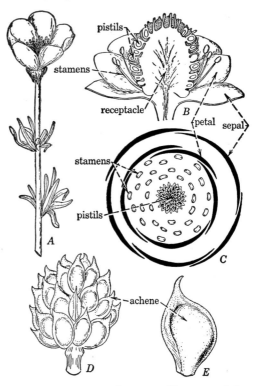

Fig. 25.3. Ranunculaceae. Flower and fruit of buttercup (*Ranunculus*). A, flower stalk; B, lengthwise section of flower; C, floral diagram; D, cluster of fruits; E, a single fruit. (A, B, and D redrawn from Korsmo.)

However, it should be noted that all flowers in one of the three main lines of ascent are hypogynous. This line culminates in the mints and places this family at a level of evolutionary advance comparable to that held by the Compositae and Orchidaceae.

SELECTED FAMILIES OF ANGIOSPERMS

Let us now proceed to examine selected families of angiosperms with two objectives in mind, (1) to learn the characteristics of some important angiosperm families and (2) to discover how these families fit into the Besseyan system of angiosperm classi-

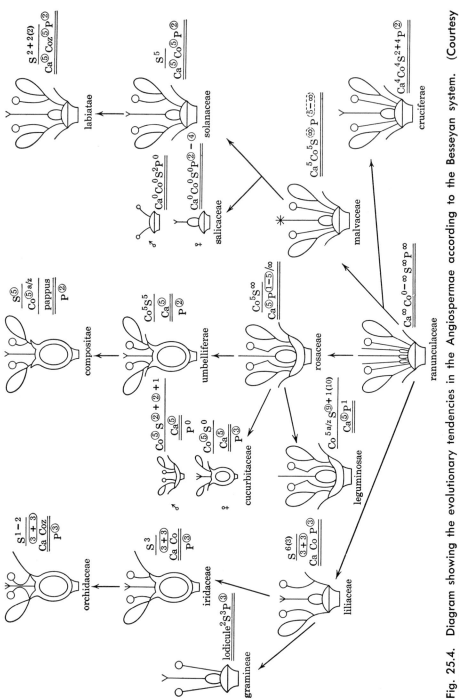

Fig. 25.4. Diagram showing the evolutionary tendencies in the Angiospermae according to the Besseyan system. (Courtesy of McMinn.)

fication. In our discussion of these matters so far, floral characteristics have been emphasized. The single exception is that of the tree form of the magnolias versus the herbaceous habit of the buttercups. The emphasis placed on floral parts is because their form and structure are little influenced by the external environment, and varies much less from generation to generation than do vegetative parts. Because of this consistency in structure, floral parts have a much greater value in both plant identification and in tracing evolutionary relationships than do vegetative characters. However, the latter cannot be neglected altogether and many of the characteristics discussed in detail in the chapters on the stem (page 81), leaf (page 154), and fruit (page 257) are used in identification and in evolutionary studies. It might be well to review briefly and independently the morphological details presented in these chapters.

Since the magnolia, the tulip-tree, and buttercups are thought to be primitive forms we shall commence our discussion with these families, then proceed first to follow through a line of ascent ending in the mint family. We shall consider the line culminating in the composites next and complete our discussion with the line of monocotyledonous families. It should be further noted that the lines are not truly straight lines but more properly trees in that each line is branched. The arrangement of the families discussed here as they occur in the Besseyan system is shown in Fig. 25.4.

FROM RANALES TO LABIATAE

In this line of ascent from the Ranales no change has occurred from the condition of hypogyny; all flowers, in all families in the line are hypogynous. Syncarpy occurred very early, as did a reduction in the number of floral parts. Other types of coales-

cence and the change to irregular flowers appeared somewhat later but still early in the line of ascent. The families involved here are the Magnoliaceae, the Ranunculaceae, the Malvaceae, the Cruciferae, the Solanaceae, the Salicaceae and the Labiatae.

The Malvaceae is a clearly marked family with relatively primitive characters as shown by its regular, perfect and hypogynous flowers. There are numerous stamens with coalesced anthers, and the five or more carpels are more or less firmly united. In the Cruciferae, flower parts are reduced in numbers and only the carpels are coalesced. In the Solanaceae, the flowers, while perfect and regular, show coalescence of sepals, petals, and carpels, with the stamens adnate to the corolla tube. The willows (Salicaceae) are an example of a family in which the reduction in both number and size of floral parts has resulted in an advanced condition. The flowers are imperfect, are grouped in catkins, and both calyx and corolla are lacking. The pistillate flowers are hypogynous and in the staminate flowers the numbers of stamens has been reduced to one or two. The willows are a part of a branch from the main line in which wind, rather than insect, pollination is the rule. The Labiatae or mints represent the most advanced family in this line of ascent. The flowers, even in this advanced family are hypogynous; they are, however, irregular, there is a reduction in the number of parts to 4 or 2; the sepals, petals, and carpels are coalescent. The stamens are not only adnate to the corolla tube but are highly specialized for insect pollination. Let us consider each family in more detail.

Magnoliaceae

The Magnoliaceae shares with the Ranunculaceae the distinction of being a **very**

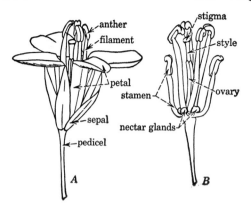

Fig. 25.5. Cruciferae. Mustard flower (*Brassica*). A, all flower parts intact; B, sepals and petals removed, note four long and two short stamens and the single pistil.

ancient group of plants. The tulip-tree, *Liriodendron*, as shown by fossil remains once had a very widespread distribution. Most species are trees or fairly large shrubs. The magnolias themselves are magnificent trees, *Magnolia grandiflora* growing to 100 feet or more with its stiff large evergreen leaves and large white blossoms 7 to 8 inches across. The magnolias are largely warm climate species, but the tulip-trees will stand northern winters. There are some 10 genera and 80 species in the family. The leaves are alternate, mostly entire, pinnately veined with large stipules generally enclosing the buds.

Flowers (Figs. 12.1, 12.2) are perfect, regular, and with distinct separate parts. There are 6 or more petals. There are generally numerous stamens and carpels all arranged spirally on the receptacle. The fruits (Fig. 13.10*B*) are follicles or samaras and are frequently grouped to form a cone-like body.

Ranunculaceae

Most members of the family are herbs, although there are a few small shrubs and woody climbers. The leaves are characteristically very much divided, a feature which has led to the common name of Crowfoot Family. There are about 300 genera and approximately 1200 species growing largely in the temperate and Arctic regions. Many of our common garden flowers belong to this family. Among these are *Delphinium*, Columbine, *Paeonia, Ranunculus, Anemone* and *Clematis.* The marsh marigold and hepatica, common spring flowers, are members of this family. One genus, *Aconitum Napellus* yields an important drug and some of the wild *Delphinium* are poisonous to livestock.

The floral parts are quite similar in structure and arrangement to those of the Magnoliaceae. They indicate a primitive angiosperm family (Fig. 25.3). There are numerous separate parts to each whorl and they are arranged in a spiral order on the receptacle. The flowers are generally regular and hypogynous. The fruit is a follicle, an achene, or sometimes a berry. There are exceptions to this arrangement of parts; for instance, the flowers of *Delphinium* are very irregular.

Cruciferae

The Cruciferae is a large, distinct family containing many cultivated forms, as well as some that are noxious weeds. The cabbages, cauliflowers, broccolis, Brussels sprouts, kohlrabies and kale are all varieties of a single species, *Brassica oleracea.* Wild mustard, another *Brassica* species, is a noxious weed in grain fields though sometimes used as cover crop in orchards. Radishes and stocks are other members of this family, as are many garden herbs. The family has a world-wide distribution in the temperate and subarctic zones; all are herbs. There are about 200 genera and 1800 species.

The flowers and fruits are very characteristic of the family. The flowers (Fig. 25.5A) are small but conspicuous because of their large numbers. They are complete, regular, and hypogynous. There are four sepals and four petals, usually somewhat sharply angled close to their midline and bending backward. There are six stamens, four longer than the other two. The single pistil is composed of four carpels and has two locules. The arrangement of the petals generally suggests a cross, whereupon the family name, Cruciferae or cross bearing. The fruit is a silque (Fig. 13.12), generally dehiscing in the typical fashion. The pod of the radish (*Raphanus*) does not dehisce.

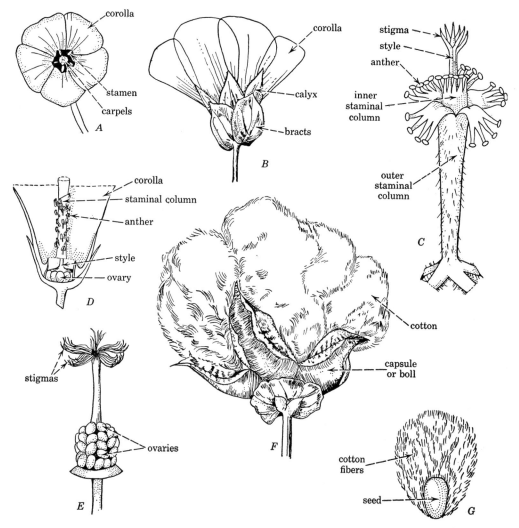

Fig. 25.6. Malvaceae. A and B, regular flowers of *Anoda* and *Malope*; C, double staminal column of *Sidalcia*; D, ovary and staminal column of *Anoda*; E, gynoecium of *Malope*; F, dehisced capsule or boll of *Gossypium* with cotton fibers; G, seed of *Gossypium* with attached cotton fibers. (Redrawn from L. H. Bailey, *Manual of Cultivated Plants*, The Macmillan Co.)

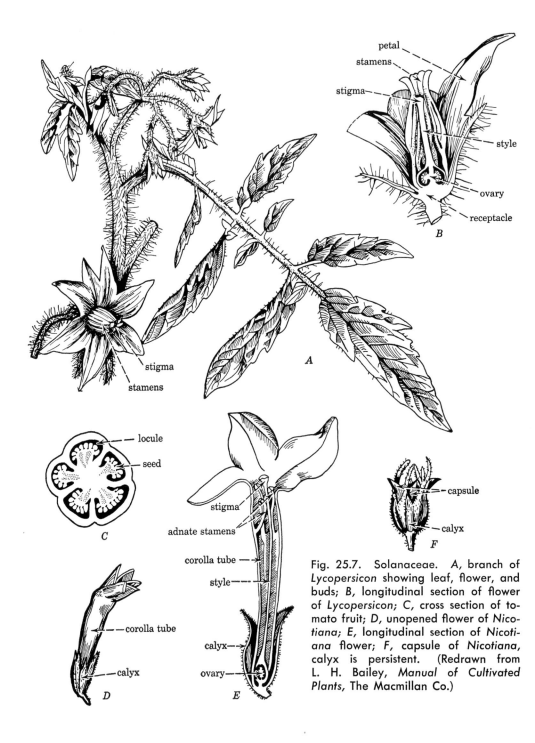

Fig. 25.7. Solanaceae. A, branch of *Lycopersicon* showing leaf, flower, and buds; B, longitudinal section of flower of *Lycopersicon*; C, cross section of tomato fruit; D, unopened flower of *Nicotiana*; E, longitudinal section of *Nicotiana* flower; F, capsule of *Nicotiana*, calyx is persistent. (Redrawn from L. H. Bailey, *Manual of Cultivated Plants*, The Macmillan Co.)

Malvaceae

This is another large family of some 50 genera and 900 species. There are no important food-producing species and the ornamentals in the family, such as *Hibiscus* and *Abutilon,* are not as outstanding as roses, irises, and orchids. The cotton, however, taken from the fruits of the various members of the genus *Gossypium,* make this family of plants as important from the viewpoint of politics, agriculture and industry as the grasses, legumes, and roses. There are herbs, shrubs, and trees in the family; their leaves are mostly palmately veined and lobed, with small deciduous stipules.

The flowers (Figs. 12.19, 25.6) are regular, generally perfect with five sepals usually united, and a tubular five-lobed corolla. The many stamens are united by their filaments to form a tube surrounding the pistil and frequently adnate at its base to the five petals. The ovary is superior with generally two to many locules, each containing one to several seeds. In most species the number of carpels can be told from the number of styles and stigmas. The fruit of most species is a capsule although in a few it is a berry. The cotton of commerce occurs as long hair or fuzz on the seeds which are borne in large capsules.

Solanaceae

This is a large family with many tropical forms but also well represented in the temperate regions. There are about 75 genera and over 2000 species, some 1200 of the latter being in a single genus, *Solanum.* To this family belong tomatoes, potatoes, tobaccos, eggplant, peppers, *Petunias* (Fig. 12.18*B, C*) and *Salpiglossis.* While the family is of world-wide distribution, most of the cultivated forms were brought under domestication in the Western Hemisphere.

There are many poisonous and drug plants, such as belladonna, in the family. Even such common things as tomatoes were long supposed to be poisonous, as appears to be indicated by its scientific name *Lycopersicon* which means "wolf peach." There are many erect and climbing herbs in the family, also some shrubs and small trees. The alternate leaves are mostly entire, although in a few species they may be variously dissected.

The perfect flowers (Fig. 25.7) are mostly regular, the calyx and corolla are coalesced and generally five-lobed. The number of adnate, hypogynous stamens, 5, corresponds to the number of corolla lobes with which they alternate. Sometimes one or more of the stamens may be sterile. The superior ovary has normally two locules, five in tomato, with a single style and a two-lobed stigma. The fruit is a berry or, less frequently, a capsule with many seeds.

Salicaceae

The willow family is comprised of only two genera (*Salix,* willows, and *Populus,* poplars) with about 200 species. They are mostly trees, but some shrubby forms are known. They are very abundant in the Northern Hemisphere, mostly in the temperate zones. Commonly planted are the weeping willow and poplars. Baskets are woven from branches of the Basket willow and paper pulp is obtained from the trunks of one species. Willows are common along water courses, frequently overhanging or even choking mountain streams to the ill comfort of fishermen. All species have alternate simple stipulate leaves.

The flowers (Fig. 25.8) are generally dioecious and are borne in catkins in the spring in advance of the leaves. The perianth is lacking, the one or more stamens and single pistil being found in the axils of bracts. There are mostly two stigmas. The

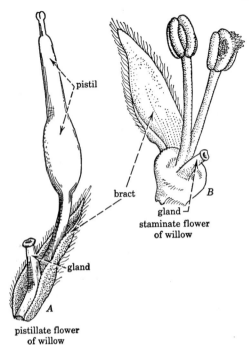

pistillate flower of willow

Fig. 25.8. Salicaceae. *A,* a pistillate flower willow (*Salix*); *B,* a staminate flower. (Redrawn from Johnson, *Taxonomy of Flowering Plants, Appleton-Century-Crofts.*)

fruits are small capsules having in a single locule many seeds with long down or hairs. Willows have one or two stamens per flower while the poplar flowers have between 8 and 10. Pussy willow is a familiar example of the flowers of this family.

Labiatae

The mints, like the orchids and composite families, represent the supposed highest advance of one of the three lines of angiosperm evolution. It is a large family of considerable economic importance, largely because of the volatile oils produced by certain of its members. Peppermint, spearmint, thyme, sage, and lavender are examples. There are about 160 genera with 3000 species well distributed over the surface of the earth. There are herbs and

shrubs in the family, generally with characteristic square stems. The leaves are simple and opposite or whorled.

The flowers (Fig. 25.9) may be showy, are generally irregular, usually complete, although some may be imperfect. The calyx is regular or two-lipped, partly coalesced and commonly five-toothed. The four or five parts of the corolla are coalesced characteristically to form two distinct lips, from which the name of the family is derived. There are four stamens, of two sizes, two shorter than the other two. The superior ovary comprised of four carpels is four-parted, each carpel containing a seed. The mature fruit consists of four single seeded nutlets.

From Ranales to Compositae

A second line of ascent from the Ranales involves the Leguminosae, the Rosaceae,

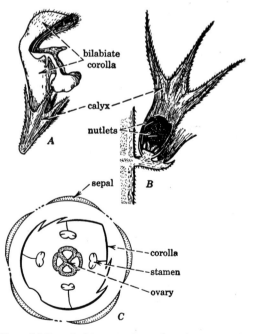

Fig. 25.9. Labiatae, irregular hypogynous flower of mint, showing union of sepals and petals.

the Umbelliferae and the Compositae, with an off-shoot family, the Cucurbitaceae. This large group of families is characterized by an early change from hypogyny to epigyny. Following this there is a division into two sublines, one being marked by a lack of coalescence and a retention of regular flowers. In the other subline coalescence and irregular flowers both occur in advanced forms.

The Rosaceae (rose family) is one of the more primitive families in this line of evolutionary development. There exists a considerable variety of flower structure within the family. The more primitive members of the family are regular, perfect, with numerous parts and showing such a slight degree of perigyny as to be recognizable only with careful observation. This is exemplified by the strawberry (Figs. 13.6, 25.10). Changes within the family involve a reduction in the number of floral parts, a shift from slight perigyny to true perigyny (Figs. 25.10, 12.21) and to epigyny (Fig. 12.22*B*). Coalescence also occurs. Members of the family generally have regular flowers.

The Leguminosae (pea family) are considered to be a more advanced family than the Rosaceae even though their flowers are hypogynous. There is a reduction in number of parts, the gynoecium having only one carpel; coalescence of stamens and of some petals occurs and the corolla parts are irregular. The Umbelliferae represent a further advance over the Rosaceae in that the flowers are epigynous and exhibit syncarpy (Fig. 25.13). This line of ascent finds its climax in the Compositae whose flowers uniformly all possess advanced characters, such as reduction in number of parts, modification of parts (pappus), irregular flowers, some imperfect flowers, the presence of coalescence in each whorl and adnation.

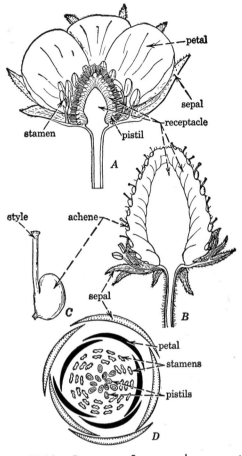

Fig. 25.10. Rosaceae, flower and aggregate fruit of strawberry (*Fragaria*). A, median lengthwise section of a flower; B, median lengthwise section of a fruit; C, single achene; D, floral diagram. (Redrawn from Robbins, *Botany of Crop Plants*, The Blakiston Co.)

The Cucurbitaceae culminate a branch line from the rose order. The flowers of the Cucurbitaceae have such advanced characters as loss of floral parts, imperfect flowers, epigyny and coalescence.

Rosaceae

Whereas grasses and the legumes supply man with bread and vegetables of basic importance, the rose family supplies dessert;

fruits and almonds and roses for decoration. There are better than 2500 species in this family and over 100 genera, not counting the almost numberless cultivated forms of roses, peaches, apples, cherries, strawberries, almonds, and so on. The family is of world-wide distribution and somewhat heterogeneous. Many of the principles of angiosperm evolution can be demonstrated with its members. There are trees, shrubs and herbs in the family. The leaves are usually alternate and bear stipules.

While the flowers of different genera show much variation they are generally perfect and regular. The parts are borne on a floral disk which as it develops after fertilization becomes responsible for certain of the fruits characteristic of the family. In the rose the disk or calyx tube is hollow and surrounds numerous pistils; the numerous stamens and corolla are adnate to this tube, the flower being perigynous. Cherries (Fig. 12.21), plums, peaches, and apricots have a similar structure except that the number of parts of the gynoecium is reduced to one or occasionally two. In the strawberry (Figs. 13.6, 25.10) the reverse situation obtains, in that instead of hollow structure bearing the parts of the gynoecium, the carpels are borne on the outside of a raised disk. In the apple (Fig. 13.21) and quince (Fig. 12.22*B*) the calyx tube or floral disk grows attached to the ovary and expands to become the edible portion of the fruit. A simple classification of the flowers of the rose family is not possible. There is much variation in the type of fruits. In the strawberry the matured ovary is an achene; in the apples and pears it is a pome; in the peaches and apricots, blackberries and cherries, it is a drupe; capsules occur in some genera and follicles in others.

Cucurbitaceae

The gourd or melon family is an interesting one, in that it is of world-wide distribution in at least the warmer regions of the world and various peoples have selected different forms for domestication. It is also probably the only group in which the fruits are highly prized for ornamental purposes and for use as vessels of various types. The pumpkins and squashes are thought to be of American origin. Cucumbers and melons have probably come from Africa and central Asia. Other species appear to have been first cultivated in the tropics of Asia, Polynesia, and India. They are frequently tendril climbing annual or perennial vines. Most are rapid growing and frost tender. There are about 90 genera with 700 species. The stems are usually soft and hairy or prickly. The generally simple leaves are large and sometimes deeply cut. Lateral tendrils are often present and they may be simple or branched.

The flowers (Fig. 25.11) are imperfect and the plants may be either dioecious or monoecious. In the pistillate flower the five-lobed calyx is adnate to the ovary. There may be five petals or they may be coalesced into a five-lobed corolla. The inferior ovary is composed commonly of three carpels with styles and stigmas also coalesced, but the latter may be lobed. The fruit is the pepo or berry so characteristic of the family. The perianth of the staminate flower is similar. There are five stamens, two of which may be fused. The anthers twist so that the stamens appear to form a solid central column.

Leguminosae

The legume family has such distinctive characteristics that its members can frequently be recognized with but little experience. It is a large family with close to 500 genera and several thousand species. All sorts of plant bodies are represented: herbs, both annuals and perennials, shrubs, vines, and trees. It is of world-wide distribution. While less heterogeneous than the rose family there is considerable variation found among its various members. It is a family of very considerable importance supplying food for man and his animals. Many legumes are used for ornaments, from shade trees to cut flowers.

Some lumber is obtained from the black locust and some of the tropical species furnish wood for fine cabinet work. The association of the nitrogen-fixing bacteria with the roots of legumes places this family in a unique position relative to the maintenance of soil fertility. Peas, beans, peanuts, clovers, lupines, are common herbaceous legumes; wisteria is a vine, brooms and redbuds are shrubs or low trees, the locusts and acacias are tree types. The *Mimosa* genus alone has some 300 species, includ-

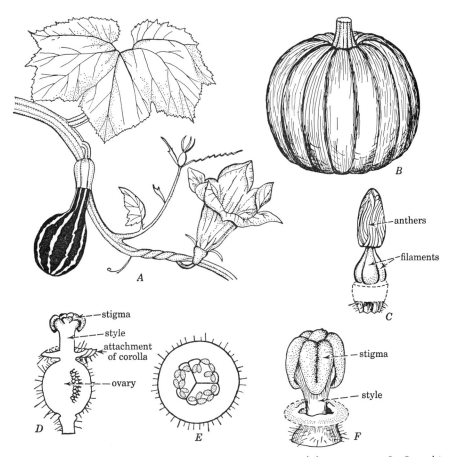

Fig. 25.11. Cucurbitaceae. A, *Cucurbita Pepo*, flowering and fruiting stem; B, *Cucurbita Pepo*, fruit; C, *C. maxima*, staminal column; D, *C. maxima* stigma, longitudinal section through pistil, corolla tube removed; E, *C. maxima*, cross section through ovary; F, *C. maxima*, style and stigma. (Redrawn from L. H. Bailey, *Manual of Cultivated Plants*. The Macmillan Company.)

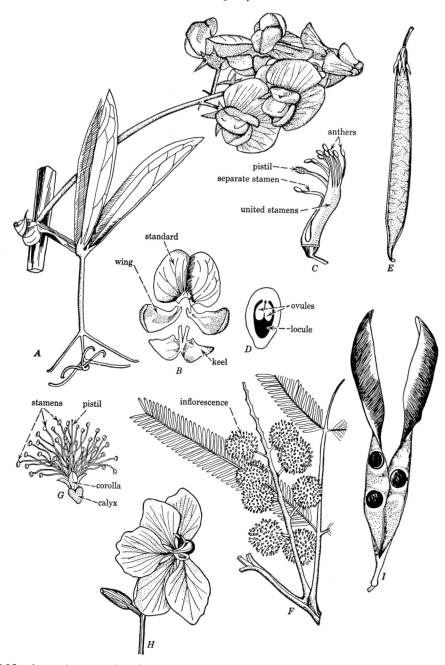

Fig. 25.12. Leguminosae. A, inflorescence and leaf of *Lathyrus*; B, exploded view of *Lathyrus* corolla; C, essential organs of *Lathyrus* flower; D, cross section of ovary; E, pod of *Lathyrus*; F, branch showing inflorescences and leaves of *Acacia*; G, a single *Acacia* flower; H, flower of *Bauhinia*; I, dehisced pod of *Bauhinia*. (Redrawn from L. H. Bailey, *Manual of Cultivated Plants*, The Macmillan Co.)

ing the sensitive plant of the florist shop; there are others of varying habit from tall trees to low herbs. The leaves of the legumes are prevailingly pinnately compound and quite generally with stipules. Sometimes a leaflet will be modified to a tendril.

The flowers of most genera are of the well-known sweet pea or "butterfly" type (Figs. 12.5, 12.17, 25.12). They are thus irregular, the five-parted corolla forming a standard, two wings, and a keel. Sepals are present. Nine of the ten stamens are united to form a tube around the ovary; the tenth stamen is free. The gynoecium is composed of a single carpel. In some genera the flowers, while quite irregular, are not of the typical sweet pea type and in *Mimosa* and allied genera the flowers are regular and small. In this group some species have numerous, free stamens. The legume (Figs. 13.2, 13.9) or pod is the characteristic fruit of the family. It forms from a single carpel, has one locule and numerous seeds. In many genera it dehisces at maturity along both sutures; in a few genera it is indehiscent.

Umbelliferae

The parsley family forms a very distinctive group of plants, many of which can be recognized with little experience as belonging to the family. There are about 250 genera and 2000 species growing in all regions of the world, though confined to the mountains in the tropic zone. The name is derived from the typical umbel type of inflorescence (Fig. 12.30). The family contains many crop plants, as well as some producing drugs and a number of kitchen herbs. Poison hemlock, made famous because of its use by the Greeks as a means of carrying out the sentence of death and which was given as such to Socrates, is a member of this family. This genus is wide-

spread, constituting a hazard to livestock not only in the pastures of Greece, but on the open ranges of California. Carrots and parsnips as well as parsley are members of this family. They are mostly herbs, rarely small shrubs with generally hollow stems. The leaves are alternate, mostly compound, and frequently much dissected. The petioles expand at the base and may somewhat sheath the stem.

The flowers are small, being borne in umbels which are in turn grouped in umbels so a large inflorescence is formed. Frequently, the umbels of all levels are subtended by bracts which form a characteristic involucre. The flowers (Fig. 25.13) are regular or the outer irregular, always epigynous and perfect, although they may not always be complete. There are five stamens alternating with the petals. The gynoecium is composed of two carpels, each with but a single seed. The fruits are indehiscent, although the carpels separate from each other when mature.

Compositae

The composite family forms an extremely large group of plants, only a few of which are woody and then not sufficiently so as to be designated as trees or shrubs. In this family of herbaceous plants there are around 800 genera and about 12,000 known species. The family is not only of worldwide distribution but in most places is relatively abundant. The family is not noted for its food plants; endive, artichokes, lettuce, sunflower, about limit its contribution in this respect. Neither is it famous as a producer of drugs or other commercial products. One species, Safflower, is now being grown for oil and another has been considered as a possible source of latex for rubber. But a paging through a seed catalog or a visit to a florist shop will show members of this family in their full grandeur. *Dahlia, Chrysanthemum,* aster, *Zinnia,* marigold, *Gaillardia,* ageratum, and many others are representatives of this family. Dandelions color lawns, and various wild species add to the fall color of meadows and fields. There are 200 species of the sagebrush genus *Artemisia* that cover arid portions of the world, and supply among other things tarragon for fancy vinegar and nectar for dessert honey. Leaves are of various shapes.

The flowers and fruits of the family have been described in detail on pages 243–244 and are shown in Fig. 25.14. They will not be further discussed here. They are, however, so characteristic of the family that any composite should be recognizable with a minimum of experience.

The Monocotyledonous Line from Ranales to the Orchids

There are many obvious differences between the Ranales and the monocotyle-

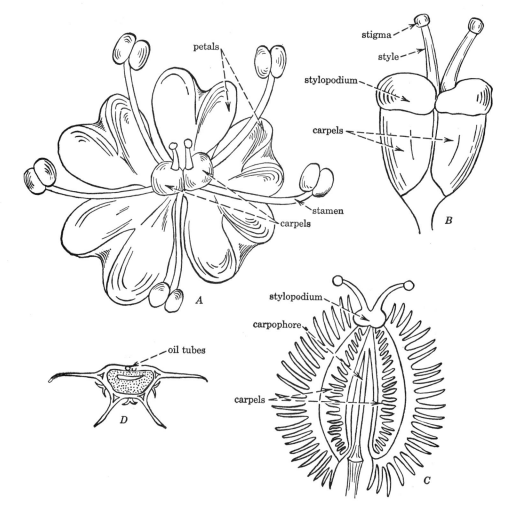

Fig. 25.13. Umbelliferae, flower and fruit of carrot (*Daucus carota*). A, flower, B, two carpels; C, mature fruit; D, cross section of a single carpel.

donous line of evolution. These have been discussed and may be briefly reviewed in table form: Table 25.5.

However, some primitive monocotyledons, particularly certain water weeds such as the arrowheads and water plantains have much in common with the buttercups and marsh marigolds. The families selected to represent this line of ascent are the Liliaceae, the Gramineae, the Iridaceae, and the

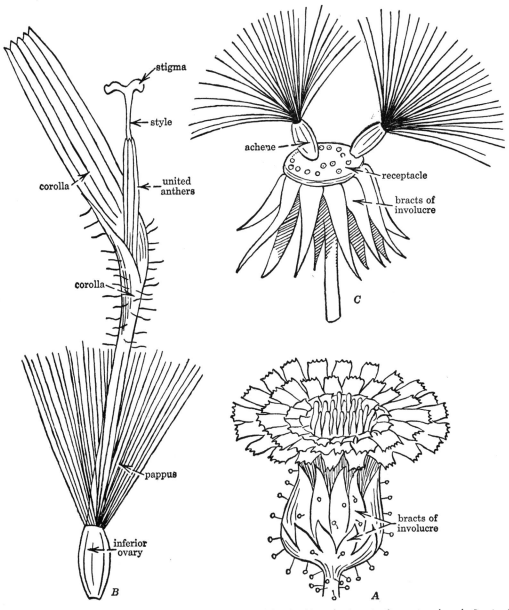

Fig. 25.14. Composite flower and fruit of sow thistle (*Sonchus*). A, flowering head; B, single ray flower; C, mature achenes. (Redrawn from Korsmo.)

Table 25.5.   Tabulation of Differences between Monocotyledons and Dicotyledons

Monocotyledons

1. One cotyledon or seed leaf.
2. Generally marked parallel leaf venation.
3. Flower parts typically in groups of three or multiples of three.
4. Vascular bundles of stems scattered throughout a cylindrical mass of ground tissue.
5. Vascular cambium lacking in most forms.

Dicotyledons

1. Two cotyledons or seed leaves.
2. Generally marked netted venation of leaves.
3. Flower parts typically in groups of four or five.
4. Vascular bundles of stems usually arranged in the form of a cylinder.
5. Vascular cambium present in those forms having secondary growth.

Orchidaceae.   The lilies differ from the Ranales in all of the distinctive monocot characters.   In addition they show a reduction in the number of floral parts and a coalescence of carpels.   The irises show a single advance over the lilies in that they are epigynous.   Many are regular, perfect, and with separate perianth parts.   The stamens show no coalescence.   Syncarpy occurs as it does in the lilies.   The orchids show evolutionary advance in that they have irregular flowers very highly specialized for insect pollination.   The stamens have been reduced in number to one or two.

The order to which the grasses belong is thought to have arisen from the order to which the lilies belong.   The primitive characters of the grasses include hypogyny, regular flowers, and only coalescence of the carpels.   The loss of perianth parts and reduction in the number of stamens and carpels marks them as a more advanced family than the Liliaceae.

Liliaceae

Unlike the grasses lilies are largely grown for ornamental purposes, although two genera, the onions (*Allium*) and asparagus are grown extensively for food.   Some species yield drugs and others have poisonous properties which may cause trouble in pastures or on the ranges of the western states.   There are about 2000 species in some 200 genera.   Most of the lilies grow from a bulb or bulblike organ, and flower in a single growing season after which the shoot dies down.   A few such as the Joshua trees (Fig. 2.15) are woody perennials.   Tulips, hyacinths, day lilies, and Aloes are other examples of the lily genera.

Members of the lily family may be generally quite easily recognized because of the typical showy flowers (Fig. 12.3).   The regular perianth has six parts, usually separate but if united they are lobed and corolla and calyx are generally not distinct from each other.   There are six stamens and one pistil.   The superior ovary is single and three-celled; there are three stigmas.   The fruit is mostly many-seeded and may be a capsule (Fig. 13.5) or a berry.

Gramineae

Not only man, but mammals in general, have been associated with the grass family for far more years than those of recorded history.   It is probably not an overstatement to say that without the grass family and man's ability to learn to exploit it, civilization, as we know it, could not have developed.   The three great civilizations domesticated different grasses, the wheats, rye, barley, and oats by the Mediterranean people; corn (*Zea mays*) by the Aztecs, Mayans, and Incas and other natives of the Western Hemisphere; and rice and millet by the Chinese.   Grasses are grown for human and animal consumption, for ornament and for uses in the arts and industry. There are over 400 genera and about 4500 species. Most grasses are herbaceous, either annuals or perennials; a few bamboos are climbers and some bamboos are woody. Grasses of one kind or another grow in all kinds of soil and situations. Grasses may be conveniently divided into five groups according to their use. 1. The bamboos, mostly evergreen, stout perennials. They are used for construction in many parts of the Orient and some have been introduced into the warmer parts of the United States for ornamental purposes. 2. The cereals, supplying grain and forage for both man and animals. 3. The sugar-producing sorts, such as sugar cane. These are strong upright perennials growing only in the tropics. 4. The sod-forming grasses, perennials that cover many square miles of the earth's surface. They are used in lawns and meadows. 5. There is a large group of grasses grown for ornamental purposes, such as pampas grass. The flowers and vegetative characteristics of the grasses have been described in some detail on pages 240–243 and shown in Figs. 12.24 and 12.25. The leaf is characteristically divided into a sheath which surrounds the stem and expands to a linear blade (Fig. 8.4).

The flowers, (Figs. 12.23 and 12.24) known as florets are small and usually grouped in spikelets. The latter may be arranged in a variety of ways, frequently in spikes or heads. The spikelet normally has two glumes at its base and a number of florets attached to the rachilla. The floret itself has two bracts, the lemma and palea, from which may extend an awn, protecting the single pistil, with its feathery stigmas, and the three stamens. Lodicles may also be present. The fruit is the typical grain or caryopsis, with a single seed whose seed coats have been attached to the ovary wall.

Iridaceae

The Iridaceae or iris family contains about 60 genera and some 1000 species. They are all herbaceous largely perennial forms, usually with rhizomes, bulbs or corms, as in the lilies. The leaves and flowering stalks last for only one season. Some of the choicest florists' plants occur in this family; the irises, gladioli, freesias, crocuses, watsonias, etc.

The regular perianth, like that of the lily, has six parts, united in some genera, separated in others (Fig. 25.15). In some genera the flowers are irregular. Three parts of the perianth may differ from the other three parts, or all may be similar. The flowers are showy and usually emerge from a spathe consisting of a pair, sometimes more, of herbaceous or scaly bracts. The single ovary is inferior and sets this family definitely apart from the Liliaceae. The ovary three-celled and has three stigmas. The fruit is always a many-seeded capsule.

Orchidaceae

The orchids are agreed by all to represent the most advanced family in the Monocotyledoneae. They are all herbaceous plants, circling the world largely in the tropics, but with a few genera extending in the colder temperate regions. There are some 15,000 recognized genera in several hundred families. All forms are perennial, with tuberous, bulbous, or otherwise thickened roots. They may be erect, prostrate, or climbing. A few are saprophytic and lack chlorophyll; others are epiphytes growing on trees without benefit of soil.

The flowers are very showy and highly specialized for insect pollination. A typical

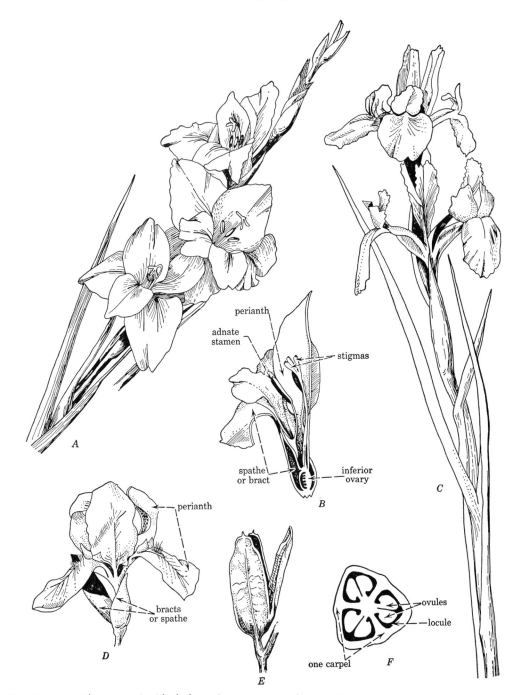

Fig. 25.15. Iridaceae. A, Gladiolus inflorescence; B, longitudinal section of a gladiolus flower; C, Iris inflorescence; D, Iris germanica; E, capsule of Iris sibirica; F, cross section of ovary of Freesia. (Redrawn from L. H. Bailey, Manual of Cultivated Plants, The Macmillan Co.)

flower is shown in Fig. 25.16: sepals are present, the corolla is irregular, and the petals united. The ovary is epigynous, one- or three-celled. The stamens unite with the pistil to form a structure sometimes called the **column**. There may be only one fertile stamen, with sometimes a number of staminodes or infertile stamenlike structures. The pollen hangs together in masses known as **pollinia**. Insects lift such a pollinium and place it with precision on the beak or projection of the stigma which may stand at the base of the anthers. The fruit is a dehiscent capsule having many minute seeds.

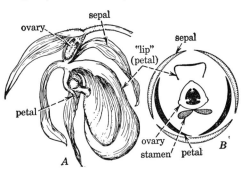

Fig. 25.16. Orchidaceae. Irregular epigynous flower of orchid. A, longitudinal section; B, floral diagram.

SUMMARY OF ANGIOSPERM INNOVATIONS

In our short discussion of the life history of an angiosperm several references were made to structures which were new to and characteristic of the angiosperms. This combination of structures has adapted the angiosperms to the present climatic conditions and resulted in their great variety and extensive vegetative growth. While this discussion has considered only reproductive structures various vegetative adaptations have also played their part in making the angiosperms such successful competitors. We shall not discuss these vegetative adaptations here. The reproductive innovations may, however, be summarized as follows:

1. The development of the carpel, involving the
  (a) ovary
  (b) style
  (c) stigma
2. The enclosure of the ovule within the ovary affording added protection to the ovule and the female gametophyte within it.
3. The style and stigma provide a precise pathway guiding the sperm cells in the pollen tube to the egg cell in the embryo sac.

4. The reduction of the female gametophyte to a seven-celled embryo sac.
5. The stamen is not an innovation of comparable rank to that of the carpel, but it has proved to be a very adaptable part, making possible various highly successful systems of pollination.
6. The reduction of the male gametophyte to a small pollen tube and the complete elimination of motile sperms.
7. The elimination of the female gametophyte as the source of nourishment for the young embryo and seedling.
8. The presence of double fertilization resulting in the formation of an endosperm as a source of nutrient, at least for the young embryo and in some cases for the seedling.
9. Food storage within the embryo itself.
10. The development of the fruit from the ovary wall.

SIGNIFICANT FEATURES OF THE ANGIOSPERM LIFE CYCLE

1. Microspores are produced by meiosis in microsporangia or pollen sacs of the anthers, the latter are a part of the microsporophylls or stamens.
2. Each pollen grain, developing from a microspore by mitosis, has a generative and tube nucleus and is provided with a thick sculptured cell wall.
3. After pollination the pollen tube or male gametophyte grows down the style to the ovule.
4. Meiosis in the megaspore mother cell within the nucellus or megasporangium of the

ovule results in four megaspores aligned in a row.

5. One megaspore commonly develops into a seven-celled embryo sac or female gametophyte.

6. The two sperms are discharged into the embryo sac and double fertilization occurs.

7. The zygote develops an embryo.

8. The primary endosperm cell forms an endosperm which may not persist into the seed.

9. The ovule after fertilization becomes the seed.

SUMMARY OF ANGIO-SPERM EVOLUTION

1. Angiosperm families, according to the Besseyan system of classification, are all derived from the primitive Ranales to which order buttercups and magnolias belong.

2. The important changes in floral evolution according to the Besseyan system are as follows: (*a*) from a spiral to a whorled arrangement of floral parts; (*b*) from many parts to few or even a loss of parts; (*c*) from separate floral parts to coalesced parts; (*d*) from a regular flower to an irregular flower; (*e*) from hypogyny to epigyny.

3. According to the Besseyan system of classification there are three branched lines of ascent from the Ranales.

4. The first line of ascent following the Ranales includes the Malvaceae (mallow family), the Cruciferae (mustard family), the Solanaceae (potato family), the Salica-

ceae (willow family), and the Labiatae (mint family).

5. A second line comprises the Rosaceae (rose family), Leguminosae (pea family), Umbelliferae (carrot family) and Compositae, with the Cucurbitaceae (melon family) as an offshoot from the Rosaceae.

6. A third line comprises the Monocotyledoneae in the following order: Liliaceae (lily family), Iridiaceae (iris family), and Orchidaceae (orchid family). The Gramineae (grass family) are an offshoot from the Liliaceae.

CLASSIFICATION

For the purpose of comparison the families studied are listed here according to the system of Engler. Note that the Gramineae are considered the most primitive.

Class	Angiospermae
Subclass	Monocotyledoneae
Family	Gramineae
	Liliaceae
	Iridaceae
	Orchidaceae
Subclass	Dicotyledoneae
Family	Salicaceae
	Ranunculaceae
	Magnoliaceae
	Cruciferae
	Rosaceae
	Leguminosae
	Malvaceae
	Umbelliferae
	Labiatae
	Solanaceae
	Cucurbitaceae
	Compositae

26

Evolution

In a broad sense the term evolution refers to a process involving gradual changes. It is well known that neither animals, nor plants, nor cities, nor states remain the same. We may speak of the evolution of means of transportation, the evolution of human clothing, the evolution of mountains and valleys, and the evolution of many other nonorganisms. Organic evolution pertains to the gradual changes that have taken place in living things (organisms). Coal, for instance, is formed from the remains of plants that were different in appearance from those growing today. The student of organic evolution may be interested in, among other things, accounting for the disappearance from the earth's flora of the Coal Age plants and the appearance of the modern flowering plants.

Organic evolution is closely allied to genetics and plant breeding. We have seen that the factors which determine the characteristics and the activities of plants are associated with the nuclei. Furthermore, these factors or genes are transmitted from generation to generation by the chromosomes during the processes of fertilization and meiosis. If the origin of new plants is to be understood, experiments on genetics will furnish important information. Many such experiments have been carried out and they have achieved two ends: (1) they have made possible clearer insight into some of the mechanisms of evolution, and (2) they have greatly increased the yield and improved the quality of agricultural crops.

THE GEOLOGIC HISTORY OF PLANTS

Since plants cannot be dissociated from their environment, some knowledge of the principal changes in the earth's crust is essential to an understanding of plant evolution. Broadly speaking, two different types of rock are found in the earth's crust. One of them, like lava, was formed from molten material. The oldest-known rocks are of this nature; granite is an example. Because of their molten origin no fossils are ever found in these rocks, but there is good reason to believe that unicellular algae inhabited the waters of the earth when these old rocks were being formed. Such rocks were predominant when the earth was young, during the period in the earth's history known as the **Archeozoic Age.** It was about 550 million years in length and

Table 26.1

Major Division	Climate and Major Geological Changes
Cenozoic Quaternary 2 million years ago	Periodic glaciation. Warming and cooling.
Cenozoic Late Tertiary	A general cooling and change to semi-arid conditions. Appearance of temperate zones and great mountain ranges.
Cenozoic Early Tertiary 60 million years ago	Began with mountain glaciers and semi-arid conditions. Ended warm and humid.
Late Mesozoic 125 million years ago	Climate generally warm with some fluctuation. Ended cool. Appearance of Rocky Mts., Sierra Nevada, and Andes.
Early Mesozoic 185 million years ago	Climate becomes drier, with periodic glaciation and much change in the earth's crust. Appalachian and Sierra Nevada Mts. form. Seas drain from continents.
Late Paleozoic 309 million years ago	Climate becomes warmer and drier.
Middle Paleozoic 381 million years ago	Climate warm over most of earth. Widespread shallow seas over North America.
Early Paleozoic 553 million years ago	Uniformly warm shallow seas over North America.
Proterozoic 1,500 million years ago	Young Laurentian Mts. form. Glaciation.

Arc diagram labels (from outer to inner):

TODAY

Man and Herbaceous Plants. Climate slowly warming. Atlantic coast eroding. Pacific coast rising and moving slowly northward. Oceans rising.

AGE OF MAN AND HERBACEOUS PLANTS

Extinction of many trees Increase in dominance of herbs such as grass

Retreat of forests from poles Reduction of forests Rise of herbaceous plants

Modernization of woody Angiosperms Development of extensive forests from equator to poles

Appearance of Man

Modern Gymnosperms

Woody Angiosperms dominant Many modern living genera present Angiosperms increasing

First Angiosperms

Gymnosperms dwindling

AGE OF GYMNOSPERMS

Gymnosperms dominant

Modern Ferns

Cycads and conifers

Extinction of many forms as climate changes from moist to dry.

AGE OF LYCOPODS, SEED FERNS, AND AMPHIBIANS

Modern Club mosses

Modern Horsetails

Seed ferns and other ferns

Extensive coal-forming swamps

Dominant club mosses horsetails

Primitive Gymnosperms

Primitive ferns, lycopods, and horsetails

Psilophytales
Rhynia

Seed ferns

First forests

First land plants

Primitive Bryophyta

?

Psilophyta
Psilotum and Tmesipteris

Bryophyta

Algae

AGE OF MARINE ALGAE

Bacteria

Algae

Algae

Bacteria

Fungi

it came to an end some 1500 million years ago.

The second type of rocks (sedimentary rocks) are formed by the deposition of large amounts of sediment in bodies of water. As layer upon layer of sediment accumulates, the pressure upon the lower layers becomes enormous and they are turned to rock. Slate, limestone, and sandstone are examples of sedimentary rocks. If plants or animals are buried in the sediment, and if decay does not occur, the buried individuals are preserved as fossils. It is important to note that plant fossils consist almost entirely of plant remains that grew in or near water or were carried by streams into lakes or other sites of deposition. Algal limestones are known from the Archeozoic Age. Plants growing in arid or mountainous regions rarely deposit their remains where conditions are favorable for their preservation as fossils. Either it is too dry or the site is undergoing erosion and the deposits are of very short duration. This means that the geological record of plants must probably remain incomplete and that the records we do have usually represent only the floras of lowlands and moist habitats. Considerable evidence indicates that the great environmental extremes prevalent in arid or semiarid mountainous areas are especially favorable to rapid evolution. This factor, we shall see, may be very important in connection with the problem of the origin of the angiosperms and, together with the rarity of fossils representing plants of arid habitats, may serve to explain peculiarities that surround the first records of the angiosperms.

The best available evidence indicates that living organisms existed at least 2 billion years ago, for sedimentary rocks that old may contain fossils. The 2 billion years since these first fossils were formed in the Archeozoic Age are divided into four ages; the oldest the **Proterozoic,** is followed in

order by the **Paleozoic,** the **Mesozoic** and the **Coenozoic.** The present Age is the Coenozoic and it is already 60 million years old. Man may have been an inhabitant of the earth for something over 2 million years but the civilized man of historical times is a newcomer of some 7000 years. By comparison with his near relatives he is hardly three days of age. The relations of these four ages, their climatic characteristics and the dominant floras are shown in Table 26.1.

Evidences of these geological ages may be seen in the exposed strata of road cuts, canyons, or mines Sometimes fossiliferous rocks lie exposed in plateau or level areas. Figure 26.1A illustrates a road cut along an Oregon highway. The dark strata contain the remains of plants that resembled modern horsetails. Chunks of this material are continually breaking away and rolling down to the shoulder (Fig. 26.1B) where they may be easily examined. In other regions fossils may be strewn around on the surface of the ground. The "stones" of Fig. 26.1C are carbonized pieces of stems of *Metasequoia*, the dawn redwood (Fig. 23.1). This tree formerly was abundant in the Western United States, but was thought to be extinct until some few living trees, virtually living fossils, were found some years ago in China. Of course, not all sedimentary rocks contain fossils, but many do; and furthermore, many fossils remain undiscovered. Probably no field of botany can be as easily enriched by the amateur collector as paleobotany.

Relation of Phyla of Plants and Geological Age

A survey of the plant kingdom shows that certain phyla growing today are but remnants of once extensive floras. A few fossils representative of them have been described. Let us now see how the differ-

Fig. 26.1. Fossils; A, a road cut along a highway showing fossil-bearing strata; B, a chunk of fosilliferous rock; C, carbonized stems of *Metasequoia*.

ent phyla are related to each other and to the geological period during which they flourished.

Fossil thallophytes are little known. The type that has been described has been found chiefly in Proterozoic rocks although fossil algae are known from the early Archeozoic. Some evidence indicates, moreover, that thallophytes were the dominant vegetation during the early Paleozoic Age. There is general agreement that the first plants to inhabit the earth were algae. Consequently, in Fig. 16.8 they are shown as the earliest plants and as those from which all other plants have been derived.

It is supposed that the bryophytes and tracheophytes have arisen, quite independently of each other, from the algae or algae-like plants. The evidence of their independent origins is not, however, conclusive.

The first vascular plants that made their appearance on the earth are known today only as fossils. They are placed in the order Psilophytales (phylum Psilophyta), members of which, it seems likely, were the ancestors of the other phyla of vascular plants. The Psilophytales (Figs. 16.3, 23.4) were apparently the first true land plants. It is interesting to note that the first air-breathing animals appeared at the time these land plants flourished.

For some hundreds of millions of years after the appearance of the Psilophytales, during the late Paleozoic Age, the horsetails, the lycopods, and the seed ferns formed the dominant vegetation. True ferns were also present in considerable numbers, but they were quite small in size. Figure 26.2 shows how a Paleozoic forest probably looked.

Four groups of plants, the horsetails, the lycopods, the ferns, and seed ferns, are thought to have originated from different representatives of the Psilophytales. Their relationship is more like that of brothers than of direct lineal descendants. As we have learned, the living herbaceous club-mosses and horsetails are the relics of a once-large clubmoss and horsetail flora. Ferns occupy a position today not unlike that which they held in the late Paleozoic Age; they may be somewhat more numerous, but they are relatively small in size. The seed ferns, however, probably gave rise more or less directly to modern gymnosperms and to angiosperms, each of which, in turn, dominated the earth's vegetation. This shift in vegetation type is likely linked to evolutionary changes that directly reflected climatic changes. The humid Paleozoic Age, illustrated in Fig. 26.2, slowly gave way to the Mesozoic, which began as a very cool, arid period and ended as a warm, wet period. The Paleozoic plants that demanded much water were at a disadvantage in the early Mesozoic, and the way was opened for the development and spread of new vegetation types.

Origin of the Angiosperms

The angiosperms as we now know them seem to have appeared already highly evolved into many families and genera without leaving us a record of the stages in their evolution or suggesting the nature of their immediate ancestors. They appeared in the later, warm, moist part of the Mesozoic Age. Their great diversity at this time can only mean a long period of development, which projects their beginnings back into the early, arid periods of the Mesozoic, or possibly even to the cool, dry period that marked the close of the Paleozoic. Therefore, it is highly unlikely that any satisfactory fossil evidence as to the origin of the angiosperms will ever be found. In addition to great aridity, much mountain building and subsequent erosion has served to destroy any chance record of the origin of the angiosperms. Studies of present-day angiosperms, however, in

Fig. 26.2.   Reconstruction of a Paleozoic forest.   Note the seeds attached to fernlike leaf in left center.   (Photo courtesy of Chicago Natural History Museum.)

which vessels are lacking or in which the carpels are not completely fused at maturity may furnish evidence as to the origin of angiosperms.

CHARLES DARWIN AND EVOLUTION

Many biologists since the time of the Greek philosophers have attempted to explain the mechanism of evolution. Great progress has been made during the twentieth century. It will be seen (page 541) that the origin of new species can in some instances be explained and that new species can still arise. Our greater understanding was made possible chiefly because the work of Charles Darwin and of Gregor Mendel (1850–1865) provided a basis that enabled biologists to approach the problem of evolution in an entirely new light.

Darwin, as a result of many years of careful study and observations on a large number of plants and animals, laid emphasis upon the following points.

1. Numbers of plants or animals may increase in a geometric ratio. For example, a given plant may produce 1000 seeds. If each seed grows into a new plant and each new plant produces 1000 seeds, 1 million new plants could result. A third generation from the one original plant would result in 1 billion plants. It may be seen from this example that plants, and animals also, potentially, could increase in numbers at a tremendous rate.

2. Actually, the number of individuals in a given plant or animal association remains fairly constant. There is no such tremendous increase in the number of individuals as seed production seemingly makes possible.

3. No two individual plants or animals are identical; there is **variation**.

Reasoning from these observations, Darwin arrived at these conclusions:

1. Any given population is usually able to reproduce many more young individuals than can adequately be raised in the region it occupies. Therefore, a struggle for existence occurs among the individuals.

2. In this struggle for existence, only those individuals survive which, because of their particular variation, are best adapted to their immediate environment. Thus, a natural selection takes place; the unfit do not survive.

3. These selected variations may be inherited, that is, passed from one generation to another, and thus may gradually give rise to new species.

Variation

Since variations play an important part in plant breeding and evolution, it will be well to examine the concept a little more closely. Variations are of two kinds: (1) environmental and (2) genetic.

Environmental Variations. Suppose that two plants are growing close together but that one is in the shade of a tree whereas the second, 6 feet away, receives full sun (Fig. 26.3). The plant in the shade is small and stunted; it has few flowers and the yield of seeds is low. The plant in full sun is large and robust; it has many flowers and a good yield of seed. Let us collect seeds from each of these plants and divide each collection into halves. If we plant seeds from the sun plant in both shady and sunny locations and do likewise with the seed from the shade plant, we shall again have poor, stunted plants in the shade and healthy plants in the sun. The conditions under which the seed was formed has not influenced in the least the type of plant produced. The environment alone has been responsible for the variation. This is an **environmental variation**, that is, a variation induced by differences in the environment.

Fig. 26.3. Environmental variation in sorghum. Shade plant, left; sun plant, right.

Genetic Variations. If we glance through a seed catalog, we shall find several varieties of beans offered for sale—green string beans, yellow wax beans, navy beans, and so on (Fig. 26.4). No matter where we plant these bean seeds, so long as the conditions permit growth and the production of seeds, we shall obtain bean seeds similar to those that we planted. Such variations are inherited variations; they are **genetic variations,** and it appears probable that they are the more important variations from an evolutionary viewpoint.

THE MECHANISM OF EVOLUTION

The conclusions of Darwin (page 537), together with those of Mendel (page 294), not only laid the foundation for much of the present knowledge of evolution, but also they were a great stimulus, and many hundreds of biologists have subsequently carried out experiments that have further increased our knowledge of the mechanism of evolution.

Let us briefly consider the nature of the gene as it has been revealed by some of these experiments. Genes are regarded as, or are related to, complex chemical compounds, and it appears probable that every gene pair differs from every other gene pair—i.e., TT is different from RR—and even the members of a pair may not be identical, for instance Tt. Genes are too small to be seen with the best light microscopes, but we know their approximate size, some of their probable physical properties, and in

Fig. 26.4. Genetic variations shown in the seed coats of beans. (Courtesy of Francis Smith.)

some plants and animals, the locations of many genes within the chromosomes. The salivary gland chromosomes of a fruit fly show dark bands thought to contain genes (Fig. 26.5). Since the majority of plants possess from seven to forty pairs of chromosomes and each chromosome contains many hundreds of genes, individual plants contain several thousands of genes. A diagram of a chromosome of Indian corn (*Zea mays*) (Fig. 26.6) shows the location of a few of the known genes of this plant. Obviously, all the associated genes of a single chromosome will move together during meiosis. They are said to be **linked.**

In our discussion of Mendel's work, we described one gene as being responsible for one aspect of a single character: the presence of the dominant gene *T* resulted in a tall pea plant. It is now known that many genes may influence one character. For instance, the color of chrysanthemum flowers is controlled by many genes. On the other hand, a single gene may be active in determining the nature of several characters. Furthermore, genes are not isolated units acting independently of each other. The action of one gene may influence the action of other genes, and all genes react in conjunction with the cytoplasm. If genes are lost, through the loss of a piece of a chromosome, some character of the plant will re-

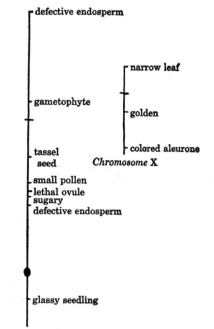

Fig. 26.6. Genetic map of fourth and tenth chromosomes of Zea mays.

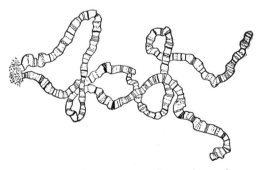

Fig. 26.5. Chromosomes from the salivary gland of *Drosophila*.

flect their absence. It is also known that genes may undergo slight alterations, with a resultant change in some character of the plant containing them. Any modification of a chromosome and the accompanying alteration of the plant in question is a **mutation** (Fig. 26.7).

In a normal, healthy plant the genes are in a delicate balance with each other and with the protoplasm containing them, with other cells, and finally with the environment in which the plant is growing. Any disturbance in this equilibrium results in some upset in the metabolism of the plant. Mutations disturb the equilibrium and, if large, are likely to result in the death of the plant containing them. As a rule, only plants with small mutations are able to survive. Furthermore, most small mutations are recessive.

Mutations occur normally in most plants

Fig. 26.7. Mutations in sunflower (Helianthus annuus). A, common wild sunflower; B, mutant known as Sun Gold. ×½. (Courtesy of Heiser.)

radiation, and certain chemicals. The mutation of a gene causes some change in the structure of a plant; mutations, therefore, are of great importance in evolution.

It is important to remember that the gene complex is in a delicate equilibrium with the external environment of the plant. Therefore, only those mutations, combinations of mutations, or other changes in the chromosomes which confer some advantage to the plant are of evolutionary significance. In other words, only the genic changes that better adapt an organism to a specific environment are likely to result in new plant or animal forms. For instance, "vestigial" is a mutation in fruit flies that results in small, underdeveloped wings. If a population composed of equal numbers of normal flies and of flies with vestigial wings is grown in still air, the normal flies increase rapidly, whereas those with the vestigial wings die and soon disappear from the population. If a similar population is placed in a windy environment, however, the small-winged mutants survive, whereas the flies with normal wings die off.

Any given gene mutates very infrequently; for instance, the gene Su, sugary, in corn changes 2.4 times in 1 million gametes. The rate of mutation of other genes in corn is given in Table 26.2.

and the rate of their occurrence has been measured in some instances. The rate varies, depending upon the particular mutation and the species involved. An average rate might be 1 mutation in 100,000 individuals. The mutation rate can be artificially accelerated by treating pollen grains, anthers, seeds, etc., with X-rays, ultraviolet

Table 26.2. Frequency of Gene Mutations in Corn, after Stadler and Demerec

(Dobzhansky, Table 4, *Genetics and the Origin of Species*)

Genes	Number of Gametes Tested	Mutations Observed	Mutation Rate per 1,000,000 Gametes
R (color factor)	554,786	273	492
I (color inhibitor)	265,391	28	106
Pr (purple)	647,102	7	11
Y (yellow)	1,745,280	4	2.2
Sh (shrunken)	2,469,285	3	1.2

It may be seen that a given gene is remarkably constant; that is, it is able to reproduce itself exactly many times without a mistake. Now, several thousand genes are present in any given gamete. If, for example, we assume that 5000 genes exist in a given species and that the average mutation rate is 1 in 100,000, then 1 out of every 20 gametes would carry a mutated gene.

A mutation rate of 1 in 100,000 genes may appear too low to be of evolutionary significance. Actually, it is not, however. Geological time is sufficiently long to permit the development of new forms even at this slow rate. Naturally, those species with a high mutation rate show greater evolutionary activity than do those with a low mutation rate. Species with a high mutation rate are plastic species. But even in plastic species the formation of new species is a complicated process involving mutations, recombinations of genes, environmental changes, and time.

For example, the effect of a desirable mutated gene, which first appears in one individual, probably as a recessive factor, must become visible; this means that two gametes each containing the mutated gene must unite. Furthermore, during succeeding years, through reproduction, the mutated gene must be distributed throughout the population in question.

The occurrence of mutations is well known, but how they have become distributed throughout a population is less well understood. Many factors are involved, four of which are listed below.

1. The mutation rate of the gene in question. A high mutation rate makes possible a more rapid distribution of the gene throughout a population.

2. The desirableness of the mutation. If the new gene confers a great advantage to the individuals possessing it their chances of survival are enhanced.

3. The number of interbreeding individuals in a population. For the most rapid spread of a mutated gene, populations of intermediate sizes are best.

4. Geographical features, such as mountain barriers or broad valleys, which either hinder or aid migration of individuals.

Hybridization, which serves to reassort the genes into various combinations, occasionally results in the immediate formation of a new species or even genus. Several examples are well known; some have occurred in experimental breeding plots, and others in nature. One concerns two species of grasses. One species *Spartina stricta,* is a native of England, and the other, *Spartina alterniflora* (smooth cordgrass), grows in the New England states. Commerce between Boston and London resulted in the accidental transportation of seeds of the New England grass across the ocean to localities in southern England. Thus *Spartina alterniflora* became established on the channel coast of England, where it grew in close proximity to the English *Spartina stricta.* Hybrids resulted from the two species, and one of them proved to be very vigorous: it is called *Spartina Townsendii* and is recognized as a distinct species. It rapidly spread over many thousand acres of southern England and crossed the channel into France. Its agricultural properties proved to be desirable and it has since been cultivated in many parts of the world. It is particularly useful in aiding in the reclamation of salt-marsh lands in Holland, France, and England.

Spartina Townsendii is very distinct from its parents. It will not backcross to either of them. It has 126 chromosomes; *Spartina alterniflora* has 70, and *Spartina stricta* has 56. Note that 70 + 56 equals 126. *Spartina Townsendii* received, in some manner, complete sets of chromosomes from each of its parents.

In nature, plants with four or six sets of chromosomes are often larger and more vigorous than those plants having only two sets. A plant with four sets of chromosomes is said to be a **tetraploid.** Any increase in chromosome numbers is known as **polyploidy.** Polyploids of snapdragons, phlox, and marigolds can now be purchased from some seed houses.

A modern theory of the mechanism of evolution can be outlined as follows:

1. The genes, contained in the chromosomes, are largely responsible for the development, structure, and metabolism of plants and animals.

2. The complement of genes does not remain absolutely constant. Mutations, changes in chromosomes and in genes, occur which modify the structure and metabolism of the individuals containing them.

3. Large mutations, because they upset the delicate equilibrium existing between the plant and its environment, are likely to kill or to greatly weaken the plant.

4. Hybrids, because of the resulting new combinations of genes, differ from their parents. Hybrids within a species are fertile; hybrids between species are usually sterile or partially so.

5. If the variants, produced by mutations or hybridization, are better adapted to the environment than the parent plants, the parent plants may be replaced by the new forms. Many complicated factors are involved in this replacement.

6. As mountains are elevated or eroded, as glaciers advance or recede, as the climate of the earth becomes more or less arid, or as the habitats of plants are changed in other ways, those plants best adapted to the new environment replace the forms less well adapted.

7. Evolution thus results from slow changes in the earth's surface, variation in plants and animals, and an adjustment between the changes in the earth and changes in the living organisms.

8. In summarizing evolutionary mechanisms, Dobzhansky writing in the *Scientific American* has said, "Evolution is a creative response of the living matter to the challenges of the environment. Evolution is due neither to chance nor to design; it is due to a natural creative process."

Glossary

Glossary of Technical Terms Including Their Origin

Abbreviations

A.S. stands for Anglo-Saxon
F.   French
Gr.   Greek
L.   Latin
M.L.   Medieval Latin

The glossary serves two purposes, (1) to define terms used in the text and (2) to give their derivation. It should be noted that in carrying out the first purpose, with few exceptions, only those meanings actually used in the text are given. Reference to dictionaries will give additional meanings, while other textbooks may define the same words in slightly different ways.

Scientific language and slang have much in common. They are both vital, growing, and changing phases of modern English. The same words will have different meanings in different parts of the country. Both slang and scientific vocabularies contribute their full share of standard everyday English words. And finally, both vocabularies are largely unintelligible to those not fully initiated into their intricacies.

Scientific language grows in a number of ways. Some botanical terms, such as seed, are used by scientist and layman alike and they can be traced back to Anglo-Saxon days, when the word *sed* was used to designate anything sown in the ground, or in our terms a seed. In other instances, words from Greek or Latin have been taken into the scientific language with their identical original meaning; for instance, the Greeks called wood *xylon,* and we use this term changed to xylem to designate the woody conducting tissue of plants. Other words have a more complex history. *Metabolos* is the Greek word *"to change."* When the scientists of Europe wrote in Latin they took this Greek word, made a Medieval Latin word from it and used it to describe the changes undergone by some insects. It was used in 1639 to mean changes in health and in 1845 the German scientist who elaborated the cell doctrine made a German word of it and first used it as we use it here, designating the changes taking place within a cell. Perhaps the newest scientific word in your text is *antibiotic.*

In using the glossary, pay as much attention to derivation as you do to the definition. To memorize the definition alone is to learn, parrot-fashion, only one word. To learn the derivation is to understand the word and possibly to introduce yourself to a whole family of new words. Pay particular attention to such combining forms as *hetero, auto, micro, phyll, angio, plast* or *plasm, spore,* etc.

Abscission zone (L. *abscissus,* cut off), zone of delicate, thin-walled cells extending across base of petiole, the breakdown of which disjoins the leaf or fruit from the stem.

Absorb (L. *ab,* away + *sorbere,* to suck in), to suck up, to drink up, or to take in. In plant cells materials are taken in (absorbed) in solution.

Accessory (M.L. *accessorius,* an additional appendage), something aiding or contributing in a secondary way, such as buds in addition to the main axillary bud.

Achene, simple, dry, one-seeded indehiscent fruit, with seed attached to ovary wall at one point only.

Acid (F. *acide,* from L. *acidus,* sharp), a substance belonging to a class of which the commonest and most typical members are sour, and are compounds of hydrogen with another element or elements; oxygen is generally the third element: Examples of inorganic acids are sulfuric acid, (H_2SO_4), hydrochloric acid (HCl); examples of organic acids are acetic acid (vinegar) and pyruvic acid.

Actinomorphic (Gr. *aktis,* ray + *morphe,* form), flowers of a regular or star pattern, capable of bisection in two or more planes into similar halves.

Active absorption (of water), the uptake of water as a result of root activity.

Active solute absorption, the intake of dissolved materials by cells against a concentration gradient and requiring an expenditure of energy.

Adaptation (L. *ad,* to + *aptare,* to fit), adjustment of an organism to the environment.

Adhesion (L. *adhaerere,* to stick to), a sticking together of unlike things or materials.

Adnation (L. *adnasci,* to grow to), in flowers, the growing together of two or more whorls to a greater or less extent. Compare adhesion.

Adsorption (L. *ad,* to + *sorbere,* to suck in), the concentration of molecules or ions of a substance at a surface or an interface (boundary) between two substances.

Adventitious (L. *adventicius,* not properly belonging to), referring to a structure arising out of its usual place: buds at other places than leaf axils, roots growing from stems or leaves.

Aeciospore (Gr. *aikia,* injury + spore), binucleate asexual spores of rust fungi formed as a result of the sexual fusion of cells but not of nuclei.

Aecium (plural, **aecia**) (Gr. *aikia,* injury), in rust, a sorus which produces aeciospores.

Aerate, to supply or impregnate with common air, such as bubbling air through a culture solution.

Aerobe (Gr. *aer,* air + *bios,* life) an organism living in the presence of oxygen.

Aerobic respiration, respiration involving molecular oxygen.

Agar (Malay, *agaragar*), a gelatinous substance obtained mainly from certain species of red algae.

Aggregate fruit (L. *ad,* to + *gregare,* to collect; to bring together), a fruit developing from the several separate carpels of a single flower.

Aleurone (Gr. *aleuron,* flour), proteinaceous and fatty material, usually in the form of small grains, occurring in the outermost cell layer of the endosperm of wheat and other grains.

Algae (L. *alga,* seaweed), the large group of thallus plants containing chlorophyll and thus able to synthesize carbohydrates.

Alkali (Arabic, *alqili,* the ashes of the plant saltwort), a substance with marked basic properties.

Alternate, referring to bud or leaf arrangement in which there is one bud or one leaf at a node.

Ammonification (*Ammon,* Egyptian sun god, near whose temple ammonium salts were first, prepared from camel dung + L. *facere,* to make), decomposition of amino acids, resulting in the production of ammonia.

Anaerobe (Gr. *a,* without + *aer,* air + *bios,* life), an organism able to respire in the absence of free oxygen, or in greatly reduced concentrations of free oxygen.

Anaphase (Gr. *ana,* up + *phasis,* appearance), that stage in mitosis in which half chromosomes or sister chromatids move to opposite poles of the cell.

Androecium (Gr. *andros,* man + *oikos,* house), the aggregate of stamens in the flower of a seed plant.

Angiosperm (Gr. *angion,* a vessel + *sperma* from *speirein,* to sow, hence a seed or germ), literally a seed borne in a vessel, thus a group of plants whose seeds are borne within an ovary.

Annual (L. *annualis,* within a year), a plant which completes its life cycle within one year's time and then dies.

Annular vessels (L. *annularis,* a ring), vessels with lignified rings.

Annulus (L. *anulus* or *annulus,* a ring), in ferns, a row of specialized cells in a sporangium, of importance in opening of the sporangium; in mosses, thick-walled cells along the rim of the sporangium to which the peristome is attached.

Anther (M.L. *anthera*—from the Greek word *anthros,* meaning flower—a medicine extracted from the internal whorls of flowers by medieval pharmacists: confined to pollen-producing parts by herbalists in 1700), pollen-bearing portion of stamen.

Antheridium (anther + *-idion,* a Gr. dimin. ending, thus a little anther), male gametangium or sperm-bearing organ of plants other than seed plants.

Anthocyanin (Gr. *anthros,* a flower + *kyanos,* dark blue), a blue, purple, or red vacuolar pigment.

Antibiotic (Gr. *anti,* against or opposite + *biotikos,* pertaining to life), natural organic substances which retard or prevent the growth of organisms, generally used to designate substances formed by microorganisms which prevent growth of other microorganisms.

Antipodal (Gr. *anti*, opposite + *pous*, foot), generally one object situated opposite another object. Specifically, the cells or nuclei at the end of the embryo sac opposite that of the egg apparatus.

Apex (L. *apex*, a tip, point, or extremity), the tip, point, or angular summit of anything: the tip of a leaf; that portion of a root or shoot containing apical and primary meristems.

Apical meristem, a mass of meristematic cells at the very tip of a shoot or root.

Apomixis (Gr. *apo*, away from + *mixis*, a mingling), the production of offspring in the usual sexual structures without the mingling and segregation of chromosomes.

Apothecium (Gr. *apotheke*, a storehouse), a cup-shaped or saucer-shaped open ascocarp.

Archegonium (L. dimin. of Gr. *archegonos*, literally a little founder of a race), female gametangium or egg-bearing organ, in which the egg is protected by a jacket of sterile cells.

Aril (M.L. *arillus*, a wrapper for a seed), an accessory seed-covering formed by an outgrowth at the base of the ovule in *Taxus*.

Ascocarp (Gr. *askos*, a bag + *karpos*, fruit), a fruiting body of the ascomycetes, generally either an open cup, a vessel, or a closed sphere lined with special cells called asci (*see* Ascus).

Ascogenous hyphae, hyphae arising from the ascogonium, after the formation of $n + n$ paired nuclei. The hymenial layer of the ascocarp develops from the ascogenous hyphae.

Ascogonium, the oogonium or female gametangium of the Ascomycetes.

Ascomycetes (Gr. *askos*, a bag + *mykes*, fungus), a large group of true fungi with septate hyphae producing large numbers of asexual conidiospores and meiospores called ascospores, the latter in characteristic cells.

Ascospore (Gr. *askos*, a bag + spore), meiospore produced within an ascus.

Ascus (plural, **asci**) (Gr. *askos*, a bag), a specialized cell, characteristic of the Ascomycetes, in which two haploid nuclei fuse, immediately after which three (generally) divisions occur, two of which constitute meiosis, resulting in eight meiospores (ascospores) still contained within the ascus.

Asexual (Gr. *a*, without + L. *sexualis*, sexual), any type of reproduction not involving the union of gametes or meiosis.

Assimilation (L. *assimilare*, to make like), the transformation of food into protoplasm.

Atom (F. *atome*, from the Greek *atomos*, indivisible), the smallest particles in which the elements combine either with themselves, or with other elements, and thus the smallest quantity of matter known to possess the properties of a particular element. Atoms were first postulated by the Greek philosopher-scientists, Leucippus and Democritus about 450 B.C.

Auricles (L. *auricula*, dimin. of *auris*, ear), ear-like structures; in grasses, small projections which grow out from the opposite side of the sheath at its upper end where it joins the blade.

Autoecius (Gr. *auto*, self + *oikia*, dwelling), having a complete life cycle on the same host.

Autophyte (Gr. *auto*, self + *phyton*, a plant), a plant which can make its own food.

Autotrophic (Gr. *auto*, self + *trophein*, to nourish with food), pertaining to a plant which is able to manufacture its own food.

Auxin (Gr. *auxein*, to increase), a plant growth-regulating substance regulating cell elongation.

Axil (Gr. *axilla*, armpit), the upper angle between a twig or petiole and the stem from which it grows.

Axillary bud, a bud formed in the axil of a leaf.

Bacillarieae (L. *baculum*, a stick), a class of the phylum Chrysophycophyta. Commonly, the diatoms.

Bacillus (L. *baculum*, a stick), a rod-shaped bacterium.

Bacteria (Gr. *bakterion*, a stick), common name for the class Schizomycetes.

Bacteriology (bacteria + Gr. *logos*, discourse), the science of bacteria.

Bacteriophage (bacteria + Gr. *phagein*, to eat), literally, an eater of bacteria; a virus that infects specific bacteria, multiplies therein, and usually dissolves the bacterial cells.

Banner (M.L. *bandum*, a standard), large, broad, and conspicuous petal of legume type of flower.

Bark (Swedish *bark*, rind), the external group of tissues, from the cambium outwards, of a woody stem or root.

Basidiomycetes (M.L. *basidium*, a little pedestal + Gr. *mykes*, fungus), group of fungi characterized by the production of meiospores on special cells, the basidia.

Basidiospore (M.L. *basidium*, a little pedestal + spore), type of meiospore borne by basidia in the Basidiomycetes.

Basidium (plural, **basidia**) (M.L. *basidium*, a little pedestal), a specialized reproductive cell of the Basidiomycetes in which nuclei fuse and meiosis occurs. It may be a special club-shaped cell, a short filamentous cell, or a short four-celled filament.

Benthon (Gr. *benthos,* the depths of the sea), attached aquatic plants and animals, collectively.

Berry, a simple fleshy fruit, the ovary wall fleshy and including one or more carpels and seeds.

Biennial (L. *biennium,* a period of two years), a plant which completes its life cycle within two years and then dies.

Bifacial leaf (L. *bis,* twice + *facies,* face), a leaf having upper and lower surfaces distinctly different.

Binomial (L. *binominis,* two names), two-named; in biology each species is generally indicated by two names, the genus to which it belongs and its own species name.

Biology (Gr. *bios,* life + *logos,* word, speech, discourse), the science which deals with living things.

Biotic (Gr. *biokitos,* relating to life), relating to life.

Bordered pit, a pit in tracheid or other cell of secondary xylem having a distinct rim of the cell wall overarching the pit membrane.

Botany (Gr. *botane,* plant, herb), the science dealing with plant life.

Bract (L. *bractea,* a thin plate of precious metal), a modified leaf from the axil of which arises a flower or an inflorescence.

Bryophyta (Gr. *bryon,* moss + *phyton,* plant), phylum including the true mosses and the liverworts.

Bud (Middle English *budde,* bud), an undeveloped shoot, largely meristematic tissue, generally protected by modified scale-leaves.

Bud-scale, a modified protective leaf of a bud.

Bud-scar, a scar left on a twig when the bud or bud scales fall away.

Bulb (L. *bulbus,* a modified bud, usually underground), short, flattened, or disk-shaped underground stem, with many fleshy scale-leaves filled with stored food.

Bundle scar, scar left where conducting strands passing out of the stem into the leaf stalk were broken off when the leaf fell.

Cactus (Gr. *kaktos,* a kind of prickly plant), any plant of the cactus family, famous plants of the desert.

Callose (L. *callum,* thick skin + *ose,* a suffix indicating a carbohydrate), an amorphous, hardened mucilaginous constituent of cell walls, common in sieve tubes.

Callus (L. *callum,* thick skin), mass of large, thin-walled cells, usually developed as the result of wounding.

Calyptra (Gr. *kalyptra,* a veil, covering), in bryophytes, an envelope covering the developing sporophyte, formed by growth of the venter of the archegonium.

Calyx (Gr. *kalyx,* a husk, cup), sepals collectively; outermost flower whorl.

Cambium (L. *cambium,* one of the alimentary body fluids supposed to nourish the body organs), a layer, usually regarded as one or two cells thick, of persistently meristematic tissue, giving rise to secondary tissues, resulting in growth in diameter.

Capillary (L. *capillus,* hair), very small spaces, or very fine bores in a tube.

Caprification, an artificial method of pollinating certain cultivated varieties of figs.

Capsule (L. *capsula,* dimin. of *capsa,* a case), simple, dry, dehiscent fruit, with two or more carpels.

Carbohydrate (chemical combining forms, *carbo,* carbon + *hydrate,* containing water), foods composed of carbon, hydrogen, and oxygen, with the hydrogen and oxygen in a 2 to 1 ratio, as in water, H_2O.

Carotene (L. *carota,* carrot), a reddish-orange plastid pigment.

Carpel (Gr. *karpos,* fruit), a floral leaf bearing ovules frequently along the margins.

Carpogonium (Gr. *karpos,* fruit + *gonos,* producing), female gametangium (in red algae).

Carpospore (Gr. *karpos,* fruit + spore), one of the spores produced in a carpogonium.

Caruncle (L. *caruncula,* dimin. of *caro,* flesh, wart), a spongy outgrowth of the seed coat, especially prominent in the castor-bean seed.

Caryopsis (Gr. *karyon,* a nut + *opsis,* appearance), simple, dry, one-seeded, indehiscent fruit, with pericarp firmly united all around to the seed coat.

Catalyst (Gr. *katalyein,* to dissolve), a substance which accelerates a chemical reaction but which is not used up in the reaction.

Catkin (literally a kitten, apparently first used in 1578 to describe the inflorescence of the pussy willow), type of inflorescence, really a spike, generally bearing only pistillate flowers or only staminate flowers, which eventually fall from the plant entire.

Cell (L. *cella,* small room), a structural and physiological unit composing living organisms, in which take place the majority of complicated reactions characteristic of life.

Cellulose (cell + *ose*, a suffix indicating a carbohydrate), a complex carbohydrate occurring in the cell walls of the majority of plants. Cotton is largely cellulose. It is composed of hundreds of simple sugar molecules linked together in a characteristic manner.

Chalaza (Gr. *chalaza*, small tubercle), the region on a seed at the upper end of the raphe where the funiculus spreads out and unites with the base of the ovule.

Chiasma (Gr. *chiasma*, two lines placed crosswise), the cross formed by breaking, during prophase I of meiosis, of two non-sister chromatids of homologous chromosomes and the rejoining of the broken ends of different chromatids.

Chitin (Gr. *chiton*, a coat of mail), a horny substance forming the outer coat of insects and crustaceans and also found in the cell walls of many fungi.

Chlamydospore (Gr. *chlamys*, a horseman's or young man's coat + spore), a heavy-walled resting asexual spore.

Chlorenchyma (Gr. *chloros*, green + *-enchyma*, a suffix meaning tissue), tissue possessing chloroplasts.

Chlorophycophyta (Gr. *chloros*, green + *phykos*, seaweed + *phyton*, plant), phylum of green, algal plants.

Chlorophyll (Gr. *chloros*, green + *phyllon*, leaf), the green pigment found in the chloroplast, important in the absorption of light energy in photosynthesis.

Chloroplast (Gr. *chloros*, green + *plastos*, formed), specialized cytoplasmic body, containing chlorophyll, in which occur important reactions of starch or sugar synthesis.

Chlorosis (Gr. *chloros*, green + *osis*, diseased state), failure of chlorophyll development, because of a nutritional disturbance or because of an infection of virus, bacteria, or fungus.

Chromatid (chromosome + *-id*, L. suffix meaning daughters of), the half chromosome during prophase and metaphase of mitosis, and between prophase I and anaphase II of meiosis.

Chromatin (Gr. *chroma*, color), substance in the nucleus which readily takes artificial staining; also that portion which bears the determiners of hereditary characters.

Chromoplast (Gr. *chroma*, color + *plastos*, formed), specialized protoplasmic body containing yellow or orange pigments.

Chromosome (Gr. *chroma*, color + *soma*, body), a group of nuclear bodies containing genes, and largely responsible for the differentiation and activity of a cell, and undergoing characteristic division stages; or, one of the bodies into which the nucleus resolves itself at the beginning of mitosis and from which it is derived at the end of mitosis.

Cilia (singular, **cilium**) (Fr. *cil*, an eyelash), protoplasmic hairs which, by a whiplike motion, propel certain types of unicellular organisms, gametes, and zoospores through water.

Cladode (Gr. *kladodes*, having many shoots), a cladophyll.

Cladophyll (Gr. *klados*, a shoot + *phyllon*, leaf), a branch resembling a foliage leaf.

Cleistothecium (Gr. *kleistos*, closed + *thekion*, a small receptacle), the closed, spherical ascocarp of the powdery mildews.

Clone (Gr. *klon*, a twig or slip), the aggregate of individual organisms produced asexually from one sexually produced individual.

Closed bundle, a vascular bundle lacking cambium.

Coalescence (L. *coalescere*, to grow together), a condition in which there is union of separate parts of any one whorl of flower parts.

Coccus (plural, **cocci**) (Gr. *kokkos*, a berry), a spherical bacterium.

Coenocyte (Gr. *koinos*, shared in common + *kytos*, a vessel), a plant or filament whose protoplasm is continuous and multinucleate and without any division by walls into separate protoplasts.

Coenogamete (Gr. *koinos*, shared in common + gamete), a multinucleate gamete, with no walls separating the many nuclei.

Cohesion (L. *cohaerere*, to stick together), union or holding together of parts of the same materials. The union of floral parts of the same whorl, as petals to petals.

Coleoptile (Gr. *koleos*, sheath + *ptilon*, down, feather), the first leaf in germination of monocotyledons, which sheaths the succeeding leaves.

Coleorhiza (Gr. *koleos*, sheath + *rhiza*, root), sheath which surrounds the radical of the grass embryo and through which the young root bursts.

Collenchyma (Gr. *kolla*, glue + *-enchyma*, a suffix, derived from parenchyma and denoting a type of cell tissue), a stem tissue composed of cells which fit rather closely together and with walls thickened at the angles of the cells.

Colloid (Gr. *kolla*, glue + *eidos*, form), matter composed of particles, ranging in size from 0.0001 to 0.000001 millimeter, dispersed in some medium. Milk and mayonnaise are examples.

Companion cells, cells associated with sieve-tube members.

Complete flower, a flower having four whorls of floral leaves: sepals, petals, stamens, and carpels.

Compound leaf, a leaf whose blade is divided in several distinct leaflets.

Conceptacle (L. *conceptaculum,* a receptacle), a cavity or chamber of a frond (of *Fucus,* for example) in which gametangia are borne.

Cone (Gr. *konos,* a pine cone), a fruiting structure composed of modified leaves or branches, which bear sporangia (microsporangia, megasporangia, pollen sacs, or ovules), and frequently arranged in a spiral or four-ranked order. For example, a pine cone.

Conidia (singular, **conidium**) (Gr. *konis,* dust), asexual reproductive cells of fungi, arising by fragmentation of hyphae, by the cutting off of terminal or lateral cells of special hyphae, or by being pushed out from a flask-shaped cell.

Conidiophore (conidia + Gr. *phoros,* bearing), conidium-bearing branch of hypha.

Conidiosporangium (Gr. *konis,* dust + sporangium), sporangium formed by being cut off from the end of a terminal or lateral hypha.

Conidiospore (conidia + spore), spore formed as described for conidia.

Conifer (cone + L. *ferre,* to carry), a cone-bearing tree.

Conjugation (L. *conjugatus,* united), process of sexual reproduction involving the fusion of isogametes.

Cork (L. *quercus,* oak), an external, secondary tissue impermeable to water and gases.

Cork cambium, the cambium from which cork develops.

Corm (Gr. *kormos,* a trunk), short, solid, vertical, enlarged underground stem in which food is stored.

Corolla (L. *corolla,* dimin. of *corona,* a wreath, crown), petals, collectively; usually the conspicuous colored flower whorl.

Cortex (L. *cortex,* bark), primary tissue of a stem or root bounded externally by the epidermis and internally by the phloem.

Cotyledon (Gr. *kotyledon,* a cup-shaped hollow), seed leaf, two, generally storing food in dicotyledons; one, generally a digestive organ in the monocotyledons.

Cross-pollination, the transfer of pollen from a stamen to the stigma of a flower on another plant, except in clones.

Crossing over, the exchange of corresponding segments between chromatids of homologous chromosomes.

Cuticle (L. *cuticula,* dimin. of *cutis,* the skin), waxy layer on outer wall of epidermal cells.

Cutin (L. *cutis,* the skin), waxy substance which is but slightly permeable to water, to water vapor, and to gases.

Cutinization, impregnation of cell wall with a substance called cutin.

Cyme (Gr. *cyma,* a wave, a swelling), a type of inflorescence in which the apex of the main stalk or the axis of the inflorescence ceases to grow quite early.

Cystocarp (Gr. *kystos,* bladder + *karpos,* fruit), a peculiar diploid spore-bearing structure formed after fertilization in certain red algae.

Cytokinesis (Gr. *kytos,* a hollow vessel + *kinesis,* motion), division of cytoplasmic constituents at cell division.

Cytology (Gr. *kytos,* a hollow vessel + *logos,* word, speech, discourse), the science dealing with the cell.

Cytoplasm (Gr. *kytos,* a hollow vessel + *plasma,* form), all the protoplasm of a protoplast outside of the nucleus.

Decay (L. *decedere,* to depart from life), to pass gradually from a sound or perfect state to an unsound or imperfect state. The breaking down of the complex compounds of dead organisms to simple inorganic or organic substances by bacteria and fungi.

Deciduous (L. *deciduus,* falling), referring to trees and shrubs which lose their leaves in the fall.

Decomposition (L. *de,* to denote an act undone + *componere,* to put together), a separation or dissolving into simpler compounds; rotting or decaying.

Dehiscent (L. *dehiscere,* to split open), opening spontaneously when ripe, splitting into definite parts.

Denitrification (L. *de,* to denote an act undone + *nitrum,* nitro, a combining form indicating the presence of nitrogen + *facere,* to make), conversion of nitrates into nitrites, or into gaseous oxides of nitrogen, or even into free nitrogen.

Diastase (Gr. *diastasis,* a separation), a complex of enzymes which brings about the hydrolysis of starch with the formation of sugar.

Diatom (Gr. *diatomos,* cut in two), member of a group of golden brown algae with silicious cell walls fitting together much as the halves of a pill box.

Dicotyledon (Gr. *dis,* twice + *kotyledon,* a cup-shaped hollow), a plant whose embryo has two cotyledons.

differentially permeable, referring to a membrane, through which different substances diffuse at different rates, some substances may be unable to diffuse through such a membrane.

differentiation (L. *differre*, to carry different ways), development from one cell to many cells, accompanied by a modification of the new cells for the performance of particular functions.

Diffusion (L. *diffusus*, spread out), the movement of molecules, and thus a substance, from a region of higher concentration of those molecules to a region of lower concentration.

Diffusion pressure, the tendency of different particles (ions or molecules) to diffuse.

Digestion (L. *digestio*, dividing, or tearing to pieces, an orderly distribution), the processes of rendering food available for metabolism by breaking it down into simpler compounds chiefly through actions of enzymes.

Dihybrid cross (Gr. *dis*, twice + L. *hybrida*, the offspring of a tame sow and a wild boar, a mongrel), a cross between organisms differing in two characters.

Dikaryon (Gr. *di*, two + *karyon*, nut), the $n + n$, paired nuclei, each usually derived from a different parent, one male, one female.

Dioecious (Gr. *dis*, twice + *oikos*, house), unisexual; having the male and female elements in different individuals.

Diploid (Gr. *diploos*, double + *oides*, like), having a double set of chromosomes, or referring to an individual containing a double set of chromosomes per cell. Usually a sporophyte generation.

Disease (L. *dis*, a prefix signifying the opposite + Middle English *aise*, comfort, literally the opposite of ease), any alteration from the state of metabolism necessary for the normal development and functioning of an organism.

Dominant (L. *dominus*, master or lord), referring, in heredity, to that gene (or the expression of the character it influences) which, when present in a hybrid with a contrasting gene, completely dominates in the development of the character. In peas, tall is dominant over dwarf.

Dormant (L. *dormire*, to sleep), being in a state of reduced physiological activity such as occurring in seeds, buds, etc.

Dorsiventral (L. *dorsum*, the back + *venter*, the belly), having upper and lower surfaces distinctly different, as a leaf.

Drupe (L. *drupa*, an over-ripe olive), a simple, fleshy fruit, derived from a single carpel, usually one-seeded, in which the exocarp is thin, the mesocarp fleshy, and the endocarp stony.

Ecology (Gr. *oikos*, home + *logos*, discourse), the study of plant life in relation to environment.

Edaphic (Gr. *edaphos*, soil), pertaining to soil conditions that influence plant growth.

Egg (A.S. *aeg*, egg), a female gamete.

Elater (Gr. *elater*, driver), an elongated, spindle-shaped, sterile, hygroscopic cell in the sporangium of liverwort sporophyte.

Element (L. *elementa*, the first principles; according to one system of medieval chemistry as recent as 1700, there were four elements composing all material bodies: earth, water, air, and fire), in modern chemistry an element is a substance which cannot be divided or reduced, by any known chemical means, to a simpler substance. Ninety-two natural elements are known, of which gold, carbon, oxygen, and iron are examples. Several have been formed in atomic piles, plutonium being an example.

Embryo (Gr. *en*, in + *bryein*, to swell), a young sporophytic plant, before the start of a period of rapid growth (germination in seed plants).

Embryo sac, the female gametophyte of the angiosperms; generally a seven-celled structure. The seven cells are: two synergids, one egg cell, three antipodal cells each with a single haploid nucleus and one endosperm mother cell with two haploid nuclei.

Emulsion (L. *emulgere*, to milk out), a suspension of fine particles of a liquid in a liquid.

Endocarp (Gr. *endon*, within + *karpos*, fruit), inner layer of fruit wall (pericarp).

Endodermis (Gr. *endon*, within + *derma*, skin), the layer of living cells with various characteristically thickened walls and no intercellular spaces which surrounds the vascular tissue of certain plants and occurs in nearly all roots and certain stems and leaves.

Endosperm (Gr. *endon*, within + *sperma*, seed), the nutritive tissue formed within the embryo sac of seed plants. It is often consumed as the seed matures but remains in the seeds of corn and other cereals.

Endosperm mother cell, one of the seven cells of the mature embryo sac, containing the two polar nuclei and after reception of a sperm cell giving rise to the primary endosperm cell from which the endosperm develops.

Enzyme (Gr. *en*, in + *zyme*, yeast), a protein of complex chemical constitution produced in living cells, which, even in very low concentration, speeds up certain chemical reactions but is **not** used up in the reaction.

Epiblast (Gr. *epi,* upon + *blastos,* a sprout or shoot), a small appendage in front of the plumule in the embryo of many grasses.

Epicotyl (Gr. *epi,* upon + *kotyledon,* a cup-shaped hollow), the upper portion of the axis of embryo or seedling, above the cotyledons.

Epidermis (Gr. *epi,* upon + *derma,* skin), a superficial layer of cells occurring on all parts of the primary plant body; stems, leaves, roots, flowers, fruits, and seeds. It is absent from the root cap and not differentiated on the apical meristems.

Epigyny (Gr. *epi,* upon + *gyne,* woman), the arrangement of floral parts in which the ovary is embedded in the receptacle so that the other parts appear to arise from the top of the ovary.

Ergastic (Gr. *ergastikos,* working, industrious), designating passive products of protoplasm including inclusions as starch grains, fat drops, and external secretions.

Ergot (F. *argot,* a spur), a fungus disease of cereals and wild grasses in which the grain is replaced by dense masses of purplish hyphae, the ergot.

Erosion (L. *e,* out + *rodere,* to gnaw), the wearing away of land, generally by the action of water.

Etiolation (F. *etioler,* to blanch), a condition involving increased stem elongation, poor leaf development, and lack of chlorophyll found in plants growing in the absence or a greatly reduced amount of light.

Evolution (L. *evolutio,* an unrolling), the development of a race, a species, genus, or other larger group of plants or animals.

Exine (L. *exterus,* outside), outer coat of pollen.

Exocarp (Gr. *exo,* without, outside + *karpos,* fruit), outermost layer of fruit wall (pericarp).

Facultative (L. *facultas,* capability), referring to an organism having the power to live under a number of certain specific conditions, e.g., a facultative parasite may be either parasitic or saprophytic.

Family, referring in plant taxonomy to a group of genera. Families are grouped in orders.

Fascicle (L. *fasciculus,* a small bundle), a bundle of pine or other needle-leaves of gymnosperms.

Fascicular cambium, cambium within vascular bundles.

Fermentation (L. *fermentum,* a drink made from fermented barley, beer), an oxidative process in foods in which molecular oxygen is not involved, such as the production of alcohol from sugar by yeasts.

Fertilization (L. *fertilis,* capable of producing fruit), that stage of a sexual life cycle involving the union of two protoplasts and hence the doubling of chromosome numbers.

Fiber (L. *fibra,* a fiber or filament), an elongated tapering, thick-walled strengthening cell occurring in various parts of plant bodies.

Fiber-tracheid, xylem elements found in pine that are structurally intermediate between tracheid and fibers.

Filament (L. *filum,* a thread), stalk of stamen bearing the anther at its tip; also a slender row of cells (certain algae).

Fission (L. *fissilis,* easily split), asexual reproduction involving the division of a single-celled individual into two new single-celled individuals of equal size.

Flagellum (plural, **flagella**) (L. *flagellum,* a whip), a long, slender whip of protoplasm.

Floret (F. *fleurette,* a dimin. of *fleur,* flower), one of the small flowers that make up the composite flower or the spike of the grasses.

Flower (F. *fleur,* L. *flos,* a flower), floral leaves grouped together on a stem and adapted for sexual reproduction in the angiosperms.

Follicle (L. *folliculus,* dimin. of *follis,* bag), a simple, dry, dehiscent fruit, with one carpel, splitting along one suture.

Food (A.S. *fōda*), any organic substance which furnishes energy and building materials directly for vital processes.

Fossil (L. *fossio,* a digging), any impression, natural or impregnated remains or other trace of an animal or plant of past geological ages which has been preserved in the earth's crust.

Fruit (L. *fructus,* that which is enjoyed, hence product of the soil, trees, cattle, etc.), a matured ovary; in some seed plants other parts of the flower may be included; also applied, as **fruiting body,** to reproductive structures of other groups of plants.

Fucoxanthin (Gr. *phykos,* seaweed + *xanthos,* yellowish brown), a brown pigment found in brown algae.

Fungus (plural, **fungi**) (L. *fungus,* a mushroom), a thallus plant unable to make its own food, exclusive of the bacteria.

Funiculus (L. *funiculus,* dimin. of *funis,* rope or small cord), a stalk of the ovule, containing vascular tissue.

Gametangium (Gr. *gametes,* a husband, *gamete,* a wife + *angeion,* a vessel), organ bearing gametes.

Gamete (Gr. *gametes,* a husband, *gamete,* a wife), a protoplast which fuses with another protoplast to form the zygote in the process of sexual reproduction.

Gametophyte (gamete + Gr. *phyton*, a plant), the gamete-producing plant.

Gel (L. *gelare*, to freeze), jellylike colloidal mass.

Gemma (plural, **gemmae**) (L. *gemma*, a bud), a small mass of vegetative tissue, an outgrowth of the thallus.

Gene (Gr. *genos*, race, offspring), a material substance in the chromosome which determines or conditions one or more hereditary characters.

Genetics (Gr. *genesis*, origin), the science of heredity.

Genotype (gene + type), the assemblage of genes in an organism.

Genus (Gr. *genos*, race, stock), a group of structurally or phylogenetically related species.

Geotropism (Gr. *ge*, earth + *tropos*, turning), a growth curvature induced by gravity.

Germination (L. *germinare*, to sprout), the beginning of growth of a seed, spore, bud, or other structure.

Glucose (Gr. *glykys*, sweet + *-ose*, a suffix indicating a carbohydrate), a simple sugar, grape sugar, $C_6H_{12}O_6$.

Glume (L. *gluma*, husk), an outer and lowermost bract of a grass spikelet.

Glycogen (Gr. *glykys*, sweet + *gen*, of a kind), a carbohydrate related to starch but found generally in the liver of animals and in some plants.

Glycolysis (Gr. *glykys*, sweet + *lysis*, a loosening), decomposition of sugar to simple compounds without involving free oxygen; early steps of respiration.

Ground meristem (Gr. *meristos*, divisible), a primary meristem which gives rise to cortex, pith rays, and pith.

Guttation (L. *gutta*, drop, exudation of drops), exudation of water from plants in the liquid form.

Grow (A.S. *growan*, probably from Old Teut. *gro*, from which grass is also derived), of living bodies generally: to increase gradually in size by natural development.

Gynoecium (Gr. *gyne*, woman + *oikos*, house), the aggregate of carpels in the flower of a seed plant.

Haploid (Gr. *haploos*, single + *oides*, like), having a single complete set of chromosomes, or referring to an individual or generation containing such a single set of chromosomes per cell. Usually a gametophyte generation.

Haustorium (plural, **haustoria**) (M.L. *haustrum*, a pump), a projection of hyphae which acts as a penetrating and absorbing organ.

Head, an inflorescence, typical of the composite family, in which flowers are grouped closely on a receptacle.

Hemicellulose (Gr. *hemi*, half + cellulose), any one of a group of carbohydrates resembling cellulose.

Herb (L. *herba*, grass, green blades), a seed plant which does not develop woody tissues.

Herbaceous (L. *herbaceus*, grassy), referring to plants having the characteristics of herbs.

Herbarium (L. *herba*, grass), a collection of dried and pressed plant specimens.

Heredity (L. *hereditas*, being an heir), the transmission of morphological and physiological characters of parents to their offspring.

Hermaphrodite flower (Gr. *hermaphroditos*, a person partaking of the attributes of both sexes, represented by Hermes and Aphrodite), a flower having both stamens and pistils.

Heterobasidiomycete (Gr. *heteros*, other + Basidiomycete), a subclass of Basidiomycetes with variable basidia, never club-shaped cells.

Heterocyst (Gr. *heteros*, different + *cystis*, a bag), an enlarged colorless cell which may occur in the filaments of certain blue-green algae.

Heteroecious (Gr. *heteros*, different + *oikos*, house), referring to fungi which cannot carry through their complete life cycle unless two different host species are present.

Heterogametes (Gr. *heteros*, different + gamete), gametes dissimilar from each other in size and behavior, as egg and sperm.

Heterogamy (Gr. *heteros*, different + *gamos*, union or reproduction), reproduction involving two types of gametes.

Heterophyte (Gr. *heteros*, different + *phyton*, a plant), a plant which must secure its food ready made.

Heterospory (Gr. *heteros*, different + spore), the condition of producing microspores and megaspores.

Heterothallic (Gr. *heteros*, different + thallus), referring to species in which male gametangia and female gametangia are produced in different filaments or by different individual plant bodies.

Heterotrophic (Gr. *heteros*, different + *trophein*, to nourish with food), referring to a plant obtaining nourishment from outside sources.

Heterozygous (Gr. *heteros*, different + *zygon*, yoke), having different genes of a Mendelian pair present in the same cell or organism, for instance, a tall pea plant with genes for tallness (*T*) and dwarfness (*t*).

Hexose (Gr. *hexa*, six + *-ose*, a suffix indicating in this usage a carbohydrate), a carbohydrate with six carbon atoms.

Hilum (L. *hilum*, a trifle), scar on seed which marks the place where the seed broke from the stalk.

Histology (Gr. *histos*, cloth, tissue + *logos*, discourse), science which deals with the microscopic structure of animal and vegetable tissues.

Homobasidiomycete (Gr. *homos*, the same + Basidiomycete), a subclass of Basidiomycetes with a typical club-shaped cell as a basidium.

Homologous chromosomes (Gr. *homologos*, the same), members of a chromosome pair; they may be heterozygous or homozygous.

Homospory (Gr. *homos*, one and the same + spore), the condition of producing one sort of spore only.

Homothallic (Gr. *homos*, one and the same + thallus), referring to species in which male gametangia and female gametangia are produced in the same filament or by the same individual plant body.

Homozygous (Gr. *homos*, one and the same + *zygon*, yoke), having similar genes of a Mendelian pair present in the same cell or organism, for instance, a tall pea plant with genes for tallness (*TT*) only.

Hormogonia (singular, **hormogonium**) (Gr. *hormos*, necklace + *gonos*, offspring), short filaments, the result of a breaking apart of filaments of certain blue-green algae at the heterocysts.

Hormone (Gr. *hormaein*, to excite), a specific organic product, produced in one part of a plant or animal body, and transported to another part where, effective in small amounts, it controls or stimulates another and different process.

Humidity, relative (L. *humidus*, moist), the ratio of the weight of water vapor in a given quantity of air, to the total weight of water vapor which that quantity of air is capable of holding at the temperature in question, expressed as per cent.

Humus (L. *humus*, the ground), decomposing organic matter in the soil.

Hyaloplasm (Gr. *hyalinos*, glossy + *plasma*, anything formed), the clear background portion of the cytoplasm, forming the continuous substance in which other protoplasmic bodies are embedded.

Hybrid (L. *hybrida*, offspring of a tame sow and a wild boar, a mongrel), the offspring of two plants or animals differing in at least one Mendelian character; or the offspring of plants or animals differing in many inheritable characters.

Hydrolysis (Gr. *hydro*, water + *lysis*, loosening), union of a compound with water, attended by decomposition into less complex compounds, usually controlled by enzymes.

Hymenium (Gr. *hymen*, a membrane), spore-bearing tissue in various fungi.

Hypertrophy (Gr. *hyper*, over + *trophein*, to nourish with food), a condition of overgrowth or excessive development of an organ or part.

Hypha (plural, **hyphae**) (Gr. *hyphe*, a web), a fungal thread or filament.

Hypocotyl (Gr. *hypo*, under + *kotyledon*, a cup-shaped hollow), that portion of an embryo or seedling below the cotyledons.

Hypogyny (Gr. *hypo*, under + *gyne*, female), a condition in which the receptacle is convex or conical, and the flower parts are situated one above another in the following order, beginning with the lowest: sepals, petals, stamens, carpels.

Hypothesis (Gr. *hypothesis*, foundation), a tentative theory or supposition provisionally adopted to explain certain facts and to guide in the investigation of other facts.

Hypotrophy (Gr. *hypo*, under + *trophein*, to nourish with food), an underdevelopment of an organ or part.

Imbibition (L. *imbibere*, to drink), the absorption of liquids or vapors into the ultramicroscopic spaces or pores found in such materials as cellulose or a block of gelatine.

Imperfect flower, a flower lacking either stamens or pistils.

Imperfect fungi, fungi reproducing only by asexual means.

Incomplete flower, a flower lacking one or more of the four kinds of flower parts.

Indehiscent (L. *in*, not + *dehiscere*, to divide), not opening by valves or along regular lines.

Indusium (plural, **indusia**) (L. *indusium*, a woman's undergarment), membranous outgrowth of the epidermis of a fern leaf which covers a sorus.

Inferior ovary, an ovary more or less, even completely, attached or united with the calyx.

Inflorescence (L. *inflorescere*, to begin to bloom), a flower cluster.

Inheritance (Old F. *enheritance*, inheritance), the reception or acquisition of characters or qualities by transmission of parent to offspring.

Inorganic, referring in chemistry to compounds which do not contain carbon.

Integument (L. *integumentum*, covering), coat of ovule.

inter, a prefix from the Latin preposition *inter* meaning between, in between, in the midst of.

intercalary (L. *intercalare,* to insert), descriptive of meristematic tissue or growth not restricted to the apex of an organ, i.e., growth at nodes.

intercellular (L. *inter,* between + cells), lying between cells.

interfascicular cambium (L. *inter,* between + *fasciculus,* small bundle), cambium that develops between vascular bundles.

internode (L. *inter,* between + *nodus,* a knot), the region of a stem between two successive nodes.

intine (L. *intus,* within), the innermost coat of a pollen grain.

intra, a prefix from the Latin preposition *intra* meaning on the inside, within.

intracellular (L. *intra,* within + cell), lying within cells.

involucre (L. *involucrum,* a wrapper), a whorl or rosette of bracts surrounding an inflorescence.

ion (Gr. *ienai,* to go), an electrified particle formed by the breakdown of substances able to conduct an electric current.

irregular flower, a flower in which one or more members of at least one whorl are of different form from other members of the same whorl; zygomorphic flower.

isobilateral leaf (Gr. *isos,* equal + L. *bis,* twice, twofold + *lateralis,* pertaining to the side), a leaf having the upper and lower surfaces essentially similar.

isodiametric (Gr. *isos,* equal + diameter), having diameters equal in all directions, as a ball.

isogametes (Gr. *isos,* equal + gametes), gametes similar in size and behavior.

karyogamy (Gr. *karyon,* nut + *gamos,* marriage), the fusion of two nuclei.

karyolymph (Gr. *karyon,* nut + *lympha,* water), the ground substance of a nucleus.

keel (A.S. *ceol,* ship), a structure of the legume type of flower made up of two petals loosely united along their edges.

kinetochore (Gr. *kinein,* to move + *chorein,* to move apart), specialized body of a chromosome which seems to direct its movement.

lamina (L. *lamina,* a thin plate), blade or expanded part of a leaf.

lateral bud, a bud which grows out from the side of a stem.

latex (L. *latex,* juice), a milky secretion.

leaf axil, angle formed by the leaf stalk and the stem.

leaflet, separate part of the blade of a compound leaf.

leaf primordium (L. *primordium,* a beginning), a lateral outgrowth from the apical meristem which will become a leaf.

legume (L. *legumen,* any leguminous plant, particularly bean), a simple, dry dehiscent fruit with one carpel, splitting along two sutures.

lemma (Gr. *lemma,* a husk), lower bract which subtends a grass flower.

lenticel (M.L. *lenticella,* a small lens), a structure of the bark which permits the passage of gas inward and outward.

leucoplast (Gr. *leukos,* white + *plastos,* formed), a colorless plastid.

liana (F. *liane* from *lier,* to bind), a plant which climbs upon other plants, depending upon them for mechanical support; a plant with climbing shoots.

lichen (Gr. *leichen,* thallus plants growing on rocks and trees), a composite plant consisting of a fungus living symbiotically with an alga.

lignification (L. *lignum,* wood + *facere,* to make), impregnation of cell wall with lignin.

lignin (L. *lignum,* wood), an organic substance or group of substances impregnating the cellulose framework of certain plant cell walls.

ligule (L. *ligula,* dimin. of *lingua,* tongue), in grass leaves, an outgrowth from the upper and inner side of the leaf blade where it joins the sheath.

linked characters, characters of a plant or animal controlled by genes grouped together on the same chromosome.

lipase (Gr. *lipos,* fat + *-ase,* suffix indicating an enzyme), any enzyme that breaks fats into glycerin and fatty acids.

liverwort (liver + Middle English *wort,* a plant; literally a liver plant, so named in medieval times because of its fancied resemblance to the lobes of the liver), common name for the Class Hepaticae of the Bryophyta.

lobed leaf (Gr. *lobos,* lower part of the ear), a leaf divided by clefts or sinuses.

locule (L. *loculus,* dimin. of *locus,* a place), a cavity of the ovary in which ovules occur.

lodicules (L. *lodicula,* a small coverlet), two scalelike structures which lie at the base of the ovary of a grass flower.

longevity (L. *longaevus,* long-lived), length of life.

lumen (L. *lumen,* light, an opening for light), the cavity of the cell within the cell walls.

lycophyta (Gr. *lycos,* wolf + *phyton,* plant) (name from the ancient fancied resemblance of some species to a wolf's foot), a phylum of vascular plants, reproducing by meiospores formed in sporangia on sporophylls which are borne, in most species, in definite strobili; leaves generally in a spiral arrangement and actively photosynthetic.

Megasporangium (Gr. *megas,* large + sporangium), sporangium which bears megaspores.

Megaspore (Gr. *megas,* large + spore), the meiospore of vascular plants which gives rise to a female gametophyte.

Megaspore mother cell, a diploid cell in which meiosis will occur resulting in four megaspores.

Megasporophyll (Gr. *megas,* large + spore + Gr. *phyllon,* leaf), a leaf bearing megasporangia and contained megaspores.

Meiosis (Gr. *meioun,* to make smaller), two special cell divisions occurring once in the life cycle of every sexually reproducing plant and animal, halving the chromosome number and effecting a segregation of genetic determiners.

Meiospore (meiosis + spore), any spore resulting from the meiotic divisions.

Meristem (Gr. *meristos,* divisible), undifferentiated tissue, the cells of which are capable of active cell division and differentiation into specialized tissues.

Mesocarp (Gr. *mesos,* middle + *karpos,* fruit), middle layer of fruit wall (pericarp).

Mesophyll (Gr. *mesos,* middle + *phyllon,* leaf), parenchyma tissue of leaf between epidermal layers.

Mesophyte (Gr. *mesos,* middle + *phyton,* a plant), a plant avoiding both extremes of moisture and drought.

Metabolism (M.L. from the Gr. *metabolos,* to change), the process, in an organism or a single cell, by which nutritive material is built up into living matter, or aids in building living matter, or by which protoplasm is broken down into simple substances to perform special functions.

Metaphase (Gr. *meta,* after + *phasis,* appearance), stage of mitosis during which the chromosomes, or at least the kinetochores, lie in the central plane of the spindle.

Microcapillary space, exceedingly small spaces, such as those found between microfibrils of cellulose.

Microfibrils (Gr. *mikros,* small + fibrils, dimin. of fiber; literally, small little fibers), the translation of the name expresses the concept very well. Microfibrils are exceedingly small fibers visible only with the high magnifications of the electron microscope.

Micron (Gr. *mikros,* small), a unit of distance 0.001 millimeter or 0.000039 inch. Symbol *μ.*

Micropyle (Gr. *mikros,* small + *pyle,* orifice, gate) a pore leading from the outer surface of the ovule between the edges of the two integument down to the surface of the nucellus.

Microsporangium (plural, **microsporangia**) (Gr. *mikros,* little + sporangium), a sporangium which bears microspores.

Microspore (Gr. *mikros,* small + spore), a spore which in vascular plants gives rise to a male gametophyte.

Microspore mother cell, a cell in which meiosis will occur resulting in four microspores.

Microsporophyll (Gr. *mikros,* little + spore + Gr. *phyllon,* leaf), a leaf bearing microsporangia and contained microspores.

Middle lamella (L. *lamella,* a thin plate or scale), original thin membrane separating two adjacent protoplasts and remaining as a distinct cementing layer between adjacent cell walls.

Mitochondrion (plural, **mitochondria**) (Gr. *mitos,* thread + *chondrion,* a grain), a small cytoplasmic particle associated with intracellular respiration.

Mitosis (Gr. *mitos,* a thread), nuclear division, involving appearance of chromosomes, their longitudinal duplication, and equal distribution of newly formed parts to daughter nuclei.

Mixed bud, a bud containing both rudimentary leaves and flowers.

Molecule (F. *môle,* mass + *cule,* a dimin.; literally, a little mass), a unit of matter, the smallest portion of an element or a compound that retains chemical identity with the substance in mass. The molecule usually consists of a union of two or more atoms, some organic molecules containing a very large number of atoms.

Monocotyledon (Gr. *monos,* solitary + *kotyledon,* a cup-shaped hollow), a plant whose embryo has one cotyledon.

Monoecious (Gr. *monos,* solitary + *oikos,* house), having the reproductive organs in separate structures, but borne on the same individual.

Monohybrid (Gr. *monos,* solitary + L. *hybrida,* a mongrel), a cross involving one pair of contrasting characters.

Morphology (Gr. *morphe,* form + *logos,* discourse), the study of form and its development.

Moss (L. *muscus,* moss), a bryophytic plant.

Multiciliate (L. *multus,* many + F. *cil,* an eyelash), having many cilia present on a sperm or spore or other type of ciliated cell.

Multiple fruit, a cluster of matured ovaries produced by separate flowers.

Mutation (L. *mutare,* to change), a sudden, heritable change appearing in an individual as the result of a change in genes or chromosomes.

Mycelium (Gr. *mykes,* mushroom), the mass of hyphae forming the body of a fungus.

Mycology (Gr. *mykes,* mushroom + *logos,* discourse), the branch of botany dealing with fungi.

Myxomycophyta (Gr. *myxa,* mucus + *mykes,* mushroom + *phyton,* plant), a phylum comprising the "slime fungi."

Naked bud, a bud not protected by bud scales.

Nectary (Gr. *nektar,* the drink of the gods), a nectar-secreting gland.

Net venation, veins of leaf blade visible to the unaided eye, branching frequently and joining again, forming a network.

Nitrification (L. *nitrum,* nitro, a combining form indicating the presence of nitrogen + *facere,* to make), change of ammonium salts into nitrates through the activities of certain bacteria.

Node (L. *nodus,* a knot), slightly enlarged portion of the stem where leaves and buds arise, and where branches originate.

Nonseptate, descriptive of hyphae lacking cross-walls.

Nucellus (L. *nucella,* a small nut), tissue composing the chief part of the young ovule, in which embryo sac develops; megasporangium.

Nucleolus (L. *nucleolus,* a small nucleus), dense protoplasmic body in the nucleus.

Nucleus (L. *nucleus,* kernel of a nut), a dense protoplasmic body essential in cellular synthetic and developmental activities; present in all living plant cells except mature sieve-tube elements.

Nut (L. *nux,* nut), a dry, indehiscent, hard, one-seeded fruit, generally produced from a compound ovary.

Obligate anaerobe, an organism obliged to live in the absence of oxygen.

Obligate parasite, an organism obliged to live strictly as a parasite.

Obligate saprophyte, an organism obliged to live strictly as a saprophyte.

Oogamy (Gr. *oion,* egg + *gamia,* reproduction), reproduction involving an egg and a sperm; heterogamy.

Oogonium (L. dimin. of Gr. *oogonos,* literally, a little egg-layer), female gametangium or egg-bearing organ not protected by a jacket of sterile cells, characteristic of the thallophytes.

Oospore (Gr. *oion,* an egg + spore), a resistant spore developing from a zygote resulting from the fusion of heterogametes.

Open bundle, a vascular bundle with cambium.

Operculum (L. *operculum,* a lid), in mosses, cap of sporangium.

Opposite, referring to bud or leaf arrangement in which there are two buds or two leaves at a node.

Organ (L. *organum,* an instrument or engine of any kind, musical, military, etc.), a part or member of an animal or plant body or cell adapted by its structure for a particular function.

Organic, referring in chemistry to the carbon compounds, many of which have been in some manner associated with living organisms.

Osmosis (Gr. *osmos,* a pushing), diffusion of a solvent through a differentially permeable membrane.

Ovary (L. *ovum,* an egg), enlarged basal portion of the pistil which becomes the fruit.

Ovulate, referring to a cone, scale, or other structure bearing ovules.

Ovule (F. *ovule,* from L. *ovulum,* dimin. of *ovum,* egg), a rudimentary seed, containing before fertilization the female gametophyte, with egg cell, all being surrounded by the nucellus and one or two integuments.

Ovuliferous (ovule + L. *ferre,* to bear), referring to a scale or sporophyll bearing ovules.

Palea (or palet) (L. *palea,* chaff), upper bract which subtends a grass flower.

Palisade parenchyma, elongated cells, containing many chloroplasts, found just beneath the upper epidermis of leaves.

Palmately veined (L. *palma,* palm of the hand), descriptive of a leaf blade with several principal veins spreading out from the upper end of the petiole.

Panicle (L. *panicula,* a tuft), an inflorescence, the main axis of which is branched, and whose branches bear loose racemose flower clusters.

Pappus (L. *pappus,* woolly, hairy seed or fruit of certain plants), scales or bristles representing a reduced calyx in composite flowers.

Parallel venation, type of venation in which veins of leaf blade that are clearly visible to the unaided eye are parallel to each other.

Paraphysis (plural, **paraphyses**) (Gr. *para,* beside + *physis,* growth), slender, multicellular hair (*Fucus,* etc.); one of the sterile branches or hyphae growing beside fertile cells in the fruiting body of certain fungi.

Parasite (Gr. *parasitos,* one who eats at the table of another), an organism deriving its food from the living body of another plant or an animal.

Parenchyma (Gr. *parenchein,* an ancient Greek medical term meaning to pour beside and expressing the ancient concept that the liver and other internal organs were formed by blood diffusing through the blood vessels and coagulating, thus designating ground tissue), a tissue composed of cells which usually have thin walls of cellulose, and which often fit rather loosely together, leaving intercellular spaces.

Parietal (F. *pariétal,* attached to the wall, from L. *paries,* wall), belonging to, connected with, or attached to the wall of a hollow organ or structure, especially of the ovary or cell.

Parietal placentation, a type of placentation in which placentae are on the ovary wall.

Parthenocarpy (Gr. *parthenos,* virgin + *karpos,* fruit), the development of fruit without fertilization.

Parthenogenesis (Gr. *parthenos,* virgin + *genesis,* origin), the development of a gamete into a new individual without fertilization.

Passive absorption of water, the absorption of water by roots due to forces of transpiration in leaves.

Passive solute absorption, absorption due only to forces of simple diffusion.

Pathogen (Gr. *pathos,* suffering + *genesis,* beginning), an organism which causes a disease.

Pathology (Gr. *pathos,* suffering + *logos,* account), the study of diseases, their effects on plants or animals, and their treatment.

Pectin (Gr. *pektos,* congealed), a white amorphous substance which when combined with acid and sugar yields a jelly. The substance cementing cells together; the middle lamella.

Pedicel (L. *pediculus,* a little foot), stalk or stem of the individual flowers of an inflorescence.

Peduncle (L. *pedunculus,* a late form of *pediculus,* a little foot), stalk or stem of a flower which is borne singly; or the main stem of an inflorescence.

Penicillin, an antibiotic derived from the mold *Penicillium.*

Perennial (L. *perennis,* lasting the whole year through), a plant which lives from year to year.

Perfect flower, a flower having both stamens and pistils; hermaphroditic flower.

Perianth (Gr. *peri,* around + *anthos,* flower), the petals and sepals taken together.

Pericarp (Gr. *peri,* around + *karpos,* fruit), fruit wall, developed from ovary wall.

Pericycle (Gr. *peri,* around + *kyklos,* circle), tissue, generally of root, bounded externally by the endodermis and internally by the phloem.

Peridium (plural, **peridia**) (Gr. *peridion,* a little pouch), external covering of the hymenium of certain fungi; in Myxomycetes, the hardened envelope which covers the sporangium.

Perigyny (Gr. *peri,* about + *gyne,* a female), a condition in which the receptacle is more or less concave, at the margin of which the sepals, petals, and stamens have their origin, so that these parts seem to be attached around the ovary.

Peristome (Gr. *peri,* about + *stoma,* a mouth), in mosses, a fringe of teeth about the opening of the sporangium.

Perithecium (Gr. *peri,* around + *theke,* a box), spherical or flask-shaped ascocarp having a small opening.

Permeable (L. *permeabilis,* that which can be penetrated), a membrane, cell, or cell system through which substances may diffuse.

Petal (Gr. *petalon,* a flower leaf), one of the flower parts, usually conspicuously colored.

Petiole (L. *petiolus,* a little foot or leg), stalk of leaf.

Phaeophycophyta (Gr. *phaios,* dusky + *phykos,* algal + *phyton,* plant), a phylum of marine algae characterized by a brown pigment.

Phelloderm (Gr. *phellos,* cork + *derma,* skin), a layer of cells formed in the stems of some plants from the inner cells of the cork cambium.

Phellogen (Gr. *phellos,* cork + *genesis,* birth), cork cambium, a cambium giving rise externally to cork and in some plants internally to phelloderm.

Phenotype (Gr. *phaneros,* showing + type), the external visible appearance of an organism.

Phloem (Gr. *phloos,* bark), food-conducting tissue, consisting of sieve tubes, companion cells, phloem parenchyma, and fibers.

Photoperiod (Gr. *photos,* light + period), the optimum length of day or period of daily illumination required for the normal growth and maturity of a plant.

Photosynthesis (Gr. *photos,* light + *syn,* together + *tithenai,* to place), a process in which carbon dioxide and water are brought together chemically to form a carbohydrate, the energy for the process being radiant energy.

Phototropism (Gr. *photos,* light + *tropos,* turning), a growth curvature in which light is the stimulus.

Phycocyanin (Gr. *phykos,* seaweed + *kyanos,* blue), a blue pigment, occurring in blue-green algae.

Phycoerythrin (Gr. *phykos,* seaweed + *erythros,* red), a red pigment occurring in red algae.

Phycomycetes (Gr. *phykos,* seaweed + *mykes,* mushroom or fungus), a class of fungi which approaches the algae in some characters.

Phylogeny (Gr. *phylon,* race or tribe + *genesis,* begining), the development of a group of related individuals.

Phylum (Gr. *phylon,* race or tribe), a primary division of the animal or plant kingdom.

Physiology (Gr. *physis,* nature + *logos,* discourse), the science of the functions and activities of living organisms.

Phytobenthon (Gr. *phyton,* a plant + *benthos,* depths of the sea), attached aquatic plants, collectively.

Phytoplankton (Gr. *phyton,* a plant + *planktos,* wandering), free-floating plants, collectively.

Pileus (L. *pileus,* a cap), umbrella-shaped cap of fleshy fungi.

Pinna (plural, **pinnae**) (L. *pinna,* a feather), leaflet or division of a compound leaf (frond).

Pinnately veined (L. *pinna,* a feather + *vena,* a vein), descriptive of a leaf blade with single midrib from which smaller veins branch off, somewhat like the divisions of a feather.

Pistil (L. *pistillum,* a pestle), central organ of the flowers typically consisting of ovary, style, and stigma.

Pistillate flower, a flower having pistils but no stamens.

Pit, a minute thin area of a cell wall.

Pith, the parenchymatous tissue occupying the central portion of a stem.

Placenta (plural, **placentae**) (L. *placenta,* a cake), the tissue within the ovary to which the ovules are attached.

Placentation (L. *placenta,* a cake + *-tion,* state of), manner in which the placentae are distributed in the ovary.

Plankton (Gr. *planktos,* wandering), free-floating aquatic plants and animals, collectively.

Plasmodesma (plural, **plasmodesmata**) (Gr. *plasma,* something formed + *desmos,* a bond, a band), fine protoplasmic thread passing through the wall which separates two protoplasts.

Plasmodium (Gr. *plasma,* something formed + mod. Latin *odium,* something of the nature of), in Myxomycetes, a slimy mass of protoplasm, with no surrounding wall and with numerous free nuclei distributed throughout.

Plasmogamy (Gr. *plasma,* anything molded or formed + *gamos,* marriage), the fusion of protoplasts, not accompanied by nuclear fusion.

Plasmolemma (Gr. *plasma,* anything formed + *lemma,* a husk or shell of a fruit), a delicate cytoplasmic membrane found on the outside of the protoplast adjacent to the cell wall.

Plasmolysis (Gr. *plasma,* something formed + *lysis,* a loosing), the separation of the cytoplasm from the cell wall, due to removal of water from the protoplast.

Plastid (Gr. *plastos,* formed), a specialized cytoplasmic structure.

Plumule (L. *plumula,* a small feather), the first bud of an embryo or that portion of the young shoot above the cotyledons.

Polar, pertaining to the opposite ends of an axis.

Pollen (L. *pollen,* fine flour), the germinated microspores or partially developed male gametophytes of seed plants.

Pollen mother cell, the cell in which meiosis will occur resulting in the formation of four pollen grains.

Pollination, the transfer of pollen from a stamen or staminate cone to a stigma or ovulate cone.

Polyploid (Gr. *polys,* many + *ploos,* fold), referring to a plant, tissue, or cell with more than two complete sets of chromosomes.

Pome (F. *pomme,* apple), a simple fleshy fruit, the outer portion of which is formed by the floral parts which surround the ovary.

Primary (L. *primus,* first), first in order of time or development.

Primary endosperm cell, a cell of the embryo sac after fertilization, generally containing a nucleus resulting from fusion of the two polar nuclei with a sperm nucleus. The endosperm develops from this cell.

Primary meristems, meristems of the shoot or root tip giving rise to the primary plant body.

Primordium (L. *primus,* first + *ordiri,* to begin to weave; literally beginning to weave, or to put things in order), the beginning or origin of any part of an organ.

Procambium (L. *pro,* before + *cambium*), a primary meristem which gives rise to primary vascular tissues and in most woody plants to the vascular cambium.

Proembryo (L. *pro,* before + *embryon,* embryo), a group of cells arising from the division of the fertilized egg cell before those cells which are to become the embryo are recognizable.

Prophase (Gr. *pro,* before + *phasis,* appearance), an early stage in nuclear division, characterized by the shortening and thickening of the chromosomes and their movement to the metaphase plate.

Protease (protein + -ase, a suffix indicating an enzyme), an enzyme breaking down a protein.

Protein (Gr. *proteios*, holding first place), naturally occurring complex organic substances (egg albumen, meat) composed essentially of carbon, hydrogen, oxygen, and nitrogen, plus sulfur or phosphorus, which are so associated as to form submicroscopic chains, spirals, or plates and to which are attached other atoms and groups of atoms in a variety of manners.

Prothallium (Gr. *pro*, before + *thallos*, a sprout), in ferns, the haploid gametophyte generation.

Protoderm (Gr. *protos*, first + *derma*, skin), a primary meristem which gives rise to epidermis.

Protonema (plural, **protonemata**) (Gr. *protos*, first + *nema*, a thread), algal-like filamentous growth, an early stage in development of the gametophyte of mosses.

Protoplasm (Gr. *protos*, first + *plasma*, something formed), living substance.

Protoplast (Gr. *protoplastos*, formed first), the organized living unit of a single cell.

Pseudopodium (Gr. *pseudes*, false + *podion*, a foot), in Myxomycetes, an armlike projection from the body by which the plant creeps over the surface.

Psilophyta (Gr. *psilo*, bare + *phyton*, plant), a phylum of primitive vascular plants.

Pteridophyta (Gr. *pteris*, fern + *phyton*, plant), a primary division of the plant kingdom including ferns and their allies (*Lycopodium, Selaginella, Equisetum*).

Pterophyta (Gr. *pteron*, feather + *phyton*, plant), a phylum of vascular plants comprised of ferns, gymnosperms, and angiosperms.

Pyrenoid (Gr. *pyren*, the stone of a fruit + L. *oïdes*, like), a denser body occurring within the chloroplasts of certain algae and liverworts and apparently associated with starch deposition.

Pyrrophycophyta (Gr. *pyrrhos*, fiery, reddish + *phykos*, seaweed + *phyton*, plant), a phylum of golden-brown algae.

Raceme (L. *racemus*, a bunch of grapes), an inflorescence in which the main axis is elongated but the flowers are borne on pedicels which are about equal in length.

Rachilla (Gr. *rhachis*, a backbone + L. dimin. ending -*illa*), shortened axis of spikelet.

Rachis (Gr. *rhachis*, a backbone), main axis of spike; axis of fern leaf (frond) from which pinnae arise; in compound leaves, the extension

of the petiole corresponding to the midrib of an entire leaf.

Radicle (L. *radix*, root), that portion of the plant embryo which develops into the primary or seed root.

Raphe (Gr. *rhaphe*, seam), ridge on seeds, formed by the stalk of the ovule, in those seeds in which the funiculus is sharply bent at the base of the ovule.

Raphides (Gr. *rhaphis*, a needle), fine, sharp, needlelike crystals.

Receptacle (L. *receptaculum*, a reservoir), enlarged end of the pedicel or peduncle to which other flower parts are attached.

Recessive character, that member of a pair of Mendelian characters which, when both members of the pair are present, is subordinated or suppressed by the other, dominant character.

Reduction (F. *reduction*, L. *reductio*, a bringing back), originally "bringing back" a metal from its oxide, i.e., iron from iron rust or ore; any chemical reaction involving the removal of oxygen or the addition of hydrogen from or to a substance. Energy is required and may be stored in the process as in photosynthesis.

Regular flower, a flower in which the corolla is made up of similarly shaped petals equally spaced and radiating from the center of the flower; star-shaped flower; actinomorphic flower.

Reproduction (L. *re*, repeatedly + *producere*, to give birth to), the process by which plants and animals give rise to offspring.

Respiration (L. *re*, repeatedly + *spirare*, to breathe), a chemical oxidation controlled and catalyzed by enzymes in which living protoplasm breaks down carbohydrate and fats, thus releasing energy to be used by the organism in doing work.

Reticulum (L. *reticulum*, a small net), a small net.

Rhizoid (Gr. *rhiza*, root + L. *oïdes*, like), one of the cellular filaments which perform the functions of roots.

Rhizome (Gr. *rhiza*, root), an elongated, underground, horizontal stem.

Rhizophores (Gr. *rhiza*, root + *phoros*, bearing), leafless branches which grow downward from the leafy stems of certain Lycopodineae and give rise to roots when they come into contact with the soil.

Rhodophycophyta (Gr. *rhodon*, a rose + *phykos*, seaweed + *phyton*, plant), a phylum of algae, largely marine, characterized by a red pigment.

Root (A.S. *rōt*), the descending axis of a plant, normally below ground, and serving to anchor the plant and to absorb and conduct water and mineral nutrients.

Root cap, a thimblelike mass of cells covering and protecting the apical meristems of a root.

Root pressure, pressure developed in the root as the result of osmosis and inducing bleeding in stem wounds.

Rootstock, an elongated, underground, horizontal stem.

Runner, a stem that grows horizontally along the ground surface.

Samara (L. *samara,* the fruit of the elm), simple, dry, one- or two-seeded indehiscent fruit with pericarp bearing a winglike outgrowth.

Saprophyte (Gr. *sapros,* rotten + *phyton,* a plant), an organism deriving its food from the dead body or the nonliving products of another plant or animal.

Scalariform vessel (L. *scala,* ladder + form), a vessel with secondary thickening resembling a ladder.

Schizocarp (Gr. *schizein,* to split + *karpos,* fruit), dry fruit with two or more united carpels, which split apart at maturity.

Schizomycetes (Gr. *schizein,* to split + *mykes,* fungus), a class of heterotrophic plants, the bacteria, which reproduce largely by cell division.

Schizophyceae (Gr. *schizein,* to split + *phykos,* seaweed), a class of autophytic plants, the blue-green algae, which reproduce largely by fission.

Schizophyta (Gr. *schizein,* to split + *phyton,* plant), a phylum of plants, bacteria and blue-green algae, which reproduce largely by cell division.

Sclereids (Gr. *skleros,* hard), more or less isodiametric cells with heavily lignified cell walls.

Sclerenchyma (Gr. *skleros,* hard + *-enchyma,* a suffix denoting tissue), a strengthening tissue composed of cells with heavily lignified cell walls.

Scutellum (L. *scutella,* a dimin. of *scutum,* shield), single cotyledon of grass embryo.

Seed (A.S. *sed,* anything which may be sown), popularly as originally used, anything which may be sown; i.e., "seed" potatoes, "seeds" of corn, sunflower, etc. Botanically, a seed is the matured ovule without accessory parts.

Self-pollination, transfer of pollen from the stamens to the stigma of either the same flower or flowers on the same plant.

Seminal root, the root or roots forming from primordia present in the seed.

Sepals (M.L. *sepalum,* a covering; "sepalum" is a modern word formed by analogy with petalum,

Gr. *petalon),* outermost flower structures which usually enclose the other flower parts in the bud.

Septate (L. *septum,* fence), divided by cross walls into cells or compartments.

Septicidal dehiscence (L. *septum,* fence + *caedere,* to cut; *dehiscere,* to split open), the splitting open of a capsule along the line of union of carpels.

Septum (L. *septum,* fence), any dividing wall or partition, frequently a cross wall in a fungal or algal filament.

Sessile (L. *sessilis,* low, dwarf, from *sedere,* to sit), sitting, referring to a leaf lacking a petiole or to a flower or fruit lacking a pedicel.

Seta (plural, **setae**) (L. *seta,* a bristle), in liverworts, a short stalk of the sporophyte which connects the foot and the capsule.

Sexual reproduction, reproduction which requires meiosis and fertilization for a complete life cycle.

Sheath, part of leaf which wraps around the stem, as in grasses.

Shoot (derivation uncertain but early referring to new plant growth, 1450, "Take a feyr schoyt of blake thorne"), a young branch which shoots out from the main stock of a tree, or the young main portion of a plant growing aboveground.

Shoot tip, that portion of the shoot containing apical and primary meristems and early stages of differentiation.

Sieve cell, a long and slender sieve element with relatively unspecialized sieve areas and with tapering end walls that lack sieve plates.

Sieve plate, perforated wall area in a sieve-tube member through which pass strands connecting sieve-tube protoplasts.

Sieve tube, a series of sieve-tube members forming a long cellular tube specialized for the conduction of food materials.

Sieve-tube member, that portion of a sieve tube comprised of a single protoplast and separated from other sieve-tube elements by sieve plates.

Silique (L. *siliqua,* pod), the fruit characteristic of Cruciferae (mustards); two-celled, the valves splitting from the bottom and leaving the placentae with the false partition stretched between.

Simple pit, pit not surrounded by an overarching border.

Solute (L. *solutus,* from *solvere,* to loosen), a dissolved substance.

Solution (Middle English *solucion,* from Old F. *solucion,* to loosen), a homogeneous mixture, the molecules of the dissolved substance; e.g., sugar, the solute, being dispersed between the molecules of the solvent. e.g., water.

Solvent (L. *solvere*, to loosen), a substance, usually a liquid, having the properties of dissolving other substances.

Soredium (plural, **soredia**) (Gr. *soros*, a heap), special reproductive body of lichens consisting of a few algal cells surrounded by fungous hyphae.

Sorus (plural, **sori**) (Gr. *soros*, a heap), a cluster of sporangia.

Species (L. *species*, appearance, form, kind), a class of individuals usually interbreeding freely and having many characteristics in common.

Sperm (Gr. *sperma*, the generative substance or seed of a male animal), a male gamete.

Spermagonium (plural, **spermagonia**) (Gr. *sperma*, sperm + *gonos*, offspring), flask-shaped structure characteristic of the sexual phase of the rust fungi; bearing receptive hyphae and spermatia.

Spermatium (plural, **spermatia**) (Gr. *sperma*, sperm), in rust fungi, a cell borne at the tip of hyphae which line the interior of spermagonia (on barberry leaves).

Spermatophyte (Gr. *sperma*, seed + *phyton*, plant), a seed plant.

Sphenophyta (Gr. *sphenos*, a wedge + *phyton*, a plant) (named for the wedge shape of many fossil leaves), a phylum of vascular plants, reproducing by meiospores formed in sporangia on special sporangiophores grouped in strobili. Leaves scalelike, whorled in arrangement, generally fused in a sheath surrounding the stem and only slightly photosynthetic. Gametophyte a prothallus.

Spike (L. *spica*, an ear of grain), an inflorescence in which the main axis is elongated and the flowers are sessile.

Spikelet (L. *spica*, an ear of grain + dimin. ending *-let*), the unit of inflorescence in grasses; a small group of grass flowers.

Spindle (A.S. *spinel*, an instrument employed in spinning thread by hand), referring in mitosis and meiosis to the spindle-shaped intracellular structure in which the chromosomes move.

Sporangiophore (sporangium + Gr. *-phore*, a root of *phorein*, to bear), a branch bearing one or more sporangia.

Sporangium (spore + Gr. *angeion*, a vessel), spore case.

Spore (Gr. *spora*, seed), a reproductive cell which develops into a plant without union with other cells; some spores such as meiospores occur at a critical stage in the sexual cycle, but others are asexual in nature.

Sporidium (dimin., meaning a little spore), the basidiospore of smut fungi.

Sporophore (spore + Gr. *phorein*, to bear), the fruiting body of fleshy and woody fungi which produces spores.

Sporophyll (spore + Gr. *phyllon*, leaf), a spore-bearing leaf.

Sporophyte (spore + Gr. *phyton*, a plant), in alternation of generations, the plant in which meiosis occurs and which thus produces meiospores.

Stamen (L. *stamen*, the standing-up things or a tuft of thready things), flower structure made up of an anther (pollen-bearing portion) and a stalk or filament.

Staminate flower, a flower having stamens but no pistils.

Starch (Middle English *sterchen*, to stiffen), a complex insoluble carbohydrate, the chief food storage substance of plants, which is composed of several hundred hexose sugar units ($C_6H_{10}O_5$) and which breaks down easily into these separate units.

Stele (Gr. *stele*, a post), the central cylinder, inside the cortex, of roots and stems of vascular plants.

Stem (Old English *stemn*), the main body of the portion aboveground of tree, shrub, herb, or other plant. The ascending axis, whether above or below ground of a plant in contradistinction to the descending axis or root.

Sterigma (plural, **sterigmata**) (Gr. *sterigma*, a prop), a slender, pointed protuberance at the end of a basidium which bears a basidiospore.

Stigma (L. *stigma*, a prick, a spot, a mark), receptive portion of the style to which pollen adheres.

Stipule (L. *stipula*, dimin. of *stipes*, a stock or trunk), a leaflike structure from either side of the leaf base.

Stolon (L. *stolo*, a shoot), a stem that grows horizontally along the ground surface.

Stoma (plural, **stomata**) (Gr. *stoma*, mouth), a minute opening bordered by guard cells in the epidermis of leaves and stems through which gases pass.

Strobilus (Gr. *strobilos*, a cone), a number of modified leaves (sporophylls) or ovule-bearing scales grouped together on an axis.

Style (Gr. *stylos*, a column), slender column of tissue which arises from the top of the ovary and through which the pollen tube grows.

Suberin (L. *suber*, the cork oak), a waxy material found in the cell walls of cork tissue.

Succulent (L. *sucus*, juice), a plant having juicy or watery tissues.

Sucrose (F. *sucre*, sugar + *-ose*, termination designating a sugar), cane sugar ($C_{12}H_{22}O_{11}$).

Superior ovary, an ovary completely separate and free from the calyx.

Suspensor (L. *suspendere*, to hang), a cell or chain of cells developed from a zygote whose function is to place the embryo cells in an advantageous position to receive food.

Suture (L. *sutura*, a sewing together; originally the sewing together of flesh or bone wounds), the junction, or line of junction of contiguous parts.

Symbiosis (Gr. *syn*, with + *bios*, life), an association of two different kinds of living organisms involving benefit to both.

Sympetaly (Gr. *syn*, with + *petalon*, leaf), a condition in which petals are united.

Synandry (Gr. *syn*, with + *andros*, a man), a condition in which stamens are united.

Syncarpy (Gr. *syn*, with + *karpos*, fruit), a condition in which carpels are united.

Synergids (Gr. *synergos*, toiling together), the two nuclei at the upper end of the embryo sac, which, with the third (the egg), constitute the egg-apparatus.

Synsepaly (Gr. *syn*, with + sepals), a condition in which sepals are united.

Tannin, a substance which has an astringent, bitter taste.

Tapetum (Gr. *tapes*, a carpet), nutritive tissue in the sporangium, particularly an anther.

Taxonomy (Gr. *taxis*, arrangement + *nomos*, law), systematic botany; the science dealing with the describing, naming, and classifying of plants.

Teliospore (Gr. *telos*, completion + spore), resistant spore characteristic of the Heterobasidiomycetes in which karyogamy and meiosis occur and from which a basidium develops.

Telium (plural, **telia**) (Gr. *telos*, completion), a sorus of teliospores.

Telophase (Gr. *telos*, completion + phase), the last stage of mitosis, in which daughter nuclei are reorganized.

Tendril (L. *tendere*, to stretch out, to extend), a slender coiling organ which aids in the support of stems.

Terminal bud, a bud at the end of a stem.

Testa (L. *testa*, a brick, shell), the outer coat of the seed.

Tetrad (Gr. *tetradeion*, a set of four), a group of four, usually referring to the meiospores immediately after meiosis.

Tetraploid (Gr. *tetra*, four + *ploos*, fold), having four sets of chromosomes per nucleus.

Tetraspores (Gr. *tetra*, four + spores), four spores formed by division of the spore mother cell, used particularly for meiospores in certain red algae.

Thallophytes (Gr. *thallos*, a sprout + *phyton*, plant), a division of plants whose body is a thallus, i.e., lacking roots, stems, and leaves.

Thallus (Gr. *thallos*, a sprout), plant body without true roots, stems, or leaves

Tissue, a group of cells of similar structure which performs a special function.

Tonoplast (Gr. *tonos*, stretching tension + *plastos*, molded, formed), the cytoplasmic membrane bordering the vacuole. So-called by de Vries as he thought it regulated the pressure exerted by the cell sap.

Toxin (L. *toxicum*, poison), a poisonous secretion of a plant or animal.

Tracheid (Gr. *tracheia*, windpipe), an elongated, tapering xylem cell, with lignified pitted walls, adapted for conduction and support.

Tracheophytes (Gr. *tracheia*, windpipe + *phyton*, plant), vascular plants.

Translocation (L. *trans*, across + *locare*, to place), the transfer of food materials or products of metabolism.

Transpiration (F. *transpirer*, to perspire), to give off water vapor from the surface of leaves.

Tropism (Gr. *trope*, a turning), movement of curvature due to an external stimulus which determines the direction of movement.

Tuber (L. *tuber*, a bump, swelling), a much-enlarged, short, fleshy underground stem.

Turgid (L. *turgidus*, swollen, inflated), swollen, distended; referring to a cell that is firm due to water uptake.

Turgor pressure (L. *turgor*, a swelling), the pressure within the cell resulting from the absorption of water into the vacuole and the imbibition of water by the protoplasm.

Tylosis (plural, **tyloses**) (Gr. *tylos*, a lump or knot), a growth of one cell into the cavity of another.

Type specimen, the herbarium specimen selected by a taxonomist to serve as a basis for the naming and descriptions of a new species.

Umbel (L. *umbella*, a sunshade), an inflorescence, the individual pedicels of which all arise from the apex of the peduncle.

Unavailable water, water held by the soil so strongly that root hairs cannot readily absorb it.

Universal veil, a membrane completely surrounding the basidiocarp of a homobasidiomycete at the button stage.

Uredinium (plural, **uredinia**) (L. *uredo,* a blight), a sorus of uredospores.

Uredosorus (L. *uredo,* a blight + *soros,* a heap), a group of uredospores.

Uredospore (L. *uredo,* a blight + spore), a red, one-celled summer spore in the life cycle of the rust fungi.

Vaccination, the injection of vaccine.

Vaccine (L. *vacca,* cow), a suspension of weakened or dead bacteria or other pathogens injected into the body to immunize against the same species of pathogen or their toxins.

Vacuole (L. dimin. of *vacuus,* empty), a watery solution of various substances forming a portion of the protoplast distinct from the protoplasm.

Vascular (L. *vasculum,* a small vessel), referring to any plant tissue or region consisting of or giving rise to conducting tissue, e.g., bundle, cambium, ray.

Vascular bundle, a strand of tissue containing primary xylem and primary phloem (and procambium if present) and frequently enclosed by a bundle sheath of parenchyma or fibers.

Vascular cambium, cambium giving rise to secondary phloem and secondary xylem.

Vector (L. *vehere,* to carry), an organism, usually an insect, which carries and transmits diseasecausing organisms.

Vegetative nucleus, a nucleus not in any active stage of either mitosis or meiosis.

Venation (L. *vena,* a vein), arrangement of veins in leaf blade.

Venter (L. *venter,* the belly), enlarged basal portion of an archegonium in which the egg cell is borne.

Ventral canal cell, the cell just above the egg cell in the archegonium.

Ventral suture (L. *ventralis,* pertaining to the belly), the line of union of the two edges of a carpel.

Vessel (L. *vasculum,* a small vessel), a series of xylem elements whose function is to conduct water and mineral nutrients.

Vessel element, a portion of a vessel derived from a single cell of the vascular cambium or procambium.

Virus (L. *virus,* a poisonous or slimy liquid), a disease principle, probably a submicroscopic organism, which can be cultivated only in living tissues, or in freshly prepared tissue bree.

Vitamins (L. *vita,* life + amine), naturally occurring organic substances, akin to enzymes, necessary in small amounts for the normal metabolism of plants and animals.

Volva (L. *volva,* a wrapper), cup at base of stipe or stalk of fleshy fungi.

Weed (A.S. *wēod,* used at least since 888 in its present meaning), generally an herbaceous plant or shrub not valued for use or beauty, growing wild and rank, and regarded as using ground or hindering the growth of superior vegetation.

Whorl, a circle of flower parts, or of leaves.

Whorled, referring to bud or leaf arrangement in which there are three or more buds or three or more leaves at a node.

Wings, lateral petals of legume type of flower.

Xanthophyll (Gr. *xanthos,* yellowish brown + *phyllon,* leaf), a yellow chloroplast pigment.

Xerophyte (Gr. *xeros,* dry + *phyton,* a plant), a plant very resistant to drought, or which lives in very dry places.

Xylem (Gr. *xylon,* wood), a plant tissue consisting of tracheids, vessels, parenchyma cells, and fibers; wood.

Zoology (Gr. *zoon,* an animal + *logos,* speech), the science having to do with animal life.

Zoosporangium (Gr. *zoon,* an animal + sporangium), a sporangium bearing zoospores.

Zoospore (Gr. *zoon,* an animal + spore), a motile spore.

Zygospore (Gr. *zygon,* a yoke + spore), a thick-walled resistant spore developing from a zygote resulting from the fusion of isogametes.

Zygote (Gr. *zygon,* a yoke), a protoplast resulting from the fusion of gametes (either isogametes or heterogametes).

Zymase (Gr. *zyme,* leaven), an intracellular, sugar-fermenting complex of enzymes.

Index

Abies, 491, 492
Abscission zone, 166–167, 319
Absorption, 148, 150; of solutes, 70–71, 198; of water, 193–198
Abutilon, 517
Acacia, 135, 169, 523
Accessory buds, 85
Accumulation, 71; of solutes, 198
Acer, 157, 270
Acetic acid fermentation, 336
Achene, 264, 269
Achras sapota, 124
Aconitum, 514
Acorn, 265, 270
Adenosine triphosphate, 216, 218
Adhesion, 193
Adnation, 239
Adsorption, 64
Adventitious buds, 85, 152
Adventitious embryo, 256
Adventitious roots, 140
Aecia, 419
Aeciospore, 419
Aeration, effect of, on root growth, 175
Aerial roots, 16, 151, 176
Aerobes, 340
Aerobic respiration, 216–217
Aesculus californica, 88
Agar, 375
Agaricales, 414
Aggregate fruits, 261, 269
Agriculture, 3–6; ancient centers of, 4
Agrobacterium tumefaciens, 340, 344
Ailanthus buds and leaf scars, 86
Air, chambers, 450; of soil, 312
Albugo, 388–393
Alcoholic fermentation, 216, 403
Aleurone layer, 277
Alfalfa stem, 108

Algae, 351–377; blue-green, 346–350; brown, 368–374; classification of, 351–352; distribution and general characteristics of, 351; fossil, 533; golden-brown, 364–368; green, 354–363; red, 374–376; reproduction of 352–354
Algal fungi, 379
Algin, 371
Alkali soils, 32
Allium cepa, 130
Almond, fruit of, 257, 258, 272
Aloe, 106
Alternate buds, 85
Alternate leaf arrangement, 85
Alternation of generations, 362–363, 372, 442; *see also plant group in question*
Amanita muscaria, 415, Plate IV
Amaryllis, 266, 480
Anaerobes, 340
Anaerobic respiration, 216
Anaphase, in meiosis, 290; in mitosis, 78
Anatomy, 10
Anchorage, by rhizoids, 444; by roots, 148, 151
Androecium, 221, 222–223
Anemone, 514
Angiospermae, 81, 503–530; classification, 461, 471, 510, 530; embryo, 507; evolution of, 510, 512; families, 511–530; female gametophyte, 507; flower, 219, 503, 506; gametophyte, 508; life cycle, 506–510; male gametophyte, 506; origin, 535; seed, 275–278, 507, 508; sporophyte, 508, 511–529; summary, 529
Annual rings, 122–123; in roots, 147
Annual herbs, 3
Annular vessels, 103–104
Annulus, of fern sporangium, 482–483; of moss sporangium, 459
Anoda, 515
Anther, 221; development of, 246, 248
Antheridia, 353, 444; *see also plant in question*

Antheridial heads of mosses, 458
Antheridiophores of *Marchantia,* 451
Anthoceros, 327, 454
Anthocerotae, 442, 453–454
Anthocyanin pigments, 58, 68
Antibiotics, 427
Antipodal cells, 232, 507
Apex, of flower bud, 227, 246; of leaf bud, 88, 168; of root, 141; of shoot, 91
Apical meristem, of fern leaves, 479; of roots, 143; of stems, 92; *see also* Bud, Flower, Leaf, Meristems, Root, Stem
Apium graveolens, 166
Apocarpy, 239
Apomixis, 256
Apothecia, 398, 407–410
Appendages, 407
Apple, flower and fruit of, 267, 274
Apricot, buds of, 85
Aralia, 307
Archegonia, 353, 365, 441, 444; *see also* plant in question
Archegonial heads of mosses, 458
Archegoniophores of *Marchantia,* 451
Archeozoic Age, 531
Aril, 493
Artemisia, 524
Ascent of water, 192–193
Asclepias, 265
Ascocarp, 398–400; of lichen, 429
Ascogenous hyphae, 398, 400
Ascogonum, 398, 400
Ascomycetes, 379, 397–412, 429; asexual reproduction, 397, 401, 406; classification, 401; sexual reproduction, 398, 402, 406; summary, 411
Ascorbic acid, 322, 323
Ascospores, 398–399
Ascus, 398–400
Asepsis, 336
Asexual reproduction, 353; Ascomycetes, 397, 401, 406; Basidiomycetes, 417; Bryophyta, 441, 451; Chlorophycophyta, 355, 356, 359, 361; Chrysophycophyta, 364, 367; Filicinae, 480; Lichens, 429; Lycophyta, 465; Phaeophycophyta, 371; Phycomycetes, 385, 389, 394; *see also* plant in question
Ash, 185
Aspergillus, 404, 426
Assimilation, 74
Atabrine, 2
Atmospheric humidity as it affects transpiration rate, 187, 188
ATP, 216, 218
Atropa belladonna, 155
Auricles, 159
Autoecism, 418, 420
Autoradiograms, 320
Autotrophic plants, 325, 351, 379
Auxin, 318
Avena sativa, 244
Avena test, 315–318

Awn, 241, 244
Axial placentation, 229
Axil, 83
Axillary buds, 83
Azotobacter, 344

Bacillarieae, 366–368
Bacillus, 333
Bacillus anthrax, 333; *Fischeri,* 338; *mycoides,* 337
Bacteria, 332–346; and milk particles, spatial relationships of, 334; and plant diseases, 344–345; capsule of, 337; classification of, 340–342; disintegration of by viruses, 433; distribution of, 335; forms of, 333–334; influence of environmental factors on, 340; nonsymbiotic, 344; nutrition of, 336; reproduction of, 338–339; respiration of, 339–340; size of, 334–335; stages in division of, 339; structure of, 336; summary of, 346; symbiotic, 344
Bacterial gummosis, 345
Bacterial nodules, 341
Bacteriology, 332
Bacteriophages, 433
Balance between shoot and root system, 136
Bald cypress, aerial roots of, 176
Banner of pea flower, 237
Barberry, aecia on, 419
Bark, 120–122
Basidia, 412, 414, 418, 423
Basidiocarp, 413, 414–417
Basidiomycetes, 379, 411–426; asexual reproduction, 417; classification, 412, 430; sexual reproduction, 412, 418; summary, 420, 426
Basidiospores, 412, 418
Bauhinia, 522
Bean, plant, 45–49; flower, fruit, 257–260; seed, 277; seedling, 282
Bees as agents of pollination, 251
Beet, root system, 137; seed, 275
Berry, 267, 272
Besseyan system of classification, 510
Beta vulgaris, 275
Big tree (*Sequoiadendron gigantea*), 34
Bignonia, 169
Binomial nomenclature, 35–39
Biological strains of *Puccinia graminis,* 421
Biotic factors, 305, 313
Black locust, stipular spine of, 132
Black stem rust (*Puccinia graminis*), 418–421
Blackberry, fruit of, 263, 269
Bladders of algal thallus, 371
Bladderwort, 171
Blade, of algal thallus, 370; of leaf, 155, 158–159
Bleeding, 194
Blight, fire, of pear, 345; late, of potatoes, 378
Blossom infection by smuts, 423
Blue-green algae, 346–350; characteristics, 346; reproduction, 347; structure, 347
Border parenchyma, 160, 165
Bordered pit, 102, 117

Boron, 181
Botanic gardens, 41
Botanical manuals, 40
Botany, 6–12
Box elder buds and leaf scars, 86
Bracket fungus, 416–417
Bract, floral, 222
Bracts, 244
Branch, gaps, 119; roots, 145–146; stems, 49, 119; traces, 119
Brassica, 38–40, 514
Bread mold (*Rhizopus nigricans*), 393–396
Bremia, 388
Brown algae, 368–374; general characteristics, 368; reproduction, 371; structure, 369
Brown rot fungus, 408–409
Bryophyllum, 169
Bryophyta, 36, 326–327, 441–460; asexual reproduction, 441, 451; classification, 442, 460; embryo, 441; gametophyte, 442, 444, 449, 453, 456; sexual reproduction, 451, 457; sporophyte, 442, 444, 451, 453, 458; summary, 447, 453, 460
Buckeye, buds, 88
Bud, classification, 85–88; definition, 86, 88, 91; development as influenced by growth substances, 318; meristems in, 89; structure, 91–92; *see also bud type in question*
Bud gap, 119
Bud primordia, 92
Bud scales, 83, 88, 170
Bud traces, 119
Budding of yeast, 401
Bud-scale scars, 83
Bulbs, 128, 131, 171
Bundle, scars, 83; sheath, 106
Bundles, carpellary, of fruit, 260, 270; closed and open, 104–107; of leaf, 165; vascular, 100
Buttercup, apex of flower, 249; apex of shoot, 168; flower and fruit of, 519

Cacti, 134
Calcium, 180
Callose, 101, 117
Calyptra, of *Marchantia*, 452; of moss, 459
Calyx, 221
Cambium, 95, 109–111; cork, 95, 110, 118, 121–122; fascicular, 108; interfascicular, 109; stages in differentiation of, 112; vascular, of stem, 95, 101–102, 110–111; vascular, of root, 147
Canna, 157
Capillary movement of water in soil, 196
Caprification, 253
Capsicum frutescens, 222
Capsule, 261–263, 266; bacterial, 337; dehiscence of in *Riccia*, 447; in ferns, 482
Carbohydrates, 59–60, 206; conduction of, 199–200; fermentation of, 403; manufacture of, 72–73, 205–206; respiration of, 74, 214; storage of, 278–279
Carbon, 178
Carbon dioxide, effect on growth, 311; in photo-synthesis, 73, 203–204, 212; in respiration, 74, 215; reduction of, 207
Carotenes, 56
Carotenoids, 56, 347, 354
Carpel, 221, 225–228; as a floral leaf, 228; development of, 226–227
Carpel primordia, 226, 227
Carpel wall, 258
Carpogonium of *Polysiphonia*, 376
Carpospores of *Polysiphonia*, 377
Carrot, chromoplasts, 55; flower and fruit, 524; stages in development of branch root, 146
Caruncle, 277
Caryopsis, 264
Casparian strip, 145
Castilla elastica, 135
Castor bean, seed, 277; seedling, 283
Catalpa, 84
Catalysts, 72
Catkin, 250
Causal agent, 344
Celery petiole, 166
Cell, 10, 50–80; parts, 51–61; physiology, 61–75; plate, 79; stages in growth, 57; types, 95–104
Cell sap, 57–58
Cell wall, 51, 59–61, 65; composition and structure of, 59–61
Cellulose, uses, 60; in cell wall, 59–60
Centaurea cineraria, 191
Central body, 347
Central cylinder of moss gametophyte, 457
Central placentation, 229
Chalaza, 276
Chaparral, 22, 28
Charophycophyta, 36
Cherry flower, 241
Chiasma, 290, 292
Chicken pox, 435
Chitin, 332, 381
Chlamydomonas, 356–357
Chlamydospores, 383
Chlorella, 355, 356
Chlorenchyma, 99
Chlorophycophyta, 354–363; asexual reproduction, 355, 356, 359, 361; classification, 373; sexual reproduction, 357, 359, 361, 362; summary, 363
Chlorophyll, 55–56, 154, 347, 354; absorption spectrum, 209; *c*, 366, 368; *d*, 374; function of, 208–210; kinds of, 56
Chloroplasts, 55–56, 154, 208–209; of algae, 354; of guard cells, 161; pigments of, 55–56
Chlorosis, 213, 437
Chromatids, 77, 289
Chromatin, 51
Chromoplasm, 347
Chromoplasts, 56
Chromosomes, 54, 76, 286, 539; homologous, 288
Chroococcus, 348
Chrysanthemum, 309, 524
Chrysophycophyta, 352, 364–368; asexual repro-

duction, 364, 367; classification, 373; sexual reproduction, 365, 368
Chytridiales, 383–384
Chytrids, 383–384
Cilia, 365
Cinchona, 2
Citrus sinensis, 256, 273
Cladodes, 132
Cladophora, 361–362
Cladophylls, 132
Class, 36
Classification, 33–44, 330; Angiospermae, 461, 478, 530, 570; Ascomycetes, 401; Bryophyta, 442, 460; characters used in, 37–38, 324–330; Chlorophycophyta, 373; Chrysophycophyta, 373; Filicinae, 461, 478; Gymnospermae, 461, 478, 502, 491–494, 530; Lycophyta, 461, 463, 477; natural, 37, 324; Phaeophycophyta, 373; Phycomycetes, 396; Psilophyta, 461, 477; Rhodophycophyta, 373; Sphenophyta, 461, 477
Claviceps, 409–411
Clay, 172
Cleistothecium, 398, 404, 407
Clematis, 235, 514
Climate, 19
Climatic factors, 172, 305, 306–311
Clone, 252
Closed bundles, 105
Clostridium, 344
Clostridium botulinum, 341; *tetani*, 341
Clover flower, 33
Club fungi, 412–426
Club mosses, 463–473
Cluster cups, 419
Coal, 531
Coalescence, 237–239
Coccus forms of bacteria, 333
Cocklebur fruit, 280
Coenocytic, 365, 382, 383
Coenogamete, 395
Coenopteridales, **485**
Coenozoic, 533
Cohesion and transpiration-pull theory, 192–193
Coleoptile, 278; of oats, experiments with, 316–318
Coleorhiza, 278
Coleus, variegated leaves of, 210
Collenchyma, 98–99
Colloids, 53
Columbine, 514
Columella, of moss sporangium, 459; of *Rhizopus nigricans*, 394
Companion cells, 100–101
Compositae, 523–525
Composite flower, 243–244
Conceptacles, 373
Conduction, by roots, 148; by stems, 82, 133, 192–193, 198–200; of foods, 199–200; of mineral salts, 198–199
Cone, 467, 486, 490–495; *see also plant in question*
Conidia, 383, 397, 429

Conidiophores, 383, 397
Conidiosporangia, 390
Conidiospores, 390, 397; formation, 398; *see also plant in question*
Coniferales, 81, 491–502
Coniferous forests, 27
Conifers, 81, 491–502
Conjugation, 79, 353, 411
Conjugation tube in *Spirogyra*, 359
Conk, 417
Contour tillage, 151
Contractile vacuoles, 357
Convolvulus arvensis, roots, 152
Copper, 183
Cork, 50, 118, 121, 147
Cork cambium, 118, 121; of root, 147; of stem, 95, 118; origin of, 110, 118
Corm, 131
Corn (*Zea mays*), commercial hybrid, 300–302; flower, 242, 245; inflorescence, 229; leaf, 159; smutted kernels, 422; stem, 106–107
Corolla, 221
Cortex, of moss gametophyte, 457; of potato tuber, 129; of root, 144–145; of stem, 94, 97–100
Cotton, 517
Cotyledon, 224
Cotyledons, 48, 276–278, 282, 501
Cover cells, 445
Crepis, fertilization and embryo development, 505
Cross-pollination, 252
Cross section of wood, 111, 113, 115, 116
Crossing over, 290, 291–293
Crown gall, 345
Cruciferae, 514
Crystals, 52, 58–59
Cucurbita, 101–102, 521
Cucurbitaceae, 520, 521
Cup fungi, 408
Cupressus macrocarpa, 34
Curly top, 431
Cuticle, of leaf, 160; of leaf as it affects rate of transpiration, 188; of stem, 97
Cutin, 59–60, 97
Cuttings, 152, 318
Cyathea, 480
Cycle, organic acid, 217
Cydonia oblonga, 242
Cyme, 231
Cystocarp of *Polysiphonia*, 377
Cystolith, 189
Cytokinesis, 75, 79
Cytology, 10
Cytoplasm, 51, 54–57
Cytoplasmic membrane, 52, 65

Dahlia, 246, 524
Damping off, 389
Dandelion, fruit of, 280
Darlingtonia, 169
Darwin, 316; and evolution, 537
Datura stramonium, 266

Daucus carota, 55, 146, 524
Day length, effect on growth, 308–310
Decay, 343
Deciduous forests, 26–28
Deciduous plants, 15
Dehiscence, 261
Dehiscent fruit, 263–265
Delphinium, 514
Denitrification, 343
Desert, 30–31
Diagrams, floral, 248
Dianthus, 231
Diatomaceous earth, 367
Diatoms, 366–368
Dicentra, parietal placentation in, 228
Dicotyledonae, 81, 513–526; comparison with Monocotyledonae, 526; flower, 216; herbaceous, 91, 107–109; leaf, 155–158; root, 136; stem, 83–89, 96–105, 111–116, 117–119
Differentiation, 304; of tissues, 92, 110–112
Diffuse porous wood, 115
Diffusion, 63–64, 66–70; gradient, 185–186, 188; pressure, 64
Digestion, 73; in seeds, 278
Digestive enzymes, 74
Digitalis, 155
Dihybrid cross, 298–299
Dikaryon, 399
Dioecious plant, 234, 457
Dionaea muscipula, 171, Plate II
Diploid, 288, 362
Disease, 344
Dissemination of seeds and fruits, 281
Dominant characters, 296
Dormant buds, 85
Dorsal suture, 226
Douglas fir, 492, 494
Downy mildews, 389–393
Drosera, 171
Drupe, 267
Duckweed, 16
Dust Bowl, 29

Echinops exaltatus, 246
Ecklonia maxima, 371
Ectocarpus, 369, 371–372, 441; life history of, 371, 372
Edaphic factors, 172, 304, 311–313
Efficiency of leaf in utilizing sun's energy, 208
Egg cell, 232, 353; *see also plant in question*
Elements essential for plant growth, 177, 183
Elodea, 51
Embryo, 48, 275–278, 281; adventitious, 256; Angiospermae, 275–278, 507; Bryophyta, 441; Filicinae, 485; Gymnospermae, 489, 500; Lycophyta, 467, 472; Phaeophycophyta, 373; Sphenophyta, 476; *see also plant in question*
Embryo sac, 230–234, 276–278; mother cell, 231; stages in development of, 230–231
Emulsion, 53
Endocarp, 258, 267

Endodermis, 144
Endomycetales, 401
Endosperm, 232, 276–278, 507; mother cell, 232; primary cell, 232; primary nucleus, 232
Energy, 202, 208; released by respiration, 215–218; stored in photosynthesis, 207; utilized in photosynthesis, 208
Environmental factors, influencing absorption, 195–198; influencing growth, 304–314; influencing photosynthesis, 211; influencing transpiration, 187–188
Enzymes, 72, 210, 214, 315
Epiblast, 278
Epicotyl, 277
Epidermal hairs, 97, 100, 163, 191
Epidermis, 96; of leaf, 160–164; of moss gametophyte, 457; of root, 143–144; of stem, 92, 96–97
Epigyny, 239
Epiphytes, 151
Equatorial plane, 78
Equisetum, 327, 473–476
Ergastic substances, 51–52, 57–59
Ergot, 409, 411
Erosion, methods of checking, 151
Erwinia amylovora, 344, 345, 346
Erysiphales, 401
Erysiphe, 406–408
Erythroxylon coca, 155
Escherichia coli, 338
Espalier, 87
Etiolation, 307
Euascomycetae, 401
Eubacteriales, 341–342
Euglenoids, 35
Euglenophycophyta, 35
Eumycophyta, 379, 380–430; general characteristics, 185, 192, 380
Evergreens, 15
Evolution, 531–542; and Darwin, 537; mechanism of, 538–542; organic, 531
Exine, 504
Exoascales, 401
Exocarp, 258, 267
"Eyes" of potato, 130

F_1, F_2, 295
False indusium, 482–483
Family, 35; form, 426
Fascicle of pine leaves, 491
Fascicular cambium, 108
Fats, 279
Female gamete (egg), 232, 353; *see also plant in question*
Fermentation, alcoholic, 403
Fern, 328, 478–486; gametophyte of, 484–485; seed, 487–488; sporophyte, 479, 484–485; staghorn, 26; tree, 480
Fertilization, 79, 219, 255–256, 281, 286, 353, 447; combination of genes, 296; double, 255, 507; effect of on fruit formation, 255; tube, 387; *see also plant in question*

Fibers, 98–100; cotton, 65; phloem, 101, 117; tractile, 77, 116; xylem, 104

Fibrous root system, 139

Ficus carica, 264

Ficus elastica leaf, 189

Ficus indica aerial roots, 151

Field capacity of soil, 173

Fig, pollination of, 253

Filament of anther, 221

Filicales, 478–486

Filicinae, 478–485; asexual reproduction, 480; classification, 461, 478; embryo, 485; gametophyte, 484, 508; sexual reproduction, 481; sporophyte, 479, 508; summary, 485

Fir, Douglas, 492

Fire blight of pear, 345

Firs, 492

Fission, 325, 331

Fission plants, 324, 331–350; classification, 350

Fixation of nitrogen, 343–344

Flagellum, 338

Floral diagram, 248

Floral tube, 269

Floras, botanical, 41

Floret, 241, 244

Flower, 219–256, 503; buds, 85, 88; coalescence, 237–239; complete, 234; composite, 243–244; cyclic, 236; development of, 246; diagram of, 244–248, 504; disk, 243; elevation of parts of, 239–240; epigynous, 239; essential organs of, 222; evolution of, 510–511; formula, 243–248; grass, 240–242; hermaphroditic, 234; hypogynous, 239; imperfect, 234; incomplete, 234; infections by smuts, 422–424; irregular, 237; morphological nature, 225–228; morphology of, 221–246; perfect, 234; perianth of, 222; perigynous, 239; pistillate, 234; primordia of, 226, 227, 249; ray, 243; regular, 237; spiral arrangement of parts of, 236; staminate, 234; symmetry of, 237; union of parts of, 237; whorled, 236; *see also plant in question*

Follicle, 263–265

Fomes applanatus, 416

Food, 74; conduction of, 133, 199–200; storage in roots, 151–152; storage in seeds, 278–279; storage in stems, 133–134

Foot, of *Anthoceros*, 454; of fern, 485; of *Marchantia*, 452; of *Selaginella*, 472

Forests, 23–28

Fossils, 461, 532–535; Algae, 533; Filicinae, 485; Gymnospermae, 488; Lycophyta, 463, 472; *Metasequoia*, 462, 533, 534; Psilophyta, 462; Sequoia, 462

Fragaria, 131–132, 238, 262, 519

Fragmentation, 353, 371

Free central placentation, 229

Freesia, 528

Fructose, 206

Fruit, 219, 257, 503, 510; aggregate, 261–262, 263, 269; classification, 261; definition of, 257; dehiscent, 263; development, 257–260; development influenced by growth substances, 319; dissemination, 279–281; dry, 263–267; fleshy, 267; indehiscent, 264; kinds, 261–273; multiple, 261, 264, 270; parthenocarpic, 260–261; seedless, 260–261; simple, 261, 263–268; summary of, 271; *see also plant in question*

Fruitfulness and sterility, 252

Fuchsia, axial placentation in, 229

Fucoxanthin, 366, 368

Fucus, 373–376

Funaria, 456, 457, 459

Fungi Imperfecti, 379, 424, 426–427

Funiculus, 226, 276

Fusarium rot on peach, 381

Fusiform initials, 110

Gaillardia, 524

Gametangium, 353

Gamete, 232, 353

Gametophyte, 372, 441, 442; Angiospermae, 508; Bryophyta, 442, 444, 449, 453, 456; Filicinae, 484, 508; Gymnospermae, 508; Lycophyta, 467; Phaeophycophyta, 372; Rhodophycophyta, 377; Sphenophyta, 475

Gametophyte, female, 469; Angiospermae, 507; Gymnospermae, 508; Lycophyta, 469

Gametophyte, male, 469; Angiospermae, 506; Gymnospermae, 489; Lycophyta, 469

Gaps, branch and leaf, 119

Garlic, 131

Geiger-Müller counter, 179

Gemmae, 441, 449, 451

Gene, 54, 286, 296; mutations, 539; segregation, 290–293

Genera, 35; form, 426

Generations, 295

Generative nucleus, 223

Genetic map of corn chromosomes, 539

Genetic variations, 538

Genetics, 293–302; application of, 300

Genotype, 298

Genus, 35; form, 426

Geologic history of plants, 531–535

Germ tube, 390

Germination, pollen grain, 254; seed, 281

Gill fungi, stages in development of, 416

Gills of mushroom, 414, 415

Ginkgo biloba, 487

Ginkgoales, 487–489

Girdling of stems, 192, 199

Gladiolus, 528; corm of, 131

Glucose, product of photosynthesis, 206; structural formula, 206; utilization, 214–218

Glumes, 241, 244

Glycogen, 347

Glycolysis, 215, 403

Gooseberry, 272

Gossypium, 65, 166, 239, 515

Grain, 264, 269; of wheat, 269, 284

Gramineae, 526

Grana, 208

Grass, flower, 240; leaves, 158–160
Grasslands, 28–30
Green algae, 351–363
Ground meristem, 92; of root, 143; of stem, 92–93
Ground pine, 464
Groups of plants, 324–330
Growth, 79, 303; as influenced by biotic factors, 313; as influenced by carbon dioxide, 311; as influenced by light, 306, 316–318; as influenced by soil moisture, 197; as influenced by temperature, 306; correlation of, 314, 323; environmental factors affecting, 304–314; intercalary, 107; mineral elements necessary for, 177–183; of a cell, 304; primary, 92–109; secondary, 109–118
Growth curvatures, 316–318
Growth regulators, 318–320
Guard cells, 97, 161
Gum, 124, 125
Guttation, 190–191
Gymnospermae, 81, 486–502; classification, 461, 478, 491–494, 502, 530; embryo, 500; female gametophyte, 496; gametophyte, 508; leaf, 160, 488–494; male gametophyte, 497; seed, 486, 487, 488, 501, 508; stem, 116; sexual reproduction, 488; sporophyte, 487, 491–496, 508; strobilus, 486, 495; summary, 502
Gynoecium, 221, 224–234

Hairs, epidermal, 97, 160, 163
Halophytes, 70
Haploid, 288, 362
Haustoria, 382, 389
Head (type of inflorescence), 243, 246, 250
Heartwood, 116, 124–125
Helianthus annuus, 247, 269
Helleborus, 224, 265
Hemlocks, 492
Hemp, 151
Hepaticae, 327, 442, 443–453
Herbaceous plants, stems of, 107–109
Herbaria, 41
Herbicides, 319
Herbs, 3
Hereditary factors, 306
Hermaphroditic flowers, 234
Hesperidium, 267, 273
Heterobasidiomycetes, 417–426
Heterocyst, 347
Heteroecism, 418, 420
Heterogamete, 353
Heterogamy, 353, 357
Heterospory, 469, 472, 482
Heterothallic, 395, 412
Heterotrophic plants, 325, 378, 418
Heterozygous plants, 296
Hevea brasiliensis, 125, 135
Hexose sugars, 206
Hibiscus, 517
Hilum, 276–277
Histology, 10

Holdfast, 360, 370, 373
Holdfast cell in *Ulothrix,* 360
Holy Fire, 409
Homobasidiomycetes, 413–416
Homologous chromosomes, 288
Homospory, 469; in ferns, 482
Homothallic, 412
Homozygous, 296, 302
Honey locust, stem thorns of, 132
Hooke, Robert, 50
Hordeum vulgare, 159, 243
Hormogonia, 347
Hormones, 315–322; discovery of, 315; flowering, 320
Horsetails, 473–476
Host plant, 344, 379
Humidity of atmosphere, as it affects growth, 310; as it affects transpiration rate, 187
Humus of soil, 173
Hyaloplasm, 51
Hybridization, 541
Hybrids, 294–299, 301
Hydathodes, 191
Hydrogen, 178
Hydrophytes, 200
Hymenium, 398
Hymenium layer, 399, 414
Hyoscyamus, 308
Hyphae, 381
Hypocotyl, 277, 501
Hypocreales, 401
Hypogyny, 239

Imbibition, 64, 192–193
Imperfect fungi, 426–427
Imperfect stage, 420
Incubation period, 439
Indehiscent, 261, 264
Indian pipe (*Monotropa*), 17
Indusium, 482–483
Inferior ovary, 240
Inflorescences, 246–251
Infrared, 208
Inheritance, 285–302; Mendelian, 293–302
Inorganic salts, accumulation, 198
Insect pollination, 251
Insect transmission of virus, 438, 439
Insectivorous plants, 170, Plate II
Integument, 230, 276, 496
Intercalary meristem, 107
Intercellular space, 99
Interfascicular cambium, 109
Internode, 49, 83
Intine, 504
Involucre, 222
Ions, 62
Iridaceae, 527–528
Iris, 528
Iron, 180
Isogamete, 353, 395
Isogamy, 353, 357

Jansen, 50
Joshua tree, 90
Juglans regia, 236, 271
Juniper (*Juniperus*), 328, 493, 494

Karyogamy, 399
Karyolymph, 51
Keel of pea flower, 237
Kelp, 353, 370–373
Keys, botanical, 41
Kinetochore, 77, 287
Knot, 120
Krebs cycle, 217

Labiatae, 518
Lamella, middle, 59, 79
Lamina, 155
Laminariales, 372–374
Larches, 492
Larix, 492, 495
Late blight of potato, 378
Latent bud, 85
Lateral buds, 86
Lateral roots, origin of, 145–146
Latex, 124, 135
Latex tubes, 135
Lathyrus, 522
Leaf, 45; abscission, 166–168; axil, 83; curl, 403; dicotyledonous, 155–158; external morphology, 155–160; floral, 219; function, 154; gaps, 119; gymnosperm, 160, 488–494; modification, 169–171; monocotyledonous, 158–160; origin, 168; primary tissues, 161–166; primitive, 486; scars, 83; sun and shade, 307; venation of, 156; *see also plant in question*
Leaf, primordia, 92; scars, 83; spines, 169
Legume, 261, 263
Leguminosae, 520–522
Lemma, 241, 244
Lemna, 16
Lenticels, 118–119
Lepidodendrales, 463, 472
Leucoplasts, 56
Libocedrus decurans, 120
Lichens, 427–430
Life cycle, 285–292, 352–354, 362; of bean, 45–49; *see also plant in question*
Light, composition of, 207; duration of, 309; effect on growth, 306; effect on rate of photosynthesis, 212; effect on rate of transpiration, 188; in photosynthesis, 207–208; quality of, 308
Lignification, 99
Lignin, 59–60, 99; waste in paper making, 126
Ligule, 159
Liliaceae, 526
Lilium, 237; *tigrinum,* 222, 240; *regale,* 262
Lily embryo sac, 231, 232–234
Linked characters, 539
Linnaeus, 39
Linum usitatissimum, 102
Liriodendron tulipifera, 220, 514

Little leaf of peach, 181
Liverwort, 442, 443–453
Lizard's tail flower, 235
Loam, 123
Locule, 228
Lodicule, 241, 244, 527
Long-day plants, 309
Lumen, 100
Lunaria annua, 268
Lycopersicon, 260, 516
Lycophyta, 328–330, 461, 463–473; asexual reproduction, 465; classification, 461, 463, 477; embryo, 467, 472; female gametophyte, 469; gametophyte, 467; male gametophyte, 469; sexual reproduction, 466; sporophyte, 464, 468; strobilus, 467, 469; summary, 476
Lycopodium, 463, 464–468

Macronutrient elements necessary for plant growth, 177–180
Magnesium, 180
Magnolia buds, 89, 221, 265
Magnolia grandiflora, 514
Magnoliaceae, 513
Maiden-hair tree, 487
Malope, 515
Malus sylvestris, 274
Malvaceae, 515, 517
Manganese, 181
Manihot, 135
Manuals, botanical, 41
Maple, fruit, 270; leaf, 157
Marchantia, 449–453
Marsileaceae, 482
Maté, 155
Matthiola incana, 268
Medicago sativa, 108
Megasporangia, 469; Angiospermae, 506; pine, 495; *Selaginella,* 469
Megaspore, 469; Angiospermae, 231, 506; mother cell, 231; pine, 496; *Selaginella,* 469
Megasporophylls, of Angiospermae, 506; of *Selaginella,* 469
Meiosis, 79, 219, 231, 286–293
Meiospores, 79, 288, 353; *see also plant in question*
Membranes, cytoplasmic, 54–55; differentially permeable, 64; living, 68–70; nonliving, 66–68; nuclear, 51, 54; permeable, 65
Mendel, 294–300
Mendelian inheritance, 294–300; important features, 294
Meristems, apical, 48; cork cambium, 95; fascicular cambium, 108; ground, 92; intercalary, 107; interfascicular cambium, 109; primary, in leaves, 168, 479; primary, in roots, 141–143; primary, in stems, 91–95; procambium, 92; protoderm, 92; secondary, in roots, 147; secondary, in stems, 95, 109–110, 118; vascular cambium, 95
Mesembryanthemum, 171
Mesocarp, 258, 267

Mesophyll of leaf, 162–164
Mesophytes, 200
Mesozoic, 533
Metaphase, in meiosis, 290; in mitosis, 77
Metasequoia, 533; distribution of, 462
Micrococcus, 349
Microfibrils, 64
Micrographia, facsimile reproduction from, 50
Microns, 334
Micronutrient chemical elements, 180–183
Micropylar chamber, 497
Micropyle, 230, 276, 277, 497
Microscope, electron, 432
Microsporangia, Angiospermae, 506; pine, 495; *Selaginella,* 469
Microspore, Angiospermae, 223, 506; pine, 495; *Selaginella,* 469
Microspore mother cell, Angiospermae, 506; pine, 495; *Selaginella,* 469
Microsporophylls, Angiospermae, 506; pine, 495; *Selaginella,* 469
Middle lamella, 59, 79
Mildews, downy, 389; powdery, 406–408
Mimosa, 521
Minerals, absorption, 198; essential elements, 177–183; conduction, 198–199; deficiency, Plate III*b;* in photosynthesis, 213; in soil, 172–173
Mitochondria, 52, 56–57
Mitosis, 75–79; and meiosis, 79; bacteria, 337; review of, 287
Mixed buds, 85, 89
Mnium, 455, 457, 458
Molds, blue and green, 405; water, 384
Molecules, 62
Molybdenum, 183
Moniliales, 426
Monocots and dicots compared, 526
Monocotyledonae, 81, 224–250; leaf, 158–160; stems, 89–91, 105–107
Monoecious plant, 234
Monohybrid cross, 294–298
Monotropa, 17
Monsoon forest, 26
Monterey cypress, 34
Morchella, 408
Morels, 408
Morning-glory rhizome, 129
Morphological factors as they affect transpiration, 185–191
Morphology, 10
Mosaic diseases, 435–439; of sugar beet, 436; of tobacco, 436
Mosses, 327, 442, 455–460
Mucilaginous substances, 135
Mucorales, 393–396
Multiple fruit, 273
Musci, 327, 442, 455–460
Mushroom, 413–417
Mutations, 539–541, Plate III*a*
Mycelium, 381–382
Mycology, 380

Mycorrhiza, 314
Myriophyllum, 16
Myxomycophyta, 379, 380–381

Naked buds, 88
Naming and classification of plants, 33–44
Natural classification, 37, 324
Natural selection, 537
Neck canal, 446
Needles of pine, 491
Nematode, 427
Nepenthes, 171
Netted venation, 156
Niacin (nicotinic acid), 321
Nicotiana tabacum, 209, 516
Nitrates, 62, 70, 174, 179, 343
Nitrification, 343
Nitrobacter, 343
Nitrobacteriaceae, 342
Nitrogen, 179, 342; cycle, 342–344; fixation, 343–344
Nitrogenous fertilizers, 344
Nitrosomonas, 343
Node, 49, 83; anatomy of, 119–120
Nodules, bacterial, 341, 344
Nomenclature, 38
Nonseptate hyphae, 383
Nonsymbiotic bacteria, 344
Nostoc, 349
Nucellus, 229, 281, 497
Nuclear membrane, 51
Nuclear nets, 54
Nuclear sap, 54
Nucleic acid, 347, 433
Nucleolus, 51, 54
Nucleoproteins, 54
Nucleus, 53–54; Angiospermae life cycle, 505–508; ascus and ascocarp, 399; bacteria, 337; basidium, 412, 421; blue-green algae, 347; egg, 232, 353; embryo sac, 230–234; evolution, 539; fertilization, 79, 219, 255–256, 447; inheritance, 293–300; meiosis, 287–290; mitosis, 75–79; pollen, 232; pollen tube, 223, 497; sperm, 223, 233, 353; vegetative 53–54
Nut, 265
Nutrient solution, 177; macronutrient elements, 177–180; micronutrient elements, 180–183

Oak, acorn, 265; wood, 114–115
Oat coleoptile, 278, 316–318
Obligate anaerobes, 340
Oenothera, 242
Oil, 17; algae, 364
Olive disease caused by boron deficiency, 181
Onion, bulb, 131; "top" or "tree," 131
Onoclea sensibilis, 499
Oogamy, 353
Oogonium, 353; *Albugo,* 392; *Fucus,* 373; *Pythium,* 391; *Saprolegnia,* 386; *Vaucheria,* 365
Oospore, 353; *Albugo,* 393; *Saprolegnia,* 388; *Vaucheria,* 365

Open bundles, 105
Operculum of moss sporangium, 459
Opposite buds, 85
Opuntia (cactus), stems of, 132
Orange flower and fruit, 273
Orchidaceae, 527–529
Order, 37
Organism, 303
Organs, 45
Oscillatoria, 348–349
Osmometer, 66
Osmosis, 67–68
Osmotic pressure, 68; of guard cells, 161, 257–258
Ovary, 221, 224–229; inferior, 240; superior, 240;
    see also Carpel, Gynoecium, Pistil
Ovulate cone of pine, 495
Ovule, 222, 229–232, 275, 509; Angiospermae, 222,
    229–232, 255, 486, 509; Gymnospermae, 486,
    489, 495, 501; pine, 495, 501
Oxidation, 74, 214–217
Oxygen, 178; and respiration, 215; end product of
    photosynthesis, 205

Paeonia californica, 77, 514
Palea, 241, 244
Paleozoic Age, 533
Paleozoic forest, 536
Palm, stem characteristics, 90; pollination, 236
Pandanus, 151
Panicle, 240, 250
Paper, 126–127
Pappus, 244
Parallel venation, 156, 158
Paraphyses, 373, 398; in mosses, 458
Parasite, 336, 379
Parenchyma, 97–99, 100; border, 165; palisade,
    164; spongy, 164; xylem, 104, 116
Parietal placentation, 229
Parkinsonia, 169
Parthenium argentatum, 135
Parthenocarpy, 260–261
Parthenocissus quinquefolia, 156
Parthenogenesis, 256
Pasteurization, 340
"Patanas," 29
Pathogenic, 379
Pathology, 380
Pea, carpel development, 226, 228; irregular flower,
    238
Peach yellows, 438
Pectates, 59
Pedicel, 250
Pellonia chloroplasts, 55
Penicillin, 427–428
Penicillium, 403–405, 426, 428
Pepo, 267
Perennials, 129
Perfect flower, 234
Perfect stage, 426
Perianth, 222
Pericarp, 258, 261

Pericycle, 145
Periderm, 118; of potato tuber, 130
Peridium, 399, 400
Perigyny, 239
Perisperm, 256, 501
Peristome of moss sporangium, 459
Perithecium, 398, 409–411
Permanent wilting, 196
Permeable membrane, 64
Permeability, 64–71
Peronospora, 391, 392
Peronosporales, 389–393
Persimmon, plasmodesmata in endosperm, 60
Petals, 221; primordia, 227
Petiole, 155, 158; anatomy, 166; modified, 169
Petunia, 238, 240, 517
Peziza, 399, 407, 410
Phaeophycophyta, 352, 368–374
Phaseolus vulgaris, 259
Phelloderm, 118
Phellogen (cork cambium), 110; of root, 147; of
    stem, 118
Phenotype, 298
Phloem, conduction in, 199; internal, 130; of leaf,
    165; primary, of root, 145; primary, of stem,
    100–101, 106; ray, 94, 113; secondary, of root,
    147; secondary, of stem, 95, 117
Phoenix dactylifera, 236
Phosphates, 210
Phosphorus, 179, 215
Phosphorylation, 215, 216
Photinia, 165
Photoperiod, 309
Photosynthesis, 202–213; chemical reaction, 203;
    chlorophyll in, 208–210; efficiency of, 208; en-
    zymes in, 210; external factors, 211–213; inter-
    nal factors, 211; light in, 207–208; phosphorus
    in, 210; principal aspects, 203; products of, 205–
    207; rate of, 211–212; raw materials, 203–205
Phototropism, 316
Phycocyanin, 332, 347, 374
Phycoertherin, 332, 374
Phycomycetes, 379, 383–396; significant features,
    396
Phyla, 34–37, 324–330; characteristics, 36; chart
    showing possible relationships, 329; of plants in
    relation to geological age, 532
Physiology, defined, 11, 61; of cell, 61–75; of
    flower, 251–256; of leaf, 154; of root, 136, 148–
    153; of seed, 278–279; of stem, 133–135
Physoderma zeae-maydis, 384
Phytomonas, 344
Phytophthora, 378, 388–390, 392
Phytoplankton, 351
Picea, 492, 493
Pierce's disease, of grapes, 439
Pigments, anthocyanins, 58; plastid, 55–56
Pileus, 414
Pinaceae, 491–493
Pine, 495–502; classification, 491; cones, 495–496;
    female gametophyte, 496; fertilization, 498;

leaves, 491; male gametophyte, 497; pollen, 495; pollination, 497; resin canals, 117; seed, 501; sugar pine, 479; wood, 103, 113

Pinus, 491–493; *cubensis*, 125; *halepensis*, 496; *jeffreyi*, 490; *lambertiana*, 490; *monophylla*, 491; *murrayana*, 490; *palustris*, 125; *ponderosa*, 490

Pistil, 221, 225

Pistillate flower, 234

Pisum sativum, 224, 228, 259

Pitcher plant, 169

Pith, 92, 104; rays, 94, 104

Pits, 98; bordered, 102, 117; canals, 98–99; membrane, 102; pair, 102; simple, 102

Pitted vessels, 103

Placenta, 226

Placentation types, 228–229

Plankton, 351

Plant body, form, 47; development, 48; functions of principal organs, 45–48; of fungi, 381; of seed plants, 45–49; primary, of stems, 92–109; secondary, of stems, 109–124

Plantain, capsule, 266

Plants, breeding, 300; classification according to water needs, 200; classification and naming, 33–40; distribution, 19–32; fission, 331; form of body, 15–16, 45–49, 325; geologic history, 531; groups, 324; harmful, 19; indicator, 32; insectivorous, 171; native and alien, 31; sciences, 9–12; seed-bearing and non-seed-bearing, 17; size, 15; succulent, 134; useful, 18

Plasma membrane, 59

Plasmodesmata, 60–61

Plasmodium, 380

Plasmogamy, 399

Plasmolemma, 65

Plasmolysis, 69–70

Plasmopara, 389, 390

Plastids, 52, 55–56

Plate, cell, 79

Platycerium andinum, 26

Pleurococcus, 355

Plywood, 125–126

Pneumococcus, 333

Pod, 261, 263, 264

Podophyllum peltatum, 76

Polar nuclei, 232

Pollen grains, 223; germination, 254–255; of pine, 495

Pollen mother cells, 223

Pollen tube, 223, 254; of pine, 498

Pollinating agents, 251–252

Pollination, 219, 223, 251–255, 497; artificial, 253; close, 252; cross, 252; in pines, 497; insect, 251; of fig, 253; self-, 252; types of, 252; wind, 251

Pollinia, 529

Polypetalous, 239

Polyploidy, 542

Polypodium, 328

Polysiphonia, 377

Polytrichum, 457

Pome, 267, 274

Poppy, capsule, 266

Populus deltoides, 156; leaves of, 155

Pore, fungus, 416, 417; spaces in soil, 173, 175

Potassium, 180

Potato, seedling of, 129; tuber of, 129–130

Powdery mildews, 406–407

Prairie, 21

Preharvest drop, as influenced by growth substances, 319

Pressure, atmospheric, 68; diffusion, 64; osmotic, 68; turgor, 66, 69; wall, 69

Primary endosperm cell, 232

Primary endosperm nucleus, 232

Primary meristems, 91–95, 141–143, 168, 479

Primary root, 139

Primary tissues, 96–109

Primary wall, 59

Primary xylem, of stem, 102–104; of root, 145

Primordia, 89, 93; flower, 226–227, 249; leaf, 168

Procambium, cells, 94; of root, 143; of stem, 92

Proembryo of pine, 500

Prop roots, 151

Propagation, by means of roots, 158; by means of stems, 318–319

Prophase, in meiosis, 289, 290; in mitosis, 76

Proplastid, 57

Proteins, 53, 279; stored in seeds, 279

Proterozoic Age, 533

Prothallia of ferns, 484

Prothallial cell of male gametophyte of *Selaginella*, 469

Protoascomycetae, 401

Protoderm, of root, 143; of stem, 92–93

Protonema of moss, 456

Protoplasm, 10, 51, 52–57; properties of, 52–53

Protoplast, 51, 52–59

Prunus, amygdalus, 258; *armeniaca*, 241; *avium*, 241

Psalliota campestris, 414

Pseudotsuga, 492, 494

Psilophyta, 328–330, 461, 462–463

Psilophytales, 535

Psilotaceae, 462

Psilotum, 326, 462; stem of, 463, 464

Pteridium, 482

Pteridospermales, 487

Pterophyta, 328–330, 461, 478–530, 508

Puccinia graminis, 418–421

Puffballs, 413

Pure line, 252

Pusztas, 29

Pyracantha, thorns of, 132

Pyrenoids, 354

Pyridoxine, 321

Pyrrophycophyta, 36

Pyruvic acid, 216

Pythium, 388, 389, 392

Quarter-sawed wood, 124

Quercus, 112, 270; *suber*, 122; *borealis*, 114–115; *lobata*, 156

Quillworts, 36
Quinine, 2

Raceme, 249
Rachilla, 241
Rachis, 158, 480
Radial section of wood, 111, 115, 117
Radicle, 48, 139, 276–278; of pine embryo, 501
Radioactive tracers in the study of conduction, 198
Radish, root tip of, 141
Rafflesia, 221
Rain forest, 24
Ranales, to Compostae, 248, 518–524; to Labiatae, 248, 513–518; to Orchidaceae, 248, 524–529
Range lands, 29
Ranunculaceae, 248, 514
Ranunculus, 511; flora apex, 249; flower and fruit of, 519; root, 114; shoot apex, 168
Raphanus, 514
Raphe, 276
Raphides, 58
Ray, conduction in, 199–200; flower, 243, 246; initials, 110; phloem, 113, 114; pith, 94, 104, 110; vascular, 110, 117; wood, 115, 116; xylem, 115, 116
Receptacle, 221
Receptive hyphae, 418–419
Recessive characters, 296
Red algae, 373–376
"Red snow," 13
Red-spore stage of *Puccinia graminis,* 420
Reduction, 74, 207; division, 286–293
Redwoods, fossil, 462
Regular flowers, 237
"Reindeer moss," 429
Relative humidity, 187
Reproduction, asexual, 353; by flowers, 251–256; by gemmae, 449, 451; by roots, 152–153; by single cells, 75–79; by stems, 82; of individuals, 79; sexual, 219, 352; types of, in different plant phyla, 354; *see also plant or phylum in question*
Resin, 117, 135; ducts, 117
Respiration, 74, 214–218; aerobic, 216; anaerobic, 217; alcoholic fermentation, 403; bacterial, 339–340; chemical reaction, 214; energy released, 214; glycolysis, 215; Krebs cycle, 217; organic acid cycle, 217; phosphorus in, 216; phosphorylation, 215; pyruvic acid formation, 216; sugar cleavage, 216
Reticulate vessels, 103–104
Reticulum, 54
Rhizobium leguminosarum, 340, 344
Rhizoids, 326, 383, 444; of fern gametophyte, 484; of *Marchantia,* 451; of moss, 456; of *Rhizopus,* 394; of *Riccia,* 444
Rhizomes, 128–129; of ferns, 480, 482; of *Psilotum,* 462
Rhizopus nigricans, 393–396; sexual and asexual reproduction of, 394–396
Rhodophycophyta, 352, 374–376
Rhynia, 463–465

Ribes, 272
Riboflavin, 323
Riccia, 443, 444–449
Ricciocarpus, 443
Ricinus communis, 156
Ring porous, 115
Robinia, 111, 169
Root, balance with shoot system, 136; crops, 138; external morphology, 137–141; functions, 147–152; hairs, 143–144; origin, 143, 145–146; primary tissues, 143–145; secondary tissues, 146; summary, 146, 147
Rootstock, 128
Rosa odorata, 156
Rosaceae, 519
Rubus ursinus, 263
Runners, 128, 131–132
Rust fungi, 418–421
Rye plant root system, 143–144

Sac fungi, 397–412
Saccharomyces, 401–403
Sage brush, 21
Saintpaulia, 237
Salicaceae, 517–518
Salix, 518
Salpiglossis, 517
Salts, absorption of inorganic, 150–151
Salviniaceae, 482
Samara, 270
Sambucus, stem, 94–96, 105
Sand, 172
Saprolegnia, 385–386
Saprolegniales, 384–388
Saprophyte, 336, 379
Sapwood, 116, 124
Sarcina, 334
Sarcobatus vermiculatus, 32
Sarcodes, 17
Sargasso Sea, 369
Sargassum natans, 369, 371
Saururus, 235
Savannah, 26, 28, 29
Savannah forest, 26
Scale, ovuliferous, 496
Scar, bud scale, 83; leaf, 83; vascular bundle, 83
Schizocarp, 265
Schizomycetes, 332–346
Schizophyceae, 346–350
Schizophyta, 331–350; nutritional requirements of, 332
Schizosaccharomyces, 402
Scientific name, 38–40
Sclereids, 99–100
Sclerenchyma, 98–100
Sclerotinia, 408–409
Scutellum, 278
Seaweed, 369
Secale cereale, 143–144
Secretory cells, 100, 117
Sections, three kinds of, 111–112

Seed coat, 501

Seedling, 282–284; infection by smuts, 424

Seed, Angiospermae, 48, 273–282, 503; bean, 276; castor bean, 276; development, 275; dispersal, 279; food storage, 278; germination, 281; Gymnospermae, 486, 489, 501; Pteridospermales, 486–488; wheat, 277

Segregation of genetic factors, 296, 299

Selaginella, 327, 463, 468–472; embryo, 472; gametophytes, 469–471; habit, 468; life history, 472; megaspores, 469; microspores, 469; sporophylls, 469; sporophyte, 468–469; strobilus, 468

Self-pollination, 252

Seminal roots, 140

Sempervivum, 171

Sepals, 221

Septa, 382

Septate hyphae, 382

Sequoia, distribution, 462; wood, 116–117

Sequoiadendron giganteum, 34

Seta, of *Marchantia,* 452; of moss sporophytes, 455

Sexual reproduction, 79, 219, 251–256, 285–293

Sheath, 159

Shoot, 48, 49, 82; apex, 48; and root systems, balance between, 136; tip, 48, 92, 278

Short-day plants, 309

Shrubland, 21, 28

Sidalcia, 515

Sieve, plate, 100–101; tube, 100

Sieve-tube member, 100–101, 117

Sieve-tube plastids, 101

Silica, 366

Silique, 263, 268

Silt, 172

Slime, layer, 332, 337; molds, 379

Smilax, leaf of, 132

Smut, blossom infecting, 423, 425; local infection, 421; seedling infecting, 424, 425

Snow plant, 17

Soil, 172–177; air, 174–176; composition, 173; conditions affecting transpiration rate, 188; environment of roots, 172; field capacity, 173; mineral matter, 172, 197; moisture and root growth, 197; optimum moisture content, 196; organic matter, 173; organisms, 176; permanent wilting percentage, 196; pore spaces, 175; relation to plant and animal nutrition, 312; solutes, 174; solutes in, effect of on growth, 312; temperature, 177; unavailable moisture in, 195–196; water, 174, 196–197; water-holding capacity, 173

Solanaceae, 516, 517

Solanum tuberosum, 129

Solute, 62

Solution, 62; concentration of, 63; molecular, 63; nutrient, 177

Solvent, 62

Sonchus, 525

Soredia of lichens, 429

Sorus, 418; of fern, 481–483; of wheat rust, 418

Sow thistle, flower of, 525

Space, microcapillary, 64

Spartina, 541

Spawn of mushroom, 414

Species, 33–35

Species novum, 39

Species Plantarum, 39

Specific name, descriptive nature of, 38

Spectrum, 208

Sperm, 223, 233, 353; nuclei of pine, 498; *see also plant in question*

Spermagonia, 418–419

Spermatia, 418–419

Sphenophyta, 328–330, 461, 473–477; classification, 461, 477; embryo, 476; gametophyte, 475; sporophyte, 473; strobilus, 475; summary, 476

Spike, 240, 243, 250

Spikelet, 241, 244

Spinach, 310

Spinacia oleracea, 310

Spindle, 77; fibers, 78

Spines, of leaves, 170; of stems, 132; stipular, 169

Spirillum, 333

Spirogyra, 354, 359–360

Spongy parenchyma, 164

Sporangiophores, 383, 390, 394, 475

Sporangium, 361, 383; defined, 383; *see also plant in question*

Spore, 18, 223, 231, 353; bacteria, 339; discharge of, Basidiomycetes, 414; mother cells, 446; print, 415; *see also spore type and plant in question*

Sporidia, 423, 425

Sporophore (basidiocarp), 414

Sporophylls, of *Lycopodium,* 466; of *Selaginella,* 468–469

Sporophyte, 372, 441, 442; Angiospermae, 508, 511–529; Filicinae, 479, 508; Gymnospermae, 487, 491–496, 508; Lycophyta, 464, 468; Phaeophycophyta, 372; Sphenophyta, 473

Sprouting, 318

Spruces (*Picea*), 492

Staghorn fern, 26

Stamens, 221–223, 239; primordia of, 249

Staminate flower, 234

Standard of pea flower, 237

Staphylococcus, 334

Starch, 279; digestion of, 73–74; first visible product of photosynthesis, 207; grains of, 52, 58–59; in roots, 151; in seeds, 279; in stems, 133–134

Stele, 95, 145

Stem, dicotyledonous, 83–89, 96–105, 111–116, 117–119; external morphology, 83–91; Filicinae, 482; functions, 82, 133–135; gymnosperm, 116–117; herbaceous dicotyledonous, 91, 107–109; industrial products from, 125–126; Lycophyta, 466; modifications, 128–132; origin, 92; primary meristems, 91–95; primary tissues, 96–109; Psilophyta, 464, 465; reproduction by, 128–129, 319; secondary meristem, 109–110, 118; secondary tissues, 110–119, 120–124; summary, 91, 109, 120, 126

Stericula platanifolia, 228

Sterigma, 413, 414, 418

Sterility, 253
Sterilization, 336
Stigma, 222, 254
Stipe, 370, 373, 414
Stipular spine, 169
Stipule, 158
Stolons, 128, 131–132; of potato, 129–130; of *Rhizopus*, 394
Stomata, behavior affecting rate of transpiration, 189; distribution affecting rate of transpiration, 190; of leaf, 161–163; of stem, 97; opening and closing, 189; sunken, affecting rate of transpiration, 190
Stomatal chambers, 164
Stone cells, 98–99
Storage, in leaves, 170; in roots, 150, 151; in seeds, 278–279; in stems, 82, 133; of food, 133–134; of water, 133
Strains, (+) and (−), sexual, 395
Strawberry runner, 132
Streptococcus, 333
Strip cropping, 151
Strobili, Coniferales, 490–495; *Equisetum*, 473–475; *Lycopodium*, 465; *Pinus*, 495; *Selaginella*, 468–470
Stroma, 208
Style, 222
Suberin, 59–60, 118
Succulent plants, 15, 133, 189
Sugar, hexose, 206; in photosynthesis, 205–207; in respiration, 214–216; in stems, 133–134
Sugar beet, leaf of, infected with mosaic virus, 436; tap root system of, 137
Sugar pine, 490
Sulfur, 179
Summary: absorption, 76, 198; Angiospermae evolution, 530; Ascomycetes, 411; bacteria, 346; Basidiomycetes, 426; cell physiology, 80; cell structure, 61; conduction of solutes, 200; external characteristics of stems, 91; fruit, 271; fruit and seeds, 278; function of tissues, 96; Gymnospermae, 502; inheritance, 299; Lycophyta, 472, 476; *Marchantia*, 453; mechanism of evolution, 542; moss, 460; photosynthesis, 213; Phycomycetes, 396; primary development, 95; primary growth in stems, 109; primary tissues of root, 146; Psilophyta, 476; Pterophyta, 508; reproduction of green algae, 363; respiration, 217, 218; *Riccia*, 447–448; Schizophyta, 349; secondary growth in roots, 147; secondary growth in stems, 120; soil and mineral nutrition, 183; Sphenophyta, 476; stem structure, 126–127; transpiration, 191; transpiration pull theory, 193
Sundew, leaf, 171
Superior ovary, 240
Support by stems, 82, 133
Suspensor, of pine embryo, 500; of *Rhizopus*, 395; of *Selaginella*, 472
Suture, 226
Sweet potatoes, propagation, 152
Symbiosis, in lichens, 429

Symbiotic bacteria, 344
Symmetry of flower, 237
Sympetaly, 239
Symphonia globulifera, 15, 16
Synandry, 239
Syncarpy, 239
Synechococcus, 349
Synergid cells, 232
Synsepally, 239
Syringa vulgaris, 89, 162–163
Systematic botany, 9

Tangential section of wood, 111, 115, 117
Tannins, 135
Tap root system, 139
Tapetum, 223, 470, 495
Taphrina, 403
Taraxacum (dandelion), fruit of, 280; latex of, 135
Taxaceae, 493
Taxodium distichum, aerial roots, 176
Taxonomy, 9
Taxus brevifolia, 494; *canadensis*, 494
Telia, 420
Teliospores, 418–421, 423, 425
Telophase, of meiosis, 290; of mitosis, 79
Temperature, effect on growth, 306; effect on photosynthesis, 211; effect on transpiration rate, 188; of soil, 312
Tendrils, leaf, 170; stem, 132
Terminal leaf bud, 86
Terracing, 151
Tetrad, 223, 290, 448
Tetraploidy, 542
Tetraspores of *Polysiphonia*, 377
Thallophyta, 36, 324, 442; characteristics of, 324–326; comparison with Bryophyta, 442; fossil, 535
Thallus, 36, 441, 444
Thiamin, 321, 322
Thorn forest, 26
Thorns, 132
Tilia, 113
Tilletia tritici, 424
Tilletiaceae, 421
Timber regions of United States, 20
Tissue, 45; collenchyma, 99; complex, 92; cork, 118; cortical, 97–100, 144; definition, 91–92; epidermal, 96–97, 143–144, 160–164; meristematic, 92–95, 101–102, 109–110, 118, 143; parenchyma, 97–99, 164; phloem, primary, 95, 100–101; primary, 96–104; primary, of stem, 94–109; secondary, 95, 109–126; sclerenchyma, 99–100; simple, 92; vascular, 100–104, 145, 164–165; xylem, primary, 102–104
Tmesipteris, 326, 462
Tobacco mosaic, 435–436
Tomato fruit, 260
Tonoplast, 65
Torreya, californica, 494, 495; *taxifolia*, 493
Toxin, botulinus, 341
Traces, bud and leaf, 47, 119
Tracheids, 102, 103, 113, 116

Tracheophytes, 327–330
Tradescantia, 77
Translocation of food, 119
Transpiration, 154, 184–192; and absorption, 197–198; conditions affecting rate, 187–191; cuticular, 185; measurement of, 186–187; pull and cohesion theory, 192–193; rate, 186–187; regulation by guard cells, 161; stomatal, 185
Tree fern, 48
Trees, determining age of, 83, 122–123; in winter condition, 86
Trifolium species, 33, 35, 37, 41
Tripsacum, 242
Triticum, 106
Tropical deciduous forests and woodlands, 26
Tropical rain forest, 24
Tropisms, 316
Tsuga, 492, 493
Tube nucleus, 223
Tuber, 128–130
Tulip, capsule of, 226; flower of, 225; infected with virus, 438
Tulipa, 225
Tundra, 31
Turgid, 66
Turgor, of guard cells, 161; pressure, 66
Turpentine, 125
Twig of walnut in winter condition, 81–85
2,4-D, effect of on grape leaves, 11, 319
Tyloses, 116, 124–125
Type specimen, 39

Ulothrix, 360–361
Ultraviolet rays, 208
Umbel, 250
Umbelliferae, 523–524
Union of flower parts, 237–239
Unit character, 248
Universal veil, 415
Uredinales, 418–421
Uredinia, 420
Uredospores, 420
Ustilaginaceae, 421–424
Ustilaginales, 421–426
Ustilago, avenae, 423; *tritici,* 423; *zeae,* 421–423
Utricularia, 171

Vaccination, 432
Vacuole, 52, 57–58
Variation, environmental, 537, 538; genetic, 538
Variegated leaves, 210
Vascular bundle, 100; at nodes, 119–120; closed and open, 105; of leaf, 164–166; scars, 83, 86
Vascular cambium, of root, 147; of stems, 95, 101–102, 110–112; stages in differentiation, 112
Vascular plants, 36, 461–530; classification, 461; general characteristics, 461
Vascular rays, 110
Vascular tissues, primary, 95, 100–104; secondary, 111–118
Vaucheria, 364–366

Vector, 438
Vegetation map of world, 20, 24
Vegetation zones, 22
Vegetative nucleus, 54
Veins of leaf, 155–158, 164–166
Venation, 156–157
Veneer, 125
Venter, 446–448
Ventral suture, 226
Venus's flytrap, Plate II
Vessel members (elements, segments), 102–104
Vessels, different types, 103–104; stages in development, 103
Virginia creeper, leaf, 132; tendril, 132
Viruses, 431–440; characteristics, 431; classification, 435; culture, 432; diseases, 431, 435–438; nature, 433–435; transmission, 438–440
Vitamins, 5, 320–323, 403; and hormones, 320; and plastids, 56; B, 321; C, 322; dependence of animal life upon, 322; plants as the source of, 322
Vitis vinifora, 11
Volva, 415

Wall, pressure, 69; primary, 59; secondary, 59
Walnut, alternate buds of, 84; flowers and fruits of, 236, 271
Washingtonia robusta, 90
Water, absorption of, by roots, 150, 193–198; and its dissolved substances of the soil, 197; available, in soil, 196, 311; capillary movement in soil, 196–197; cohesion, 193; conduction, 192–193; content of plant parts, 184; continuity in xylem, 193; forces concerned in ascent, 192–193; in photosynthesis, 204, 212; path of movement in plant, 186; quantity transpired, 186–187; rate of movement in stems, 192; respiration, 215; role in plant, 184; unavailable in soil, 196
Water molds, 384–388
Water-holding capacity of soil, 173, 196
Weeds, 19, 32; perennial, 152; seeds, 280
Wheat, 277–278; coleoptile, 284; embryo, 277–278; grain, 277–278; seed, 277–278; stages in germination, 284; stem, 106
"White rusts," 390–393
White-mottled rot, 416
Whorled buds, 85
Whorled leaf arrangement, 84
Willow, pistillate and staminate flowers, 518
Wilting percentage, permanent, of soil, 196
Wind, movements affecting growth, 311; pollination by, 251; transpiration affected by, 188
Wings of pea flower, 237
Wood, 122–127; industrial products, 125–127; quarter-sawed, 126; rays, 116; spring, 114, 122–123; summer, 114, 122–123; various sections, 112, 114–116, 125–126
Woody plants, age, 123; external characters, 120–122

Xanthium (cocklebur), fruit, 280
Xanthophylls, 56
Xerophytes, 200
Xylem, conduction in, 192, 198–199; of leaf, 164–165; primary, of root, 145; primary, of stem, 95, 102–104, 106; ray, 114, 116; secondary, of root, 147; secondary, of stem, 112, 114–117

Yeast, 401–403; ascospores, 402; budding, 401, 402; economic importance, 403; fermentation by, 403

Yew, 493
Yucca, 106

Zantedeschia aethopica, 235
Zea mays, flowers, 229, 245; leaf, 159; origin of, 242; smutted kernels, 422; stem, 107
Zinc, 182
Zinnia, 524
Zoospores, 353
Zygospore, 353, 395
Zygote, 232, 281, 353, 362